Rogers' Inorganic
Pharmaceutical Chemistry

CHARLES H. ROGERS, Sc.D.

Rogers' Inorganic Pharmaceutical Chemistry

Taito O. Soine, Ph.D.
Professor of Medicinal Chemistry, University of Minnesota

Charles O. Wilson, Ph.D.
Dean of the School of Pharmacy and Professor of Pharmaceutical Chemistry,
Oregon State University

Eighth Edition

Lea & Febiger

Philadelphia   1967

Preface

This work has been revised so that it may be used advantageously with the United States Pharmacopeia XVII and the National Formulary XII by students of pharmacy and pharmacists. Since the first edition of the textbook may not be readily available, we have recognized the desirability of reproducing the Preface to the First Edition in its entirety adjoining the present Preface. In this way it becomes possible to once again examine the basic principles on which Dr. C. H. Rogers wrote the original text and to assess the changes that thirty-seven years of experience may have wrought. Such an examination reveals that the basic principles were soundly conceived and continue to guide the present authors although, certainly, some of the detail has been modified as deemed desirable.

It may be well to again assert that this book *is not intended* to be a general chemistry text. There is a surfeit of these on the market already. It *is meant* to be a useful descriptive compendium of inorganic pharmaceutical and medicinal agents in which the history, chemistry, testing, manufacture, utilization and pharmacology of such agents is gathered together for whatever instructive value it may have. In the present edition the pharmacological treatments have been examined critically and given more than cursory treatment wherever indicated. It is our belief that the pharmacy student taking a course dealing with inorganic pharmaceuticals and medicinals has, or should have had, an adequate background in modern general chemistry prior to a study of these agents. To attempt a consideration of inorganic medicinals without such a background is tantamount to building a house without a foundation. To attempt integration of the teaching of general chemistry with a consideration of these agents in any detail does not appear possible within the time usually allotted to inorganic pharmaceutical chemistry. The average pharmacy student with the proper background is no longer interested in a purely chemical treatment of medicinal and pharmaceutical agents but eagerly seeks to relate them to the general scheme of things medicinal and pharmaceutical. It is on this basis that the present edition has expanded the pharmacological aspects of these agents although still keeping in mind that this is not intended to be a pharmacology text. The instructor using this text has at his disposal a wealth of material which he can use in any way he sees fit. It is believed that the informed instructor will develop his own mode of presentation of the material rather than being slavishly bound to the order of presentation in any textbook. This text should permit such teaching.   It is our sincere hope that the text will be useful in this context and criticisms and suggestions for its betterment will be welcomed.

The authors are especially indebted to Dr. Herbert Jonas, College of Pharmacy, University of Minnesota, Minneapolis, for his significant contribution in reviewing, rewriting, and updating the chapter entitled "Radioactivity and the Radioactive Elements."

TAITO O. SOINE
CHARLES O.WILSON

Minneapolis, Minnesota
Corvallis, Oregon

Preface to the First Edition

THE subject matter of this text-book has been formulated and arranged especially for those students of pharmacy who have a foundation in general inorganic and qualitative chemistry. The most extensive courses in these basic chemical subjects are not too long, nor too comprehensive to establish this foundation. It is of the utmost importance that the pharmacy student be as well trained in these prerequisite branches as the student who intends to major in pure chemistry. Incomplete and cursory considerations of the principles of chemistry written particularly for students of pharmacy have been published in the past as books on "Pharmaceutical Chemistry." I believe this title to be a misnomer for such treatises.

The study by students of pharmacy of the composition of matter, the changes that take place therein and the laws and theories advanced to explain these transformations, does not constitute pharmaceutical chemistry any more than the study of chemical philosophy by students of medicine comprises medical chemistry. When possessed with a working knowledge of the fundamentals of chemistry, the medical student may interest himself in the chemistry of the human organism in health and disease, *viz.* medical chemistry, whereas the student of pharmacy may consider those chemical things that are of specific pharmaceutic interest. It was with this latter conception of the meaning of pharmaceutical chemistry that this book was written.

I have attempted to present the elements and their compounds in such a manner as to make them interesting to pharmacists and students of pharmacy; to make available the physical constants of inorganic compounds of pharmaceutical importance; to consider collectively the chemistry of the elements and their compounds, the pharmacological actions of the various ions and pharmaceutical preparations; and to include in these considerations any other information of professional interest. By virtue of their training the pharmacist and student of pharmacy turn naturally to the U. S. Pharmacopoeia and *National Formulary* for guidance and information. There they find official Latin and English titles, common names, empirical formulas showing structural characteristics, definitions, purity rubrics, descriptions and physical properties, tests for identity and purity, assays, methods of preservation, etc. The very purpose of these books precludes a more detailed treatise. If historical information is required students must search the chemical

(vii)

and pharmaceutical histories; if advices on natural sources are desired they must refer to general chemistries or to economic geologies; if explanations of qualitative tests and quantitative methods are sought they must consult books on qualitative and quantitative chemistry; if information about the pharmacological actions of the ions and the therapeutic uses of drugs is desired they must look to manuals of pharmacology, etc. For those to whom these sources of information are not readily available this book may prove valuable as a reference work. However, as stated at the outset, it is not intended to replace a text on general chemistry, and the inclusion of the qualitative, quantitative and industrial treatises does not qualify it as a manual on these subjects. There have been presented only such portions of these chemical subjects as are directly or indirectly explanatory of the processes of manufacture, the tests for identity and the assays of Pharmacopoeial and *National Formulary* compounds.

With a few exceptions, the elements have been considered in the order in which they occur in natural groups or families. Their history, occurrence, physical and chemical properties, tests for identity, metallurgy, preparations of the non-metals from raw materials, the pharmacological actions of their ions, and industrial and medicinal uses are presented. The inorganic compounds and a few of the official salts of some organic acids follow in alphabetical order. They are treated as follows:

Properties.—Each compound is described and its physical constants, *e.g.*, specific gravity, melting- and boiling-points, solubilities in different solvents, crystalline forms, etc., are stated.

Tests for Identity.—Directions are given for carrying out pharmacopoeial and other qualitative tests for anions and cations. Each reaction is described and chemical equations are presented wherever it is possible to do so. Chemical equations that may not represent accurately and completely that which takes place in the reactions are designated by the dagger(†).

Commercial Methods of Manufacture.—The old and new methods employed in the industrial production of these compounds are described. Thus, by comparison it is possible to acquire an appreciation of the enormous advancement made by the chemical industries. Many of the descriptions are accompanied by diagrammatic representations of the manufacturing plants.

Laboratory Preparation.—For a number of the compounds there has been selected a laboratory preparation exercise which is intended to simulate closely one of the industrial methods of production. These exercises will assist students to acquire a better understanding of the industrial methods of manufacture. The quality of the products which they prepare in the laboratory gives them confidence in their operative ability, and the practice in synthetic methods soon develops a technique which is a decided asset to them in their professional work.

Quantitative Determinations.—Detailed directions are given for the assay of many of the compounds. Pharmacopoeial and other analytical methods are annotated and all reactions are represented by equations.

Pharmaceutical Preparations and Uses.—Pharmaceutical preparations in which the respective compounds occur are considered in the alphabetical order of their official Latin titles. Official English titles, common names or synonyms, cursory statements as to the ingredients and methods of compounding, equations to represent chemical reactions, therapeutic uses and pharmacopoeial average doses are given for each preparation.

In order to facilitate study and also to parallel the alphabetical arrangement in the U. S. Pharmacopoeia and *National Formulary*, the inorganic acids are treated in a separate chapter instead of being considered among the compounds of the characterizing elements.

In writing this textbook I have secured information from many excellent works on general inorganic chemistry, qualitative and quantitative analysis, industrial chemistry, medical chemistry and pharmacy. The U. S. Pharmacopoeia and *National Formulary* are acknowledged as the basic works upon which this book is a commentary. I wish to thank those chemical and pharmaceutical manufacturers who have opened their laboratories for inspection. Especially do I wish to acknowledge my indebtedness to Dr. M. C. Sneed, who wrote the treatises on zirconium, titanium, vanadium, columbium, tantalum, tungsten and the rare-earth metals; and to Dr. A. D. Hirschfelder for his contributions to those parts dealing with the pharmacological actions of the ions. I wish to express my sincere appreciation to Mr. J. Lewis Maynard, who wrote the chapter on the Inert Gases, and to Dr. C. A. Mann, Prof. G. Bachman, Mr. C. V. Netz, Miss Rose Weinerman and others for the valuable suggestions and generous assistance they have given in the preparation of this book.

C. H. R.

Minneapolis, Minn.

Contents

Contents

1

Atomic Structure and Chemical Bonding

ALL matter is made up of elements, which are either combined or uncombined. How these combinations occur and what the composition of an element is have been questions of man for centuries.

The Greek philosophers proposed the "continuous" theory of infinite subdivision with no unit and the "atomistic" theory of multiple units called atoms.

About 1805 John Dalton proposed his "Atomic Theory." In brief it is:

1. All elements consist of minute discrete particles called atoms.
2. Atoms of a given element are alike and have the same mass.
3. Atoms can not be subdivided nor those of one element changed into another.
4. Atoms are incapable of being destroyed or created.
5. Atoms of different elements differ, each element having unique atoms.
6. Chemical reaction is the combination of atoms in definite numerical proportions.

The points of Dalton's theory are all quite well agreed on and have guided chemical thinking since their inception. Statements 2, 3, and 4 are not necessarily true in light of recent research on atomic structure.

Due to some brilliant research, we now have a fairly clear picture of atomic structure. The particles of an atom which are of concern to pharmaceutical inorganic chemistry are the electron, proton and neutron. The general configuration of an atom is often likened to a planetary system with protons and neutrons as the nucleus and electrons moving in elliptical or circular paths about the nucleus.

The modern interpretation, however, is that electrons *do not* travel in fixed orbits and that the electron cloud concept is more valid. In the hydrogen atom, for example, one pictures a spherical cloud which has the greatest density near its nucleus, *i.e.*, where the electron is found most often. Nevertheless, the older representation shown in Figure 1 is useful as a bookkeeping method and rather vividly portrays the two main divisions of the atom, namely the nucleus and the orbital electrons. The carbon atom is represented as having a nucleus of six neutrons and six protons (a mass of 12) surrounded by six electrons in two shells of 2 and 4 electrons each.

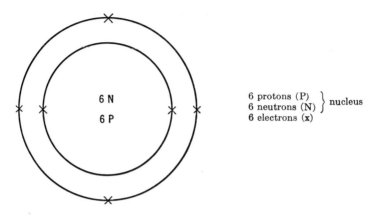

6 protons (P) ⎱
6 neutrons (N) ⎰ nucleus
6 electrons (x)

FIG. 1.—Typical Carbon Atom.

The electron represents the elementary unit of negative electricity and a mass of $\frac{1}{1839}$ of a proton, so small that it is ignored for practical purposes. The proton has a mass of one and a positive electrical charge equal to that of the electron (negative). The hydrogen ion is identical with the proton. Neutrons have been found to be neutral particles within the nucleus having about the same mass (one) as the proton.[1] It might be that a neutron is a specific union of a proton and an electron to give a neutral mass of approximately one but yet differs from a hydrogen atom.

Atoms, of the elements then, in simple terms are represented by a systematic addition of neutrons and protons to the nucleus and addition of electrons to the outer area equal to the number of protons so that electrical neutrality is maintained. A series can now be visualized starting with one proton and one electron (Hydrogen atom), next two protons and two neutrons with two electrons (Helium atom), etc. The number of protons are always equal to the number of electrons (Atomic Number). The number of neutrons and protons are equal only for the lightest elements. Within the same element, atoms containing different numbers of neutrons account for isotopes. Isotopes are atoms of elements differing only in mass but having the same electron configuration and, therefore, the same chemical properties. An example is natural oxygen containing O^{16} (99.757%) with 8 neutrons, O^{17} (0.039%) with 9 neutrons and O^{18} (0.204%) with 10 neutrons. These isotopes account in part for the fractional atomic weights of the elements. For example, if natural carbon atoms all had 6 neutrons the atomic weight would be 12 but, as we know, this is not the case.

[1] The actual atomic weights are:

H atom = 1.00785	Neutron = 1.00866
Proton = 1.0073	Electron = 0.00055

For convenience, as indicated earlier, the electron arrangement about the nucleus is considered to be planetary with the electrons moving about the nucleus in characteristic orbits. Each electron spins on its axis in a manner similar to the earth. The electrons arrange themselves about the nucleus in energy levels (shells) or quantum states.

Table 1 shows the elements arranged according to their atomic number and increasing number of electrons. Usually the electrons in the outer shell are responsible for chemical reactions in compound formation. Up to chromium this is quite true but from here on with the heavier elements some electrons in the next to last shell are available for chemical reaction. This, as will be seen later, helps explain the several valence possibilities of some elements (Cu, Cr, Mn, Au, Fe, etc.).

Considering the nuclei of atoms to be made up primarily of protons and neutrons one wonders what holds this together. Protons are positive and should repel each other and the neutrons should have no effect. Physicists are undecided as to the right explanation but "Nuclear Forces" are at play. We must, at present, accept the theory of nuclear positive charge equal to the negative charge of surrounding electrons.

Periodic Table.—During the growth of chemistry and the discovery of the elements it became more and more evident that the elements were related in some way. We are all now familiar with the various families: alkali metals, alkaline earth metals, coinage metals, halogens, etc. By 1868–1870, sufficient chemical data was available to prompt Mendeléeff of Russia and Lothar Meyer of Germany, each working independently, to suggest a periodic table. They assumed that the properties of elements were a function of their atomic weights but today it is known that the properties are better based on atomic number.

Table 1 shows that, in general, elements with the same number of electrons in their outer orbits will have similar chemical properties. The Periodic Table was based on this observation of similar chemical properties but was done before electron distribution was fully understood. There have been several forms or arrangements of the Periodic Table. The one given as Table 2 suits explanations in pharmaceutical chemistry quite well.

In examining the Periodic Table note that there are eight groups or, that after every eighth element (for Periods II and III) the properties begin repeating themselves which necessitates listing sodium under lithium, magnesium under beryllium, etc., thus "building" the Periodic Table. The name implies that the properties of elements occur in periods.

With each increase in atomic number (a like increase in electrons) the valence possibilities of the elements change. Every so often (Group O or the inert gases) an element appears with no chemical properties (completely unreactive). These are always preceded by an element with seven electrons in the outer shell and succeeded by an element with one electron in the outer shell. The atoms of the elements in each group in the Periodic Table nearly always have the same number of electrons in the outer shell. This fact accounts for the similarity in chemical properties for elements in the same group.

TABLE 1.—ELECTRONIC DISTRIBUTIONS

Element	Atomic No.	1s	2s	2p	3s	3p	3d	4s	4p	4d	5s
H	1	1									
He	2	2									
Li	3	2	1								
Be	4	2	2								
B	5	2	2	1							
C	6	2	2	2							
N	7	2	2	3							
O	8	2	2	4							
F	9	2	2	5							
Ne	10	2	2	6							
Na	11	2	2	6	1						
Mg	12	2	2	6	2						
Al	13	2	2	6	2	1					
Si	14	2	2	6	2	2					
P	15	2	2	6	2	3					
S	16	2	2	6	2	4					
Cl	17	2	2	6	2	5					
A	18	2	2	6	2	6					
K	19	2	2	6	2	6		1			
Ca	20	2	2	6	2	6		2			
Sc	21	2	2	6	2	6	1	2			
Ti	22	2	2	6	2	6	2	2			
V	23	2	2	6	2	6	3	2			
Cr	24	2	2	6	2	6	5	1			
Mn	25	2	2	6	2	6	5	2			
Fe	26	2	2	6	2	6	6	2			
Co	27	2	2	6	2	6	7	2			
Ni	28	2	2	6	2	6	8	2			
Cu	29	2	2	6	2	6	10	1			
Zn	30	2	2	6	2	6	10	2			
Ga	31	2	2	6	2	6	10	2	1		
Ge	32	2	2	6	2	6	10	2	2		
As	33	2	2	6	2	6	10	2	3		
Se	34	2	2	6	2	6	10	2	4		
Br	35	2	2	6	2	6	10	2	5		
Kr	36	2	2	6	2	6	10	2	6		
Rb	37	2	2	6	2	6	10	2	6		1
Sr	38	2	?	6	2	6	10	2	6		2
Y	39	2	2	6	2	6	10	2	6	1	2
Zr	40	2	2	6	2	6	10	2	6	2	2
Cb	41	2	2	6	2	6	10	2	6	4	1
Mo	42	2	2	6	2	6	10	2	6	5	1
Tc	43	2	2	6	2	6	10	2	6	6	1
Ru	44	2	2	6	2	6	10	2	6	7	1
Rh	45	2	2	6	2	6	10	2	6	8	1
Pd	46	2	2	6	2	6	10	2	6	10	
Ag	47	2	2	6	2	6	10	2	6	10	1
Cd	48	2	2	6	2	6	10	2	6	10	2

TABLE 1.—ELECTRONIC DISTRIBUTIONS—(*Continued*)

Element	Atomic No.	1s	2s	2p	3s	3p	3d	4s	4p	4d	4f	5s	5p	5d	5f	6s	6p	6d	7s
In	49	2	2	6	2	6	10	2	6	10		2	1						
Sn	50	2	2	6	2	6	10	2	6	10		2	2						
Sb	51	2	2	6	2	6	10	2	6	10		2	3						
Te	52	2	2	6	2	6	10	2	6	10		2	4						
I	53	2	2	6	2	6	10	2	6	10		2	5						
Xe	54	2	2	6	2	6	10	2	6	10		2	6						
Cs	55	2	2	6	2	6	10	2	6	10		2	6			1			
Ba	56	2	2	6	2	6	10	2	6	10		2	6			2			
La	57	2	2	6	2	6	10	2	6	10		2	6	1		2			
Ce	58	2	2	6	2	6	10	2	6	10	2	2	6			2			
Pr	59	2	2	6	2	6	10	2	6	10	3	2	6			2			
Nd	60	2	2	6	2	6	10	2	6	10	4	2	6			2			
Pm	61	2	2	6	2	6	10	2	6	10	5	2	6			2			
Sm	62	2	2	6	2	6	10	2	6	10	6	2	6			2			
Eu	63	2	2	6	2	6	10	2	6	10	7	2	6			2			
Gd	64	2	2	6	2	6	10	2	6	10	7	2	6	1		2			
Tb	65	2	2	6	2	6	10	2	6	10	9	2	6			2			
Dy	66	2	2	6	2	6	10	2	6	10	10	2	6			2			
Ho	67	2	2	6	2	6	10	2	6	10	11	2	6			2			
Er	68	2	2	6	2	6	10	2	6	10	12	2	6			2			
Tm	69	2	2	6	2	6	10	2	6	10	13	2	6			2			
Yb	70	2	2	6	2	6	10	2	6	10	14	2	6			2			
Lu	71	2	2	6	2	6	10	2	6	10	14	2	6	1		2			
Hf	72	2	2	6	2	6	10	2	6	10	14	2	6	2		2			
Ta	73	2	2	6	2	6	10	2	6	10	14	2	6	3		2			
W	74	2	2	6	2	6	10	2	6	10	14	2	6	4		2			
Re	75	2	2	6	2	6	10	2	6	10	14	2	6	5		2			
Os	76	2	2	6	2	6	10	2	6	10	14	2	6	6		2			
Ir	77	2	2	6	2	6	10	2	6	10	14	2	6	9					
Pt	78	2	2	6	2	6	10	2	6	10	14	2	6	9		1			
Au	79	2	2	6	2	6	10	2	6	10	14	2	6	10		1			
Hg	80	2	2	6	2	6	10	2	6	10	14	2	6	10		2			
Tl	81	2	2	6	2	6	10	2	6	10	14	2	6	10		2	1		
Pb	82	2	2	6	2	6	10	2	6	10	14	2	6	10		2	2		
Bi	83	2	2	6	2	6	10	2	6	10	14	2	6	10		2	3		
Po	84	2	2	6	2	6	10	2	6	10	14	2	6	10		2	4		
At	85	2	2	6	2	6	10	2	6	10	14	2	6	10		2	5		
Rn	86	2	2	6	2	6	10	2	6	10	14	2	6	10		2	6		
Fr	87	2	2	6	2	6	10	2	6	10	14	2	6	10		2	6		1
Ra	88	2	2	6	2	6	10	2	6	10	14	2	6	10		2	6		2
Ac	89	2	2	6	2	6	10	2	6	10	14	2	6	10		2	6	1	2
*Th	90	2	2	6	2	6	10	2	6	10	14	2	6	10		2	6	2	2
*Pa	91	2	2	6	2	6	10	2	6	10	14	2	6	10	2	2	6	1	2
*U	92	2	2	6	2	6	10	2	6	10	14	2	6	10	3	2	6	1	2
*Np	93	2	2	6	2	6	10	2	6	10	14	2	6	10	4	2	6	1	2
*Pu	94	2	2	6	2	6	10	2	6	10	14	2	6	10	5	2	6	1	2
*Am	95	2	2	6	2	6	10	2	6	10	14	2	6	10	6	2	6	1	2
*Cm	96	2	2	6	2	6	10	2	6	10	14	2	6	10	7	2	6	1	2
*Bk	97	2	2	6	2	6	10	2	6	10	14	2	6	10	8	2	6	1	2
*Cf	98	2	2	6	2	6	10	2	6	10	14	2	6	10	9	2	6	1	2

* Probable structures.

(Inorganic Chemistry by Therald Moeller, John Wiley & Sons, Inc., pp. 98–101, 1952.)

TABLE 2.—THE LONG PERIODIC TABLE

Metals   *Nonmetals*

Transition Metals

Group	I	II	IIIA	IVA	VA	VIA	VIIA	VIII			IB	IIB	III	IV	V	VI	VII	O
Period I	H 1																	He 2
Period II	Li 3	Be 4											B 5	C 6	N 7	O 8	F 9	Ne 10
Period III	Na 11	Mg 12											Al 13	Si 14	P 15	S 16	Cl 17	A 18
Subgroups	IA	IIA	IIIA	IVA	VA	VIA	VIIA	VIII			IB	IIB	IIIB	IVB	VB	VIB	VIIB	O
Period IV	K 19	Ca 20	Sc 21	Ti 22	V 23	Cr 24	Mn 25	Fe 26	Co 27	Ni 28	Cu 29	Zn 30	Ga 31	Ge 32	As 33	Se 34	Br 35	Kr 36
Period V	Rb 37	Sr 38	Y 39	Zr 40	Cb 41	Mo 42	Tc 43	Ru 44	Rh 45	Pd 46	Ag 47	Cd 48	In 49	Sn 50	Sb 51	Te 52	I 53	Xe 54
Period VI	Cs 55	Ba 56	57 — 71	Hf 72	Ta 73	W 74	Re 75	Os 76	Ir 77	Pt 78	Au 79	Hg 80	Tl 81	Pb 82	Bi 83	Po 84	At 85	Rn 86
Period VII	Fr 87	Ra 88	89 — 96															

Elements 57—71	La 57	Ce 58	Pr 59	Nd 60	Pm 61	Sm 62	Eu 63	Gd 64	Tb 65	Dy 66	Ho 67	Er 68	Tm 69	Yb 70	Lu 71
Elements 89—101	Ac 89	Th 90	Pa 91	U 92	Np 93	Pu 94	Am 95	Cm 96	Bk 97	Cf 98	Es 99	Fm 100	Mv 101	— 102	— 103

Beyond Argon (2–8–8) the electron structure becomes more complicated and necessitates a division into A and B subgroups. The horizontal periods II and III are called the "typical elements." Within these the elements in each vertical group show some similarity. In the following periods, IV to VII, the subgroups are expressed as A and B. In following through with the atomic numbers it will be noted that elements in A come first and in B come later in their respective periods. Group VIII elements in the center of the table bring together the subgroups A and B. The complexity of the larger elements allows grouping elements of atomic number 58 to 71 which all resemble lanthanum 57 into Group IIIA (Period VI). Likewise, the elements of atomic number 89–101 are similar to actinium 89 and are arranged as part of Group IIIA (Period VII).

It may easily be seen that the elements within a group, in general, possess the same number of electrons in their outer shell. Likewise, across a period the elements progressively increase by one electron. Chemical activity in general increases for the listed elements in descending order for a group except for Group IB and the halogens.

In a given period metallic properties decrease as the atomic number increases. In a group the metallic properties increase downward. This change in metallic character is gradual and there are certain intermediate elements possessing both metallic and non-metallic character which are termed *metalloids* (*e.g.*, germanium and arsenic).

Valence and Chemical Combination.—Much has been learned in recent years about how and why chemical combinations occur. Valence is concerned with the combination of elements and how the attraction is maintained. It explains the completely ionic compounds (NaCl), partly ionized compounds ($MgSO_4$), non-ionized compounds (CCl_4) and complex compounds ($Ag(NH_3)_2NO_3$).

Valence is difficult to define in that atoms unite in different ways but in all cases there is an electrostatic attraction. Perhaps it is simply best to consider it the power or ability of elements to combine with one another. A chemical bond is more definite because we visualize two chemical units as being held together by some force. Going back to Table 1 of electron distribution we note that the ability of elements to combine depends upon their extranuclear structural arrangement and the number of electrons. Generally speaking, the electrons in the outer shell of an element determine much of its valence characteristics.

Valency may be considered under the following four categories: (*1*) electrovalency, (*2*) covalency, (*3*) co-ordinate covalency, and (*4*) other bonding forces.

(*1*) *Electrovalence* exists between two chemical entities of opposite charge. This situation occurs when electrons are taken up or surrendered by the uniting particles. Valence of this type is present

TABLE 3.—ELECTRONEGATIVITIES OF THE ELEMENTS,* ACCORDING TO PAULING
(Nature of the Chemical Bond, Cornell University Press)

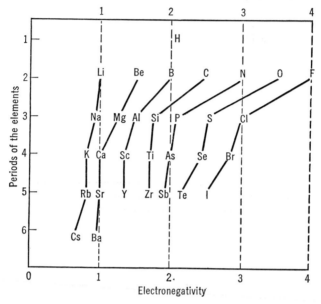

Electronegativity

* Electropositivity is another term, usually used in referring to the relative tendency of metals to give up an electron and thus go to a more electropositive condition.

particularly between the strongly metallic (Group I and IA) or
strongly electropositive elements (see Table 3) and the strongly
non-metallic (Group VII and VIIB) or strongly electronegative elements.[1] It also is found to a degree in many acids and bases. Electrovalence is common in most salts where the anion is complex (made
up of two or more elements).[2]

Table 1 notes that all of the inert gases (except helium) have
eight electrons in their outer shell. Because of their stability this
configuration is recognized as a non-reactive form and has led to
the establishment of the octet theory (nearly all stable ions have an
electron arrangement of an inert gas).

The formation of sodium chloride can be used to illustrate electrovalence. From Table 1 it may be noted that sodium has one
electron in the outer shell and chlorine has seven. The transfer is
one electron from a sodium atom to join with a chlorine atom,
thereby forming two oppositely charged ions with each having
eight electrons in their outer shells which is the configuration of an
inert gas.

[1] Thus, sodium and chlorine are far apart and would tend to form ionic bonds but
this is not so with carbon and chlorine.
[2] Groups of elements, or radicals, have the property of accepting electrons and account for most anions such as SO_4^{--}, NO_3^-, $S_2O_3^{--}$, etc.

The force holding the ions together is the electrostatic attraction between the ions.

$$\text{Na} \cdot + \cdot \overset{\cdot\cdot}{\underset{\cdot\cdot}{\text{Cl}}} \colon \rightarrow \text{Na}^+ \; \overset{\cdot\cdot}{\underset{\cdot\cdot}{\text{Cl}}} \colon^-$$

In the case of calcium:

$$\text{Ca} \colon + \; 2 \cdot \overset{\cdot\cdot}{\underset{\cdot\cdot}{\text{Cl}}} \colon \rightarrow \; \colon \overset{\cdot\cdot}{\underset{\cdot\cdot}{\text{Cl}}} \colon^- \text{Ca}^{++} \; \colon \overset{\cdot\cdot}{\underset{\cdot\cdot}{\text{Cl}}} \colon^-$$

In electrovalence the atom surrendering the electron or electrons takes on the configuration of the next lower inert gas structure, while the atom attracting the electron(s) assumes the structure of the next higher inert gas. However, as the atoms become larger or more complex the octet rule is less obvious. A number of metals such as Cu, Cr, Mn, Fe, Ni, Au, etc. will exhibit variable positive valences by using electrons from the next electron shell or are said to have "inner shell electrons." Copper first forms cuprous ions, Cu^+ and then under other conditions loses another electron to form cupric ions, Cu^{++}. There is also "odd electron valence" which will be discussed later.

The ionic bond formation depends upon the relative attraction of the reacting atoms for the other valence electrons. If the attraction is decisive and strong enough, ions will be formed.

Generally speaking, metals lose electrons to form positive ions and nonmetals attract electrons to form negative ions. The atoms that have one valence electron lose it more readily than those atoms having two or more. Also it is observed that the heavier elements in a group of the Periodic Table will lose their electron(s) more easily than the lighter elements. A reason for this is that in large atoms (many electrons) the valence electrons are at a greater distance from the attracting protons in the nucleus and, therefore, are "held" more loosely. An index to this property is noted in the electromotive series of metals (see Appendix) and from Table 3.

The tendency of an atom to gain electrons to form negative ions is called its electronegativity. This property is expressed in Table 3. According to Pauling the most electropositive element is cesium whereas the most electronegative is fluorine.

(2) *Covalence* is the sharing of a pair of electrons by two atoms, each supplying one electron, to form the typical chemical bond. This is most common to organic chemistry but found throughout inorganic compounds as well. In this bonding each atomic nucleus has an extra electron associated with it. In this type of valence there is not sufficient electropositivity or electronegativity to bring about a complete loss or gain of electrons. Chemical stability of a compound depends upon each atom sharing the electron pair to make up its outer shell to a stable octet.

Hydrogen exists in nature as a molecule of two hydrogen atoms held by a covalent bond (note stable helium electron shell).

$$H. + .H \rightarrow H : H$$

Water can be considered a good example of covalent bonding.

$$H. + .\overset{..}{O}. + .H \rightarrow H : \overset{..}{\underset{..}{O}} : H$$

Double bonds are the sharing of two pairs of electrons and triple bonds of three.

$$: \overset{..}{O} :: C :: \overset{..}{O} : (CO_2) \text{ and } H : C \overset{..}{::} N \text{ (HCN)}$$

The covalent bond is most characteristic between the same kind of atoms (H_2, Cl_2, N_2, S_8, etc.) or ones of closely similar electronegativity. The more unlike (see Table 3) the atoms the greater is the electronegativity difference and the less possible is the covalent bond.

(3) *Co-ordinate covalence* is a modified type of covalence in that the "bonding" of two atoms is the result of one atom supplying both electrons. It is expressed as an arrow ($\rightarrow$) pointing toward the electron-pair-accepting-atom. There are a number of examples of the co-ordinate covalence in the higher oxidation states of non-metals. In particular, it may be observed in the oxyacids (*e.g.*, sulfuric, nitric, phosphoric, chloric, etc.).

(4) *Other Bonding Forces.*—Why do many inorganic compounds show existence of partial ionic valence and covalence? In other words, why are they all not completely ionized? One explanation is the effect of polarization on ionic union. The degree of polarization of an ion depends upon its polarizability and the polarizing power of surrounding ions.

Atoms and molecules are the building blocks of chemistry. Their comparative size is of some interest; the nuclear radii vary from 1×10^{-12} to 1×10^{-13} centimeters (see Table 4) whereas the atomic radii are nearer 1×10^{-8} centimeters. This indicates that there is much "open" space in atoms and molecules.

It is now generally accepted that electrical charge of a neutral atomic system can be altered by a rearrangement of the electrons. The nuclei of the atoms or molecules are unchanged.

There are three factors that play a very important part in the chemical and physical properties of atoms, molecules and ions.

(a) *Polarizability* is a term to suggest that the negative electrons shift from a normal distribution to an abnormal or lopsided arrangement. In the Periodic Table the polarizability of the elements increases from top to bottom.

(b) *Polarizing power* is the ability of one atom or molecule to cause polarization in another atom or molecule. In other words there are electron-repelling or electron-attracting properties. In a given period of the Periodic Table the increase in electron-attracting power is from left to right due to increase of protons; it decreases from top to bottom for a given group (compare with Table 3).

(c) *Polarization* means the extent to which an anion or a cation can be polarized.

In polarized molecules one part is relatively positive and the other negative due to displacement of electrons in relation to atomic nuclei. In diatomic molecules this situation occurs because of a difference in electronegativities of the two atoms. This causes molecules to have *two poles* in which the center of positive charge is separated some distance from the negative charge. A polarized molecule is referred to as having a dipole moment. The term permanent dipole also is used for molecules that by themselves exhibit polarization, such as water. The term induced-dipole implies that the property was created by surrounding ions, atoms or molecules. The dipole moment is the electrical charge at one center multiplied by the distance between charges. This electrical property can be measured and is reflected in the dielectric constant.[1]

In the case of water, oxygen has more attraction for electrons than does hydrogen. Oxygen is more electronegative than hydrogen and the molecule is said to be polarized. A polarized molecule is not

an ionized molecule.[2] However, because the electrons are in dynamic motion a position is reached at a given "moment" that allows some ionization. The following are polar molecules that show some ionization: H_2S, H_2O_2, NH_3, HCN, C_2H_5OH, and $C_6H_5NH_2$. Partially ionized inorganic compounds such as $HgCl_2$, $CaCl_2$, $FeCl_2$, etc., probably are influenced by this phenomenon.

Ion Deformation

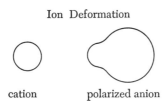

cation   polarized anion

When ions come close to each other the cations, being positive, attract the negative electrons surrounding the anion. The positive nucleus of the anion at the same time repels the cation. This leads

[1] Please see the section "Electrostatic Forces" in Chapter 11 for a more detailed discussion.

[2] As the difference in electronegativity of two atoms increases, the chemical bonds increase in polarity becoming more and more ionic in character.

to a distortion of the electron cloud around the anion which is called ion deformation or polarization. The ions usually may be visualized as having normal electron distribution while a polarized ion has a lopsided form. Polarization is greatest with anions because of their usual large size but does occur to a small extent in cations. As ion polarization increases the electrons are shared to a greater degree and a more covalent-type of bond exists.

The effect of polarization upon the passage from electrovalency to covalency was developed to a great extent by K. Fajans who proposed the following four principles as favoring the transition:—

(*a*) A large charge on the ion.
(*b*) A small size of the cation.
(*c*) A large size of the anion.
(*d*) The possession by the cation of a structure that is not that of an inert gas.

(*a*) A large charge on an ion, particularly if it is small, will have a pronounced distorting effect in comparison to less highly charged ions. Thus, one would expect a greater distortion of the anion by Al^{+++} than by Mg^{++} which in turn would have a greater effect than Na^+ (see Table 4).

(*b*) A small size of the cation coupled with a large charge or, in other words, a large ratio of charge-to-size in the cation promotes the polarization effect. Thus, for cations of the same charge but with differing sizes, the greater polarizing effect will be associated with the smaller ions ($Be^{++} > Mg^{++} > Ca^{++} > Sr^{++} > Ba^{++}$).

(*c*) Anions of large size, particularly if they have more than one negative charge (*e.g.*, $S^=$, $Se^=$, $N^{\equiv}$), are easily distorted or deformed. This is partly due to the fact that the electrons are at a relatively great distance from the positively charged nucleus and can be influenced more readily by a neighboring cation. Combinations of small cations and large easily distorted anions almost always lead to covalent bonding (*e.g.*, HI, AlN, etc.).

(*d*) Cations that have a non-inert-gas configuration of the electrons seem to have greater deforming power on anions than do those that possess the inert gas configuration. This is believed to be due to the rather incomplete shielding of the nuclear charge in the non-inert-gas configurations which is said to permit more of the excess positive charge to come through the electron shell. The difference is particularly apparent when comparing the polarizing abilities of cations with the same charge-to-size ratio but with differing electron configurations. Thus, the covalent character of CuCl as compared to the ionic character of NaCl can be rationalized.

Each compound (cation and anion) would be expected to be affected differently (a specific degree of ionization). The larger an ion and the looser its electronic structure, the more easily the electrons are polarized (distorted). In the same way the smaller ions

TABLE 4.—THE CRYSTAL RADII OF IONS

(After Pauling, Nature of the Chemical Bond, Cornell University Press.)

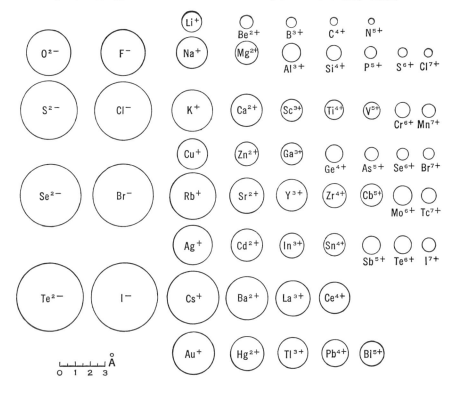

(few electrons) will have less distortion. A main point is that small ions have the protons (positive charge) nearer the "surface" thus exerting powerful polarizing power.

Van der Waals forces (or London forces) are electrical in character even though the molecules or atoms are uncharged. The electrons and protons present induce electrical charges in neighboring molecules which in turn attract oppositely charged molecules and atoms near them and tend to bring the units closer together. An index to Van der Waals forces is the boiling point of non-associated (non-polar) liquids since this is the temperature required to develop thermal agitation of the molecules to overcome the attractive force. Van der Waals forces arise from the polarizability of the molecule. Because of the dynamic motion of electrons their distribution does not always coincide with the center of density of protons in the nuclei. This situation gives a slight electrical unbalance to the molecule with one end positive and one end negative. It is referred to as an electrical dipole or a polarization of the molecule. Van der Waals forces account for the crystal structure of many compounds.

When the atoms approach "too" close a Van der Waals repulsive force (nuclear effect) exerts itself. Van der Waals force, however, is 10 to 20 times less in magnitude than the attraction of ionic bonds. Compounds are formed on this basis, though, mostly in organic compounds. Examples are the compounds of picric acid with aromatic hydrocarbons.

In crystals these two forces balance each other to maintain a distance between the atoms. Also in such properties as volatility, solubility, miscibility, viscosity, plasticity and surface tension there is a dependence on intermolecular interaction. The cohesion energy of solids and liquids is determined by Van der Waals forces.

Low Van der Waals forces of helium account for the difficult liquefaction of this gas. It has few electrons and all are in the same shell.

Hydrogen bonding (or hydrogen bridge) is observed between highly electronegative atoms such as fluorine, oxygen, chlorine, nitrogen and (sometimes) sulfur. The hydrogen atom serves to hold two other atoms together.[1] It appears to be divalent but, of course, is not. One can visualize that when an electronegative atom exerts a strong pull for the hydrogen electron it tends to induce a positive charge on the hydrogen atom (creating a proton-like

character, $-\overset{(-)}{\underset{..}{\overset{..}{O}}} : \overset{(+)}{H} ---$). This positive charge then attracts nearby

electronegative atoms (named above) to produce a definite steric arrangement of the molecules. The type of bond established is electrostatic in character and is expressed as a dashed line (----).

Some examples are: F---HF, N---HN, O---HF, O---HO, N---HO, and O---HCl. These bonds are comparatively weak, being about one-tenth as strong as most covalent bonds. The difference in the properties of HF, H_2O and HNH_2 from other hydrides is due to hydrogen bonding. The high boiling point of water is due to hydrogen bonding between the molecules: ---H-O---H-O---

$$\underset{H}{|} \qquad \underset{H}{|}$$

(Note that the water molecule is really angular at 105°). This type of bonding is also noted in hydrogen cyanide and hydrogen peroxide. Hydrogen bonding plays an important part in solution formation and in water of crystallization (see Appendix).

Resonance.—Chemical systems, molecules, can exist in several quantum mechanical energy states or molecular configurations. The normal state, most stable, is that having the lowest energy and the other "states" are called "excited states." When a structure can exist in two structural forms one may be much more stable than the other and so it will exist in this form. However, if the structures

---

[1] May be looked upon as related to electrovalence.

are nearly equal in stability the normal state will involve both and the system or the molecule will be a resonance hybrid of the two. When two or more structures for a molecule are possible the actual one is considered as involving resonance among the structures only by re-arrangement or exchange of electrons. Using carbon dioxide we have the following structural forms having the same number of

$$\overset{+}{:}O:::C:\overset{-}{\ddot{O}}:\leftrightarrow:O::C:\overset{+}{\ddot{O}}\overset{-}{:}\leftrightarrow\overset{..}{\ddot{O}}:C::O:\leftrightarrow\overset{-}{\ddot{O}}:C::O:\overset{+}{\leftrightarrow}\overset{-}{\ddot{O}}:C:::O:\overset{+}{:}$$

electrons. None of these forms exist as the result of an equilibrium but each contributes to the over-all structure. For example, there are several structures possible for the sulfate ion and measurements indicate that the S–O bond is partly a double and partly a single bond and that all S–O bonds are identical.

Coordination Compounds and Complex Ions.—There are many "addition" compounds of certain metallic ions that vary widely in their properties and stabilities. They are said to have *coordination numbers*.[1] The coordination number appears to be established after all of the normal valence requirements have been satisfied. These are referred to as *coordination compounds* and when in solution produce *complex ions*. There are those that exist only in a solid crystal form and decompose in solution while others in solution form complex ions.

Common examples in pharmacy are:[2] $[Ag(NH_3)_2]^+$, $[HgI_4]^{--}$, $[Cu(NH_3)_4]^{++}$, $[Fe(SCN)]^{++}$, $[Ag(CN)_2]^-$ and $[Ag(S_2O_3)_2]^{---}$, $[Fe(CN)_6]^{---}$ and $[Au(S_2O_3)_2]^{---}$, and $[Fe(CN)_6]^{----}$.

The binding may be electrovalent, covalent and in some cases may be unknown.

Complex ions of some metallic ions with neutral molecules or other anions[3] have long been observed in chemistry. These are difficult to explain but the best theory appears to be that of A. Werner. It is said that he came upon the key to it through a dream and after twenty years of study was awarded the Nobel Prize for its development. Using $PtCl_4$ with water and/or hydrochloric acid well known addition or coordination compounds are shown:

$$PtCl_4 + 2HCl \rightarrow H_2[PtCl_6]$$
$$PtCl_4 + H_2O + HCl \rightarrow H_2[Pt(OH)Cl_5]$$
$$PtCl_4 + 2H_2O \rightarrow H_2[Pt(OH)_2Cl_4]$$

Most coordination compounds exhibit the properties of adding different agents to form "mixed" anions or cations (see Table 6). The main points of Werner's theory are:[4]

---

[1] Not to be confused with the coordination number of crystals that refers to the number of nearest neighbors that a particular chemical species may have.

[2] The ion should be in brackets [ ] to indicate that it ionizes as a particle. This, however, is not always so written.

[3] In a very few cases cations are also found coordinated with cations.

[4] Inorganic Chemistry by Therald Moeller, John Wiley & Sons, 1952, pp. 230.

1. Two types of valency are observed for metals—primary (ionizable or principal) and secondary (non-ionizable).
2. Each metal exhibits a specific number of secondary valences called coordination number (see Table 5).
3. The primary valences of each metal are filled by negative ions but the secondary valences (coordination number) may be satisfied by negative anions and/or neutral molecules. Positive groups sometimes (but rarely) are present.
4. These secondary valences are arranged spatially around the metallic ion. Those of coordination number 2 are either linear or bent chain; 3 are triangular coplanar or a trigonal pyramidal configuration; 4 are usually tetrahedral or square coplanar; 6 have the attraction at octahedral points about the metallic ion, and a few such as molybdenum have an arrangement of 8. Using the cupric ammonia chloride complex $[Cu(NH_3)_4]Cl_2$ the structural formula is:

$$\left[\begin{array}{c} NH_3 \\ \vdots \\ H_3N\text{----}Cu\text{----}NH_3 \\ \vdots \\ NH_3 \end{array} \right]^{++} \quad 2\ Cl^-$$

It is customary to express the coordination number by dotted lines and primary valence with solid lines. One finds formulas using arrows (see below) but this indicates coordinate covalence and is *not* universally accepted as being correct.

$$\begin{array}{c} NH_3 \\ \downarrow \\ Ag\text{---}Cl \\ \uparrow \\ NH_3 \end{array} \qquad [Ag(NH_3)_2]^+ \ Cl^-$$

It is assumed that all complexes formed due to coordination numbers are not of the same type of valence. There are some where electron pairs are donated to a central cation. In others such as the transition elements of Group VIII, the bond may be a result of hybrid bond formation due to slight energy differences of the electrons between orbitals d, s and p. A redistribution of electrons can occur among these orbitals to provide hybrid bonds and normally four or six are developed. Hybrid bond formations require the bond to be covalent.

In general, there should be no attempt to formulate a rigid valence theory. Many types are indicated and some even appear to be ion-dipole in character. It is interesting to note that *some* metallic ions coordinate with sufficient electron pairs to establish an inert gas electron structure (Fe^{++}, Co^{+++}, Pd^{++++}, Ir^{+++}, and Pt^{++++}).

The most stable complexes are formed by the ions of the transition elements (Group VIII) and those immediately preceding and following in Group VIA, VIIA, IB, IIB and IIIB.[1] The most notable in Group IIIB from a pharmacy standpoint is aluminum. The following table lists the main elements as ions having coordination numbers that may be of interest to pharmacists.

TABLE 5.—METALLIC ION COORDINATION NUMBERS

Ion	No.	Ion	No.
Cr^{+++}	6	Pt^{++}	4
Mo^{+++}	8	Cu^+	2
Mn^{+++}	6	Cu^{++}	4
Fe^{++}	6	Ag^+	2
Fe^{+++}	6	Au^+	2
Co^{+++}	6	Au^{+++}	6
Ni^{+++}	6	Zn^{++}	4
Ni^{++}	4	Cd^{++}	4
Pd^{++++}	6	Hg^{++}	4
Pd^{++}	4	Al^{+++}	6
Pt^{++++}	6		

TABLE 6.—COORDINATING AGENTS[1]

Neutral Agents			Negative Agents*
NH_3	H_2O	R_3As	CN^-
NH_2R	HOR	R_3P	$S_2O_3^{--}$
NHR_2	ROR	R_2S	F^-
NR_3	$RCOR$	PX_3	OH^-
	$RCHO$		Cl^- Br^-
			I^-

(Neutral Agents: decreasing stability downward; Negative Agents: decreasing stability downward)

R = Alkyl or aryl radical   X = halogen

[1] Taken from Inorganic Chemistry, T. Moeller, John Wiley & Sons, Inc., New York, 1952, pp. 236.

* Others are NO_2^-, SO_3^{--}, SO_4^{--}, $C_2O_4^{--}$, and CO_3^{--}.

The atoms of smaller atomic volume have the lower coordination number (see Table 5). This seems to fit the theory that coordinating agents must "cover" the metallic ion. Generally the metallic ion in the highest valence state forms the most stable complex.

The strength or desire to form coordination compounds decreases from Group VIII elements in both directions. No cases of coordination compounds have been observed for the elements of Group IA and IIA. It is apparent that the small cations of high ionic charge

[1] Even in group IVB mention of a coordination number for carbon is made. In group VB, nitrogen and, especially, antimony have a coordination number.

are best. These as one might expect would have great attraction for an electron pair or cooperate in an ion-dipole relationship.

Substances that are complexed by the above-mentioned ions include neutral molecules and ions (primarily negative). These are called *coordinating agents* and vary greatly in the ease with which they coordinate and also in the stability of the coordination complex. Any groups would be included that possess a pair of unshared electrons. In Table 6 are listed the coordinating agents with an indication as to stability.

From Table 6 it is apparent that the usual coordinating agents common to pharmacy are NH_3, H_2O and CN^-. In pharmaceuticals, OH^- and the halide ions are frequently encountered. In Table 6 the order of decreasing stabilities is not *always* true. In the case of halides with mercuric ions the stability is iodide > bromide > chloride > fluoride (HgI_4^- is most stable).

The addition of negative ions can alter the positive charge of a metallic ion, in fact, sufficient negative anions establish a negative charge to the coordination complex.

$$2Na_2S_2O_3 + AgCl \rightarrow Na_3[Ag(S_2O_3)_2] + NaCl$$

No groups transfer a positive charge to the complex or decrease a negative one. However, a complex anion containing neutral agents can have them replaced by negative agents (see Table 6). For example:

$$[Co(NH_3)_6]^{+++} \quad [Co(NH_3)_5Cl]^{++} \quad [Co(NH_3)_3Cl_3]^{\circ}$$

Coordination compounds are well distributed throughout the minerals. Many plant and animal compounds are of this type such as chlorophyll, hemin, and hemocyanin. Industrial uses are found also such as for pigments, metal lakes, and the cyano complexes of metallurgy. Analytical chemistry finds wide application of this phenomenon. An important one to pharmacy is Ammoniacal Silver Nitrate.

Auto-Complexes are in the same area as coordination compounds. In pharmacy we encounter the examples of $ZnCl_2$ and $CdCl_2$.

$$2ZnCl_2 + H_2O \rightarrow Zn^{++} + [ZnCl_4]^-$$

2

Oxygen and Ozone

OXYGEN

Oxygen, U.S.P. XVII

O_2

Symbol, O.   Valence, 2.   Atomic Weight, 16; Atomic Number, 8

History.—Duckworth's study of an old work on chemistry by Klaproth led him to conclude that the Chinese, as early as the eighth century, recognized the existence of an active element in the air. They designated it as *yne* and believed it to be a component of water. Its action upon various metals and also its power to combine with sulfur and carbon were known to them. Furthermore, they made the substance by heating saltpeter and certain minerals, such as native manganese dioxide.

The phenomenon of combustion was studied during the fifteenth century by Leonardo da Vinci. In 1668, Mayow determined the amount of a particular gas present in the atmosphere, and showed that it was consumed during oxidation and during the respiration of animals. He concluded that these processes were analogous. In 1727, Steven Hales obtained oxygen by strongly heating minium (Pb_3O_4), but apparently did not realize that he had obtained a new element. In 1774, Bayen obtained the gas from mercuric oxide. In August of the same year, J. Priestley published a description of the properties of a gas which he obtained by heating mercuric oxide. He named it "dephlogisticated air." K. W. Scheele, a Swedish apothecary, working independently during the years 1771 to 1773, also announced the discovery of this element which he named "empyreal air." He prepared the gas from nitrates, observed many of its properties and contributed much to the knowledge of this element. A. L. Lavoisier, a French chemist of great renown, repeated Priestley's experiments and correctly interpreted the part played by oxygen in combustion, respiration, etc. Because of the acidic nature of many of the compounds formed by the combustion of substances in this gas, he named the element "oxygen," from the Greek: ὀξύς, sour; γεννάω, I produce, signifying "acid former."

Occurrence.—Oxygen in the free state constitutes 20.9 per cent by volume (nearly 23.1 per cent by weight) of the atmosphere.[1] In combination with other elements it is found in very large quantities. About 88.81 per cent by weight of water is oxygen and nearly 50 per cent by weight of terrestrial matter is composed of it. Growing plants possess the power of absorbing carbon dioxide from the air, assimilating the carbon and liberating the oxygen. Oxygen is necessary to animal life in every form.

Physical Properties.—Oxygen is a colorless, tasteless and odorless gas. It is slightly heavier than air, its density being 1.10532 (air = 1). One liter of oxygen weighs 1.429 Gm. at 0° C. and 760 mm. pressure. Oxygen can be liquefied when cooled below −118.82° C., which is its critical temperature.[2] Liquid oxygen has a density of 1.13, boils at −182.96° C., and may be frozen to a light blue solid which melts at −218.4° C. One volume of oxygen dissolves in approximately 32 volumes of water and in about 7 volumes of alcohol, at 20° C. and at 760 mm. pressure. It quite readily dissolves also in some molten metals, especially silver.

Oxygen is a paramagnetic[3] substance, a property shown more strongly by the liquid and the solid form. The electron distribution around this diatomic molecule ($\cdot \ddot{\text{O}} : \ddot{\text{O}} \cdot$) is such as to give each atom one odd, or unpaired, electron. Liquid oxygen will actually cling to a permanent magnet.

Chemical Properties.—Oxygen functions primarily as an oxidizing agent. In this capacity one must consider both the diatomic (molecular) form and the atomic form. Considering both forms it may be said that oxygen is one of the most active elements. It supports combustion more readily than does air. Under ordinary conditions molecular oxygen reacts very slowly with most substances. Dissociation increases with rise in temperature until at 5000° C. it is complete.

In the molecular form the reactions of oxygen (O_2) are often much slower than the reactions of other oxidizing agents. This may be due to the two-phase (gas-liquid) nature of such reactions but mostly it is in the difficulty of breaking the oxygen-to-oxygen bond. The few fast reactions of molecular oxygen are ones in which the oxygen-to-oxygen bond is not broken. This is supported by the fact that alkali metals, except lithium, burn in air to form peroxides, such as Na_2O_2 and K_2O_2 or superoxides such as KO_2. It is difficult to prepare Na_2O and other normal oxides of the alkali

---

[1] For an isotopic consideration of the composition of the atmosphere see: Asimov, I., J. Chem. Education, **32**, 633 (1955).

[2] The *critical temperature* of a gas is that temperature at or below which it can be liquefied by pressure, but above which it cannot be liquefied regardless of the pressure applied. The *critical pressure* of a gas is that pressure which will just liquefy a gas at its critical temperature.

[3] Paramagnetic substances are those that tend to move into a strong magnetic field such as that between the poles of a magnet. Diamagnetic substances tend to move out of the field.

metals.   Other examples are the oxidation of iron in hemoglobin to a Fe-O-O compound and the attack on the double bond of organic molecules to form organic peroxides.   Generally speaking, however, molecular oxygen at ordinary temperature is relatively unreactive.   The presence of moisture is important since dry oxygen is not very reactive.

It unites directly with most metals and non-metals, the rapidity of the reactions depending upon the purity and temperature of the gas.   The presence of a catalyst[1] greatly stimulates the combination. Non-metals, *e.g.*, sulfur, phosphorus, and carbon, combine when heated or burned with oxygen to form oxides (1, 2 and 3).

(1) $S + O_2 \rightarrow SO_2$
(2) $4P + 5O_2 \rightarrow 2P_2O_5$
(3) $C + O_2 \rightarrow CO_2$

At high temperatures, oxygen unites with several other nonmetals (silicon, boron and arsenic).   Union between oxygen and nitrogen takes place only at exceedingly high temperatures ($3000°$ C.) and then only to a limited degree (2 per cent or less). The Birkeland-Eyde Process of nitrogen fixation for preparing nitrates made use of this reaction.   Oxygen does not combine *directly* with the halogens or the inert gases (He, Ne, A, Kr, Xe, Rn), although the oxides of chlorine and iodine can be prepared by other chemical methods (see Chlorine, p. 87).   All of the common metals, excepting gold, silver, and platinum, when heated, combine with oxygen with varying degrees of avidity (4, 5 and 6).

(4) $4Fe + 3O_2 \xrightarrow{\Delta} 2Fe_2O_3$
(5) $4Al + 3O_2 \xrightarrow{\Delta} 2Al_2O_3$
(6) $2Mg + O_2 \xrightarrow{\Delta} 2MgO$

Oxygen is responsible for oxidative changes in paint, fats and oils, rubber goods, fabric, leather, etc.   Many materials contain an antioxidant to reduce the effect of oxidation and some pharmaceuticals (Potassium Iodide Solution, Diluted Hydriodic Acid, etc.) have a reducing agent present for the same purpose.

Although oxygen is looked upon as an oxidizing agent, it is worth noting that in the usual diatomic form this property is negligible. When oxygen functions as an oxidizing agent it is in the atomic form (see peroxides, sodium perborate, potassium permanganate).

Oxygen in the molecular state is not a very active oxidizing agent.   In the assay, therefore, a very active reducing agent is

---

[1] A catalytic agent is "a substance which accelerates whether positively or negatively, the speed of a chemical reaction by contact or by entering into the reaction, the agent having the same chemical composition at the end of the change as at the beginning."

3

necessary to be quantitatively oxidized by the molecular oxygen. The reducing agent used is ammonium chloride-ammonium hydroxide T.S. with a coil of copper wire. Some copper is dissolved in the ammonia solution to form a cuprous ammino chloride ($CuNH_3Cl$) which is readily oxidized by oxygen when in the presence of ammonium chloride and excess ammonia (7).

$$(7) \quad 4NH_4Cl + 8CuNH_3Cl + 8NH_3 + 2H_2O + O_2 \rightarrow$$
$$4CuCl \cdot CuCl_2 \cdot 4NH_3 + 4NH_4OH$$

In the assay carbon dioxide and other acid anhydrides are also absorbed in the basic solution. The technique of the assay using a calibrated nitrometer is described in the U.S.P., page 435.

Official Test for Identity.—A glowing splinter of wood bursts into flame when it is introduced into oxygen (3).

Commercial Manufacture.—Oxygen is now or has been manufactured on a large scale for commercial purposes by the following processes: (1) By the fractionation of liquid air; (2) the electrolysis of water; (3) the Boussingault-Brin Brothers' process; (4) the Thessie du Motay-Marechal process. The last two are obsolete.

1. *The Fractionation of Liquid Air—Linde-Fränkl Process.*—This process is based upon the fractional distillation of liquefied air and has superseded all other processes for the commercial production of oxygen. When air is liquefied in a suitable apparatus, it boils at a temperature of about $-191°$ C. The boiling-point of liquid air ($-191°$ C.) is higher than the boiling-point of liquid nitrogen ($-195.8°$ C.) and lower than the boiling-point of liquid oxygen ($-182.96°$ C.), hence the nitrogen evaporates from liquid air much more rapidly than does the oxygen. The "boiling off" of the nitrogen from liquid air may be so thoroughly accomplished that a liquid oxygen of better than 96 per cent purity may be obtained. Nitrogen is also produced commercially by this procedure.

The commercial production of oxygen from air involves two general procedures, *viz.*: (a) *The purification and compression of air*, and (b) *the liquefaction and fractionation of the product.*

(a) Before going to the compressors, all dust and carbon dioxide must be removed from the air. Atmospheric moisture is removed at some several stages during the compression. The dust and carbon dioxide are taken out by passing the air upward through two towers working in series. These towers are packed with coke over which trickles a solution of caustic soda or potash. After its downward passage over the coke, the caustic liquor is returned to the top of the towers and used over again. Over 99 per cent of the moisture in the air is removed by liquefaction as the air is cooled in its passage from one compression cylinder to another. The small amount of water still remaining in the so-called "fourth-stage air" is removed in a cylindrical vessel, using the counter-flow principle, with fused calcium chloride or caustic potash. The compressing of the purified air is accomplished in either four- or five-stage compressors (depending on the output of the plant). In its passage from one cylinder to the next in the compressor, the air passes through a set of coils immersed in running cold water so that it enters the next cylinder at practically room temperature. In the compressor the air is reduced to about 2 per cent of its volume and is under a pressure of about 2900 pounds per square inch (about 200 atmospheres).

(b) The clean, dry, carbon dioxide-free, high-pressure air is now ready to be liquefied and fractionated. These operations are usually effected in a combination liquefier and fractionator. Due to the consumption of heat necessary to overcome molecular cohesion, all gases upon expansion become somewhat cooled. The lower the temperature of a gas, the greater is the attraction between the molecules. Because more heat is required to overcome this increased cohesion, the cooling effect upon expansion is greater. The various processes for the liquefaction of air are based upon this principle.

2. *The Electrolysis of Water.*—In those plants where both oxygen and hydrogen are needed, this method may be used successfully. A direct current is passed between iron or steel electrodes that are immersed in 10 to 25 per cent aqueous solution of sodium or potassium hydroxide with oxygen being liberated at the anode and hydrogen at the cathode; the method of collecting the gases depending upon the construction of the cell. Water only must be added to the cell during the electrolysis. The efficiency of this type of cell (said to yield an average of about 7.5 cubic feet of hydrogen and 3.8 cubic feet of oxygen per kilowatt hour) is increased by carrying out the electrolysis under pressure.

Pharmacological Action of Oxygen.—Evolutionary processes, in the case of land mammals, have not made it necessary for them to develop any elaborate apparatus for extensive storage of oxygen against periods of deprivation. The obvious reason is that they live submerged in an "ocean" of air containing more than enough oxygen for their needs. It is for this reason, however, that severe oxygen deprivation results in quick extinction of life. Even lesser degrees of oxygen deprivation cause anatomic and physiologic disorders if not permanent local damage. The mechanism whereby the body makes use of the atmospheric oxygen is illustrated in Figure 2, a diagrammatic representation of the human circulatory system. The venous blood enters the heart from where it is pumped to the lungs for aeration and, back to the heart for pumping into the arterial system. The arterial system carries the blood to the capillaries where it is in intimate contact with tissue cells and from which it is discharged into the venous system for conveyance back to the heart and lungs. The entire process takes about one minute in the

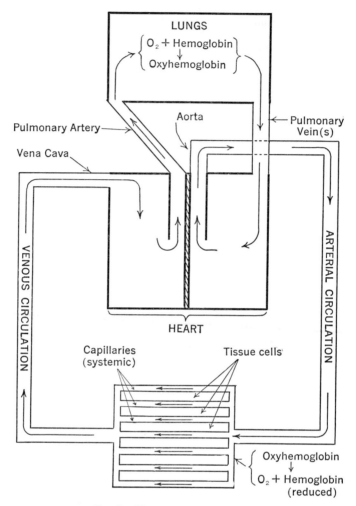

Fig. 2.—Diagram of the circulation.

normal state and as little as ten to fifteen seconds when the body is being exerted. The oxygenation of the blood takes place from the alveoli of the lungs where the alveolar air and venous blood are separated by a pulmonary membrane (0.004 mm. thick) consisting of the alveolar and capillary wall. The surface area of the membrane is estimated at from 70 to 90 square meters. All of the blood corpuscles, which contain hemoglobin, must pass through the lung capillaries in single file and, therefore, offer a tremendously large surface for oxygenation. The process is continuous because there is always residual air in the alveoli. The process by which oxygen reaches the tissues consists of three steps:

(a) Diffusion from alveolar air to blood plasma.

(b) Surrender from blood plasma to red blood corpuscles to form oxyhemoglobin.

(c) Abstraction of oxygen from oxyhemoglobin by the tissues via complex physiochemical processes and also by diffusion.

It is necessary for the successful transport of oxygen from air to the tissues that there be a progressive lessening of oxygen tension in each of the above steps—lower tension in plasma than in alveolar air, lower in red corpuscles than in the plasma, and lower in the tissues than in the red corpuscles. This is well illustrated in Figure 3 illustrating gaseous exchange in lungs and tissues.

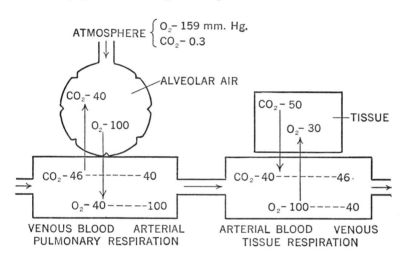

FIG. 3.—Diagram illustrating the exchange of gases in the lungs and the tissues. The values as stated are mm. Hg pressure. (Zoethout and Tuttle, *Textbook of Physiology*, courtesy of C. V. Mosby Co.)

The diffusion of oxygen into the plasma would be of limited value if it were not for the hemoglobin present in the red corpuscles. It has been pointed out that, if the body were dependent on only the amount of oxygen that would diffuse into the plasma and be held in solution (without binding to hemoglobin) it would require 300 quarts of plasma to carry all of the oxygen necessary for body functions. This is a patently absurd situation because this volume is four times that of the whole body. Therefore, the hemoglobin content of the blood is a vital factor in successful oxygen transport and it is present to the extent of 15 Gm. per 100 ml. of blood. Each gram of hemoglobin can hold 1.34 ml. of oxygen so that 100 ml. of blood can hold 20 ml. of oxygen. Under normal conditions, the arterial blood is approximately saturated.

Oxygen wants in the body are conveniently classified into four major divisions: (1) anoxic (2) anemic (3) stagnant (4) histotoxic.

(1) In the anoxic type the oxygen supply to the tissues is inadequate because the blood arrives with its oxygen at a lowered tension. The cause for this may be lowered oxygen tension in the inspired air as a result of high altitudes, increase in the inert gases normally present or abnormal presence of other inert gases. Lowered oxygen tension in the plasma may be another cause which results from interference with diffusion of alveolar air into the plasma because of disturbed pulmonary function or a defect in the cardiac septum (allowing mixing of arterial and venous blood). Studies showing that the inhalation of oxygen-enriched atmospheres containing 40 to 60 per cent oxygen raised the oxygen saturation of arterial blood to or near normal value in patients with pneumonia and cardiac insufficiency placed this therapy on a sound basis. It has since found use in asthma, massive collapse of the lungs, atelectasis of the lungs of the newborn, bronchopneumonia, congestive heart failure, coronary thrombosis, cerebral thrombosis, etc. In these cases the oxygen is administered by mask or in tents. Apparently, its use in high concentrations is quite safe although uninterrupted inhalation of pure O_2 for one or two days could cause harmful effects (edema of the lungs, etc.). In premature infants a condition known as *retrolental fibroplasia* may occur due to the administration of high concentrations of O_2 at birth. This is a vascular proliferative disease of the retina and may lead to blindness by progression to retinal detachment. Limitation of the concentration of inhaled O_2 to 35 to 40 per cent when possible minimizes the danger.

(2) In the anemic type the oxygen tension is normal, but the amount of hemoglobin is inadequate to supply enough oxygen to the tissues. This condition may result from hemorrhage or from carbon monoxide poisoning because CO has a much greater affinity for hemoglobin than O_2. Oxygen administration for this type has no rationale although in the case of carbon monoxide poisoning a carbon dioxide-oxygen mixture is said to be of value based on the fact that CO_2 has a specific stimulating effect on the respiratory center and aids in the swifter elimination of CO. Increase of the O_2 tension of the inspired gas is more effective than if administered at atmospheric pressure, however.

(3) The stagnant type occurs when the general circulation is inadequate or when circulation is locally retarded. In this type tension and rate of oxidation is normal, but each portion of the blood tarries in the capillaries, permitting surrender of a larger portion of its oxygen. Therapy of this type with oxygen is without value and this type is treated with cardiotonic drugs to speed up the circulation.

(4) In the histotoxic type tissue cell oxidation may be interfered with in several ways. It may depend on failure of that form of oxida-

tion which is chemically dehydrogenation. Various toxic substances of exogenous origin, of which cyanides are the notable example, may paralyze cell respiration. Again, oxygen administration is theoretically without value and treatment has traditionally been directed toward neutralization of the toxic materials.

It has become increasingly apparent, however, that in spite of theory, oxygen administration, particularly at about 2.5 atmospheres pressure, is dramatic in countering the effects of lethal doses of cyanide. Many suggest that it be a routine procedure, together with sodium nitrite and sodium thiosulfate, in the antidotal treatment of cyanide poisoning.[1]

In summary, the efficient utilization of oxygen by the body in its normal processes demands a smooth functioning of oxygen transport from inspired air to utilization in the tissues. It is beyond the scope of this text to consider the metabolic processes that utilize molecular oxygen but it should be emphasized that the ultimate conversion of oxygen to H_2O and CO_2 is the net result of all the complex physiochemical processes.

Use.—*Oxygen*, U.S.P. XVII contains not less than 99 per cent of O_2. It usually is available in green colored cylinders or the label is green. Oxygen is widely used in medical practice as well as in surgery. All pathological conditions, *e.g.*, pneumonia, angina, asthma, bronchitis, etc., that are accompanied by cyanosis and dyspnea (difficulty in breathing) are relieved by inhalations of the gas, using the "oxygen tent" or other suitable devices. It is administered in chloroform poisoning and in threatened death from inhalations of coal gas or nitrous oxide (*q.v.*). Oxygen is used in the resuscitation of individuals apparently drowned. Under conditions in which there is a scarcity of oxygen, *e.g.*, in airplanes at high altitudes, in diving bells and in submarines, this essential gas is supplied from tanks.

Oxygen (20%) is often used mixed with *Helium* U.S.P. (*q.v.*) for therapeutic purposes. The mixture is available in brown-green colored cylinders. Likewise a mixture of oxygen and carbon dioxide is also available in gray-green cylinders.

Liquid oxygen is an effective local destructive agent in treating growths such as warts. Application is made with a cotton swab resulting in a thorough freezing of a small lesion in a few seconds.

Oxygen is of great importance in industry because of its use in the steel industry, steel fabrication, and industrial maintenance. Other miscellaneous uses include breathing oxygen, automotive and aircraft, chemicals and petroleum. Liquid oxygen has been useful as an ingredient in the fuel of rockets.

[1] See, however, "The Importance of Oxygen in the Treatment of Cyanide Poisoning." C. Cope, J. Am. Med. Assn., **175**, 1061 (1961); also "Cyanide Poisoning" by F. G. Hirsch, Arch. Environmental Health, **8**, 622 (1964).

OZONE

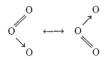

Formula, O₃. Molecular Weight, 48

History.—In 1785, Van Marum, a Dutch chemist, called attention to the fact that oxygen or air, through which electric sparks had been passed, possessed a peculiar, irritating odor and also the property of tarnishing mercury. In 1840, the German chemist, Schönbein, demonstrated that these phenomena were caused by a new gaseous substance formed from oxygen during the electrical discharge, and he named it *ozone* from the Greek, *to smell.* He prepared fairly high concentrations of the gas in oxygen by the electrolysis of water and also by the slow combustion of phosphorus. In 1856, Andrews established the constitution of ozone.

Occurrence.—Ozone is found in very small quantities (ca 0.05 p.p.m.) in the atmosphere as a result of solar ultraviolet radiation of atmospheric oxygen. It has been found in smog over Los Angeles and other large cities. Electrical discharges through the air (lightning) produce ozone. The characteristic odor of the gas is usually very pronounced around electrical generating machines in operation.

Physical Properties.—Ozone, an allotrope of oxygen, is a bluish gas having a peculiar, irritating odor (suggesting sulfur dioxide). One liter of water at 0° C. dissolves 490 milliliters. One liter of ozone weighs 2.144 Gm. at 0° C. and 760 mm., and is, therefore, one and a half times heavier than oxygen. When ozonized air is cooled to —180° C., the ozone condenses to a blue liquid, which boils at —111.9° C. and freezes at —250° C. Both liquid ozone and liquid oxygen are strongly magnetic. Ozone dissolves in and unites with the double bonds of substances such as oil of turpentine, oil of cinnamon and olive oil to form ozonides, some of which possess antiseptic properties. Some commercial ozonide preparations derived from olive oil are Oilzo (a liquid) and Ozettes (vaginal suppository).

$$R—CH=CH—R+O_3 \rightarrow \begin{array}{c} R—CH—O—CH—R \\ | \qquad\qquad | \\ O————O \end{array}$$
$$\text{Ozonide}$$

$$\xrightarrow{H_2O} R—\overset{\overset{\displaystyle H}{|}}{C}=O + R—\overset{\overset{\displaystyle H}{|}}{C}=O + H_2O_2$$

This is a general reaction but the important thing pharmaceutically is the release of hydrogen peroxide when an ozonide comes in contact with water.

Chemical Properties.—The transformation of oxygen into ozone involves the changing of electrical energy into chemical energy. The energy, expressed as heat units, required to change oxygen into ozone is 68,820 calories (1) (an endothermic reaction).

(1) $3O_2 + 68,820$ calories $\rightleftarrows 2O_3$

From this equation it is evident that a definite weight of ozone contains more internal energy than does an equal weight of oxygen, and it may be correctly concluded that ozone is a more active chemical agent than is oxygen. Because of the instability and high energy content, ozone is an ideal oxidizing agent for both organic and inorganic substances. Oxygen is usually the by-product of oxidation since ozone decomposes according to equation (2). Unlike oxygen, ozone at ordinary temperatures oxidizes certain metals, e.g., mercury (3) and silver (4).

(2) $O_3 \rightarrow O_2 + (O)$
(3) $Hg + O_3 \rightarrow HgO + O_2$
(4) $2Ag + 2O_3 \rightarrow Ag_2O_2$ (silver peroxide) $+ 2O_2$

From equations (3) and (4) it may appear that one-third of the "oxygen" of ozone is more active than the remaining two-thirds. However, the fact that 1 molecule of ozone completely oxidizes 3 molecules of sulfur dioxide to sulfur trioxide (5) indicates that *all* of the "oxygen" of ozone is chemically active and not merely one-third, as might be concluded from the above equations (see also ozonides).

(5) $3SO_2 + O_3 \rightarrow 3SO_3$

Ozone is fairly stable at very low temperatures. At ordinary temperatures it slowly decomposes into oxygen (2). Ozonized air (air containing one to two per cent ozone) can be compressed and stored for limited periods of time. However, ozone is usually manufactured at the point of ultimate use. The velocity of this chemical change increases as the temperature increases until, at about 250° C., the decomposition is complete. Van't Hoff's law of mobile equilibrium states that when the temperature of a system in equilibrium is raised, the equilibrium is displaced in the direction that absorbs heat. From this law it follows according to the thermochemical equation (1) that more ozone is formed the higher oxygen is heated. The presence of a catalyst causes ozone to decompose violently.

Ozone is a powerful oxidizing agent, exceeding all ordinary chemicals except fluorine, fluorine oxide (F_2O) and atomic oxygen in its oxidation potential. Also, liquid ozone is highly explosive unless diluted with liquid air or oxygen.

Tests for Identity.—1. Ozone in the atmosphere may be identified by its characteristic odor.

2. When a piece of absorbent paper that has been moistened with starch test solution containing a little sodium or potassium iodide is introduced into an atmosphere containing ozone, the starch is colored blue due to liberated iodine (6).

$$(6)\ 2I^- + O_3 + H_2O \rightarrow I_2 + O_2 + 2OH^-$$

Oxides of nitrogen, the halogens, and particularly acidulated hydrogen peroxide liberate iodine from iodides and are, therefore, interfering substances.

3. A piece of red litmus paper, one-half of which has been dipped into a solution of potassium iodide, will turn blue when held in an atmosphere containing ozone. This is caused by the hydroxide formed by the action of ozone upon potassium iodide (6).

4. Slightly heated silver is tarnished by ozone (4).

Preparation of Ozone.—1. Ozone may be prepared by subjecting cold, dry oxygen or air to an electric discharge. The apparatus used for this purpose is called an *ozonizer*, and consists of 2 glass tubes, one within the other. The outside of the outer tube is covered with tin-foil and the inner tube is lined with the same material. The electrical discharge is produced through the space between the tubes by connecting the foils with the poles of an induction coil. Cold, dry, carbon dioxide-free oxygen or air is slowly passed between the tubes where, under ordinary conditions, from 5 to 6 per cent of the oxygen is converted into ozone. Under the most favorable conditions, *e.g.*, using a silent discharge, low temperature and very pure, dry oxygen, the yield of ozone can be increased to better than 18 per cent.

2. *Welsbach Method.*—Prior to 1946 ozone was of only limited commercial importance because no economical method of preparation was available. Air is cleaned by passing it through an electrostatic precipitator and paper filter. After the removal of moisture the clean dry air under a pressure of 8 to 10 psig.* passes through a bank of Welsbach ozonators, which produces ozone as a gas diluted with large amounts of air. Using air, a concentration of 1 per cent ozone is obtained and with oxygen the yield is 2 per cent. Ozone even in this dilution of 1% with air is of great practical use as an oxidizing agent and is of use in industry.

3. Ozone is formed in small quantities by: (*a*) Slow oxidation (especially of phosphorus and zinc); (*b*) by the electrolysis of dilute sulfuric acid; (*c*) by the action of an active acid, *e.g.*, concentrated sulfuric acid upon a highly oxidized compound, *e.g.*, barium peroxide (7); (*d*) by burning hydrogen in oxygen; (*e*) by plunging a heated platinum coil into liquid oxygen; (*f*) by the decomposition of potas-

---

* Pounds per square inch by gauge.

sium chlorate; and (*g*) by bombarding oxygen with high speed electrons under controlled thermal, mechanical, electrical and chemical sensitizing influences.

(7) $2H_2SO_4 + 2BaO_2 \rightarrow 2BaSO_4 + 2H_2O + O_2$ (with high per cent of ozone)

Uses.—The improved industrial methods for preparing this active oxidizing agent have made possible its utilization in the arts and industries. General advantages of ozone use are ease of control and absence of solid oxidative residues. Ozone *per se* is rarely used, but air or oxygen containing it is employed as a bleaching agent for oils, waxes, delicate silk or wool fabrics, flour, starch, ivory, etc.; as a disinfectant for drinking water; as a deodorant of foul animal matter, especially in ventilating large public halls and food warehouses; and as an inhibitor of molds and bacteria on meats and fruits in cold storage rooms (1 to 3 p.p.m.). Electronic air deodorizers are available which will keep large volumes of air deodorized. It is also used in the manufacture of synthetic camphor, cortisone and many other organic compounds.

Ozone, in acute exposure, is a highly toxic and lethal substance. Most individuals commonly experience headache and throat dryness after continued exposure above 0.1 p.p.m. Detection by odor of ozone is usually possible when the concentration is only a few hundredths of a part per million. Even at this concentration ozone can deodorize the air. Studies show that less than 5 p.p.m. of ozone kill 50 per cent of exposed rats whereas 10.5 p.p.m. is fatal to 50 per cent of exposed hamsters. An increased tolerance is developed by repeated exposures. Unlike carbon monoxide, ample warning is given by headache, cough and general pulmonary irritation.

3

Hydrogen

H_2

Symbol, H. Valence, 1. Atomic Weight, 1.008; Atomic Number, 1

History.—There is evidence that hydrogen was recognized by Paracelsus in the sixteenth century. During the seventeenth century, Turquet de Mayenne called attention to its combustible nature, and in 1700 N. Lemery showed that upon ignition a mixture of hydrogen and air detonated. The first experiments to determine the nature of hydrogen were made by Cavendish in 1766. He produced it by the action of dilute hydrochloric or sulfuric acids upon certain metals, and called the gas "inflammable air," which name conformed to the generally accepted "phlogiston" theory of the day. Later (1781), Cavendish and Watt showed that water was the only substance produced when hydrogen was burned in air or oxygen and, as oxygen was then known to be the substance with which combustibles united, they correctly concluded that water was a compound of hydrogen and oxygen. In 1783, Lavoisier named the gas *hydrogen*, from the Greek, ὕδωρ, water, and γεννάειν, to produce.

Occurrence.—Very small quantities of hydrogen are found in the free state in some volcanic gases, in fumaroles and in pockets in carnallite and rock salt deposits. It also occurs in very small quantities in the air, in some meteorites, in the stars and nebulæ and in the envelopes of the sun. Hydrogen gas is sometimes a product of the decomposition of organic matter. It is produced also by anaërobic fermentation. Hydrogen in combined form is an integral part of many compounds, minerals, and most animal and vegetable tissues. It is an essential constituent of all acids.

Physical Properties.—Pure hydrogen is a colorless, tasteless and odorless gas. It has a specific gravity of 0.06947 (air = 1) and is, therefore, about fourteen and a half times lighter than air. One liter of hydrogen weighs 0.08987 Gm., whereas the same volume of air weighs 1.293 Gm. At its critical temperature of −239.9° C. hydrogen may be liquefied by a pressure of 12.8 atmospheres. Liquid hydrogen is colorless and has a boiling-point of −252.7° C. Hydrogen has been solidified to a colorless solid melting at −259.14° C. The specific heat of hydrogen gas is 3.4041 (water = 1). Hydro-

(32)

gen is only sparingly soluble in water (1.8 ml. dissolves in 100 ml. of water at 15° C.). It diffuses very rapidly through porous membranes and through some metals at red heat. Hydrogen is absorbed or "occluded" by many metals. The quantity of gas "taken up" depends upon the metal, its physical condition, and upon the temperature and pressure during the operation. At ordinary temperatures and pressures, 1 volume of palladium black absorbs 873 volumes of hydrogen, whereas finely divided iron, gold, and platinum occlude 19.2, 46.3 and 49.3 volumes of the gas, respectively.

Chemical Properties.—At ordinary temperatures hydrogen is chemically inactive. Its activity may be greatly increased by passing it through an ozonizer (*q.v.*), by subjecting it to high potential electrical discharges in vacuum, or by exposing it to the action of alpha-rays from radium emanations. At high temperatures or in one of its activated forms hydrogen is a powerful reducing agent. When molecular hydrogen (H_2) is passed through an electric arc it forms atomic hydrogen (H) which again recombines to form molecular hydrogen (H_2), liberating much heat. This knowledge is made use of in atomic hydrogen welding torches which develop temperatures of 4000° to 5000° C.

Hydrogen burns in air with a pale blue, non-luminous flame. When mixed with oxygen in a suitable burner (oxyhydrogen torch) and ignited, it burns with a flame giving very little light but a temperature of over 2500° C. The oxyhydrogen flame will melt all metals, even platinum. When this flame is directed upon a piece of quicklime (CaO), the latter becomes white-hot at the point of contact. The emitted light is called a "calcium" or "lime light."

Hydrogen and oxygen unite very slowly at ordinary temperatures. However, if finely divided platinum is held in the mixture, the union is hastened and the heat of the reaction is sufficient to make the platinum glow, thereby causing the explosion of the mass. Automatic lighters for illuminating gas operate on this principle.

Occluded hydrogen or hydrogen in its activated state is a vigorous reducing agent. The gas occluded by palladium (1 volume of palladium absorbs up to 873 volumes of hydrogen) is especially active in this respect and readily reduces ferric salts to ferrous salts, chlorates to chlorides, nitrates to nitrites and ammonia, etc. One of the most important uses of hydrogen with palladium (also nickel, or platinum) is for the reduction of organic compounds. It adds to aliphatic double bonds of organic compounds which is the basis for preparing oleomargarine and hydrogenated fats. Hydrogen unites with many metals and non-metals to form innumerable compounds, *e.g.*, H_2S, NH_3, PH_3, CH_4, HCl, CaH_2, NaH, etc.

Commercial Manufacture.—Hydrogen has considerable industrial and military value, and its manufacture has likewise assumed importance. Because it is not economical to ship unliquefied gases for long distances, the manufacture of hydrogen (a difficultly compressible gas) is, of necessity, a more or less local undertaking. Thus, the method of manufacture depends on the required purity, raw materials, power supply, etc., of the area being supplied by the hydrogen plant.

Hydrogen may be obtained by: (1) The steam-hydrocarbon process using natural gas or propane as hydrocarbon; (2) catalytically oxidizing CO of water gas with steam; (3) electrolysis of water containing caustic soda; (4) passing steam over incandescent iron; (5) pyrolysis or breaking down of hydrocarbons at relatively high temperatures; (6) catalytically breaking down ammonia; (7) the fractionation of water gas or coke oven gas; (8) steam-methanol process; (9) the "Silicol" process from ferrosilicon and caustic soda; (10) fermentation of corn mash in the production of acetone and butanol; and (11) the action of caustic on some metals. (12) It is also a by-product of the electrolytic caustic cell.

1. The steam-hydrocarbon process depends upon using a source of relatively pure hydrocarbon (propane free of sulfur compounds) mixed with steam and passed over a nickel catalyst at about $1500°$ C (1).

$$(1) \ C_nH_{2n+2} + nH_2O \rightarrow nCO + (2n+1)H_2 \uparrow$$

The gas mixture is cooled with steam to $700°$ C. and the carbon monoxide added to steam to produce CO_2 and H_2 (2).

$$(2) \ CO + H_2O \rightarrow CO_2 + H_2 \uparrow$$

The combined gas mixture is cooled and carbon dioxide removed with aqueous ethanolamine.

2. The carbon monoxide in water gas is removed by catalytically oxidizing it with steam to carbon dioxide, which is then dissolved out completely under pressure in cold water followed by a scrubbing with caustic soda. During the oxidation additional hydrogen is produced (3).

$$(3) \ CO + H_2O \rightarrow CO_2 + H_2$$

3. When electric power is available at low rates, and particularly when oxygen as well as hydrogen can be marketed, the electrolysis of water is the preferred process for preparing hydrogen. A very pure hydrogen is obtained by passing a direct current between iron electrodes immersed in a 10 to 25 per cent caustic soda solution. Hydrogen by this process is used mostly for making synthetic ammonia.

4. It is claimed that by the Messerschmidt process hydrogen of better than 99 per cent purity may be obtained. The process is based upon the decomposition of superheated steam by metallic iron with the subsequent reduction of the iron oxides so formed by a mixture of carbon monoxide and hydrogen (blue water gas).

At 700° to 800° C., iron oxide reacts with the carbon monoxide and hydrogen of the water gas to form metallic iron, carbon dioxide and water (4).

(4) $FeO.Fe_2O_3 + 2CO + 2H_2 \rightarrow 3Fe + 2CO_2\uparrow + 2H_2O\uparrow$

When this reaction is complete the water gas and air are shut off and steam is introduced. The steam is superheated and as it ascends through the heated iron, it is reduced, producing magnetic iron oxide and hydrogen (5).

(5) $3Fe + 4H_2O \rightarrow 4H_2\uparrow + Fe_3O_4$

The hydrogen passes out of the apparatus and is cooled and freed from dust by washing with a spray of water. Carbon dioxide is removed with lime and any hydrogen sulfide present is taken out with oxide of iron.

5. Carbon and hydrogen are the ultimate products obtained by the pyrolysis of all hydrocarbons. The various processes differ materially from one another and are dependent principally upon the type of carbon (carbon black, lampblack, etc.) desired. In general, methane, propane or natural gas is heated either with or without a catalyst (nickel) at relatively high temperatures. When either of these gases is passed through an alundum tube heated to 1300° to 1700° C., hydrogen and carbon, uncontaminated with intermediate products, are produced. In some of the other processes, iron, cobalt, and nickel (if kept clean of accumulated carbon) are employed to catalyze the production of carbon and hydrogen.

6. Ammonia when catalytically decomposed breaks down into nitrogen and hydrogen at 450° to 500° C. but catalysts such as iron, nickel, osmium, zinc and uranium lower the temperature to 300° C.

7. Water gas (a mixture of approximately equal parts of CO and H_2) is cooled and compressed by the Linde method to the point where the CO liquefies and can be removed as a liquid. The same is true of coke oven gas which is a mixture composed largely of hydrogen together with other gases (mainly CH_4, N_2, CO, C_2H_4, and CO_2).

The other processes are relatively unimportant and will not be discussed here.

Uses.—Hydrogen is used in the Haber process for nitrogen fixation (*q.v.*); for inflating balloons; for the production of high temperatures when burned with oxygen; and for the hydrogenation of oils used for edible and other purposes.

The work of Dr. Irwin Langmuir of the General Electric Company made it possible to obtain one of the highest temperatures ever produced and also to effect a weld in a reducing atmosphere. Hydrogen is passed through an electric arc wherein molecular

hydrogen is converted into atomic hydrogen (6). Immediately
upon issuing from the arc the atomic hydrogen combines to form
molecular hydrogen and a tremendous quantity of heat is evolved.
This hydrogen then burns with the oxygen of the air. In short,
the flame consists of a nucleus of combining hydrogen atoms surrounded by a shell of burning molecular hydrogen. A temperature
of about 5000° C. has been obtained.

(6) $H_2 + 98,000$ cal. $\rightleftarrows H + H$

Other than its use in the activated state as a laboratory agent in
the preparation of many chemical compounds it is never used in
pharmacy or medicine.

4

Water and Hydrogen Peroxide

WATER

Water, U.S.P. XVII
Purified Water, U.S.P. XVII
Water for Injection, U.S.P. XVII
Sterile Water for Injection, U.S.P. XVII
Bacteriostatic Water for Injection, U.S.P. XVII

Formula, H_2O. Molecular Weight, 18.02

History.—The nature of water was held to be elementary until the latter part of the eighteenth century. In Robert Boyle's time (1627–1691) it was known that some metals, *e.g.*, tin, iron, zinc, etc., dissolved in aqueous solutions of hydrogen chloride with the evolution of a vile-smelling gas, which was thought to be air contaminated with "obnoxious oils." This view was held by all chemists until 1781, when Cavendish showed that the evolved gas could be purified of its odor and then possessed constant physical and chemical properties differing widely from those of air. He not only demonstrated that this gas burned in air with the evolution of heat and the formation of water, but also determined the quantitative relations and found that it took nearly 1000 volumes of air to burn 423 volumes of "hydrogen" gas. This important discovery was confirmed by the subsequent experiments of Humboldt and Gay-Lussac. In 1783 Lavoisier decomposed water into its elements and showed that it was composed of about 1 part by weight of hydrogen and about 8 parts by weight of oxygen. It was not until 1805 that Gay-Lussac and Humboldt proved the volume composition of water.

Occurrence.—The ocean is by far the most abundant of all natural sources of water. About 25 per cent of the water vapor rising therefrom is condensed to rain, snow, sleet, etc., and precipitated on the land. In this way lakes and rivers are formed; or the water is absorbed by the soil and used by plant life; or, perhaps, it reappears again in springs, etc. *Mineral waters* are natural spring or well waters which contain in solution sufficient quantities of mineral

(37)

4

or gaseous matter to render them unfit for domestic use. The nature and quantity of the dissolved substances make these waters of more or less value as medicinal agents. The Council on Pharmacy and Chemistry of the American Medical Association, however, has this to say about the therapeutic values of mineral waters: "The Council has declared artificial mineral waters to be non-essential modifications of natural waters, that natural mineral waters are only one feature prescribed by spas and health resorts and that mineral waters are not eligible for consideration for acceptance as individual products, since there is no convincing evidence to show that the many therapeutic claims which are made for these preparations as bottled for individual use are valid." They are usually designated according to the character of their most important medicinal constituent. Thus:

Alkaline waters usually contain appreciable quantities of sodium and magnesium sulfates together with some sodium bicarbonate. Apollinaris, Vichy and the waters from the Capon Springs (W. Va.) are examples.

Carbonated waters are those which have been charged while in the earth with carbon dioxide under pressure. They usually effervesce on coming to the surface. Such waters contain calcium and magnesium carbonates in solution as bicarbonates. Springs in Colorado and Yellowstone Park (Wyoming) yield waters of this class. Artificial carbonated waters may be made by charging water under pressure with carbon dioxide.

Chalybeate waters contain iron in solution or in suspension and are characterized by a ferruginous taste. Upon exposure to the atmosphere the iron is usually precipitated as hydroxide or oxide. Spring and well waters containing iron are very common.

Lithia waters, as a rule, do not contain appreciable quantities of lithium. If present, it occurs in the form of the carbonate or chloride.

Saline waters are sometimes called "purgative waters" and contain relatively large amounts of magnesium and sodium sulfates with sodium chloride. The waters from springs located at Saratoga Springs, N. Y., and from the Blue Lick Springs in Kentucky are examples.

Sulfur waters contain hydrogen sulfide. These waters, *e.g.*, the waters from White Sulphur Springs, W. Va., Richfield Springs, N. Y., etc., deposit sulfur upon exposure to the atmosphere.

Siliceous waters occur in Yellowstone Park and Iceland and contain very small quantities of soluble alkali silicates.

Water constitutes from 75 to 90 per cent of green plants; from 80 to 98 per cent of fruits; and about 70 per cent of the animal body. In the form of water of hydration it enters into the composition of many chemicals.

Physical Properties.—Pure water is a tasteless, odorless, limpid liquid which is colorless in small quantities but greenish-blue in

deep layers. It is only slightly compressible and is a poor conductor
of heat and electricity. At atmospheric pressure (760 mm.) water
exists as a liquid between 0° and 100° C., reaching its greatest
density at 4° C. Below 0° C. it becomes a solid and above 100° C.
a vapor. Viscosity of water decreases very rapidly with rise of
temperature, and is actually eight times as great at 0° C. as at
100° C. This is an important property in filtering and washing
precipitates. When water passes from one physical state to that of
another, heat (energy) is either consumed or liberated. Thus, when
1 Gm. of ice at 0° C. changes to 1 Gm. of water at 0° C., 79.71 calories of heat are required to effect the transformation (heat of fusion
of ice). Likewise, when 1 Gm. of water at 100° C. turns to 1 Gm. of
steam at 100° C., 539.55 calories of heat are consumed (heat of
vaporization). The temperatures at which these transformations
occur are known as melting- or freezing-points (solids to liquids or
vice versa) and as boiling-points (liquids to vapors), respectively.
The boiling-point of a liquid is that temperature at which the pressure of its saturated vapor is equal to the standard atmospheric
pressure (760 mm.). The *specific heat* of a substance is that quantity
of heat expressed in calories required to raise 1 Gm. of it 1° C.
The specific heat of water at 14.5° C. is 1. The unit quantity of
heat is called the *calorie* (cal.). It is the amount of heat required
to raise 1 Gm. of water at 14.5° C. to a temperature of 15.5° C.
The large calorie, or kilocalorie, is 1000 times larger than the calorie.

Water has a high dielectric constant which is extremely important
in its capacity as a solvent dipole. The dielectric constant is related
to the separation of charge within the water molecule as a result of
its nonlinear "bent" shape (angle of 105°). The negative charge
may be considered as being localized at the oxygen end of the molecule whereas the positive charge is localized at the hydrogen end.
A more extended discussion of its effects as a solvent dipole may
be found on p. 168.

Most natural waters will contain suspended or colloidal solids
such as dirt, silt, rust, etc., which may be removed by sedimenta-
tion, coagulation, or filtration. Bacteria are always present and
are reduced in number usually by chlorination or other processes.
There are always dissolved electrolytes producing ions of Na^+, K^+,
Ca^{++}, Mg^{++}, Fe^{+++}, Sr^{++}, Ba^{++}, etc. with HCO_3^-, $CO_3^=$, Cl^-
$SO_4^=$, NO_3^-, etc. Actually, then, all water is in a sense mineral water.

A concentration of solid in water of most municipalities ranges
from about 20 ppm. for New York City to about 500 ppm. for Kala-
mazoo, Michigan. A pharmaceutical can be altered in clarity,
color, taste and, oftentimes, in therapeutic effect by the water used.
The U.S.P. and N.F. in most products recommend a suitable form of
water. It is somewhat difficult to explain the choice of "water" for
some U.S.P. and N.F. preparations (see discussion, p. 46).

The dissolved impurities (including minerals) in all ordinary potable waters amount to very little, usually less than 0.1 of 1 per cent. One of the chief factors that determines the value of a water for domestic and commercial purposes is its hardness. This property is occasioned by the presence in solution of varying amounts of calcium, iron, and/or magnesium salts, which convert the ordinary soap (water-soluble sodium and/or potassium salts of high molecular weight fatty acids) into water-insoluble calcium, iron, and/or magnesium salts of the fatty acids (1). These same metals present as bicarbonate (temporary hard water) will likewise react with soap.

$$(1) \quad 2RCOONa + CaSO_4 \rightarrow (RCOO)_2Ca \downarrow + Na_2SO_4$$

Water-soluble   Hardening   Water-insoluble
   soap   agent   soap

Only when all of the hardening substances have been precipitated as a water-insoluble curd by the above mechanism will the soap begin to lather. It is apparent that hard water may be undesirable in many respects and, therefore, methods of removing hardness have received much attention. Water may possess *temporary* or *permanent* hardness or both.

Temporary hardness is caused by the presence in the water of soluble calcium or magnesium bicarbonates. These bicarbonates are formed by the action of water charged with carbon dioxide percolating through limestone deposits to cause the following reaction to take place (2).

$$(2) \quad CaCO_3 + H_2O + CO_2 \rightarrow Ca(HCO_3)_2$$

Water-insoluble   Water-soluble

Temporarily hard water may be "softened" by the following procedures:

1. *Boiling.*—The carbon dioxide that has held the insoluble calcium and magnesium carbonates in solution as bicarbonates is driven off by boiling and the insoluble normal carbonate is precipitated (3).

$$(3) \quad Ca(HCO_3)_2 + heat \rightarrow CaCO_3 \downarrow + H_2O + CO_2 \uparrow$$

This method, of course, is not too satisfactory when large volumes of "softened" water are needed.

2. *Clark's Lime Process.*—Clark, in 1841, suggested that slaked lime, in quantities just sufficient to react with the bicarbonate ion, be added to the water, thus precipitating the normal carbonate (4).

$$(4) \quad Ca(HCO_3)_2 + Ca(OH)_2 \rightarrow 2CaCO_3 \downarrow + 2H_2O$$

Care must be taken not to add too much slaked lime since this will impart a new hardness to the water which is more difficult to remove than the original.

3. *Addition of Soluble Alkali Carbonates or Hydroxides.*—Sodium carbonate, for example, when added to temporarily hard water will precipitate the normal carbonate (5).

(5) $Ca(HCO_3)_2 + Na_2CO_3 \rightarrow CaCO_3 \downarrow + 2NaHCO_3$

This manner of softening water is familiar to the housewife through the use of *washing soda* ($Na_2CO_3.10H_2O$) as a water softener in the laundry.

By furnishing hydroxyl ions, sodium hydroxide, or borax (sodium borate), on the other hand, converts the bicarbonates to slaked lime (6) which reacts with the calcium or magnesium bicarbonate still remaining (4).

(6) $2NaOH + Ca(HCO_3)_2 \rightarrow Ca(OH)_2 + 2NaHCO_3$
$Na_2B_4O_7 + 3H_2O \rightleftarrows 2NaBO_2 + 2H_3BO_3$
$NaBO_2 + 2H_2O \rightleftarrows NaOH + H_3BO_3$

4. *Addition of Ammonia.*—Household ammonia is also used for softening water (7).

(7) $Ca(HCO_3)_2 + 2NH_3 \rightarrow CaCO_3 \downarrow + (NH_4)_2CO_3$

5. *Zeolite Process.*—Artificial zeolites were introduced by Gans (1910) as a means of softening both temporarily and permanently hard waters. They make use of an ion-exchange reaction for softening water. It is a sodium aluminum silicate (said to be $Na_2H_6Al_2Si_2O_{11}$), and may be simply represented by the symbol, Na_2Zeol. By passing the hard water through the zeolite, an exchange of the "water-hardening" cations is made for "non-hardening" sodium ions (8).

(8) $Na_2Zeol + Ca(HCO_3)_2 \rightarrow CaZeol + 2NaHCO_3$

When the zeolite is all converted to the CaZeol form it obviously can no longer furnish sodium ions. To restore its activity a strong solution of sodium chloride is allowed to flow through the inactivated zeolite, converting it to the sodium form again (9).

(9) $CaZeol + 2NaCl \rightarrow Na_2Zeol + CaCl_2$

6. *De-ionized or Demineralized Water.*—The latest method for softening both types of water is an outgrowth of the desire to obtain water approximating distilled water in purity without going through the wasteful and expensive distillation procedure. Water may be de-ionized for one to ten per cent of the cost of preparing it by distillation. Practically all of the procedures previously mentioned leave some chemical in the water, although the water may be "softened" in the ordinary sense of the word. The presence of salts in water is undesirable in many manufacturing processes. The development of commercial *resinous ion-exchangers* in 1935 made possible the removal of both cations and anions from water. The removal of salts

from water by this process consists of two steps. The *first step* is a removal of the cations by passing the water through a *hydrogen-exchange resin* (HResin or cation exchange resin) which converts any salt to the corresponding acid by giving up a hydrogen ion in exchange for the metal ion (10).

(10) $2HResin + Ca(HCO_3)_2 \rightarrow Ca(Resin)_2 + 2H_2CO_3 (2H_2O + 2CO_2 \uparrow)$

The *second step* accomplishes the removal of all anions (now in the form of acids) by passage of the water through another resin (usually an amine-formaldehyde resin, anion resin) whereby the $-NH_2$ groups neutralize the acids (11). Usually the process is carried out

(11) $Resin{-}NH_2 + HCl \rightarrow Resin{-}NH_2 \cdot HCl$

with four columns (two of each type resin, alternately and in series) because the highly ionized cations (Na^+ and K^+) are removed first as are the anions of the highly ionized acids (Cl^- and $SO_4^=$).

Carbonic acid is not completely removed in a single pass through the anion resin bed since the weak acids are not removed until after the strong acids have been eliminated.

The water which finally issues from the de-ionizer compares very favorably with distilled water in purity and it can be produced at a lower cost. Indeed, the U.S.P. XV modified the name and monograph of the traditional Distilled Water to permit the use of deionized water (*q.v.*) under the title of Purified Water. Ion-exchange resins will only remove ionizable impurities such as sodium, potassium, calcium, magnesium, chlorides, sulfates, bicarbonates, carbonates, hydroxides, etc. Demineralized water is not suitable when bacteria, pyrogens, organic impurities, etc. are objectionable. When sterility is necessary in pharmacies, hospitals, and biological plants, de-ionized water is not recommended.

Permanent hardness is caused by the presence in solution of the sulfates, chlorides or hydroxides of calcium and/or magnesium. These objectionable salts cannot be removed by boiling or by lime treatment of the water. Permanently hard water may be softened by the following procedures.

1. *Addition of Soluble Carbonates.*—By adding soluble carbonates (*e.g.*, Na_2CO_3) to the hard water the insoluble carbonates of calcium and magnesium are precipitated (12).

(12) $MgSO_4(or\ CaSO_4) + Na_2CO_3 \rightarrow MgCO_3(or\ CaCO_3) \downarrow + Na_2SO_4$

2. *Zeolite Process.*—As previously indicated, this process applies equally well to temporarily and permanently hard waters (13).

(13) $Na_2Zeol + CaSO_4 \rightarrow CaZeol + Na_2SO_4$

3. *De-ionized or Demineralized Water.*—The resinous ion ex-
changers also soften both types of water, inasmuch as all anions and
cations are removed irrespective of the salts. The removal of $CaSO_4$
from permanently hard water is carried out by the typical two-step
mechanism (14) (15).

$$(14) \quad 2HResin + CaSO_4 \rightarrow Ca(Resin)_2 + H_2SO_4$$
$$(15) \quad 2Resin{-}NH_2 + H_2SO_4 \rightarrow (Resin{-}NH_2)_2 \cdot H_2SO_4$$

4. *Sequestration and Chelation.*—The principle of sequestration
has been utilized in pharmaceuticals for many, many years. A
general definition of the word means the act of withdrawing or retir-
ing, also to take possession of by confiscating or appropriating.
Chemically, *sequestering agents* decrease the concentration of a
multivalent positive ion (copper, calcium, ferrous, ferric, etc.) in
solution, by combining with it to form a complex negative ion.
Usually the concentration of the multivalent positive ion remaining
is insufficient to enter into any of its characteristic chemical reactions, *i.e.*, oxidation or precipitation. By sequestration the multivalent positive ion has disappeared from the solution without
being evolved as a gas, removed as a precipitate or deposited as
an element. The element, however, is still in solution but not in the
form of its ions.

Perhaps one of the most widely used sequestering agents is
Graham's Salt or sodium metaphosphate $(NaPO_3)$ that has been
converted to a polymer by controlled crystallization. This polymer,
known commercially as Calgon is a very effective water-softener by
acting to remove the calcium ions as a very slightly ionized complex.
The polymerized salt, sodium hexametaphosphate,[1] when placed in
water ionizes as follows:

$$(NaPO_3)_6 \rightleftarrows 2Na^+ + Na_4(PO_3)_6^= \rightleftarrows 2Na^+ + Na_2(PO_3)_6^{==}$$

When multivalent ions such as calcium ions are present in hard
water, they are removed by the anion.

$$Ca^{++} + Na_4(PO_3)_6^= \rightleftarrows 2Na^+ + Na_2Ca(PO_3)_6^=$$

A complete equation would be:

$$Ca^{++} + (NaPO_3)_6 \rightarrow 4Na^+ + Na_2Ca(PO_3)_6$$

Bivalent metal ions that respond to sequestering agents are calcium, barium, strontium, magnesium, copper, zinc, lead, manganese,
ferrous, cobalt, and nickel. Trivalent metal ions such as ferric and
aluminum are not so readily sequestered. However, bismuth and
antimony are readily sequestered by tartrates or citrates.

---

[1] Actually, the polymerized form is not a hexametaphosphate but is probably
made up of chains of molecules of variable length, possibly up to 1000 units. For
our purposes, however, the hexametaphosphate will serve to illustrate the principle
of sequestration.

Another efficient sequestering agent is Trilon B (Versene). It is the sodium salt of ethylene diamine tetraäcetic acid (EDTA) and may be more precisely described as a *chelating agent* (Greek: chelos, claw).

It ionizes in solution as follows:

$$Na_4EDTA \rightarrow 2Na^+ + Na_2EDTA^=$$

In the presence of calcium ions or other sequesterable ions the following reaction occurs:

$$Na_4EDTA + Ca^{++} \rightarrow 2Na^+ + Na_2CaEDTA$$
$$\text{(soluble)}$$

The structural representation shows graphically how the metal ion is chelated, *i.e.*, is held in the "claw" of the ligand (EDTA).

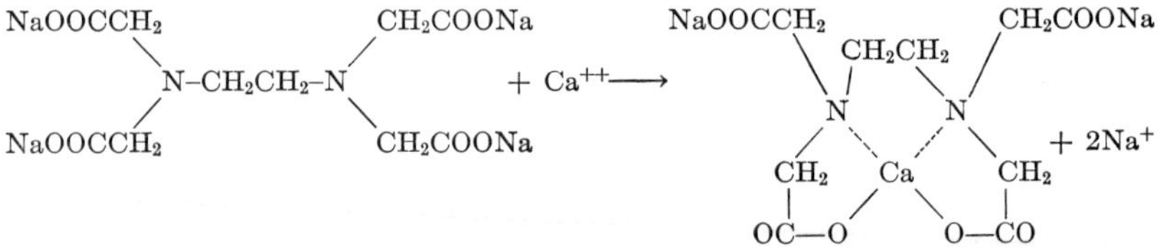

Calcium Disodium Edetate U.S.P. is used orally or intravenously as a sequestering agent for treating lead poisoning presumably by exchanging calcium for lead which is removed as a water-soluble complex. For further discussion of sequestration see page 228.

The hardness of water is variously expressed. On Clark's scale (English) it is the number of grains of calcium carbonate per gallon of 70,000 grains of water; in Germany, it is expressed as the number of parts of calcium oxide per 100,000 parts of water; and in France as the number of parts of calcium carbonate per 100,000 parts of water. In the United States, hardness is represented as 1 part of calcium carbonate or its equivalent in 1,000,000 parts of water (1 milligram per liter). Hardness may be determined by shaking a measured quantity of the sample of water with gradually added portions of a soap solution (standardized against known calcium chloride solution) until a permanent lather is produced. It may also be determined by titration of the water sample with the Edetates using a suitable indicator (*e.g.*, Eriochrome Black T).

Chemical Properties.—In most chemical reactions, water plays merely a mechanical part, *viz.*, that of a solvent for reacting substances to ionize in since most chemical reactions do not take place without ions. Nevertheless, this relatively stable substance does possess certain well-defined chemical properties which are exhibited on certain occasions. For example, it combines with many oxides to form acids and bases (16 and 17);

(16) $SO_3 + H_2O \rightleftarrows H_2SO_4$

(17) $Na_2O + H_2O \rightarrow 2NaOH$

Oxides of the non-metals such as nitrogen dioxide (NO_2), sulfur dioxide (SO_2), sulfur trioxide (SO_3), phosphorus pentoxide (P_2O_5) are the so-called acid anhydrides and react with water to form acids.

$3NO_2 + H_2O \rightarrow 2HNO_3 + NO \uparrow$

$SO_2 + H_2O \rightarrow H_2SO_3$

$SO_3 + H_2O \rightarrow H_2SO_4$

$P_2O_5 + 3H_2O \rightarrow 2H_3PO_4$

Also, the gas ammonia (NH_3) reacts to form a basic solution (see p. 72).

$NH_3 + H_2O \rightleftarrows NH_4OH$

Hydrates are formed with many salts (18 and 19);

(18) $FeSO_4 + 7H_2O \rightleftarrows FeSO_4 \cdot 7H_2O$

(19) $CuSO_4 + 5H_2O \rightarrow CuSO_4 \cdot 5H_2O$

     (white)   (blue)

It reacts chemically with some substances in such a manner that double decomposition (metathesis) takes place (20). Such an interaction is called *hydrolysis*.

(20) $PCl_3 + 3H_2O \rightarrow H_3PO_3 + 3HCl$

Certain elements such as aluminum, lead, arsenic, antimony, bismuth, manganese, and iron form salts which are prone to hydrolysis (21, 22, 23).

(21) $Al(CH_3COO)_3 + H_2O \rightarrow Al(OH)(CH_3COO)_2 + CH_3COOH$

(22) $Bi (NO_3)_3 + 2H_2O \rightarrow Bi(OH)_2NO_3 \downarrow + 2HNO_3$

                      (white)

(23) $Fe_2(SO_4)_3 + 2H_2O \rightarrow Fe_2(OH)_2(SO_4)_2 \downarrow + H_2SO_4$

Properties of salts of these elements make possible the pharmaceuticals of Aluminum Subacetate Solution U.S.P. and Bismuth Subcarbonate U.S.P.

A mere trace of moisture very often exerts what is thought to be a catalytic influence upon many chemical changes. For example, perfectly dry hydrogen and oxygen cannot be made to unite when exposed to the action of an electric spark. However, under like conditions, a trace of moisture causes them to combine with explosive violence. Also the presence of water in ointments of some substances is quite essential for therapeutic effect. Boric acid and calomel, for example, are much less effective in anhydrous ointment bases.

Other materials such as digitalis are adversely affected by water. The U.S.P. XVII describes three methods for the determination of water in drugs and chemicals on page 924. The N.F. XII includes a method on page 515.

Recognition of Water by U.S.P. XVII With Tests for Purity.—The U.S.P. XVII recognizes WATER, PURIFIED WATER, WATER FOR INJECTION, BACTERIOSTATIC WATER FOR INJECTION and STERILE WATER FOR INJECTION.—Water (H_2O), U.S.P. XVII, must conform to the following requirements and tests: It is a clear, colorless, odorless liquid.

It should have a range of hydrogen-ion concentration corresponding to a pH of approximately not less than 6.3 and not more than 8.3. The limit of the former may be determined by adding 2 drops of methyl red pH indicator (transition interval, 4.2 [red] to 6.3 [yellow] pH) to 10 ml. of Water contained in a clean test-tube. No pink or red color should be produced. The latter limit may be determined by adding 2 drops of phenolphthalein T.S. (transition interval, 8.3 [colorless] to 10.0 [red] pH) to another 10 ml. portion of Water contained in a clean test-tube. No pink or red color should develop.

When heated nearly to the boiling-point and agitated, Water should not evolve a disagreeable odor. The soluble impurities should not exceed 100 mg. per 100 ml.

Dissolved carbon dioxide in Water attacks untarnished lead, copper and some other heavy metal surfaces and forms soluble bicarbonates which may be poisonous. Therefore, the limit of the amount of heavy metals present in Water is specified and tested for as follows: 1 ml. of diluted acetic acid and then 10 ml. of freshly prepared hydrogen sulfide T.S. are added to 40 ml. of Water, heated to 50° C., and allowed to stand for ten minutes. The color of the liquid when viewed downward over a white surface is no darker than the color of a mixture of 40 ml. of the same Water with 1 ml. of diluted acetic acid and 10 ml. of Purified Water, using matched Nessler tubes for the comparison.

The limit of soluble zinc salts is tested for as follows: 3 drops of glacial acetic acid, then 0.5 ml. of potassium ferrocyanide T.S. are added to 50 ml. of Water contained in a glass tube. The solution should not show more turbidity than that produced by 50 ml. of Purified Water in a similar glass tube, treated in the same manner, and viewed downward over a dark surface (24).

$$(24)\ K_4Fe(CN)_6 + 2ZnSO_4 \rightarrow Zn_2Fe(CN)_6 \downarrow \text{ (white)} + 2K_2SO_4$$

The U.S.P. XVII requires that Water meet the standards for freedom from bacteriological impurities (*e.g.*, *coliform organisms*) required for potable water by the United States Public Health Service.

Water U.S.P. is used in many U.S.P. and N.F. preparations. The selection of Water U.S.P. for only external preparations is not true in actuality since it is used in most fluidextracts and tinctures, some elixirs, syrups and mucilages. Many external pharmaceuticals such as Aluminum Acetate Solution and Benzyl Benzoate Lotion, employ Water U.S.P. Several factors such as alkalinity and the possible presence of reducing substances are the disadvantages of Water U.S.P. Water when used as a solvent for reagents or in preparing test solutions must always be Purified Water (see U.S.P. XVII, pp. 7 and 928). "Carbon dioxide-free water" is Purified Water that has been boiled for 5 minutes or more and protected from reabsorption of carbon dioxide while cooling.

Purified Water, U.S.P. XVII (Distilled Water U.S.P. XIV), is defined as "water obtained by distillation[1] or by ion-exchange treatment." The present revision of the U.S. Pharmacopeia does not include a specific method for its preparation.

Official Purified Water is described as a "clear, colorless, odorless liquid." It should have a pH approaching neutrality as determined by no red color developing when 2 drops of methyl red T.S. is added to 10 ml. of Purified Water contained in a test-tube and by no blue color being produced when 5 drops of bromothymol blue T.S. (transition interval, 6.0 [yellow] to 7.6 [blue] pH) is added to 10 ml. of Purified Water. One hundred milliliters of Purified Water when evaporated on a water-bath and dried to constant weight at 105° C., should not leave a residue weighing more than 1 mg. (10 parts per million). Purified Water should not respond to appropriate limit tests for sulfate, chloride, calcium, ammonia, carbon dioxide, oxidizable substances and heavy metals. Chlorine is often present in municipal water and to prevent it coming over during distillation some sodium thiosulfate may be added to the still. When Purified Water is allowed to stand, minute stringy or flocculent particles occasionally make their appearance. These particles are microsopic plants (confervae) developed from spores which have fallen into the Purified Water. They may be minimized or entirely prevented by allowing only air that has been passed through a pledget of cotton, to come in contact with the Purified Water. Purified Water has the same tests for bacteriological purity as does Water U.S.P.

A caution for its use is given by the U.S.P. to the effect that Purified Water is not to be used for parenteral administration or in preparations to be used parenterally. Water for Injection, Bacteriostatic Water for Injection or Sterile Water for Injection is required for such products.

The N.F. and U.S.P. require that Purified Water U.S.P. be used in all tests. Purified Water is employed as a solvent in many U.S.P. and N.F. preparations. It is not used in any of the official fluid-extracts. Of the tinctures only Iodine Tincture U.S.P. and those using Diluted Alcohol utilize Purified Water. Most solutions, syrups, and elixirs, and all aromatic waters employ Purified Water as a solvent. In pharmaceuticals, Purified Water is the most widely used of the official forms.

---

[1] Distilled Water Preparation, Lane, Manzelli, and Flock, Am. Prof. Phar., **19**, 204, 1953.

Water for Injection, U.S.P. XVII, is water purified by distillation and contains no added substances. The U.S.P. cautions:—*Water for Injection is intended for use as a solvent for the preparation of parenteral solutions. For parenteral solutions that are prepared under aseptic conditions and are not sterilized by appropriate filtration or in the final container, first render the Water for Injection sterile and thereafter protect it from bacterial contamination.* It is important to note that this water has no sterility requirement and is not intended to be put up in packages for pharmaceutical use as such. Many official Injections, however, are to be made using Water for Injection as the solvent with suitable provisions for sterilization following preparation of the solution. Because it is to be used for parenteral solutions it is necessary that it be free of pyrogens (bacterial decomposition products causing fever). This is determined by a requirement that Water for Injection meets the requirements of the *Pyrogen Test* (U.S.P. XVII, p. 863). The other tests that the product must conform to are those that are specified for Purified Water (*q.v.*).

Water for Injection is to be preserved in tight containers which may be stored at a temperature below or above the range in which the growth of microbes may occur.

Sterile Water for Injection, U.S.P. XVII (Water for Parenterals) is Water for Injection which has been sterilized and suitably packaged for pharmaceutical use. It contains no bacteriostatic agent. This official water is required to be a clear, colorless, odorless liquid. The U.S.P. sets up a requirement for chloride content so that it does not exceed 0.5 parts per million. This test employs the *Special Distilled Water* described in U.S.P. XVII (p. 900) and compares the turbidity produced with silver nitrate T.S. in a standard against the sample. Not only is there a sterility requirement (U.S.P. XVII, p. 829) but pyrogen is also required to be absent. The total solids content of the product depends on the size of the container used: 40 parts per million for glass containers up to and including 30 ml.; 30 parts per million for 30 to 100 ml. glass containers; and 20 parts per million for larger glass containers. Inasmuch as none of the containers now available is able to withstand completely the solvent action of hot water it is necessary to provide allowances for the increased solids content thus introduced during the heat sterilization procedure. These allowances take into account the fact that the dissolved solids will be roughly proportional to the exposed surfaces of the container so that the smaller the container, the higher the limit. This accounts for the three "stages" of exemption with respect to container sizes. In any event it is noticeably higher than that of Water for Injection (10 parts per million) which is not heat sterilized. The other requirements that this official water must meet are the same as those for Purified Water except as noted above.

The product is stored in single dose glass containers (preferably Type I or Type II glass [U.S.P. XVII, p. 901]) not larger than 1000 ml. and is to be labeled to indicate that it contains no bacteriostatic agent or other added substance, and that it is not suitable for intra-vascular injection without first being made approximately isotonic by addition of a suitable solute.

HYDROGEN PEROXIDE

Hydrogen Peroxide Solution, U.S.P. XVII

Formula, H_2O_2.   Molecular Weight, 34.02

History.[1]—Hydrogen peroxide was discovered by Thenard in 1818 when he found that the solution produced in the reaction of barium peroxide and nitric acid (1) could be made to evolve oxygen. This liquid was at first called "oxygenated acid" until further work showed that both the barium and acid radicals could be eliminated. He, therefore, concluded that the substance he had produced was "oxygenated water"—or, as we know it, hydrogen peroxide.

(1) $BaO_2 + 2HNO_3 \rightarrow H_2O_2 + Ba(NO_3)_2$

It took about 50 years before its potential usefulness as a bleach was recognized and it is believed that the first commercial production took place in Berlin in 1873. Its use in medicine began in this period as well as its use as a hair bleach, a use which was even then greeted with mixed emotions, *e.g.*, "that offensive blonde shade . . . attracts attention and curiosity."

Occurrence.—Because of its instability, hydrogen peroxide is found occurring naturally only in very small quantities in air, dew, rain, and snow.

Physical Properties.—Pure hydrogen peroxide is a rather unstable colorless, astringent, syrupy liquid at room temperature having a specific gravity of 1.463 (0° C.) and a boiling point of 62.8° C./21 mm. Pure hydrogen peroxide will decompose only very slowly. When heated to 100° C. it decomposes with explosive violence to form water and oxygen (2). It may be separated with very little decomposition from its aqueous solutions by fractional distillation under reduced pressure. When a concentrated solution (96 per cent) of hydrogen peroxide is cooled sufficiently, colorless, transparent, prismatic crystals separate out.[2]   These crystals melt at −1.7° C.

---

[1] For a review and bibliography see ACS monograph No. 128: W C. Schumb, C. N. Satterfield, R. N. Wentworth, *Hydrogen Peroxide* (Reinhold, New York, 1955).

[2] Production of 100% anhydrous hydrogen peroxide by continuous fractional crystallization is described by Crewson and Ryan in U.S. pat. 2,724,640 (to Becco).

Cryoscopic determinations show its molecular weight to be 34.016 and its formula H_2O_2 (available O_2, 47.03%). At ordinary temperatures hydrogen peroxide is miscible in all proportions with water, alcohol or ether. It is more soluble in ether than in water and, therefore, may be extracted from its aqueous solution by shaking the two liquids in a separatory funnel.

Chemical Properties.—Hydrogen peroxide is stable in solutions of high purity but due to contaminants will decompose unless a stabilizer is present. Several concentrations are available including 90, 50, 35, and 27.5 per cent solutions. The decomposition is exothermic but the rate of decomposition is very slow in the absence of catalysts (impurities).

$$(2) \quad 2H_2O_2 \rightleftarrows 2H_2O + O_2 \ (46{,}200 \text{ cal.})$$

Its structural formula may be represented by: H-O-O-H. The oxygen-to-oxygen bond is a very weak covalent bond and many substances in minute amounts cause the decomposition of hydrogen peroxide. Those metals having more than one valence state, i.e. chromium, copper, iron, and mercury, increase the loss of oxygen from peroxide solutions. Dust and dirt of most types will catalyze decomposition. Aluminum does not catalyze decomposition of hydrogen peroxide solutions and therefore tanks of this metal are good storage containers.

Numerous substances have been suggested as hydrogen peroxide "stabilizers." Acids or acid salts are satisfactory and phosphates and tin salts are used commercially. However, the hydrogen peroxide used in therapeutics must be readily decomposed by catalase and many good stabilizers poison or inactivate this enzyme. A distinct retardation of catalase is exhibited by 0.1 per cent of chloral hydrate, salts of alkali metals, and phenol; and complete inactivation is given by sulfuric or phosphoric acids. For pharmaceutical preparations an excellent stabilizer is 0.02 per cent quinine sulfate.

Stabilizers are of three types: (1) acidic, (2) complex-forming, and (3) adsorptive.

(1) All acids, inorganic or organic, increase the stability of hydrogen peroxide. Alkaline solutions of hydrogen peroxide, even if pure, are much more unstable.

(2) Complex-forming stabilizers include acetanilid,[1] phenacetin, quinine sulfate, and 8-hydroxyquinoline. They supposedly remove heavy metal ions from solution by forming a coordination complex. Another hypothesis suggests that, because hydrogen peroxide is light sensitive and will be decomposed by ultraviolet rays, these compounds act as "screening-agents." In this way they protect the peroxide from the effects of sunlight.

[1] Acetanilid at 0.03% is usually present in official hydrogen peroxide.

(3) The adsorptive power of alumina, silica, hydrous antimony oxide, or hydrous stannic oxide is used in peroxide solutions to remove impurities.

Hydrogen peroxide is very slightly ionized in water.

(3) $H_2O_2 \rightleftarrows H^+ + OOH^-$
$Ka = 2.4 \times 10^{-12}$ (pH 5.8)

(4) $H_2O_2 \rightleftarrows 2H^+ + O_2^=$
$Ka = 1.55 \times 10^{-12}$ (pH 5.9)

The hydronium ion concentration is about 12 times that of pure water. It is a weaker acid than boric acid or carbonic acid. The presence in trace amounts of acidic substances such as sulfuric acid, phosphoric acid (used commercially), benzoic acid, citric acid, or acid salts will greatly increase the stability of hydrogen peroxide solutions. Solutions containing 0.05 per cent phosphoric acid in clean containers protected from light are claimed to have a loss of about 1 per cent per year.

Hydrogen peroxide in water solution ionizes to yield the peroxide ion:

(5) $H_2O_2 \rightleftarrows 2H^+ + O_2^=$

It reacts with alkaline hydroxides of barium and strontium to form peroxides which easily become hydrated and appear as crystalline precipitates (6) (7).

(6) $Ba(OH)_2 + H_2O_2 \rightleftarrows BaO_2 + 2H_2O$
(7) $BaO_2 + 8H_2O \rightleftarrows BaO_2 \cdot 8H_2O$

The existence of the peroxide ion may also be shown by reaction (1) and also by the fact that sodium peroxide may be formed by adding hydrogen peroxide to sodium hydroxide.

Alkalies generally are considered to increase decomposition of peroxide solutions and such is actually the case. The real cause, however, is not the alkalinity of the medium but the traces of catalysts inherently present in the alkalies used. Six per cent hydrogen peroxide solution with 20 per cent specially purified sodium hydroxide showed a decomposition of only 5 per cent in twenty-four hours in contrast to 53 per cent when U.S.P. Sodium Hydroxide was used.

Addition compounds are formed with many organic and inorganic compounds:

$(NH_4)_2SO_4 \cdot H_2O_2$; $K_2CO_3 \cdot 2H_2O_2$; $Na_2CO_3 \cdot 1\frac{1}{2}H_2O_2$

A crystalline compound forms with some nitrogen (amine) compounds such as urea, $H_2NCONH_2 \cdot H_2O_2$, which is stabilized by a trace of citric acid (also acetanilid). In anhydrous media urea peroxide is a useful source of peroxide in therapy.

Hydrogen peroxide unites with some anhydrides to form the per-acids in a manner similar to that of water in forming acids (8, 9, 10).

(8) $H_2O + SO_3 \rightarrow H_2SO_4$

(9) $H_2O_2 + SO_3 \rightarrow H_2SO_5$
        peroxysulfuric acid

(10) $H_2O_2 + 2SO_3 \rightarrow H_2S_2O_8$
        peroxydisulfuric acid

The oxidation number of oxygen in the peroxide ion is -1. When hydrogen peroxide functions as an oxidizing agent each oxygen atom changes from a -1 to -2. This shows then that each molecule of H_2O_2 has an oxidation number of 2 or requires the reducing agent to supply 2 electrons (11). An acid medium is most efficient.

(11) $H_2O_2 + 2H^+ + 2\,\epsilon \rightarrow 2H_2O$

The two electrons (ϵ) are furnished by a reducing agent, $e.g.$, iodide

(12) $H_2O_2 + 2HI \rightarrow 2H_2O + I_2$

(12). It is an active oxidizing agent that resembles ozone and has a wide field of application. It is better than iodate, hypobromite or lead dioxide. Sulfides are converted into sulfates (13); sulfites are oxidized to sulfates (14); arsenites to arsenates (15); and ferrous salts changed to ferric salts (16).

(13) $PbS + 4H_2O_2 \xrightarrow{\ H^+\ } PbSO_4 + 4H_2O$

(14) $Na_2SO_3 + H_2O_2 \xrightarrow{\ H^+\ } Na_2SO_4 + H_2O$

(15) $Na_3AsO_3 + H_2O_2 \xrightarrow{\ H^+\ } Na_3AsO_4 + H_2O$

(16) $2FeCl_2 + H_2O_2 + 2HCl \longrightarrow 2FeCl_3 + 2H_2O$

Hydrogen peroxide also acts as a reducing agent. In this case it is generally used in acid media where it is better than ferrous ions but less useful than iodide ions.

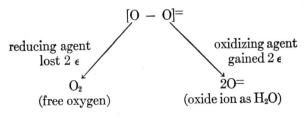

reducing agent
lost 2 ϵ

O_2
(free oxygen)

oxidizing agent
gained 2 ϵ

$2O^=$
(oxide ion as H_2O)

Silver oxide is reduced with a rapid evolution of oxygen (17); potassium permanganate, in acid (H_2SO_4) solution, is rapidly changed to manganese sulfate, potassium sulfate and oxygen (18); and both hydrogen peroxide and ozone are reduced when they interact (19). Usually hydrogen peroxide acts as a reducing agent with those metallic oxides which easily lose all or part of their oxygen, *e.g.*, Ag_2O. Oxygen is always evolved when hydrogen peroxide functions as a reducing agent.

(17) $Ag_2O + H_2O_2 \rightarrow 2Ag + H_2O + O_2 \uparrow$

(18) $2KMnO_4 + 3H_2SO_4 + 5H_2O_2 \rightarrow K_2SO_4 + 2MnSO_4 + 8H_2O + 5O_2 \uparrow$

(19) $H_2O_2 + O_3 \rightarrow H_2O + 2O_2 \uparrow$

The official assay of hydrogen peroxide depends on its reducing properties in the reaction expressed by equation 18.

Official Tests for Identity.—1. When 1 ml. of Hydrogen Peroxide Solution is shaken with 10 ml. of distilled water containing 1 drop of diluted sulfuric acid, and then 2 ml. of ether and a drop of potassium dichromate test solution are added, an evanescent blue color will appear in the aqueous layer. The color may be transferred to the ether layer by shaking the liquid and allowing it to stand. When sulfuric acid acts upon potassium dichromate, dichromic acid and potassium sulfate are formed (20).

(20) $K_2Cr_2O_7 + H_2SO_4 \rightarrow H_2Cr_2O_7 + K_2SO_4$

The dichromic acid then reacts with the hydrogen peroxide to form a perchromic acid, thought to have the formula $HO.CrO_2.O.O.CrO_2.OH$ (blue color). This perchromic acid is more soluble in ether than in water and in ethereal solution the blue color is much more permanent.

All peroxides in solution will give the same reaction. For examples, one may refer to zinc peroxide, barium peroxide, sodium peroxide, sodium carbonate peroxide, sodium pyrophosphate peroxide. calcium peroxide, and magnesium peroxide.

Solutions of sodium perborate likewise give the reactions of a peroxide.

2. When a solution of hydrogen peroxide is added to a mixture of a diluted tincture of guaiac and malt infusion, a blue color is produced. Tincture of guaiac contains substituted diphenyl phenols which are readily oxidized to colored (blue) quinones. The malt infusion contains the enzyme, catalase, that decomposes the peroxide. A similar and better test is to use benzidine (p,p'-diaminodiphenyl) in place of the tincture of guaiac. This a modification of the test for blood.

5

Commercial Manufacture.—The commercial manufacture of hydrogen peroxide was influenced greatly by World War II. The most significant progress was not made so much in methods of synthesis, as in the large scale methods for concentrating hydrogen peroxide by distillation under reduced pressure. Solutions containing 35 per cent of H_2O_2 were the highest concentrations available in commercial quantities previous to the war, but now it is possible to obtain up to 100 per cent concentrations.

The methods used for the commercial production of hydrogen peroxide for medicinal and industrial use may be divided into two major classifications: (A) non-electrolytic and (B) electrolytic.

A. Methods of this class include: (1) Barium peroxide with sulfuric or phosphoric acid (eq. 21 and 22); (2) sodium peroxide with sulfuric acid at about $-2°$ C. (eq. 23); and (3) direct synthesis from hydrogen and oxygen.

$$(21)\ BaO_2 \cdot 8H_2O + H_2SO_4 \rightarrow BaSO_4 \downarrow + H_2O_2 + 8H_2O$$

$$(22)\ 3BaO_2 \cdot 8H_2O + 2H_3PO_4 \rightarrow Ba_3(PO_4)_2 \downarrow + 3H_2O_2 + 24H_2O$$

$$(23)\ Na_2O_2 + H_2SO_4 \rightarrow H_2O_2 + Na_2SO_4$$

Because of shortage of electrical power due to intensive Allied bombing during World War II, the reduction of 2-ethyl anthraquinone and the subsequent oxidation of the resultant 2-ethyl anthranol offered an attractive non-electrolytic peroxide synthesis to German chemists. The process in general is known as the "autoxidation process" and involves cyclic oxidation and reduction of some easily oxidized organic substance. The net result of the complete cycle is the formation of a molecule of H_2O_2 and the restoration of the organic to its state at the beginning of the cycle.

While actual production of hydrogen peroxide by this method had not had time to expand before the end of the war, the method nevertheless offered a good, non-electrolytic process not requiring an elaborate setup. It is now used by industry and offers a high grade inexpensive hydrogen peroxide.

B. *Electrolytic* hydrogen peroxide is prepared (1) by the electrolysis of sulfuric acid to peroxydisulfuric acid which is hydrolyzed to yield the product and (2) by the electrolysis of ammonium bisulfate solutions to ammonium peroxydisulfate which may be treated in various ways to yield hydrogen peroxide.

1. In this process sulfuric acid is oxidized anodically to peroxydisulfuric acid, $H_2S_2O_8$, (24) which when heated forms peroxysulfuric acid, H_2SO_5 (25) (Caro's acid).

$$(24)\ 2H_2SO_4 \rightarrow H_2S_2O_8 + H_2 \uparrow$$

$$(25)\ H_2S_2O_8 + H_2O \xrightarrow{\Delta} H_2SO_5 + H_2SO_4$$

The peroxysulfuric acid (H_2SO_5) is then hydrolyzed by further heating to yield hydrogen peroxide (26).

(26) $H_2SO_5 + H_2O \xrightarrow{\Delta} H_2O_2 + H_2SO_4$

2. A more usual way is to mix ammonium sulfate and sulfuric acid in the proportions to form ammonium bisulfate (27) and electrolyze the cold solution to form ammonium peroxydisulfate (28) at the anode.

(27) $(NH_4)_2SO_4 + H_2SO_4 \rightarrow 2NH_4HSO_4$
(28) $2NH_4HSO_4 \rightarrow (NH_4)_2S_2O_8 + H_2 \uparrow$

The ammonium peroxydisulfate that is formed is usually treated in one of three ways to yield hydrogen peroxide.

(a) It may be reacted with potassium bisulfate (29) to form relatively insoluble potassium peroxydisulfate which can be hydrolyzed by live steam to yield hydrogen peroxide and potassium bisulfate (30), the vapors being condensed and rectified to obtain the hydrogen peroxide.

(29) $(NH_4)_2S_2O_8 + 2KHSO_4 \rightarrow K_2S_2O_8 + 2NH_4HSO_4$
(30) $K_2S_2O_8 + 2H_2O \rightarrow 2KHSO_4 + H_2O_2$

(b) The ammonium peroxydisulfate may be treated with sulfuric acid and distilled at reduced pressures to give a distillate of water and hydrogen peroxide (31) (32).

(31) $(NH_4)_2S_2O_8 + H_2SO_4 \rightarrow H_2S_2O_8 + (NH_4)_2SO_4$
(32) $H_2S_2O_8 + 2H_2O \rightarrow 2H_2SO_4 + H_2O_2$

(c) According to the Kufstein procedure hydrogen peroxide may be distilled directly from the ammonium peroxydisulfate solution (33).

(33) $(NH_4)_2S_2O_8 + 2H_2O \rightarrow 2NH_4HSO_4 + H_2O_2$

All of the procedures, non-electrolytic and electrolytic, produce a solution of hydrogen peroxide which may be concentrated by distillation under reduced pressure in a suitable apparatus to produce concentrations up to 90 per cent H_2O_2. Until 1955 this was the practical limit of concentration but since then continuous fractional crystallization of the 90 per cent form gives up to virtually 100 per cent concentrations.

Physiological Properties.—Hydrogen peroxide solutions and vapors are nontoxic. However, 30 per cent solutions are caustic. Internal use of solutions, even the 3 per cent, should be avoided because sufficient irritation may develop to cause bleeding and decomposition with the evolution of much oxygen which can be dangerous. Injection of a peroxide solution into body cavities or abscesses is not recommended for the same reason.

The vapor is irritating to the nose and eyes. Contact of the liquid with the skin gives a stinging sensation (more intense with strong solutions) causing the skin to whiten. Usually, the epidermis returns to normal showing no apparent damage. The eyes should be protected with goggles when solutions stronger than 3 per cent are handled.

Hydrogen peroxide in excessive concentrations on the skin is best counteracted by a thorough washing of the area with water.

Uses.—*Hydrogen Peroxide Solution,* U.S.P. XVII, is an aqueous solution containing, in each 100 ml., not less than 2.5 Gm. and not more than 3.5 Gm. of H_2O_2. Not over 0.05 per cent of a suitable preservative may be present. It is a clear, colorless liquid, odorless or having an odor resembling that of ozone. Incompatibilities of hydrogen peroxide, of course, include any substance that may be oxidized (reducing agent) and basic compounds. It forms insoluble calcium and strontium salts and is decomposed by most organic materials. The solution, when free from impurities, keeps fairly well. However, it freezes at 29° F. (−1.5° C.) and should be protected in cold weather. The U.S.P. XVII suggests that it be stored below 35° C. and be in tight, light-resistant containers. A trace of free acid and acetanilid (0.03%) increases its stability by catalytically retarding its decomposition. Other stabilizers may be better but acetanilid does not inactivate catalase. When exposed to the air at ordinary temperatures or when heated, decomposition takes place. When rapidly heated it frequently decomposes suddenly. Because of impurities in the reacting substances used in the manufacture of solutions of hydrogen peroxide, the U.S. Pharmacopeia XVII specifies that the official solution be practically free from arsenic, barium and heavy metals. The amount of non-volatile matter is limited to 30 mg. in 20 ml. of the solution; the free acidity in 25 ml. must not exceed an equivalent of 2.5 ml. of tenth-normal sodium hydroxide solution; and the preservative (usually acetanilid) must not exceed 50 mg. per 100 ml. of solution.

This solution is used as an antiseptic because of the active liberation of oxygen when it comes in contact with tissue (*e.g.*, pus and blood).

Often this property is referred to as "auto-oxidation" (2) and is promoted by catalase of the body tissues. The foaming caused by the liberation of O_2 mechanically cleanses wounds by dislodging fixed bacteria, particles of dirt, etc. Indeed, some authorities feel that the chief virtue of hydrogen peroxide as an antiseptic is its mechanical cleansing action rather than the antiseptic action. Both, however, undoubtedly play a role.

This mechanical action is an important function of hydrogen peroxide which is useful in removing surgical dressings and in loosening ear wax.

The official solution is also used in treating Vincent's stomatitis, the undiluted solution being used as a mouth wash several times daily. Continued use may cause a condition known as "hairy tongue" (hypertrophied filiform papillæ), which disappears on discontinuation of the medication.

The official solution is mildly germicidal but should not be diluted with water to more than twice its volume for antiseptic purposes. Antiseptic action is not fast, but the oxygen released will destroy most pathogenic micro-organisms such as typhoid bacilli, anthrax, staphylococci, etc. Because of its lack of toxicity it is a favorite disinfectant for use in the nose and throat. It is also a chemical antidote for cyanide and phosphorus poisoning through oxidation of the poisonous materials to more or less harmless oxidation products.

2. Stronger solutions of hydrogen peroxide are used as hair bleaches, fabric bleaches, etc. They are particularly desirable because of the harmless nature of the reaction products. Usually a 6 per cent solution (20 volume) is considered adequate as a hair bleach. A small amount of dilute ammonia solution (alkaline media increases decomposition) is usually combined with the peroxide for hair application to soften the hair, remove oils, and hasten the bleaching process.

The action of the normal bacterial flora present in milk is retarded by a concentration of 0.1 per cent hydrogen peroxide and thus the period required for "souring" is greatly extended. This is known as the "buddizing" process and apparently has only a minor effect on the nutritive qualities of the milk. Solutions may be rendered nonpyrogenic by heating with hydrogen peroxide.

Solutions of hydrogen peroxide are frequently said to be of a certain "volume" strength (i.e., 10 volume, 20 volume, etc.). Ordinary 3 per cent hydrogen peroxide solution is a 10 volume peroxide, 6 per cent peroxide is 20 volume, etc. A common commercial strength is 100 volume or 30 per cent hydrogen peroxide (Superoxol and Perhydrol). The volume specification is based on the number of milliliters of oxygen, measured at standard temperature and pressure, liberated by 1 ml. of the peroxide solution when decomposed (2). Thus, if 1 ml. liberates 10 ml. of oxygen it is a 10-volume peroxide, etc.

Hydrogen peroxide is available in several strengths ranging from 3 to 100 per cent. Industrially it is used as a bleach and antiseptic for sugar, soap, oils, paper, etc. Millions of pounds are used annually of which the pharmaceutical applications consume about 5 per cent. A preparation Neoxyn (Rorer) contains H_2O_2 and is recommended for poison ivy

Products that utilize hydrogen peroxide include: urea peroxide and glycerite of hydrogen peroxide.

Urea peroxide (Perhydrit or carbamide peroxide) ($H_2NCONH_2 \cdot H_2O_2$) contains 34 per cent H_2O_2, occurs as a white crystalline solid and is stable in closed containers protected from light and heat. It is very soluble in water but decomposes rapidly. A 10 per cent solution is stable for only about ten days. Solubility in most organic solvents is good, especially in the alcohols, glycols, or glycerin. Anhydrous solvents are recommended, and a common preparation is made by dissolving 4 per cent of urea peroxide in anhydrous glycerin containing 0.1 per cent 8-hydroxy-quinoline. This is equivalent to 1.5 per cent H_2O_2. Remarkable antiseptic properties have been reported for this solution. Using *Cl. welchii* and *Cl. tetani* it showed greater bacteriotoxic action than thirty-two other antiseptic solutions with the exception of Tincture of Iodine U.S.P.

Glycerite of hydrogen peroxide is an anhydrous glycerin solution usually containing 1.5 per cent hydrogen peroxide. A highly concentrated solution (90 per cent) of hydrogen peroxide should be used as the source of H_2O_2. Except for convenience of preparation this solution possesses all the properties of one containing urea peroxide.

Other peroxides in current use include sodium peroxide, sodium carbonate peroxide, sodium pyrophosphate peroxide, calcium peroxide, barium peroxide, magnesium peroxide, and zinc peroxide. Also note that sodium perborate is essentially a form of hydrogen peroxide.

5

Nitrogen, Nitrous Oxide, and Ammonia

NITROGEN

Nitrogen, U.S.P. XVII

N_2

Symbol, N.   Valence, 3 and 5.   Molecular Weight, 28.01
Atomic Number, 7

History.—In 1772, Dr. D. Rutherford of Edinburgh, observed that when oxygen was removed from air there remained a gas which was incapable of supporting either combustion or respiration. In the published results of his work, he designated this gas as "mephitic air."   Scheele was the first to understand the true nature of the principal gases composing the atmosphere. He showed that one gas (oxygen) supported combustion and respiration and that the other (nitrogen) did not.   Lavoisier proved conclusively the correctness of Scheele's findings, and he named the inert gas *azote* from the Greek meaning "without life."   Because this element was found to be a constituent of saltpeter, Chaptal proposed the name *nitrogen*, from the Greek, νιτρον, niter, and γενναω, I produce, and it was generally accepted.   In 1894, Rayleigh and Ramsay showed that atmospheric nitrogen was in reality an admixture of nitrogen and slightly over 1 per cent of inert gases.

Occurrence.—Nitrogen constitutes approximately 79 per cent by volume of the atmosphere.   Free nitrogen is found in some natural waters.   Spectroscopic observations have shown it to be present in certain nebulæ and probably in the sun.   In combination with sodium and oxygen, it occurs in Nature in enormous quantities as Chile saltpeter ($NaNO_3$).   When united with hydrogen, it forms ammonia (free or combined) and, in organic combination as protein, alkaloids, amino-acids, etc., it is an integral part of animal and vegetable tissues and liquids.   It is invariably present in soil, wherein nitrogen compounds are formed by the action of nitrifying bacteria.

Physical Properties.—Nitrogen is a colorless, tasteless and odorless gas. Its density is 0.9682 (air = 1). One liter of nitrogen at 0° C. and 760 mm. weighs 1.251 Gm. Nitrogen can be liquefied; the critical temperature being −147.13° C. and the critical pressure 33.49 atmospheres. It forms a colorless liquid, boiling at −195.8° C. and a white solid melting at −209.8° C. Under standard conditions (0° C. at 760 mm.), 2.4 volumes of nitrogen dissolve in 100 volumes of water. At 20° and 760 mm. pressure one volume of nitrogen dissolves in about 65 volumes of water or in about nine volumes of alcohol.

Chemical Properties.—Nitrogen is a rather inert gas. Like hydrogen, it may be activated by high voltage discharges at low pressure or by subjecting the gas at normal pressure to a silent electrical discharge. It will neither burn nor support the combustion of ordinary combustibles. At high temperatures, it combines directly with Li, B, Si, Ba, Ca, Sr and Mg to form nitrides. Thus, when magnesium ribbon is burned in air, the white powder that is formed is composed of large quantities of magnesium oxide (MgO) and smaller quantities of magnesium nitride (Mg_3N_2). The latter compound may be detected by moistening the ash with water and testing the evolved gas with moistened red litmus paper. The paper is turned blue by the ammonia produced by the hydrolysis of the nitride (1).

$$(1)\ Mg_3N_2 + 6H_2O \rightarrow 3Mg(OH)_2 + 2NH_3 \uparrow$$

When the rare earth metals are mixed with magnesium and heated in a current of nitrogen, nitrides are produced.

Nitrogen forms six oxides:

Oxides of Nitrogen	Formula	Oxidation No.
Nitrous oxide	N_2O	+1
Nitric oxide	NO	+2
Nitrogen trioxide	N_2O_3	+3
Nitrogen dioxide	NO_2	+4
Nitrogen tetroxide	N_2O_4	+4
Nitrogen pentoxide	N_2O_5	+5

Actually nitrogen does exhibit valences of three and five when combined with other elements besides oxygen, hydrogen and the halogens (also phosphorus in a few cases).

Nitrous oxide will be discussed as an official product.

Nitrogen tetroxide (N_2O_4) is a commercially available compound. It is a heavy brown liquid, boiling at 21° C., and has a specific gravity greater than water. The oxide is readily handled and resembles ozone and hydrogen peroxide in many of its reactions. Use has been made of the product in detergents, metallurgy, explosives, for bleaching flour, as a nitrating agent, and for preparing oxidized derivatives of cellulose.

Compounds with hydrogen are as follows:

Name	Formula	Oxidation No.
Hydroxylamine	NH_2OH	-1
Hydrazine	N_2H_4	-2
Ammonia	NH_3	-3

Also there is the unusual linear compound hydrazoic acid (N_3H) which forms the salt, sodium azide (NaN_3) wherein one nitrogen atom exists in the pentavalent form and the other two in trivalent form.

Chlorine unites with it to form a very volatile, oily, yellow substance, nitrogen trichloride (NCl_3), which has a very pungent smell, powerful lachrymatory properties, and is a most dangerous explosive. The corresponding iodine compound, nitrogen triiodide (NI_3) in the dry state is a sensitive explosive. It may be prepared from ammonium hydroxide and iodine as a black amorphous material.

Official Test for Identity.—The flame of a burning wood splinter held in an atmosphere of Nitrogen is extinguished. Other than the identity test, the U.S.P. XVII sets a limit on the amount of carbon dioxide (300 parts per million) and oxygen (1%) present.

Commercial Manufacture.—Nitrogen may be obtained experimentally by (1) removing the oxygen from the atmosphere or (2) by decomposing compounds in which it occurs.

The first may be accomplished by:

1. Burning phosphorus in a confined volume of air. The phosphorus combines with the oxygen of the air to form phosphorus pentoxide, P_2O_5. The gas remaining in the container is nearly pure nitrogen.

2. The action of an alkaline solution of pyrogallol on air. An alkaline solution of pyrogallol energetically absorbs oxygen from the air, turns brown, and finally decomposes into carbon dioxide, acetic acid, and brown substances. Nitrogen is unaffected by the pyrogallol solution.

3. Passing air over red-hot copper filings. Copper at red heat combines with the oxygen of the air to form cupric oxide, whereas the nitrogen is unaffected and passes on into a reservoir.

4. A solution of sodium hydrosulfite ($Na_2S_2O_4$) will absorb oxygen from the air quantitatively. By a similar setup as that used in (1) and (2) nitrogen may be obtained.

For the production of quantities sufficient for industrial use (manufacture of cyanamid, etc.) it is made by (1) fractional distillation of liquid air by the same process used for oxygen; (2) the fractional separation by liquefaction of producer gas which contains about 67 per cent of nitrogen; (3) by catalytically oxidizing the CO in producer gas to CO_2; (4) by decomposing ammonia into H_2 and N_2 by passage over heated iron and then liquefying the nitrogen.

Nitrogen Fixation.—Plants do not have the power of fixing atmospheric nitrogen as they do oxygen and, therefore, must obtain it from nitrogenous compounds formed in the soil mainly by the action of nitrifying bacteria. Because these compounds are essential to plant life, it is necessary to replace them as they are extracted from the soil; hence the use of nitrogenous manures or artificial fertilizers containing soluble nitrates. The enormous demands made upon the natural niter deposits brought about the realization that eventually these natural sources of nitrogen would be used up. The attention of chemists has turned increasingly to the development of processes for the fixation of atmospheric nitrogen in order to establish independence from the rapidly diminishing natural sources of nitrates and also for economic reasons. Combination of nitrogen, obtained directly or indirectly from the air, has been effected by forming (1) cyanamides, (2) ammonia, (3) oxides of nitrogen and then nitric acid, (4) decomposable nitrides, (5) cyanides, and (6) urea.

1. *The Cyanamide Process.*—By means of the electric furnace calcium oxide is induced to react with carbon (2).

$$(2) \quad CaO + 3C \rightarrow CaC_2 + CO \uparrow$$

The calcium carbide is treated with nitrogen while hot to form calcium cyanamide (3).

$$(3) \quad CaC_2 + N_2 \rightarrow CaCN_2 + C$$

Calcium cyanamide by treatment with excess carbon and sodium chloride will yield about 50 per cent sodium cyanide. This is used in cyanidation of ores to make ferrocyanides or acidified to yield HCN.

2. *The Haber Process.*—The synthesis of ammonia from its constituent elements is one of the most important methods of nitrogen fixation (see p. 70).

If it is desired to use the nitrogen, fixed as ammonia, for the production of nitrates, it is necessary to first convert the ammonia into nitric acid. This is accomplished by means of the *Ostwald Process*, whereby ammonia is mixed with air (21 per cent of oxygen), the mixture heated and rapidly passed through a fine wire gauze of activated platinum raised to a glowing heat. Better than 95 per cent of the ammonia is oxidized to NO, and then to NO_2 (4, 5, 6), which is absorbed by water to form nitric acid.

$$(4) \quad 4NH_3 + 5O_2 \rightarrow 4NO + 6H_2O$$

$$(5) \quad 4NO + 2O_2 \rightarrow 4NO_2$$

$$(6) \quad 3NO_2 + H_2O \rightarrow 2HNO_3 + NO \uparrow$$

The nitric acid so formed may be used as such or converted into sodium nitrate, calcium nitrate, etc.

Uses.—*Nitrogen*, U.S.P. XVII, contains not less than 99 per cent by volume of N_2. It is usually available in a blue-pink cylinder. The usual pharmaceutical applications are to retard oxidation, in the identity test for carbon monoxide, and to provide an inert atmosphere for some organic reactions. Cod-liver oil, olive oil, castor oil, etc., are often packaged with a nitrogen atmosphere above the oil to retard oxidation and consequent rancidity or loss of vitamins during storage. The U.S.P. XVII (p. 4) allows nitrogen (as well as carbon dioxide) to replace air in containers of parenterals, solutions for topical application, and injections without the need of declaring its presence on the label.

Elementary nitrogen is used principally in connection with nitrogen fixation. The Haber process for ammonia production uses the largest amount. Considerable quantities of nitrogen are also used in the cyanamide process. Inorganic nitrogen consumption in the United States has expanded considerably in recent years, but it is difficult to conceive of a possible shortage in the future.

Liquid nitrogen is useful to obtain temperatures as low as $-320°$ F, and, as a result, may be used to freeze warts, angiomas, etc. This low temperature is also used to freeze gums, waxes, rubber, resins, etc., so as to prevent their tenacious (sticky) property from interfering during grinding or powdering operations. Mercury thermometers that are intended for use at elevated temperatures > 200° have the space above the mercury column filled with nitrogen gas to decrease the evaporation of the mercury and to prevent its oxidation. Electric light bulbs filled with nitrogen are now in general use, thus giving longer life by reducing the volatilization of the filaments.

NITROUS OXIDE

Nitrous Oxide, U.S.P. XVII

$$N \equiv \overset{+}{N} - \overset{-}{O} \longleftrightarrow \overset{-}{N} = \overset{+}{N} = O$$

Formula, N_2O.   Molecular Weight, 44.01

History.—Nitrogen monoxide or nitrous oxide was first made in 1772 by J. Priestley. He obtained it by the action of nitric oxide (NO) upon moist iron filings. While studying the physical and chemical properties of this gas, he observed that ignited substances burned in it with greater luminosity than in the atmosphere. Sir H. Davy, who determined its composition, observed that the gas produced exhilarating effects when inhaled, hence its common name "laughing gas."

Had the 21-year-old Davy written nothing else, his fame would be secure for this passage in his first book, *Researches on Nitrous Oxide* (1780):

> "As nitrous oxide in its extensive operation appears capable of destroying physical pain, it may probably be used with advantage during surgical operations in which no great effusion of blood takes place."

Unfortunately, no surgeon of the age availed himself of this tip from the chemist Davy.[1]

Physical Properties.—Nitrous oxide is a colorless gas without appreciable odor or taste. Its aqueous solutions have a somewhat sweetish taste. Its specific gravity is 1.530 (air = 1). One liter of the gas at 0° C. and one atmosphere pressure weighs about 1.96 Gm. and it is readily soluble in water at low temperatures. One volume of nitrous oxide dissolves in about 1.5 volumes of water under normal pressure at 20° C. It is about three times more soluble in alcohol than in water, and readily dissolves in ether or in oils. Fats also readily dissolve large volumes of nitrous oxide, a principle used in making modern aerosol whipped cream formulations. In closed containers cream is saturated with N_2O which forms many small bubbles in the cream as the pressure is released. Since N_2O is not an acid anhydride there is no obnoxious taste. The gas may be liquefied to a thin, mobile, colorless liquid boiling at $-89.5°$ C. This property is utilized in the official assay. When it is further cooled, white crystals melting at $-102.4°$ C. separate out.

Chemical Properties.—Nitrogen monoxide is not inflammable but it supports the combustion of many substances almost as well as oxygen.

At about 500° C. nitrous oxide decomposes (1)

$$(1) \quad N_2O \xrightarrow{500°C.} N_2 \uparrow + (O)$$

thus providing oxygen for combustion of any burning material. It supports the combustion of a glowing splinter of wood and phosphorus and sulfur burn in it.

Due to this endothermic decomposition certain oxidations take place more readily than in air. Some application of it as an oxidizing agent is possible. At ordinary temperatures metals do not rust in nitrous oxide and the hemoglobin of the blood is unable to use it as a source of oxygen.

In contrast to nitric oxide (NO), nitrogen dioxide (NO_2), and nitrogen tetroxide (N_2O_4), nitrous oxide is *not* an acid anhydride. It has no reaction with water.

Official Test for Identity.—There is no official test for identity of Nitrous Oxide other than its description. However, the U.S.P. sets limits on a number of impurities such as carbon dioxide,

---

[1] The Laboratory, **28**, 37 (1960); *see also* Metz, W. C., J.A.M.A., **141**, 363 (Oct. 8, 1949).

oxidizing substances, reducing substances, halogens and excessive acidity or alkalinity.

Commercial Manufacture.—The manufacture of Nitrous Oxide has undergone some engineering changes in the past several years although the basic chemistry remains the same. Until recently, the gas was produced by the thermal decomposition of ammonium nitrate (2) by a "batch" process wherein the solid salt, free from

$$(2)\ NH_4NO_3 \xrightarrow[240°]{\triangle} 2H_2O + N_2O \uparrow$$

chlorides and other impurities, was melted and fed into reactors where it was decomposed by controlled heat into the desired gas and water. The principal difficulty was in controlling the rate of decomposition (dependent on heating rate) and a secondary difficulty was the explosive nature of the dry salt which necessitated careful handling. Modern procedures employ a "continuous" process in which a concentrated aqueous solution of the salt is fed to the reactor at exactly the same rate as its decomposition rate. There is no possibility of super-heating and no handling is required because the solution can be pumped wherever desired. The gas is cooled in a condenser, washed with sodium dichromate solution to remove nitric oxide, with a solution of sodium hydroxide to take out the nitric acid, and lastly with water. Nitric oxide (NO) is readily oxidized by dichromate to NO_2 which forms nitric acid with the water present. It is then compressed in steel cylinders under a pressure of about 100 atmospheres.

Uses.—*Nitrous Oxide* (Nitrogen Monoxide), U.S.P. XVII, "contains not less than 97 per cent by volume of N_2O." It is officially recognized as a general anesthetic for use by inhalation and is to be used as required. For this purpose it is often used with 20 to 25 per cent of oxygen as a diluent since permanent neurological damage due to hypoxia can result from even several minutes of administration of the pure gas. Since the safe concentrations are not completely anesthetic, modern practice dictates a judicious combination of "sleep producing" barbiturates, nitrous oxide, and other anesthetic gases as well as muscle relaxants for production of the most suitable anesthesia. The administration of nitrous oxide in concentrations less than that required for anesthesia, however, is definitely anesthetic in man. The optimum concentration for this purpose is 35 per cent admixed with air or oxygen, preferably the latter. The use of pure nitrous oxide for a few minutes together with alternate use of pure oxygen is condoned in the second stage of labor where it is of considerable value and does not impair uterine contraction nor interfere with oxygen saturation of the patient's blood.*

---

* For a more extended discussion of the use of nitrous oxide see H. L. Price and R. D. Dripps in *The Pharmacological Basis of Therapeutics*, 3rd Ed., ed. by L. S. Goodman and A. Gilman, N. Y., The Macmillan Co., 1965, p. 71 *et seq.*

AMMONIA

Strong Ammonia Solution, N.F. XII

Formula, NH_3.   Molecular Weight, 17.03

History.—An aqueous solution of ammonia was prepared during Geber's time (eighth century) by destructively distilling the hoofs and horns of animals and absorbing the gas in water.   The solution was called "spirit of hartshorn."   In 1756 Black differentiated between ammonia and ammonium carbonate.   Priestley was the first to obtain almost pure ammonia which he called "alkaline air." Berthollet determined its composition in 1803.

Physical Properties.—Ammonia is a colorless gas having a strong, pungent, characteristic odor.   It is about one-half as heavy as air, having a specific gravity of 0.5967 (air = 1).   One liter of ammonia weighs 0.7714 Gm.   The gas may be liquefied either by subjecting it to intense cold ($-60°$ C.) or by cooling it to about $10°$ C. and increasing the pressure to 6.5 or 7 atmospheres.   Liquid ammonia boils at $-33.35°$ C. (760 mm.) and the white crystals of solid ammonia melt at $-77.7°$ C.   Liquid ammonia is a good solvent and ionizing medium.

It dissolves salts, forming ionic solutions and also alkali metals and alkaline-earth metals without chemical reaction.   The solutions of metals are blue and will slowly decompose in the presence of impurities giving up hydrogen and leaving the amide, *i.e.*, $NaNH_2$.

One milliliter of water at $0°$ C. dissolves 1298.9 volumes of ammonia, and at $15°$ C. 1 ml. of water dissolves 727 volumes of the gas. Its solutions are lighter than water.   The pH of a 1N solution is 11.6 and that of a 0.1N solution is 11.1.   It is also soluble in alcohol and ether.   All of the gas may be expelled from its solutions by boiling. Ammonia exists in aqueous solution mainly in the form NH_3, only a small amount reacting with water to form NH_4OH.   For all

$$NH_3 + HOH \rightleftarrows NH_4OH$$

practical purposes, however, ammonia water may be considered as containing NH_4OH.

Chemical Properties.—At low temperatures ammonia (NH_3) is stable.   At red heat and by the action of an electric spark, it is completely decomposed into hydrogen and nitrogen.   The reaction is reversible (1).   Reaction (1) at $450°$ to $500°$ C. is the basis for producing hydrogen from ammonia (see Hydrogen, p. 35).

(1) $2NH_3 \rightleftarrows 3H_2 + N_2$

To all intents and purposes ammonia is noninflammable although under suitable conditions it can be oxidized (2).

(2) $4NH_3 + 3O_2 \rightarrow 2N_2 + 6H_2O$

Ammonia may be shown to be an active *reducing agent* by the following reactions.

1. Heated oxides of many metals are reduced when ammonia is passed over them (3).

(3) $3CuO + 2NH_3 \rightarrow 3Cu + 3H_2O + N_2 \uparrow$

2. When a mixture of ammonia and air is heated in the presence of a catalyst (platinum), the ammonia is oxidized to water and oxides of nitrogen which combine to form nitric acid. (see Ostwald Process.)

3. When a current of either chlorine or bromine vapor is passed into a flask containing ammonia, the halogen ignites and free nitrogen and ammonium chloride or ammonium bromide are formed (4 and 5).

(4) $2NH_3 + 3Cl_2 \rightarrow N_2 \uparrow + 6HCl$

(5) $NH_3 + HCl \rightarrow NH_4Cl$ (white)

4. Hypochlorites oxidize ammonia to nitrogen and water (6).

(6) $2NH_3 + 3NaClO \rightarrow 3NaCl + 3H_2O + N_2 \uparrow$

5. Potassium permanganate is reduced to MnO_2 (7).

(7) $2NH_3 + 2KMnO_4 \rightarrow 2KOH + 2MnO_2 + 2H_2O + N_2 \uparrow$

Also, ammonia exhibits properties of an *oxidizing agent*.

1. When lithium, calcium, magnesium or boron are heated in a stream of ammonia gas, hydrogen is evolved and the respective nitride formed (8).

(8) $2NH_3 + 3Mg \rightarrow Mg_3N_2 + 3H_2 \uparrow$

These nitrides are solids and are easily hydrolyzed by water to ammonia (9).

(9) $Mg_3N_2 + 6H_2O \rightarrow 2NH_3 \uparrow + 3Mg(OH)_2$

2. Sodium and potassium replace only part of the hydrogen of ammonia. The resulting compounds are known as amides (10).

(10) $2Na + 2NH_3 \rightarrow 2NaNH_2 + H_2 \uparrow$

Sodamide, like the nitrides, yields ammonia upon hydrolysis (11).

(11) $NaNH_2 + H_2O \rightarrow NH_3 \uparrow + NaOH$

Ammonia, as noted above, is a basic substance causing it to react with acidic materials to form ammonium compounds (12).

(12) $NH_3 + HCl \rightarrow NH_4Cl$

It is actually a proton (H^+) acceptor and in this role will react with some substances in solution that exhibit a pH greater than 7, *i.e.*, bicarbonates (HCO_3^-) (13), as they occur in temporarily hard water.

(13) $Ca(HCO_3)_2 \rightleftarrows Ca^{++} + 2HCO_3^-$
$HCO_3^- \rightleftarrows H^+ + CO_3^=$
$NH_3 + H^+ \rightarrow NH_4^+$

Complete reaction:
$Ca(HCO_3)_2 + 2NH_3 \rightarrow CaCO_3 \downarrow + (NH_4)_2CO_3$

In the qualitative test for the phosphate ion ($PO_4^\equiv$) or the magnesium ion (Mg^{++}) ammonia is utilized to increase the concentration of the $PO_4^\equiv$ ion (14).

(14) $Na_2HPO_4 \rightleftarrows 2Na^+ + 2HPO_4^=$
$HPO_4^= \rightleftarrows H^+ + PO_4^\equiv$
$NH_3 + H^+ \rightarrow NH_4^+$

Complete reaction:
$NH_4^+ + Mg^{++} + PO_4^\equiv + 6H_2O \rightarrow MgNH_4PO_4 \cdot 6H_2O \downarrow$

Ammonia as ammonia water readily forms soluble complex ions with the cations of Cu, Ag, Au, Zn, Cd, Cr, Ni, Co and Mn (less important ones are Rh, Pd, Ir, and Pt). (See coordination number.) The hydroxide or insoluble salts of these are soluble in ammonia[1] solution. A common example is the formation of the soluble complex (called ammines) silver-ammonia ion when AgCl (insoluble) is treated with ammonia water in excess (15). This property is utilized in Ammoniacal Silver Nitrate Solution N.F.

(15) $AgCl + 2NH_3 \overset{H_2O}{\rightleftarrows} Ag(NH_3)_2^+ + Cl^-$

The above mentioned elements form soluble ions with ammonia solution usually having twice the number of molecules of ammonia (NH_3) as the valence of the ion (a probable exception being cuprous ions, $CuNH_3^+$). Thus, we note $Cu(NH_3)_4^{++}$; $Au(NH_3)_2^+$; $Zn(NH_3)_4^{++}$; $Cd(NH_3)_4^{++}$; $Ni(NH_3)_4^{++}$; $Co(NH_3)_6^{+++}$.

Ammonia of crystallization occurs with some compounds such as $CaCl_2 \cdot 8NH_3$, $ZnCl_2 \cdot 4NH_3 \cdot H_2O$, $ZnSO_4 \cdot 5NH_3$, $CdCl_2 \cdot NH_3$, $Hg_2Cl_2 \cdot 2NH_3$, and $CuCl_2 \cdot 2NH_3$. These, however, are obtainable by adding ammonia (NH_3) to alcoholic solutions, to the dry salt, or to saturated aqueous solutions of the salt (called ammoniates).

Bases such as sodium and potassium hydroxide, being stronger bases than NH_3, will remove a hydrogen ion (proton) from the

---

[1] For corresponding solubility in fixed alkali see those given under sodium hydroxide (Au, Zn, Al, Pb and Sn). Note the Au and Zn salts are soluble in both types of alkali.

ammonium ion (NH_4^+) forming free ammonia (NH_3) and water. All ammonium salts will react in this manner (16) (see test for identity).

(16) $NH_4Cl + NaOH \rightarrow NH_3 \uparrow + H_2O + NaCl$

Ammonia reacts with active chemical groups in a way similar to water. The process of forming ammonia-basic salts is analogous to hydrolysis and has been designated "ammonolysis." In the case of mercuric chloride both reactions take place.

$$HgCl_2 + H_2O \rightarrow Hg\Big\langle{{OH}\atop{Cl}} + HCl \text{ (hydrolysis)}.$$

$$HgCl_2 + NH_3 \rightarrow Hg\Big\langle{{NH_2}\atop{Cl}} + HCl \text{ (ammonolysis)}$$
$$\text{(ammoniated}$$
$$\text{mercury)}$$

In organic chemistry ammonia reacts with phosgene, acid chlorides, and some alkyl esters to form amides (R—CO—NH_2).

The assay of the ammonia solutions is carried out by a straightforward titration with sulfuric acid utilizing methyl red as the indicator.

Official Test for Identity.—When ammonia (NH_3) or ammonium ions (NH_4^+) are present in colorless solutions their detection and quantitative estimation are possible with Nessler's Reagent. Since the reaction that takes place involves ammonia (NH_3) it is not possible to distinguish between the ammonium ion and ammonia. Due to the alkalinity of Nessler's Reagent ammonia is released from the ammonium ion (see qualitative test for ammonium ion).

Nessler's Reagent (Alkaline Mercuric-Potassium Iodide T.S.) is a solution of potassium iodide, mercury bichloride, and potassium hydroxide having present several of the possible salts (17, 18) (see chemical properties of mercury).

(17) $4KI + HgCl_2 \overset{KOH}{\rightleftarrows} K_2HgI_4 + 2KCl$

   $K_2HgI_4 \rightleftarrows 2K^+ + HgI_4^=$

(18) $K_2HgI_4 \rightleftarrows HgI_2 + 2KI$

6

When the reagent is added to a solution containing ammonia or ammonium ions the free ammonia causes ammonolysis of the mercuric iodide (HgI_2) (19).

$$(19)\ \ Hg\Big\langle{{I}\atop{I}} + NH_3 \rightarrow Hg\Big\langle{{NH_2}\atop{I}} + HI$$
$$(A)$$

Also the hydrolysis product of HgI_2 is present (20).

$$(20)\ \ Hg\Big\langle{{I}\atop{I}} + H_2O \rightarrow Hg\Big\langle{{OH}\atop{I}} + HI$$
$$(B)$$

The two products, A and B, interact in basic media to form a yellow to brown colored solution or in high concentration a brown precipitate (21), a qualitative or quantitative reaction.

$$(21)\ \ Hg\Big\langle{{OH}\atop{I}} + {{H_2N}\atop{I}}\Big\rangle Hg \xrightarrow{\text{KOH}} HO{-}Hg{-}NH{-}Hg{-}I + KI + H_2O$$
$$\text{(yellow to brown)}$$

The completed equation is usually given as follows (22):

$$(22)\ \ NH_3 + 2K_2HgI_4 + 3KOH \rightarrow Hg(OH)NHHgI + 7KI + 2H_2O$$

Commercial Manufacture.—Present day techniques for producing ammonia vary as do the conditions for the interaction of nitrogen and hydrogen as well as the source of these two vital gases. Ammonia is produced at the present time almost exclusively by the Haber Process or some modification of it. The wash-waters of the gases obtained by the destructive distillation of coal (production of coke and illuminating gas) are also a source of ammonia. Ammonia, as a constituent of *crude* illuminating gas combines in part with various other impurities to form salts. In most gas works, the mixture composed of gas-condensate and scrubber-water will have an ammonia content of about 3 per cent by weight. This *ammoniacal gas liquor* is first concentrated to 16 per cent ammonia and shipped in tank cars to ammonia refineries.

The Haber Process.—When nitrogen and hydrogen are mixed in volume proportions of 1 to 3 and the mixture under high pressure (between 100 and 1000 atmospheres) passed through a promoted iron catalyst at a temperature of 400° to 550° C. they unite to form ammonia.

The volumes of gases are adjusted so as to give a ratio of 1 of nitrogen and 3 of hydrogen, and the mixed gases, under a pressure of about 50 atmospheres, are scrubbed with water and finally with a solution of caustic soda to remove any remaining carbon dioxide. The pressure is then stepped up to 200 atmospheres, the gases scrubbed with ammoniacal copper formate to remove carbon mon-oxide and passed on to the catalyzing elements. The catalyst is said to be a mixture of metallic oxides, *e.g.*, Fe_3O_4, Fe_2O_3, and Al_2O_3, containing about 1 per cent of K_2O. The gases leaving the catalyzing element contain about 8 per cent by volume of ammonia, which is cooled and absorbed in water. The uncombined nitrogen and hydrogen are dried and again passed through the apparatus. The reaction taking place may be represented as follows (23):

$$\text{(23)} \quad N_2 + 3H_2 \underset{\xrightarrow{\hspace{1cm}}}{\overset{400\text{–}550°C.}{\rightleftharpoons}} 2NH_3 + 2 \times 12{,}200 \text{ calories}$$

The ammonia may be recovered easily from the ammonia water in continuously operating stills and then, if desired, it may be lique-fied. In this physical state it may be used for refrigeration or other purposes. The gas is available as a liquid in steel cylinders.

Uses.—*Strong Ammonia Solution,* (Stronger Ammonia Water) N.F. XII, is an aqueous solution of ammonia (NH_3) containing not less than 27 per cent and not more than 30 per cent, by weight, of NH_3. This solution deteriorates rapidly in open containers due to loss of ammonia by evaporation. Strong Ammonia Solution is prepared by passing ammonia gas into cooled water until the water is saturated with ammonia (NH_3).

Caution.—Use care in handling Strong Ammonia Solution because of the caustic nature of the Solution and the irritating properties of its vapor. Cool the container well before opening, and cover the closure with a cloth or similar material while opening. Do not taste Strong Ammonia Solution and avoid inhalation of its vapor.

Strong Ammonia Solution is a colorless, transparent liquid, hav-ing an exceedingly pungent, characteristic odor, and a very caustic and alkaline taste. It is strongly alkaline to litmus and has a specific gravity of 0.90.

A dilute solution of ammonia was official in U.S.P. XVI under the title *Diluted Ammonia Solution* and contained in each 100 ml. not less than 9 Gm. and not more than 10 Gm. of NH_3. It was prepared by diluting 398 ml. of Strong Ammonia Solution with enough

Purified Water to make 1000 ml. of finished solution. Since it could be made extemporaneously from the stronger solution when needed the official compendia apparently saw no need for its separate recognition and, therefore, it was deleted. This was the product usually dispensed on demand for "household ammonia" in pharmacies. It is also known as "ammonia water."

On account of its ability to unite directly with acids, an aqueous solution of ammonia is used in the manufacture of ammonium salts (*q.v.*). The identification test for this solution, in fact, is the production of dense white fumes of NH_4Cl when a glass rod wet with hydrochloric acid is held near the surface of Strong Ammonia Solution. It is also used in the manufacture of sodium carbonate and bicarbonate (*q.v.*), nitric acid (*q.v.*), etc. One reason for its recognition officially as a pharmaceutical aid is for the preparation of *Aromatic Ammonia Spirit* (*q.v.*).

When hydronium ions (from HCl, for example) are introduced into the solution, the equilibrium is disturbed by the union of hydroxide ions with hydronium ions to produce water, and the ammonium ions and chloride ions form ammonium chloride. As rapidly as water is formed by the hydroxide ions uniting with hydronium ions, more ammonium hydroxide dissociates into its cation and anion, and concurrently more ammonia combines with water to form undissociated ammonium hydroxide. This effort to re-establish an ionic equilibrium continues until the reaction is complete (24) and (25). The weak basic property of an aqueous

(24) NH_3 (gas) $\rightleftarrows NH_3$ (solution) $+ H_2O \rightleftarrows NH_4OH \rightleftarrows NH_4^+$
$+ OH^-$

(25) $NH_4^+ + OH^- + H_3O^+ + Cl^- \rightarrow NH_4Cl + 2H_2O$

solution of ammonium hydroxide is due to the presence of relatively few OH^-, produced by the slight dissociation of ammonium hydroxide into NH_4^+ and OH^-. The molar concentration of OH^- is about 0.5 per cent that of a comparable solution of sodium hydroxide.

The basic property of solutions of ammonia is utilized in its quantitative determination. Sulfuric acid of known normality with methyl red T.S. is employed in a volumetric procedure (26).

$$\text{(26) } 2NH_4OH + H_2SO_4 \xrightarrow{\text{methyl red}} (NH_4)_2SO_4 + 2H_2O$$

Ammoniacal Silver Nitrate Solution (Ammoniacal Silver Nitrate, Howe), N.F. XII is an aqueous solution of silver diammino nitrate, containing in each 100 Gm. the equivalent of not less than 28.5 Gm. and not more than 30.5 Gm. of silver (Ag), and not less than 9 Gm. and not more than 9.7 Gm. of ammonia (NH_3).

The silver nitrate (704 Gm.) is powdered in a glass mortar and dissolved in 245 ml. of distilled water, warming if necessary. The solution is cooled to room temperature and Strong Ammonia Solution (680 ml.) added from a burette until all but the last trace of black precipitate is dissolved (27, 28, 29).

(27) $AgNO_3 + NH_4OH \rightarrow AgOH \downarrow + NH_4NO_3$

(28) $AgOH + 2NH_4OH \rightleftarrows Ag(NH_3)_2OH + 2H_2O$

(29) $Ag(NH_3)_2OH + NH_4NO_3 \rightleftarrows Ag(NH_3)_2NO_3 + NH_4OH$

This solution may be filtered if necessary.

The solution does contain some silver diammino nitrate $(Ag(NH_3)_2NO_3)$. Silver ions, in alkaline solution, are readily reduced just as are cupric and bismuth ions and this property is utilized in dentistry. Silver may be deposited on exposed dentine and in cavities prior to filling. This solution is unstable when exposed to light and air. It must be stored in small, well-filled, glass-stoppered, light-resistant containers or ampuls. Upon opening, the reversible reaction (28, 29) takes place slowly. For oral use—mix Ammoniacal Silver Nitrate Solution with a reducing agent, such as 10 per cent formaldehyde or eugenol, so as to deposit the metallic silver in the infected area in a state of fine subdivision.

Uses of Ammonia.—Anhydrous ammonia is consumed mostly in the production of sodium nitrate, calcium nitrate, ammonium sulfate, ammonium chloride, alum, ammonium nitrate, ammonium phosphate, ammoniated superphosphate, urea, and aqueous ammonia. Applied directly to the soil by special machines, anhydrous ammonia is itself a widely used fertilizer. It is also the starting point for the manufacture of almost all military explosives and an industrial source of hydrogen. Ammonia goes into the making of soda ash, nitric acid, nylon, plastics, lacquers, resins, dyes, refrigerants, rubber, sulfa drugs, and antimalarials. Liquid ammonia is used for refrigeration and for the manufacture of artificial ice. Ammonia is one of the truly fundamental reagents of industrial chemistry.

Pharmaceutical applications have been pointed out in its preparations and include antacid, counterirritant, stimulant, salt and soap formation, and basic properties.

THE HALOGEN FAMILY: Group VIIB

Introduction.—A discussion of these elements at this early point in the text is in order for two principal reasons: 1) the halogen family is one of the best illustrations of gradations of properties of a group of similar elements to be found in the Periodic Table, and 2) many of the subsequent salts to be discussed will employ anions derived from the halogen group. However, the lack of any pronounced relationships between Group VIIA and the halogens permits them to be discussed later in the text.

Berzelius suggested the word "halogen," which is derived from the two Greek words meaning "sea salt" and "to produce," and consequently means "the producer of sea salt." The term is applied to four elements—fluorine, chlorine, bromine and iodine, because the sodium salts of their respective hydro-acids are very similar to ordinary sea salt. These four elements and their compounds show a great resemblance to one another in general chemical properties. The physical properties of the elements exhibit a gradual transition that is evident upon consulting the accompanying table. Thus, as the atomic weight increases, the physical state changes from that of a gas (F and Cl) to that of a liquid (Br) and then to that of a solid (I); the melting- and boiling-points rise; the colors deepen; the densities increase; etc. There appears to be a relationship between the ease of removal of an electron (ionization potential) and the energy necessary for excitation of the halogen molecule so far as color formation is concerned. Iodine requires the least energy for excitation (and absorption of visible light) whereas fluorine requires high energy radiation. Thus iodine absorbs low energy yellow and green radiations to give a violet color and fluorine absorbs high energy violet radiation to give a yellow color.

The gradual transition from gaseous fluorine to solid iodine may be explained on the basis of the increasing atomic radius. As the radius increases the outermost electrons get further away from the influence of the nucleus and, thus, have a greater opportunity to exert an influence on neighboring nuclei. As the attraction for neighboring nuclei increases it is to be expected that liquefaction and, finally, solidification will take place. This attraction may be ascribed to van der Waals forces (weak attractive forces between uncharged bodies), which should be greater between heavier molecules than between lighter ones, and also to the greater deformability of the electron clouds of the heavier elements.

The important chemical properties of the halogens are those in which they are reduced and promote an oxidation of something else. Fluorine is the best oxidizing agent we have and consideration of the oxidation potentials will show that the oxidizing property decreases with increasing atomic number. On the other hand, the tendency to be oxidized is, of course, greatest with iodide and least with fluoride. In fact, the two heaviest halides may be used as reducing agents whereas the two lightest halogens are commonly used as oxidizing agents. A halogen of lower atomic weight will always displace one of higher atomic weight from its binary hydrogen compounds or from the salts thereof (1). This illustrates again that the

$$(1) \quad 2HI + Cl_2 \rightleftarrows 2HCl + I_2 \text{ or } 2I^- + Cl_2 \rightleftarrows I_2 + 2Cl^-$$

force with which the respective halogens hold electrons diminishes from fluorine to iodine.

All four halogens unite with hydrogen but the affinity toward this element decreases as the atomic weights increase. Thus, we find that, although hydrogen and fluorine unite explosively, hydrogen and iodine need a catalyst to promote the reaction. The hydrides of the halogens are all colorless gases and, as anhydrous gases, have considerable covalent character with this character increasing with the size of the halogen. However, when dissolved in water, it is found that the hydrogen halide with the greatest ionic character is the weakest acid (and, in fact, is classed as a weak acid), namely, HF. In order of decreasing acidity in aqueous solution we have HI > HBr > HCl > HF. With the exception of HF, the hydrogen halide molecules ionize rather completely in water and are classed as *strong acids*. In general, series of halides such as the above as well as others (*e.g.*, stannic salts) will have the greatest ionic character with the smallest halogen.

The affinity of the halogens for oxygen increases as the atomic number increases. Thus, iodine pentoxide is a well-defined crystalline solid while chlorine monoxide, peroxide and heptoxide are very unstable even at ordinary temperatures. The oxides of fluorine and bromine are exceedingly difficult to make and are correspondingly unstable. When treated with water, the oxides of the halogens yield acids, thereby indicating that the simple halogens are non-metals.

In combination with hydrogen or the metals, the halogens are univalent and negative. When combined with oxygen or in the form of their oxygen salts, they have valences that are often greater than 1 and are positive. Of the halogens, fluorine exhibits the most marked tendency to become negative and the greatest resistance toward becoming positive, whereas iodine shows the greatest inclination to become positive and the least to become negative. The simple derivatives of the halogens (binary combinations) can form either ionic or covalent compounds. With the ionic types which are derived from combinations with metals early in the Periodic Table it is noted that the greatest ionic character is associated with the smallest halide. This is apparent from the trends in melting and boiling points which are high with lithium fluoride but fall off with increasing atomic weight of the halogen. On the other hand, the covalent halides (*e.g.*, HX, CX_4, SiX_4, GeX_4) present low melting and boiling points with the lower halogens which increase with the heavier ones. These results may be rationalized on the basis that, with the ionic compounds, the electrostatic attraction diminishes as the ions are further apart and, therefore, less work is required to separate them as the ionic radius increases. The covalent molecules do not have a strong external field and it is to be expected that as the atomic weight increases the work necessary to fuse or boil them should increase. Of course, the covalent compounds have a much lower boiling and melting point to begin with than the ionic compounds. The covalent types of combinations are found with the metals in the middle groups of the Periodic Table where the combination of small size and high charge lends itself to this type of bonding.

There are four types of oxyacids of the halogens (not including F): (1) HXO (hypohalous acid), (2) HXO_2 (halous acid), (3) HXO_3 (halic acid), (4) HXO_4 (perhalic acid). Their salts are accordingly the hypohalites, halites, halates and perhalates. A number of them will be encountered among the salts used in pharmaceutical practice. Insofar as the acids are concerned their acidity and thermal stability increases for any particular halogen with the increasing number of oxygens coördinated with the central atom. In general, the hypohalous and halous acids are classed as weak acids whereas the halic and perhalic are strong acids. This may be looked upon as a result of each additional oxygen atom (each of which has a strong electron affinity) exerting its attraction to help pull the bonding electrons away from the hydrogen in the acid. The progressive "loosening" of the hydrogen as a proton leads to stronger acids. Although the thermal stability increases with increasing oxygen attached to the central atom, the stability of all of these acids is low. The oxidizing action of these acids is usually believed to be the greatest with the greater number of oxygens. Actually, this measures the capacity for oxidation rather than the readiness to oxidize and, indeed, the lower the thermal stability, the greater the ability to oxidize. As an illustration of this, we may cite the well-known activity of sodium hypochlorite as an antiseptic and the recognized deficiency of potassium chlorate as an oxidizing antiseptic.

Fluorine exhibits some peculiar differences from the other members of this family. For example, silver chloride, bromide and iodide are nearly insoluble in water, whereas silver fluoride is appreciably soluble. Sodium chloride, bromide and iodide are readily soluble in water, whereas sodium fluoride is much less soluble and interesting because it is the only one having antiseptic properties.

Concerning the solubility of halides, a general rule is that they
are soluble except in the case of Ag^+, Hg_2^{++}, and Pb^{++} which are
insoluble. This pertains, obviously to the halides formed from
metallic elements and not to those from non-metallic ones which
present a more complicated picture.

PROPERTIES OF THE HALOGENS

Properties	Fluorine	Chlorine	Bromine	Iodine
Atomic Number . .	9	17	35	53
Atomic Weight . .	18.998	35.453	79.909	126.904
Isotopes	19	35, 37	79, 81	127
Electrons	2–7	2–8–7	2–8–18–7	2–8–18–18–7
Density	1.14 ($-200°$)	1.56 ($-33.6°$)	3.12	4.94
M.P.	$-223°$	$-102°$	$-7.3°$	114°
B.P.	$-187°$	$-34.5°$	58.8°	183°
Common oxidation states	0, -1	0, -1, $+1$, $+3$, $+5$, $+7$	0, -1, $+1$, $+3$, $+5$	0, -1, $+1$, $+3$, $+5$, $+7$,
Radius (X^-), Å . .	1.36	1.81	1.95	2.16
Radius (cov.), Å .	0.64	0.99	1.14	1.33
Electronegativity, Pauling's scale. .	4.0	3.0	2.8	2.4
Oxidation Potential, volts, $2X^-\rightarrow X_2 + 2e$.	-2.8	-1.359	-1.065	-0.535
Ionization Potential, volts, first . . .	17.3	13.0	11.8	10.6
Usual physical state	gas	gas	liquid	solid
Color	Pale yellow	Greenish yellow	Reddish brown	Black (solid) Violet (gas)

6

Fluorine

F₂

Symbol, F. Valence, 1. Atomic Weight, 18.998; Atomic Number, 9

History.—In 1886, Moissan, a French chemist, succeeded in isolating fluorine by the electrolysis of anhydrous hydrofluoric acid in molten potassium hydrogen fluoride. In 1860, Gore succeeded in liberating small quantities of the gas by heating potassium fluoplumbate (1). The addition of fluorspar, CaF_2, to various minerals for the purpose of facilitating their fusion was recorded by both Basil Valentine in the fifteenth century and by Agricola in the sixteenth century. The fact that fluorspar had been used for centuries as a flux was no doubt responsible for naming the element *fluorine*, which is derived from the Latin *fluo*, "to flow."

(1) $K_2PbF_6 \rightarrow 2KF + PbF_2 + F_2 \uparrow$

Occurrence.—The great activity of this element would preclude its occurrence as such in Nature. However, it is claimed that minute traces of free fluorine have been detected. In combination, its principal minerals are *fluorite* or *fluorspar* [CaF_2], *apatite* or *fluorapatite* [$CaF_2.3Ca_3(PO_4)_2$], and *cryolite* [$AlF_3.3NaF$]. The first two minerals are widely distributed while the latter is found in large deposits in Greenland and Iceland. The bones and enamel of teeth of mammals contain small amounts of calcium fluoride.

Fluorine is the seventeenth most plentiful element in the earth's crust which places it below chlorine but above bromine.

Physical Properties.—Fluorine is a pale yellow gas having a characteristic odor resembling a mixture of ozone and chlorine. It may be condensed below the critical temperature of $-129°$ C. to a pale yellow liquid, boiling at $-188°$ C. Solid fluorine melts at $-217.8°$ C. The density of the gas is 1.695 (air$=1$). Its critical pressure is 55 atmospheres.

Chemical Properties.—Fluorine is an intensely active substance, if not the most active element known. It combines directly with all of the elements excepting oxygen, nitrogen, chlorine, and the inert gases (helium family). All organic compounds are attacked by it. Hydrogen, sulfur and many other elements ignite spontaneously in an atmosphere of fluorine. Ordinary illuminating gas is ignited by it, hence the use of a stream of illuminating gas to detect leaks in a fluorine apparatus. Most metals unite with it to form fluorides. Gold and platinum do not react with it below red heat. Fluorine abstracts hydrogen from its compounds. It decomposes water to form hydrofluoric acid and ozone (2).

$$(2)\ 3F_2 + 3H_2O \rightarrow 6HF + O_3 \uparrow$$

Commercial Manufacture.—The electrolytic generation of fluorine is possible under varying conditions of temperature and electrolyte composition. One commercially practical cell of the diaphragm type draws approximately 1000 amperes. Ordinary carbon steel is used for the major parts, including the cell body, the hot water jacket, the HF feed line, the cathode, and the solid part of the diaphragm. The anodes are carbon rods impregnated with copper and the diaphragm is a Monel screen. The electrolyte is fused $KF.2HF$ to which has been added 1 to 1.5 per cent LiF. The cell operates at 95° to 115° C. with an anode current efficiency close to 95 per cent and an overall potential drop of 9 volts. These cells can operate continuously for more than a year and produce 99 per cent fluorine after removal of 4 to 8 per cent HF.

Prior to 1942, only a few pounds per day of fluorine were produced. During World War II the demand for fluorine increased, so that by 1945 production was measured in tons per day. The production and use of hydrogen fluoride and other fluorides has also increased tremendously and new applications for these chemicals are continually developed.

Fluorine gas can be handled satisfactorily at ordinary temperatures and atmospheric pressure in piping, tubing, and other vessels constructed of copper, iron, magnesium, nickel, or Monel. A protective coat of the metal fluoride develops on the metal. If it is free of hydrofluoric acid (HF) fluorine may be placed in glass or quartz vessels for short periods.

Pharmacology of Fluorine.—Gaseous fluorine, like the more familiar chlorine, is highly irritating to the skin, eyes, and mucous membranes. It reacts with water to form hydrofluoric acid and will liberate chlorine and iodine from the respective chlorides and iodides. Upon contact with body fluids, the liberated chlorine forms sodium chloride which contributes to the irritation. Fluorine is so reactive and difficult to handle that it has limited use in industry. Hydrofluoric acid is the primary fluorine compound.

The fluorides have been most useful in pharmacy and are discussed with sodium fluoride.

In contrast to the chloride, bromide, or iodide ions, the fluoride ion is extremely germicidal. Sodium fluoride is useful to prevent the growth of bacteria or mold and will preserve blood specimens.

In 1 per cent concentration it inhibits growth and acid production of *L. casei*. Fluorine substitution in otherwise active germicidal compounds, such as the phenols, does not appreciably alter the bactericidal properties.

Uses.—Fluorine is used almost exclusively in the form of inorganic or organic compounds.

In the organic field, simple fluorine-containing compounds have been used for more than a decade as refrigerants, known as *Freon* (CF_2Cl_2). These are good solvents and dispersants for aerosol insecticides. Fluorocarbons, because of their extreme stability, are used as lubricants and inert solvents. A polymer of tetra fluoroethylene (Teflon) is now used for containers of hydrofluoric acid.

Inorganic compounds available are quite varied and are used for many purposes. Sulfur hexafluoride is finding its principal application as a gaseous dielectric in high-voltage generators. Sodium fluoride, stannous fluoride, and sodium monofluorophosphate are employed to prevent dental caries. Sodium fluorosilicate solution is an effective antimoth preparation whereas cryolite (Na_3AlF_6) has long been used as an insecticide. Di-isopropyl fluorophosphate (DFP) is used for the reduction of intraocular tension in glaucoma.

7

Chlorine

Cl_2

Symbol, Cl.   Valence, 1, 3, 5, 7.   Atomic Weight, 35.453;
Atomic Number, 17

History.—This gaseous chemical element takes its name from Greek, χλωρός, (chloros), meaning "greenish yellow." Scheele discovered it in 1774 and called it "dephlogisticated muriatic acid." In 1785, C. L. Berthollet expressed his belief that it was a compound of oxygen and hydrochloric acid and named it "oxygenized muriatic acid." He pointed out its usefulness as a bleaching agent, but James Watt was responsible for the application. In 1810–1811, Sir H. Davy proved conclusively that it was an element and gave it the name *chlorine*.

Occurrence.—Chlorine never occurs as such in Nature. In combination with the alkali metals it occurs widely distributed as *rock salt* (NaCl), as *carnallite* ($KCl.MgCl_2.6H_2O$), and as *sylvite* (native KCl) at Stassfurt. It is found in combination with the alkali metals in sea salt, in various spring waters, and in the tissues of plants and animals. The blood contains about 0.25 per cent of chloride. Sea water contains about 2.07 per cent of combined chlorine. Volcanic gases contain chlorine in the form of hydrochloric acid (*q.v.*).

Physical Properties.—Chlorine is a greenish yellow gas, having a characteristic unpleasant, suffocating odor and an astringent taste. The vapor density of chlorine is 3.214 (air = 1). Its critical temperature is 146° C. and its critical pressure 93.5 atmospheres. Its vapor pressure at 21° C. is 5.72 atmospheres. It can be liquefied at −34.05° C. under atmospheric pressure and at ordinary temperatures by compression. It solidifies and crystallizes at −101.6° C. Two hundred and thirty cubic centimeters of the gas dissolve in 100 ml. of water at 20° C. It is only slightly soluble in a concentrated solution of sodium chloride.

Chemical Properties.—At ordinary temperatures, chlorine unites directly with many other elements. In direct sunlight, or in the actinic light of burning magnesium, it combines explosively with hydrogen. Powdered arsenic, antimony, copper, and phosphorus

(82)

ignite spontaneously in an atmosphere of chlorine to form the corresponding chlorides (1, 2 and 3).

(1) $2Sb + 3Cl_2 \rightarrow 2SbCl_3$

(2) $2P + 3Cl_2 \rightarrow 2PCl_3$

(3) $PCl_3 + Cl_2 \rightarrow PCl_5$

It does not combine directly with carbon, nitrogen, or oxygen. Many compounds containing hydrogen are readily decomposed by chlorine. For example, if a few drops of hot turpentine are placed upon a strip of paper and then immersed in an atmosphere of chlorine, a violent reaction takes place with the formation of hydrochloric acid and carbon (4).

(4) $C_{10}H_{16} + 8Cl_2 \rightarrow 16HCl + 10C$

Furthermore, a lighted taper burns in chlorine with a very luminous flame. Therefore, it may be concluded that chlorine does not *readily* unite with carbon.

Chlorine is the most active of the halogens in reacting with a hydrocarbon to form a chlorinated compound (5) and in adding to double bonds of organic compounds.

(5) $CH_3CH_2CH_3 + Cl_2 \rightarrow CH_3CH_2CH_2Cl + HCl$

A saturated solution of chlorine in distilled water (Chlorine Water) is listed among the Test Solutions of the U.S.P. XVII. A freshly prepared solution of chlorine in water was official as Aqua Chlori in U. S. Pharmacopœia, 1890. It has a yellow color, which disappears on standing. At room temperature about a 0.6 per cent solution is attained. This is caused by the action of chlorine upon water to form hydrochloric and hypochlorous acids (6), both of which are colorless.

(6) $H_2O + Cl_2 \rightleftarrows HCl + HClO$

In a one-half saturated chlorine water solution at 10° C., 33 per cent of the chlorine is changed to hydrochloric and hypochlorous acids. The equilibrium thus established is readily destroyed by the action of sunlight, ultraviolet light or some contact catalysts on hypochlorous acid forming hydrochloric acid and oxygen (7).

(7) $2HClO \rightarrow 2HCl + O_2 \uparrow$

The oxidizing and bleaching properties of chlorine are due to the oxygen evolved in the breakdown of hypochlorous acid (7) (see Oxygen, p. 20). Consequently, in an effort to re-establish the equilibrium, more chlorine reacts with water according to equation (6). In the presence of light these reactions continue until the colorless solution contains only a small quantity of dissolved chlorine and is mostly a dilute solution of hydrochloric acid. Freshly prepared chlorine water contains free chlorine, hydrochloric acid, and hypochlorous acid. In order to retain as much chlorine *per se* in solution as possible, chlorine water should be kept in a dark place or in light-resistant containers.

In basic solutions chlorine may form hypochlorous or chloric salts depending upon the temperature. A cold aqueous solution of sodium hydroxide reacts with chlorine to form sodium hypochlorite (8).

$$(8)\ Cl_2 + 2NaOH \rightarrow NaCl + NaClO + H_2O$$

In warm or hot solutions a chlorate is produced (9).

$$(9)\ 3Cl_2 + 6NaOH \overset{\triangle}{\rightarrow} 5NaCl + NaClO_3 + 3H_2O$$

As stated previously, chlorine has the property of displacing halogens of higher atomic weight from the hydrogen halides or their salts (10).

$$(10)\ 2HX + Cl_2 \rightarrow 2HCl + X_2 \qquad (X = Br\ or\ I)$$

and

$$2MX + Cl_2 \rightarrow 2MCl + X_2 \qquad (M = any\ metal)$$

When water at $0°$ C. is saturated with chlorine, a pale green compound, chlorine hydrate $(Cl_2.8H_2O)$, crystallizes out. At higher temperatures this compound is readily decomposed into its constituents. Chlorine hydrate is of historical interest because, in 1823, Faraday prepared the first liquid chlorine by placing this compound in one arm of a U-tube, sealing the open end and placing the empty limb in a freezing mixture. When the hydrate was warmed gently, chlorine was driven off and liquefied by its own pressure in the empty part of the tube.

Tests for Identity.—1. Free chlorine may be recognized by its characteristic odor.

2. It liberates iodine from solutions of potassium iodide (10).

3. Litmus, indigo, etc., are bleached by chlorine.

4. Chlorine acts as a powerful oxidizing agent (7).

Commercial Manufacture.—Chlorine is made by the electrolysis of sodium chloride or potassium chloride in an electrolytic cell of which there are several designs. The diaphragm cell is the most generally used type. It is so named because of its porous asbestos diaphragm which permits the free flow of ions, yet, by obstructing the interaction of cell products, it minimizes the formation of sodium chlorate. A cell is usually run at 10,000 amperes and 3.75 volts and produces 500 pounds of chlorine per day. This method of preparation not only produces chlorine but also hydrogen and sodium hydroxide (potassium hydroxide if KCl replaces NaCl). Sodium chloride in aqueous solution will ionize into sodium ions, Na^+, and chloride ions, Cl^-. The water will supply hydronium ions, H_3O^+, and hydroxide ions, OH^-. The passing of an electric current through such a solution causes the positively charged ions (Na^+ and H_3O^+) to travel toward the cathode, whereas the negatively charged ions (Cl^- and OH^-) migrate toward the anode. Being a much more reactive element than hydrogen, sodium requires a higher voltage to accept an electron and thereby convert the sodium ion to sodium atom.[1] The voltage may be regulated so that the hydronium ion does accept an electron and thus liberates hydrogen (11).

$$(11) \quad H_3O^+ + 1\epsilon \rightarrow H° + H_2O$$
$$H° + H° \rightarrow H_2 \uparrow$$

The liberation of chlorine at the anode (rather than OH^- ions liberating an electron) takes place at the same time and in a similar manner (12).

$$(12) \quad Cl^- \rightarrow Cl° + 1\epsilon$$
$$Cl° + Cl° \rightarrow Cl_2$$

The residue is purified and fused into sticks or pellets.

Other methods of production are the electrolysis of fused sodium chloride (see sodium production) and the interaction of sodium chloride and nitric acid.

Pharmacological Action of Chlorine.—Chlorine is an irritant to the skin, mucous membranes and the respiratory tract. Overexposure to the gas causes restlessness, sneezing and excessive salivation. These symptoms increase and are accompanied by vomiting until death occurs by asphyxiation.

Physiological effects of various concentrations of chlorine gas are presented in the following table.[2]

Effect	Parts of Chlorine Gas per Million Parts of Air
Minimum amount required to produce slight symptoms of irritation after several hours of exposure	1.0
Minimum detectable odor	3.5
Maximum amount that can be breathed for one hour without serious effects	4.0
Minimum amount required to cause irritation of the throat	15.5
Minimum amount required to cause coughing	30.2
Amount dangerous in 30 minutes to one hour	40–60
Amount likely to be fatal after a few deep breaths . . .	1000

[1] An alternative explanation is that the sodium ion migrates to the cathode and accepts an electron, thus becoming sodium metal (a) which, of course, cannot exist as such in an aqueous solution and, therefore, forms NaOH and H_2 (b).

$$(a) \quad Na^+ + 1\epsilon \rightarrow Na$$
$$(b) \quad 2Na + 2H_2O \rightarrow 2NaOH + H_2 \uparrow$$

Chlorine forms by simply giving up an electron to the anode (12).

[2] Information taken from U. S. Bureau of Mines Technical Paper 248 "Gas Masks for Gases Met in Fighting Fires."

Liquid chlorine will cause blistering of the exposed skin. Shallow breathing in a chlorine atmosphere is best and persons afflicted with asthma or chronic bronchitis are particularly bothered by chlorine.

The antiseptic action of chlorine solutions is thought to be due mostly to the non-ionized hypochlorous acid or in slightly alkaline solutions to the non-ionized molecules of hypochlorite salt. Chlorine is present as positive chlorine in hypochlorites. The following equations may be used to explain hypochlorite formation (13).

$$(13) \quad \begin{matrix} Cl\ (a) \\ | \\ Cl\ (b) \end{matrix} + H_2O(H^+ + OH^-) \rightleftarrows HCl + HClO$$

Chlorine atom (a) will unite with the hydrogen ion (H^+) and be reduced to form HCl while at the same moment the chlorine atom (b) is oxidized to positive chlorine and will unite with hydroxide ions to form HClO.

In hypochlorite solutions (Diluted Sodium Hypochlorite Solution N.F.) the most effective condition is at a pH near 7. Acidification with boric acid also produces an effective solution. In the presence of bacterial protein the antiseptic property is thought to be due to the chlorination of the amide group present in proteins (14).

$$(14) \quad \begin{matrix} O & H \\ \| & | \\ R-C-N-CH_2-R \end{matrix} + NaClO \rightarrow \begin{matrix} O & Cl \\ \| & | \\ R-C-N-CH_2-R \end{matrix}$$
$$+ NaOH$$

It is known that a hypochlorite will chlorinate the amide group of a benzamide or sulfonamide (15).

$$(15) \quad p\text{-}CH_3-C_6H_4-SO_2-NH_2 + NaClO \rightarrow$$
$$p\text{-}CH_3-C_6H_4-SO_2-NHCl + NaOH$$

The organic compounds such as chloramine-T and dichloramine-T probably function as antiseptics because of the slow liberation of hypochlorous acid (HClO) when in solution. Antiseptic property was found to be greatest at pH 7 and to decrease as the solution was made more alkaline or acidic.

Although solutions of hypochlorite are strong oxidizing agents and do possess available chlorine, they are not necessarily antiseptic because of these properties. The mere function of supplying oxygen does not seem to be the whole factor when compared to hydrogen peroxide, potassium permanganate, chlorates, etc. Some organic chlorine structures and inorganic hypochlorites, however, are mentioned because of their long association with chlorine. Most are standardized on the basis of "active" chlorine or "available" chlorine. This is the chlorine which is liberated from a substance when treated with an acid.

Uses.—Chlorine as the pure element has little use in medicine. Chlorine Test Solution is a reagent listed in U.S.P. XVII. However, the oxidizing property is utilized when in the form of a hypochlorite or the organic N-chloro compounds. Examples of these are *Sodium Hypochlorite Solution, Labarraque's Solution, Chlorinated Lime* and *Halazone.*

Since the early part of the century chlorine has been used to purify the drinking water of our cities. Long before this, however, chlorine was known to prevent putrefaction and remove the odor of decay. The most important use of chlorine today is in water purification. Water is treated with an excess of gaseous chlorine and then carbon is added which adsorbs certain objectionable impurities and reduces the chlorine concentration to 0.2 part per 1,000,000. The water-carbon mixture is then filtered. Some chlorine is allowed to remain in the water to protect it while moving through the mains. Chlorinated water is often unpalatable due to chlorine compounds formed from the impurities. Phenolic compounds, for example, will be converted to chlorophenols which have a characteristic unpleasant taste and odor. Algæ growth in water presents a similar difficulty.

A few of the principal uses of chlorine are in the manufacture of explosives, insecticides and herbicides, organic and intermediate chemicals, refrigerants, etc. It is also used in cellulose processing.

Chlorine dioxide (ClO_2) has been used to purify drinking water and besides having two and a half times the oxidizing power of chlorine does not chlorinate contaminating compounds (16, 17), but oxidizes them to odorless and tasteless products.

(16) $ClO_2 + 2\frac{1}{2}H_2 \rightarrow HCl + 2H_2O$

(17) $Cl_2 + H_2 \rightarrow 2HCl$

Chlorine dioxide is a good bactericide, but it is not economical to use it for sterilizing drinking water. Therefore, to purify drinking water, chlorine is first added to disinfect it and then chlorine dioxide added to destroy unpleasant tastes and odors.

Chlorine dioxide is also the best compound for bleaching flour, fats, oil, paper, textiles, etc. Its action is instantaneous and it does not weaken the fiber of materials.

8

Bromine

Br_2

Symbol, Br. Valence, 1, 3, 5. Atomic Weight, 79.909;
Atomic Number, 35

History.—In 1826, A. J. Balard isolated this element from the concentrated mother liquor of the salines of Montpellier. He named it *bromine* (Greek, βρῶμος, a stench) because of its pungent, unpleasant smell. Prior to its discovery, Joss had confused it with selenium and Liebig thought that it was iodine monochloride. Balard's investigations established the elemental character of the substance and demonstrated that its chemical properties were very similar to those of chlorine and iodine.

Occurrence.—Bromine does not occur in Nature in the uncombined condition, but is always united with various metals. The mineral *bromyrite* (AgBr) is naturally occurring. Sodium, potassium, calcium and magnesium bromides are found in mineral waters (kissingen, kreuznach, etc.), in river and sea water, and occasionally in marine plants and animals. Its principal commercial sources are: (*a*) Sea water (0.007 per cent $MgBr_2$); (*b*) Dead Sea (9 per cent $MgBr_2$); (*c*) the carnallite deposits at Stassfurt in Prussian Saxony, where, after the extraction of the potassium chloride from the impure mineral, the mother liquor is found to contain appreciable quantities of magnesium and sodium bromides; and (*d*) the brines of Michigan, Ohio, Pennsylvania, Kentucky, and West Virginia. These brines contain about 25 per cent solids and 1300 parts per 1,000,000 of bromine. In the form of bromides, it is also found in small quantities in the mother liquors from kelp and Chile saltpeter.

Physical Properties.—At ordinary temperatures, bromine is a dark reddish-brown mobile liquid, which in any quantity appears almost black. It has a density of 3.119, and boils at 58.2° C., forming a deep red, poisonous vapor which is very irritating to the respiratory organs. Bromine vapors are about 5.5 times as heavy as air. At ordinary temperatures, it has a high vapor pressure (150 mm. at 18° C.) and hence evaporates very quickly. When cooled to −21° C., it forms red, needle-shaped crystals (melting-point,

−7.3° C.).   One Gm. of bromine dissolves in about 30 ml. of water at 20° C., and is freely soluble in alcohol, ether, chloroform, carbon disulfide and acetic acid.   Alcohol and ether are gradually decomposed by bromine, forming bromine substitution products.   Solubility in water may be increased by the use of potassium bromide.

Containers are usually glass vessels for small quantities or glass lined metal drums.   Recently introduced are fiber drums having a liner only 0.00045 inch thick of polyethylene.   These are available in sizes up to 55 gallons or 400 pounds capacity.

Chemical Properties.—In general, the chemical properties of bromine are intermediate between those of chlorine and iodine (*q.v.*). It does not combine directly with oxygen, nitrogen, or carbon and will unite with hydrogen only in the presence of a catalyst or at fairly high temperatures (heat of formation of HBr = 8600 calories).

Chlorine tends to gain an electron more readily than does bromine and will unite more easily with hydrogen.   Bromine combines directly with the active alkali and alkaline earth metals to form bromides.   It also will react with the non-metals, phosphorus and arsenic, just as does chlorine and iodine (1).

(1) $2P + 3Br_2 \rightarrow 2PBr_3$

Bromine is less reactive with water than is chlorine but more so than iodine (2).

(2) $Br_2 + H_2O \rightleftarrows HBr + HBrO$

The hypobromous acid is slowly decomposed just as is hypochlorous acid to yield oxygen which is responsible for the bleaching property (3).

(3) $HBrO \rightarrow HBr + (O)$

Bromine reacts vigorously with alkalies to produce hypobromites and bromides (4).   If the reaction mixture is heated the hypobromites undergo auto-oxidation forming bromates and more bromide (5).

(4) $Br_2 + 2KOH \rightarrow KBr + KBrO + H_2O$
(5) $3KBrO \rightarrow 2KBr + KBrO_3$
(6) $6KOH + 3Br_2 \rightarrow 5KBr + KBrO_3 + 3H_2O$

The sum of reactions (4) and (5) is shown by (6).

Bromine is the halogen of choice for reacting with the double bond of organic structures because the decolorization is readily observed and it is more easily handled than chlorine (7).

(7) $R—CH = CH—R + Br_2 \rightarrow R—CHBr—CHBr—R$

In contrast to iodine a yellow color is produced by starch and bromine.   Iodine forms a blue starch-iodide complex.

Chemically, bromine is a very active oxidizing agent either as a vapor, liquid or in solution. Of the halogens, iodine, even though a weaker oxidizing agent, is commonly used because of its ease in handling.

Bromine will be decolorized by most reducing agents in a manner similar to that of iodine (8, 9, and 10).

(8) $Br_2 + 2Na_2S_2O_3 \rightarrow 2NaBr + Na_2S_4O_6$

(9) $Na_2SO_3 + Br_2 + H_2O \rightarrow Na_2SO_4 + 2HBr$

(10) $2Br_2 + HPH_2O_2 + 2H_2O \rightarrow 4HBr + H_3PO_4$

Tests for Identity.—1. Bromine may be recognized by its characteristic, unpleasant odor.

2. It destroys organic matter and bleaches litmus, indigo and other coloring materials.

3. It imparts a yellow color to starch test solution.

4. When an aqueous solution of bromine is shaken with carbon disulfide, the latter acquires a reddish yellow color.

Commercial Manufacture.—The methods of bromine preparation depend upon the oxidation of the bromide ion to elemental bromine.

1. *Recovery From Sea Water.*—Sea water contains 3.5 per cent total solids and 65 to 70 parts per 1,000,000 of bromine. Bromine is present in sea water as bromide and is liberated by introducing chlorine gas. In order to have the bromine liberated, the sea water is acidulated with sulfuric acid (0.27 pound of 96 per cent sulfuric acid per ton of sea water) to a pH of about 3.5. This is necessary because if the sea water is just brought to neutrality or allowed to remain basic and then chlorine added, the following reactions will take place (11 and 12).

(11) Br_2 (or Cl_2) + $H_2O \rightleftharpoons HBr + HBrO$

(12) $3Br_2$ (or $3Cl_2$) + $6OH^- \rightleftharpoons 5Br^- + BrO_3^- + 3H_2O$

The excess sulfuric acid causes the reaction to remain completely on the left-hand side due to the hydrogen ions released from the sulfuric acid. Chlorine is passed through the acidulated sea water to oxidize the bromide to free bromine (13).

(13) $2Br^- + Cl_2 \rightarrow 2Cl^- + Br_2 \uparrow$

The bromine thus generated is blown out of the solution and absorbed by a sodium carbonate solution to concentrate the bromine as sodium bromide and bromate in a small volume (14).

(14) $3Br_2 + 3Na_2CO_3 \rightarrow 5NaBr + NaBrO_3 + 3CO_2 \uparrow$

The solution of bromide and bromate so obtained is treated with sulfuric acid (15, 16 and 17). The bromine vapors are then steamed out of the acidified solution and are condensed to pure liquid bromine.

(15) $2NaBr + H_2SO_4 \rightarrow 2HBr + Na_2SO_4$

(16) $2NaBrO_3 + H_2SO_4 \rightarrow 2HBrO_3 + Na_2SO_4$

(17) $5HBr + HBrO_3 \xrightarrow{H^+} 3H_2O + 3Br_2 \uparrow$

2. *Recovery From the Dead Sea and From Natural Bromide-containing Brine.*—The procedure is the same as that used for sea water except acidification with sulfuric acid is unnecessary.

3. *Electrolysis.*—Bromine may be obtained by the electrolysis of bitterns. These aqueous solutions of various bromides and chlorides yield upon electrolysis free bromine until all of the bromides have been decomposed. During the operation, chlorine is also liberated from the chlorides present, but it immediately displaces the bromine from its salts and becomes fixed. The current is stopped as soon as chlorine begins to come off (see Chlorine Production).

Pharmacological Action of Bromine.—Bromine is a very irritant poison and a powerful escharotic and is, therefore, rarely used in medicine.

Solutions of free bromine, 1:5000 in distilled water, have been found to be between comparable solutions of chlorine and iodine in antiseptic power. A 0.2 p.p.m. bromine solution is effective for *E. coli* but higher concentrations (15 to 50 p.p.m.) are necessary for most other organisms. Organic bromine compounds such as 4-bromothymol which has a phenol coefficient of 12.5 have been studied but none are in general use.

Liquid bromine quickly attacks the skin and other tissue producing a burn that is slow to heal. *When handling bromine it is always advisable to have ammonia water within reach to stop its action* (18).

(18) $3Br_2 + 8NH_4OH \longrightarrow 6NH_4Br + N_2 \uparrow + 8H_2O$

It helps also to wash the affected area quickly with alcohol. A concentration of one p.p.m. or less in air is said to be safe for eight hours and is readily detected by its odor. Concentrations of ten p.p.m. in air can hardly be tolerated.

Relief from inhaled bromine may be obtained by breathing ammonia vapors followed after a period of time by oxygen. Bromine on contact with skin is cooling (just as are all volatile liquids) followed by a brown stain and burn. The burn is treated by washing the area with an abundance of water followed by a solution of sodium thiosulfate (hypo) (see equation 8). After thorough washing, packs of moist sodium bicarbonate are applied.

Uses.—Bromine is used in making bromides for medicinal purposes, in analytical chemistry, in photography, and in the preparation of organic dyes.

Bromine is listed among the Reagent Standards of the U.S.P. XVII. Standards for its quality, *i.e.*, specific gravity, limits for non-volatile matter, organic bromine compounds, iodine, and sulfur compounds are specified and appropriate tests given.

Bromine T.S. (Bromine Water) is included in the list of Test Solutions given in the U.S.P. XVII. It is a saturated solution of bromine prepared by agitating from 2 to 3 ml. of bromine with 100 ml. of cold distilled water in a glass-stoppered bottle, the stopper of which should be lubricated with petrolatum. It is to be preserved in a cool place, protected from light. Bromine water is a useful oxidizing agent in qualitative chemistry.

Bromine, Tenth-Normal Solution (U.S.P. XVII) (Koppeschaar's Solution) is a solution of potassium bromate (3 Gm.) and potassium bromide (15 Gm.) in water sufficient to make a liter. It is a clear solution and free bromine is only released upon the addition of an acid (19).

(19) $5KBr + KBrO_3 + 6HCl \rightarrow 3Br_2 + 6KCl + 3H_2O$

Other solutions of bromine include:

Iodobromide T.S. (U.S.P. XVII, p. 1076),
Bromine-Acetic Acid Solution (U.S.P. XVII, p. 881).

9

Iodine

Iodine, U.S.P. XVII

I₂

Symbol, I.   Valence, 1, 3, 5, 7.   Atomic Weight, 126.90;
Atomic Number, 53

History.—The accidental discovery of iodine in 1811 by B. Courtois, a saltpeter manufacturer of Paris, is an interesting example of serendipity. The process for making saltpeter at this time was to expose heaps of decaying organic matter mixed with lime to atmospheric action. The crude calcium nitrate formed was extracted from the heaps with water and the nitrate solution then treated with wood ash (principally K_2CO_3), filtered, and concentrated to obtain saltpeter (KNO_3). In seeking to lower costs of manufacture because of the high cost of wood ashes, Courtois turned to seaweed ash which, however, contained sodium carbonate instead of potassium carbonate. In this manner, he ended up with a solution of sodium nitrate which could be converted to potassium nitrate with wood ash more economically than by the other process. In the process of repeatedly extracting sodium carbonate from seaweed ash, however, Courtois was bothered by a thick liquid encrusted with insoluble material forming in the bottom of the metal vats. He customarily cleaned them out with sulfuric acid and one day, accidentally, used a stronger concentration of the acid than he usually did. A strange phenomenon took place wherein beautiful violet vapors rose into the air and formed irregular deposits of dark metal-like crystals on the cooler parts of the vat. He suspected that they might be a new element but, being too busy with his work, turned them over to a friend who subsequently gave them to Gay-Lussac. This distinguished French chemist eventually reported in 1813 on his observations and named the new substance "Iode." At about the same time England's Sir Humphrey Davy, who had also received samples, reported his proof of the elemental character of the product. As often happens, the discoverer, Courtois, found himself in a poor economic position when the war which had created a demand for saltpeter ended. An effort to extract iodine on a commercial basis was doomed to failure because of the lack of demand. He did, however, receive a prize from the Royal Society in 1831 "for having improved the art of healing" in recognition of the value shown for iodine in treating goiter (Coindet, 1820).

Occurrence.—Iodine does not occur as such in Nature, but is found widely but sparingly distributed in the form of iodides and iodates, chiefly of potassium and sodium. Small quantities are also found in some minerals in combination with silver, lead, mercury and other metals. Sea water, seafoods, seaweed and sponges contain small quantities of iodides. The ashes obtained by burning seaweeds are known in Scotland as kelp; in Norway as varec; and in Spain as barilla. They often contain as much as 2 per cent of iodine as iodides, etc. Japan is a current producer of iodine from seaweed. Iodine also occurs in the thyroid glands of animals in organic combination as a part of the thyroid hormone in which it is present as part of the two amino-acids triiodothyronine and thyroxin. Chile saltpeter (impure sodium nitrate) contains approximately 0.2 per cent of a mixture of sodium iodide and sodium iodate.

Physical Properties.—Iodine occurs in the form of a grayish black solid, having a metallic luster and a characteristic penetrating odor. It crystallizes in large rhombic plates or granules. At ordinary temperatures it volatilizes slowly and when heated to 113.5° C., it melts, giving off a violet-colored vapor which is one of the heaviest known gases, 8.8 times as heavy as air. The liquid boils at 184.4° C. It has a specific gravity of 4.93 and is the heaviest non-metallic element. The molecular weight of iodine (by vapor density method from 184° to 700° C.) is 253.8; hence its molecular formula I_2. At 1700° C. the dissociation of the diatomic iodine molecule into monatomic molecules is complete and its molecular weight is equal to its atomic weight (1).

$$(1) \quad I_2 \rightleftarrows I + I - 28{,}500 \text{ calories}$$

One Gm. of iodine is soluble in about 2950 ml. of water, in 12.5 ml. of alcohol, in about 80 ml. of glycerin, and in about 4 ml. of carbon disulfide. Solutions of iodides, *e.g.*, potassium iodide, dissolve large quantities of iodine because of the formation of the I_3^- ion (2). This property is also true for bromine and bromides, but chlorides do not increase the solubility of chlorine. The I_3^- ion is formed by the union of I_2 and an iodide ion (I^-) which is attracted to the iodine molecule by a coordinate covalent bond. The I_3^- ion *per se* has been found to have no antiseptic property.

$$(2) \quad KI + I_2 \rightleftarrows KI_3$$

The electronic structure of the anion may be represented as:

$$\overset{\text{xx}}{\underset{\text{xx}}{\overset{x}{\underset{x}{I}}}} \overset{\cdot\cdot}{\underset{\cdot\cdot}{\overset{x}{I}}} \overset{\text{xx}}{\underset{\text{xx}}{\overset{x}{\underset{}{I}}}}{}^{\overset{x}{\underset{x}{I}}} \,^{-}$$

Iodine gives brown solutions with most polar solvents. Relatively non-polar solvents such as carbon disulfide, carbon tetrachloride and chloroform give violet solutions, a property utilized by the U.S.P. as an identity test. It is thought that the brown color of solutions of iodine in certain solvents is due to the products of a weak combination of iodine with these solvents, and that the violet-colored solutions represent iodine in solution in an uncombined form.

Chemical Properties.—The chemical properties of iodine resemble those of chlorine and bromine. In substitution reactions (replacing the hydrogen of hydrocarbons) and addition reactions (3) it is less reactive than the other halogens.

$$(3)\ R—CH = CH—R + I_2 \rightarrow R—CHI—CHI—R$$

Iodine acts as an oxidizing agent but is a weaker oxidizing agent than either chlorine or bromine. Even when heated, it unites very slowly with hydrogen, the presence of a catalyst (platinum black) being necessary to effect the combination. It combines directly with some non-metals and with a majority of the metals. For example, yellow phosphorus melts and then inflames when mixed with iodine (4); antimony burns in iodine vapor; and mercury or

$$(4)\ 2P + 3I_2 \rightarrow 2PI_3$$

iron when heated combine rapidly with it (5, 6).

$$(5)\ Hg + I_2 \rightarrow HgI_2$$
$$(6)\ Fe + I_2 \rightarrow FeI_2$$

In aqueous solution, the most common chemical property is that of an oxidizing agent. It is less reactive with water than chlorine or bromine but is considered to function as an oxidizing agent via the formation of hypoiodous acid (7, 8).

$$(7)\ I_2 + H_2O \rightleftarrows HI + HIO$$
$$(8)\ HIO \rightarrow HI + (O)$$

Many reducing agents react with iodine in aqueous solutions as follows:

$$(9)\ HPH_2O_2 + 2I_2 + 2H_2O \rightarrow 4HI + H_3PO_4$$
$$(10)\ H_3AsO_3 + I_2 + H_2O \rightarrow 2HI + H_3AsO_4$$
$$(11)\ H_2SO_3 + I_2 + H_2O \rightarrow 2HI + H_2SO_4$$
$$(12)\ H_2S + I_2 \rightarrow 2HI + S \downarrow$$
$$(13)\ 2FeCl_2 + I_2 + 2HCl \rightarrow 2HI + 2FeCl_3$$
$$(14)\ 2Na_2S_2O_3 + I_2 \rightarrow 2NaI + Na_2S_4O_6$$

Since nitrites (sodium nitrite) are frequently used in pharmacy as reducing agents, it is pointed out that no reaction takes place with iodine.

Iodine can be oxidized (decolorized) by strong oxidizing agents and thus functions as a reducing agent. Potassium chlorate solutions will oxidize iodine to iodic acid (15) and a similar reaction occurs with nitric acid (16).

(15) $3I_2 + 5KClO_3 + 3H_2O \rightarrow 6HIO_3 + 5KCl$

(16) $I_2 + 10HNO_3 \rightarrow 2HIO_3 + 10NO_2 \uparrow + 4H_2O$

Excess chlorine water added to an iodide will decolorize the liberated free iodine by oxidizing it at once to iodic acid (17) (see potassium chlorate).

(17) $I_2 + 5Cl_2 + 6H_2O \rightarrow 2HIO_3 + 10HCl$
    (excess)

With alkali, iodine forms the iodide and iodate, especially with the aid of heat, reacting in a manner similar to that of bromine and chlorine (18).

(18) $3I_2 + 6NaOH \overset{\Delta}{\rightarrow} 5NaI + NaIO_3 + 3H_2O$

Ammonium hydroxide will also decolorize an iodine solution by what is thought to be the same type of reaction. Although the formation of ammonium iodide and ammonium hypoiodite are possible, the main reaction is most important (19). Application was made of this in *Decolorized Iodine Tincture*, N.F. IX.

(19) $3I_2 + 6NH_4OH \rightarrow 5NH_4I + NH_4IO_3 + 3H_2O$

If pure iodine is added to Strong Ammonia Solution U.S.P. the following reaction (20) takes place:

(20) $2NH_3 + 3I_2 \rightarrow NI_3 \cdot NH_3 + 3HI$

The iodine compound with ammonia is more stable than those of chlorine or bromine and is called "nitrogen iodide." It is an insoluble brownish-black solid which decomposes in light and is *very* explosive in the dry state.

The assay of iodine is carried out by first dissolving it with the aid of potassium iodide and then titrating a slightly acidified solution with sodium thiosulfate solution according to equation 14.

Official Tests for Identity.—1. Iodine can be readily detected by the blue color it immediately gives with starch test solution. The color vanishes when the mixture is boiled, but reappears on cooling, provided the boiling has not been too prolonged.

2. The color of its solutions in chloroform, carbon tetrachloride or carbon disulfide is violet.

Commercial Manufacture.—Iodine is obtained from (1) iodates in crude Chile saltpeter (caliche), (2) iodides in oil-well brines, or (3) iodides present in the ashes of burned seaweed.

1. *The Recovery of Iodine from Iodates.*—Iodine is obtained in large quantities from the mother liquors of Chile saltpeter where it occurs in a concentration of 6 to 12 grams per liter as sodium iodate. The liquor is mixed with a stream of sulfur dioxide to liberate the iodine (21).

$$(21)\ 2NaIO_3 + 4H_2O + 5SO_2 \rightarrow Na_2SO_4 + 4H_2SO_4 + I_2 \downarrow$$

The precipitated iodine is filtered in canvas bags, which are pressed to remove the water. The iodine is sublimed in cement-lined retorts. The product is 99 to 99.5 per cent iodine. The yield represents only about 70 per cent of the original iodine content of Chile saltpeter.

2. *The Recovery of Iodine from Iodides in Oil-well Brines of California.*—Iodide is present in brine from 10 to 135 p.p.m. The more important extraction processes used are: (a) the silver iodide method; and, (b) blowing iodine out with air after chlorinating and SO_2 absorption.

(a) *Silver Iodide Method.*—To clean brine is added 2 per cent silver nitrate solution in the presence of ferric chloride. The precipitate of $AgI-Fe(OH)_3$ is treated with hydrochloric acid to dissolve the ferric hydroxide. [Iron scrap is added which forms ferrous iodide and free silver. A solution of ferrous iodide is obtained by filtration and treated with chlorine gas (22).

$$(22)\ FeI_2 + Cl_2 \xrightarrow{H_2O} FeCl_2 + I_2 \downarrow$$

The solid iodine is purified by sublimation.

(b) *Chlorinating and SO_2 Absorption.*—Chlorine gas is passed through clean brine and the liberated iodine mixed with air is blown into absorption towers of SO_2 and water (23).

$$(23)\ I_2\ (air) + SO_2 + 2H_2O \rightarrow 2HI + H_2SO_4$$

More chlorine is passed into the iodide solution to precipitate iodine.

3. *Recovery of Iodides from Seaweed.*—The seaweed is burned, producing an ash known as varec or barilla. Japan is a current producer by this method. About 25 tons of seaweed produce only a few pounds of iodine as the ash contains from 0.2 to 2 per cent iodine.

The ash is lixiviated with water to extract the soluble salts. When the liquid is concentrated, the less soluble salts (chiefly alkali chlorides, carbonates and sulfates) crystallize out and are removed. Sulfuric acid is added to the liquid to decompose any alkaline sulfides and sulfites present. The sulfuric acid also converts the iodides and bromides into sulfates, and hydrogen iodide and hydrogen bromide are produced and go into solution. Then the liquid is run into the iodine still, warmed, and manganese dioxide is added from time to time (24). The liberated iodine volatilizes and is condensed in suitable receivers.

$$(24)\ 2HI + MnO_2 + H_2SO_4 \rightarrow MnSO_4 + 2H_2O + I_2$$

The iodine thus obtained is purified by mixing it with a small quantity of potassium iodide and subliming. In this way, traces of bromine and chlorine are removed.

Pharmacological Action of Iodine.[1]—Iodine when administered orally will be converted to inorganic iodide ion in the gastrointestinal tract regardless of the form of medication. Its systemic effect is therefore the same as a corresponding quantity of inorganic iodide. A comprehensive review of the metabolism of iodine compounds was published in 1949.[2]

The first recorded use of iodine in medicine was in 1820 by Dr. Jean Coindet of Geneva, Switzerland, who successfully used it as a cure for goiter. This led to the gradual acceptance of iodine into medicine and its first recorded use as a germicide in wounds.[3,4] Its sporicidal action was demonstrated in 1873 by Davaine[5] on anthrax. Since then it has been established as an effective germicide, fungicide, amebicide, and virucide. Apparently it acts by oxidizing and/or iodizing the protoplasm of organisms. Thus, in the presence of organic material the antiseptic value is usually greatly reduced. Although chlorine is considered to be germicidal by virtue of the formation of HClO, free iodine is about six times more effective than hypoiodous acid (HIO).

Iodine solutions in concentrations of 1:5000 (0.02 per cent) in distilled water or isotonic solution of sodium chloride display more effective antibacterial activity against many common bacteria than do solutions of chlorine (1:5000) or free bromine (1:5000). The addition of 5 per cent citrated human plasma does not alter the results.

Pharmaceutically, iodine preparations are usually used externally as antiseptics or internally as a source of iodine (iodide ion). Since iodine is necessary in thyroxin formation, some is required in the diet for proper functioning of the thyroid gland. Due to the size of the iodine atom, it is placed in organic compounds which are used as an opaque medium in X-ray studies.

Uses.—*Iodine*, U.S.P. XVII, should contain not less than 99.8 per cent of I. Iodine has been used in medicine for over 140 years, mainly as a counterirritant and disinfectant. Elemental iodine can only exert its characteristic action when used externally. Regard-

[1] See discussion of iodide ion under Hydriodic Acid (page 129).
[2] J. Am. Pharm. Assoc. Sci. Ed., **38**, 626–41 (1949).
[3] Davies, J.: Selections in Pathology and Surgery, Longman, Orme, Green and Longmans, London, 1839, Part II.
[4] Boinet, A. A.: Iodotherapie, 2nd Ed., Paris, Masson, 1865.
[5] Davaine: Dictionaire Encyclopedique des Sciences Med., P. Asselin and G. Masson, Paris, 1873, p. 335.

less of whether iodine is administered internally as iodine, a salt of hydriodic acid, or organically combined, it is converted primarily to the iodide ion in the body. The iodide ion is *not* a disinfectant nor a counterirritant, but possesses therapeutically useful characteristics (see p. 129).

The only official preparation containing elemental iodine and which is designated as a source of iodine for internal use is the familiar Lugol's Solution (*Strong Iodine Solution*) introduced to medicine over a century ago by the French physician Lugol. It consists of an aqueous solution of potassium iodide and iodine and its dose is usually 0.3 ml. three times a day with a range of from 0.1 to 1 ml. A similar commercial preparation is marketed as Lugol Caps (Burnham).

For its antibacterial and irritant properties elemental iodine is officially recognized in a variety of preparations including *Iodine Tincture, Iodine Ampuls* (Iodine Swabs), *Iodine Ointment, Iodine Solution, Phenolated Iodine Solution* (Boulton's Solution) and *Strong Iodine Tincture*. The last named also has antifungal properties. Some of these preparations utilize sodium iodide as a solubilizing agent in preference to the traditionally used potassium iodide. It has been noted, however, that the ratio of iodine to sodium iodide in Iodine Solution does not provide a sufficient excess of sodium iodide to exert the desired solubilizing influence on iodine under some conditions.[1] It is believed[2] that sodium iodide reacts more favorably on the tissue cells and allows deeper penetration of iodine.

All tinctures and solutions of iodine were found to lose less than 0.5 per cent iodine in thirty months.[3] This slight loss occurred under normal conditions of use with care being taken to keep the containers closed. Alcohol evaporates more rapidly than iodine and alcoholic solutions in open containers will increase in iodine concentration. Cork or metal stoppers are least desirable with rubber being suitable for short periods and glass or plastic being best. Light appears to have little effect on the stability of iodine solutions or tinctures.

Iodine Tincture and Iodine Solution employ the same concentrations of active ingredients but differ in the solvent medium. The tincture is prepared with diluted alcohol as solvent and the solution is completely aqueous. Both are very effective antibacterials and can be diluted with an equal volume of water without serious loss of antiseptic efficiency. Iodine Solution has the advantage over the Tincture in that it is less irritating because of the lack of alcohol, but at the same time it dries much more slowly when applied. Another consideration is that the alcoholic solution is much less apt to freeze under extreme weather conditions than the aqueous

[1] J. Am. Pharm. Assoc., Sci. Ed., **41**, 333 (1952).
[2] Am. Prof. Pharm., **13**, 51 (1947).
[3] J. Am. Pharm. Assoc., Sci. Ed., **36**, 203 (1947).

solution. Both of these preparations are virtually as effective as the original Strong Iodine Tincture which was formerly the only official tincture. However, they possess the advantage of causing little or no tissue destruction. In contrast, the Strong Iodine Tincture often caused more tissue damage than was warranted for any beneficial results obtained.

OFFICIAL IODINE COMPOUND

Povidone-Iodine, N.F. XII

Physical Properties.—Povidone-Iodine occurs as a yellowish brown, amorphous powder, having a slight, characteristic odor. It is soluble in water and alcohol but insoluble in chloroform, carbon tetrachloride, ether and acetone. Aqueous solutions are acid in reaction.

Chemical Properties.—Both the powder and solutions made from it are quite stable to storage, the vapor pressure of the contained iodine being virtually zero. The iodine content, however, is titratable with thiosulfate (1) and is termed "available iodine." Similarly, the product gives the characteristic deep blue iodine color with starch solution.

$$(1) \quad 2Na_2S_2O_3 + I_2 \longrightarrow Na_2S_4O_6 + 2NaI$$

There is no staining comparable to that experienced with uncomplexed iodine and solutions may easily be washed from the skin or clothing without leaving a stain. Apparently, the iodine is not simply in an equilibrium combination in the complex because it cannot be extracted out by the use of the usual continuous extraction techniques. It has been postulated that iodine added to polyvinylpyrrolidone (PVP) causes the PVP to assume a helical shape with the iodine atoms trapped within the helix. The fact that the ultraviolet absorption spectrum of iodine is altered from normal in the complex indicates that some interaction with PVP must take place.

Since a certain amount of iodide ion is formed during the preparation of the complex due to the oxidizing action of iodine on the unsaturated end groups of PVP one can expect the usual chemical reactions associated with iodide ion (*q.v.*).

Official Tests for Identity.—(A) The infrared absorption spectrum of Povidone-Iodine shows maxima at about 6μ, 7μ, and 7.7μ when examined as a 1-in-200 dispersion in a potassium bromide disc, the product having been dried prior to preparing the disc.

(B) One drop of a 1-in-10 solution of Povidone-Iodine in water when added to a solution containing 1 ml. of starch T.S. and 9 ml. of water produced a deep blue color.

(C) If 1 ml. of a 1-in-10 solution of the material in water is spread over an approximately 20 cm. by 20 cm. area on a clean glass plate and allowed to dry overnight at room temperature and under low humidity a brown, dry, non-smearing film forms, the film being readily soluble in water.

Commercial Manufacture.—According to Siggia[1] the product can be made by either dry-mixing the PVP powder with the requisite amount of iodine crystals or by drying an aqueous solution of PVP and iodine. Heat may be employed in the dry mixing procedure to facilitate the combination. The capacity of PVP for picking up iodine is about one part iodine to 2 or 3 parts of PVP. Greater concentrations of iodine will not be complexed in the characteristic manner as indicated by the enhanced vapor pressure and the fact that it can be extracted from the mixture with carbon tetrachloride. Below the above ratio any combination is satisfactory. The one that is recognized officially as Povidone-Iodine contains approximately 10 per cent available iodine, 85 per cent PVP and 5 per cent iodide ion.

Uses.—*Povidone-Iodine* (Betadine, Isodine, Polyvinylpyrrolidone-Iodine Complex), N.F. XII, is a complex of iodine with polyvinylpyrrolidone. Dried at 105° to constant weight, it contains not less than 9 per cent and not more than 12 per cent of available iodine (I).

It has all the antiseptic qualities associated with comparable solutions of elemental iodine (*q.v.*) and has several advantages. Among the more important advantages are a markedly reduced potential for irritation of tissues, a sharply reduced oral toxicity, the lack of staining potential on skin and clothing, and a low incidence of idiosyncrasy to the drug. Numerous studies have shown the Povidone-Iodine complex to be useful in a variety of applications to mucous tissue as well as to the skin. For example, Gershenfeld[2] describes its use as a vaginal microbicide. On the other hand, more conservative opinion[3] rates the "iodophors"[4] (including Povidone-Iodine) as being inferior to alcoholic iodine solutions of comparable strength. Because there have been few if any controlled studies comparing the sensitizing potential of iodine preparations vs. that of the iodophors it is stated that the claimed advantage for the iodophors on this point may not be well founded. Nevertheless, it is pointed out by such conservative opinion that the iodophors are superior to hexachlorophene in most respects and that they are effective against both gram-negative and gram-positive organisms. Furthermore, the lack of irritation to skin and mucous membranes is considered to be an advantage over the elemental iodine solutions.

[1] Siggia, S., J. Am. Pharm. Assoc. (Sci. Ed.), **44**, 201 (1957).
[2] Gershenfeld. L., The Am. J. of Pharm., **134**, 278 (1962).
[3] The Medical Letter, **6**, 89 (1964).
[4] An iodophor is a product in which iodine is loosely combined with a suitable solubilizing agent or carrier which will slowly liberate iodine in solution. In many iodophors a non-ionic surfactant is employed as the carrier.

8

The official form in which Povidone-Iodine is used is *Povidone-Iodine Solution* which is a transparent, reddish-brown colored liquid containing 6, 7.5, 10 or 30 per cent of the complex, equivalent to 0.5, 0.75, 1, and 3 per cent of available iodine. Expressing the concentrations in terms of available iodine in the following the product may be used for: (*a*) *Intravaginal* application as a 1 per cent douche or a 0.1 per cent gel (*b*) *Topical* application as a 0.5 per cent aerosol spray, a 1 per cent ointment, a 0.75 per cent shampoo, a 0.75 per cent skin cleanser, a 1 per cent solution, or as a 0.75 per cent surgical scrub.

Non-Official Iodine Compounds

Diglycocoll Hydroiodide—Iodine (Bursoline).—This is an organic preparation that releases free iodine in water. It contains 30.5 to 32.0 per cent of active iodine and is a stable and convenient form of iodine. When dissolved in a liter of water, tablets that are available will provide an iodine concentration of 7.4 p.p.m. Iodine in this concentration is effective against E. coli, E. typhosa, S. dysenteriæ, etc. The product is used primarily to disinfect drinking water. Iodine is better than chlorine for purifying drinking water because it is not affected by nitrogen containing compounds.

Undecoylium Chloride-Iodine N.D. (Virac).—This iodophor is a complex of iodine with a complex organic quaternary compound. It is soluble in water and forms a solution from which iodine is slowly released on contact with skin and mucous membranes. Although the quaternary ammonium compound accompanying the iodine is also antiseptic, its value lies more in its ability to aid in the penetration of iodine to skin surfaces by way of its surface active properties. There is no precipitation with tissue proteins as there is with the iodine tinctures. The compound is useful for treatment of surface infections as well as for pre- and post-operative disinfection. It may also be applied to sensitive mucous membranes because it lacks the irritative action of elemental iodine in tincture and solution preparations.

It is usually used in solutions containing 0.2 per cent available iodine or in stronger (0.6 and 0.8 per cent available I_2) solutions for topical use.

10

Acids

ACIDITY, BASICITY AND pH

At the present time there are several concepts of acidity and basicity, all of which are extensions of the well-known classical or Arrhenius concept. Two of these, the Brönsted-Lowry and the Lewis concepts, will be considered briefly together with the Arrhenius approach. There is really no question of *correctness* in the application of these various concepts because each is correct in the capacity for which it was intended. Nevertheless, it also is true that one interpretation may be suited better than another for some particular need. For example, although the classical concept is correct for aqueous systems, it cannot be extended to non-aqueous systems. It is for this reason that broader concepts of acid-base relationships have been sought and have resulted in those of Brönsted-Lowry and Lewis as well as others.

Classical Concept.—According to the classical concept acids are substances which contain hydrogen and which, when dissolved in water, will furnish hydrogen ions. Bases are substances which contain hydroxide groups and which, when dissolved in water, will furnish hydroxide ions. Neutralization of an acid with a base is merely the combination of hydrogen ions with hydroxide ions to form relatively non-ionized water. It may be observed that the distinction accorded to the hydrogen and hydroxide ions in the classical approach is merely a reflection of their being the component ions of the most common solvent, water. As long as the systems are aqueous, this concept is adequate.

Brönsted-Lowry Concept.—For many years this has been the most popular of the extensions of the classical system of acids and bases. It is sometimes termed the *protonic concept of acidity*. According to definition an acid is a substance, molecular or ionic, capable of giving up a proton to another substance. It is apparent that this definition does not cause any substantially different definition of the acid than that for the Arrhenius definition. However, there is a substantial difference when the definition of a base is considered. A base is defined as *any* substance, ionic or molecular, capable of combining with a proton. Whereas the base, in the classical sense, is limited to the hydroxide ion, the Brönsted-Lowry definition broadens the possibilities considerably (OH^- is just one of many) and has a wider applicability. Acids ionize according to the following reaction forming a hydrogen ion and a *conjugate base;*

$$HA \rightleftharpoons H^+ + A^-$$

Acid ... Conjugate base

A few examples of this will suffice to illustrate.

Acid ... *Conjugate base*

$$HCl \rightleftharpoons H^+ + Cl^-$$
$$H_2CO_3 \rightleftharpoons H^+ + HCO_3^-$$
$$HCO_3^- \rightleftharpoons H^+ + CO_3^=$$
$$NH_4^+ \rightleftharpoons H^+ + NH_3$$
$$H_3O^+ \rightleftharpoons H^+ + H_2O$$

Brönsted bases are usually neutral molecules or anions although a few cases of cations accepting protons are known. The species formed when a proton is added to a base is known as the *conjugate acid* of that base. A few examples will illustrate:

Base ... *Conjugate acid*

$$OH^- + H^+ \rightleftharpoons H_2O$$
$$SO_4^= + H^+ \rightleftharpoons HSO_4^-$$
$$H_2O + H^+ \rightleftharpoons H_3O^+$$
$$HCO_3^- + H^+ \rightleftharpoons H_2CO_3$$

In a few instances, notably water and bicarbonate ion, the conditions of a reaction will determine whether the chemical species will act as an acid or base. Thus, water may function as an acid by giving up a proton or as a base by picking up a proton to form H_3O^+. In a similar way, if bicarbonate ion gives up a proton to form carbonate ion it is acting as an acid but if it accepts a proton to form carbonic acid it is behaving as a base.

It must be pointed out that the half-reactions given in the preceding illustrations do not take place spontaneously but are rather the result of a base actually pulling the hydrogen ion off of the conjugate base. A typical acid-base reaction according to Brönsted requires the transfer of hydrogen ion from an acid to a base to form the conjugate acid and conjugate base. A few illustrations are as follows:

Acid		Base		Conjugate acid		Conjugate base
H_3O^+	+	OH^-	$\rightleftharpoons$	H_2O	+	H_2O
H_2O	+	SH^-	$\rightleftharpoons$	H_2S	+	OH^-
H_2SO_4	+	H_2O	$\rightleftharpoons$	H_3O^+	+	HSO_4^-

Brönsted acids vary in strength considerably. According to the definitions it follows that the strongest acids have the weakest conjugate bases and vice versa. This implies that strong acids lose their protons because they are not attracted very strongly and it is, therefore, not to be expected that the proton would come back to the anion to which it was not attracted very strongly in the first place.

Lewis Acid-Base Concept.—This concept was developed at approximately the same time as the Brönsted-Lowry concept and is broader in its scope. Although it did not enjoy immediate popularity it has, in recent years, become of increasing importance. It is based on the concept that an electron pair is donated from the base to the acid. Lewis acids are often termed *electrophilic* because the acidic property may be looked upon as a "seeking" of electrons from the electron donating base. In contrast to the classical and Brönsted-Lowry definitions where the acidity feature is based on the unique character of the proton, Lewis considers the proton as only one of many atoms and molecules that can form a covalent bond by sharing two electrons with a donor atom. Considered in this light the Lewis definition can be seen to have far reaching implications. On the other hand, Brönsted-Lowry bases are also bases in the Lewis sense because the reaction with a proton is noted in both. However, all Lewis bases are not Brönsted-Lowry bases because all Lewis bases may not react with a proton.

Thus, molecules with an "open sextet" of electrons are included in the definition as acids because they are able to accept a pair of electrons from the donor atom or molecule to form a covalent bond and so complete the octet. Examples of this are BF_3, $AlCl_3$, SO_3, etc. Each of these can be drawn with electron configurations to show a sextet of electrons around the central atom.

$$\overset{..}{\underset{**\ *\ **}{:F:B:F:}}\quad\quad \overset{..}{\underset{**\ *\ **}{:Cl:Al:Cl:}}\quad\quad \overset{..}{\underset{**\ *\ **}{:O:S:O:}}\quad\quad *\ =\ \text{acidic site.}$$

It is not even necessary for the Lewis acid to have an open sextet if it is able to expand its shell of electrons beyond the normal octet to accommodate the extra pair of electrons. An example of this is $SnCl_4$ which possesses an octet that can be expanded. Another common example of shell expansion is that of the formation of the triiodide ion by interaction of acidic iodine with the base iodide, with expansion of the shells of the iodine atoms.

$$:\overset{..}{I}:\overset{..}{I}: \quad + \quad \left[:\overset{..}{\underset{..}{I}}:\right]^{-} \rightleftarrows \left[:\overset{..}{\underset{* \ \ *}{I}}:\overset{..}{I}::\overset{..}{I}:\right]^{-} \quad * = \text{Expanded shells.}$$

Many positive ions are conveniently regarded as Lewis acids. An example in this respect is the reaction of silver ion with ammonia, with ammonia being the electron donor:

$$Ag^+ + :NH_3 \rightarrow [Ag:NH_3]^+$$

Almost all anions can act as Lewis bases. The reaction illustrated above in the formation of triiodide ion illustrates the fact that iodide ion is a base as well as that iodine is an acid. However, neutral molecules can also behave as bases provided they have atoms with two or less unshared pairs of electrons. The basicity of ammonia has been illustrated above in its reaction with silver ion. Water is another good example of a Lewis base with its two unshared pairs of electrons.

Hydrogen-ion Concentration or pH.—The hydrogen ion (symbol H^+) is a hydrogen atom with a positive electric charge resulting from the loss of the one and only electron from its outer shell. Strictly speaking, it is a proton. According to modern ideas of ionization of acids it is believed that the hydrogen ion, as such, exists only to a very limited extent in solution because protons cannot exist in polar[1] solvents without combining with the solvent. For example, in aqueous solutions the proton of an acid combines with a molecule of water resulting in the hydronium ion (H_3O^+) according to the following reaction (7):

$$(7) \quad HCl + H_2O \rightleftarrows H_3O^+ + Cl^-$$

This combination of a proton with solvent is also true of other polar solvents such as alcohol which is of considerable pharmaceutical importance (8).

$$(8) \quad HCl + C_2H_5OH \rightleftarrows C_2H_5OHH^+ + Cl^-$$

However, hydrocarbons such as benzene, etc., are not polar and and are incapable (in an anhydrous form) of accepting protons. They are spoken of as *aprotonic* solvents, and acids dissolved in them exist in a wholly undissociated form and do not behave as acids in the usually accepted sense of the word.

For the sake of simplicity this discussion will be confined to aqueous solutions because they illustrate ionization phenomena as well as any solvent. Thus, to be exact in discussing the ionization of acids in water, the hydronium-ion concentration should be spoken of rather than the hydrogen-ion concentration. The hydronium ion characterizes all acids, is responsible for their acidic properties when in aqueous solution, and may be taken as an index of the rate at which a metal will dissolve in the solution, the rate at which cane sugar will be inverted in the acid solution, etc.

The hydroxide ion (symbol OH^-) is a radical composed of a hydrogen atom, an oxygen atom, and an electron giving the radical a negative electric charge. It is the hydroxide ion which is responsible for the chemical properties of all alkalies.

From the preceding discussion of the Brönsted-Lowry concept it is apparent that water may act either as an acid or as a base and is therefore spoken of as being *amphoteric*. This is illustrated by the equation for the ionization of water:

[1] Polar compounds are those in which the centers of negative and positive electricity do not coincide, thus creating an electrical field about the molecule. The molecules may be considered as differentially charged bodies, somewhat similar to small magnets (positive at one end and negative at the other).

$$H_2O + H_2O \rightleftarrows H_3O^+ + OH^-$$

Acid$_1$ Base$_1$ Acid$_2$ Base$_2$

When 1 molecule of water ionizes as shown above, it forms one hydronium ion and one hydroxide ion. Thus, pure water is always neutral because it contains just as many hydronium ions as hydroxide ions. If a solution contains a greater number of hydronium ions than hydroxide ions it is acidic (acid), and if it contains less hydronium ions than hydroxide ions it is basic (alkaline). There is always a constant relationship between the concentrations (expressed as normality) of the two ions present, namely, the *product of the concentrations is equal to a constant.*

$$C_{H_3O^+} \times C_{OH^-} = K$$

For pure water the constant $K = (1 \times 10^{-7}) (1 \times 10^{-7}) = 1 \times 10^{-14}$ $\left(\dfrac{1}{100,000,000,000,000} \text{ or } 0.00000000000001\right)$ at 25° C. Therefore, if one concentration is high the other must necessarily be low in order that the product of the two concentrations will always be the same, namely 1×10^{-14}. For example, if the concentration of H_3O^+ (expressed as $C_{H_3O^+}$ or $[H_3O^+]$) is 1×10^{-3}, then the concentration of OH^-(C_{OH^-} or $[OH^-]$) must be 1×10^{-11} in order to equal the constant.[1] Thus,

$$(1 \times 10^{-3}) (1 \times 10^{-11}) = 1 \times 10^{[-3+(-11)]} = 1 \times 10^{-14} = K.$$

Because of this definite mathematical relationship it readily can be seen that the hydroxide-ion concentration is being stated indirectly whenever the hydronium-ion concentration is given.

A possible source of confusion in considering hydronium-ion concentration lies in the fact that acids can be and are thought of in two ways:

1. *Total (Titratable) Acidity.*—Expressing acidity in this way simply means that the acid concentration is stated in terms of the amount of the acid substance present in a definite amount of the solution. For example, we may consider 0.1 N solutions of HCl and CH_3COOH. There is no difference in the total acid concentration of these two solutions. This expression of concentration does not show what portion of the acid is dissociated, but merely the total amount of acid, dissociated and undissociated, that is present. This acidity is commonly expressed in terms of per cent (by weight), Gm. per 100 ml., molarity,[2] molality,[3] or

---

[1] In multiplying two powers of the same number, the exponents are added to get the exponent of the product, and in dividing two powers of the same number the exponent of the divisor is subtracted from the exponent of the dividend to get the exponent of the quotient.

[2] A molar solution contains a gram-molecular weight of the substance in 1000 ml. of solution.

[3] A molal solution contains a gram-molecular weight of the substance in 1000 Gm. of solvent.

normality.[1] Procedures for the determination of these expressions are known as acidimetry and alkalimetry.

2. *Hydronium-ion Concentration*.[2]—This expression of acidity is the one representing the actual acidic "intensity" of a solution which in turn depends upon the amount of hydronium-ion present through dissociation of the acid molecules. Acids are usually spoken of as

TABLE 7.—pH AND pOH RELATIONSHIPS

$[H^+]$ or moles/L.	$[H_3O^+]$ gm.-equ./L.	pH*		pOH
1.0	1×10^0	0 ↑		↑ 14
0.1	1×10^{-1}	1		13
0.01	1×10^{-2}	2	Increasing	12
0.001	1×10^{-3}	3	acidity	11
0.0001	1×10^{-4}	4		10
0.00001	1×10^{-5}	5		9
0.000001	1×10^{-6}	6		8
0.0000001	1×10^{-7}	7	neutral	7
0.00000001	1×10^{-8}	8		6
0.000000001	1×10^{-9}	9		5
0.0000000001	1×10^{-10}	10	Increasing	4
0.00000000001	1×10^{-11}	11	alkalinity	3
0.000000000001	1×10^{-12}	12		2
0.0000000000001	1×10^{-13}	13		1
0.00000000000001	1×10^{-14}	14 ↓		↓ 0

* A tenfold change in $[H^+]$ takes place from one pH unit to another.

being "strong" or "weak." The "strong" acids are those which are highly ionized (*e.g.*, HCl, HNO_3, H_2SO_4, etc.), whereas the "weak" acids are those which are ionized only slightly (*e.g.*, HCN, H_3BO_3, organic acids, etc.). Therefore, although we find no difference in *total* acidity between 0.1 N HCl and 0.1 N CH_3COOH, there is a considerable difference in the hydronium-ion concentration because HCl in that concentration is almost completely ionized, whereas CH_3COOH is ionized very little. Bases, also, are designated as being "strong" and "weak" depending upon the extent of ionization. Hydronium-ion concentration can be expressed in the same way as total acidity, *e.g.*, as grams of hydronium ion per 100 ml. of solution, or more commonly as gram-equivalents of H_3O^+ per liter.

The expression of hydronium-ion concentration in aqueous solution is generally considered as being limited by the ionization constant of water to a range of between 1×10^0 and 1×10^{-14}. The normal limits of pH are usually given as 0 to 14. However, in concentrated solutions of highly ionized acids or bases higher values are

[1] A normal solution contains a gram-equivalent weight of substance in 1000 ml. of solution. A gram-equivalent weight of a substance is the gram-molecular weight divided by a number representing the number of gram-atomic weights of hydrogen or its equivalent present in the compound.

[2] Often designated as hydrogen-ion concentration but in keeping with the preceding discussion the above nomenclature is preferred.

obtained. A 6N hydrochloric acid contains about 2 Gm. of hydrogen ions per liter (pH-0.7). Likewise, the pH of 7N potassium hydroxide is greater than 14. Because the numbers expressing hydronium-ion concentration are mathematically cumbersome to use in expressing acidity, it was suggested by Sörenson that they could be more practicably expressed as negative logarithms to the base 10. This number (the negative log) is called the "hydrogen-ion exponent" and is designated by the symbol pH.[1] Therefore, we have the following relationships.[2]

$$pH = -\log[H^+] = -\log[H_3O^+] = \log \frac{1}{[H_3O^+]}$$

The U.S.P. has departed from this conventional definition of pH and now bases it on the modern conventional pH scale defined by the equation:

$$pH = pH_S + (E - E_S)/k,$$

where pH_S is the pH value assigned to the specified *Standard Buffer Solution* (see U.S.P. XVII, p. 913), E and E_S represent electromotive force values of a suitable galvanic cell of the type usually employed in pH meters (E being the value obtained when the cell contains the solution under test and E_S that obtained with the same cell when a buffer of pH represented by pH_S is substituted, and k is the value calculated by the equation $k = 0.05916 + 0.0001984 (t - 25°)$ volts for any temperature t. The U.S.P., however, recognizes that, for practical purposes, the older definition is not in serious disagreement with the modern convention.

The calculation of pH from the hydronium-ion concentration and *vice versa* offers some difficulty to the average student, usually because of unfamiliarity with logarithmic manipulations. The authors have taught a rather simplified method of calculation for a number of years with considerable success. Briefly, for the conversion of $[H_3O^+]$, expressed in normality, to pH it consists of the following steps:

1. Obtain the $[H_3O^+]$ as gram-equivalents per liter (normality).
2. Convert the decimal expression of normality to the exponential form (*i.e.*, to a number multiplying a whole number power of 10).
3. Take the log of the number and add it to the exponent.
4. Change the sign of the exponent and call it pH.
(The conversion of pH to $[H_3O^+]$ is essentially the converse.)

[1] The derivation of pH is from the German where the "p" refers to the German word for "power," namely "Potenz," in a mathematical sense. The "H" of course is the symbol for hydrogen. Combining the two terms gives us "power for hydrogen" which is appropriate because the expression is a logarithm which in turn is a power.
[2] The reader will note that in agreement with the previous discussion the $[H_3O^+]$ is to be considered $[H^+]$, and, indeed, in *aqueous solutions* it is immaterial whether the expression "hydronium ions" or "hydrogen ions" is used. Exceptions arise only when other solvents are considered.

To illustrate: What is the pH of a solution containing 0.0000343 gram-equivalents of H_3O^+ per liter?

Step 1.
The information is already given, the $[H_3O^+]$ being 0.0000343 N.

Step 2.
$$[H_3O^+] = 0.0000343 \text{ N} = 3.43 \times 10^{-5} \text{ N}$$

Step 3.
log of 3.43 = 0.54
$$\therefore [H_3O^+] = 3.43 \times 10^{-5} = 1 \times 10^{(-5+0.54)} = 1 \times 10^{-4.46}$$

Step 4.—According to definition pH is equal to the negative log ($-log$ *of* $[H^+]$) *then:*

$$[H_3O^+] = 1 \times 10^{-4.46}$$
$$\therefore \text{pH} = 4.46.$$

To illustrate the conversion of pH to $[H_3O^+]$:
Calculate the $[H_3O^+]$ of a solution having a pH of 11.56.

Step 1.—Change the sign of the pH and make it a power of 10.
pH = 11.56
$$[H_3O^+] = 1 \times 10^{-11.56}$$

Step 2.—Convert the exponent to a negative whole number and a positive log having a zero characteristic.

$$[H_3O^+] = 1 \times 10^{-11.56} = 1 \times 10^{(-12+0.44)}$$

Step 3.—Convert the log to a number and remove from the exponent. Using the log table find the antilog of 0.44 which is 2.8.
$$[H_3O^+] = 1 \times 10^{(-12+0.44)} = 2.8 \times 10^{-12}$$

Step 4.—Convert the exponent form of the number to the decimal form.
$$[H_3O^+] = 2.8 \times 10^{-12} \text{ N} = 0.0000000000028 \text{ N}$$

As further typical examples of the solution of these problems the following may be solved by three methods: (*A*) the above method, (*B*) the use of the negative log of $[H_3O^+]$, (*C*) the use of the log of the reciprocal of the $[H_3O^+]$.

1. What is the pH of a solution containing 0.00001 gram-equivalents of H_3O^+ per liter? (See Table 1.)

A. $[H_3O^+] = 0.00001 \text{ N} = 1 \times 10^{-5}$
   pH = 5
B. pH $= -\log 0.00001 = -[-5] = 5$
C. pH $= \log \dfrac{1}{0.00001} = \log \dfrac{1}{1 \times 10^{-5}} = \log (1 \times 10^{5}) = 5$

2. What is the pH of a solution containing 2.86×10^{-4} gram-equivalents of H_3O^+ per liter?

A. $[H_3O^+] = 2.86 \times 10^{-4} = 1 \times 10^{(-4+0.46)} = 1 \times 10^{-3.54}$
pH $= 3.54$

B. pH $= -\log (2.86 \times 10^{-4}) = -[0.46 + (-4)] = -[-3.54]$
$= 3.54$

C. pH $= \log \dfrac{1}{2.86 \times 10^{-4}} = \log \dfrac{10^4}{2.86} = \log 10^4 - \log 2.86$
$= 4 - 0.46 = 3.54$

pH $= \log \dfrac{1}{.000286} = \log 3496 = 3.54$

3. What is the hydronium-ion concentration of a solution having a pH of 5.62?

A. $[H_3O^+] = 1 \times 10^{-5.62} = 1 \times 10^{(-6+0.38)} = 2.4 \times 10^{-6}$

B. pH $= -\log[H_3O^+]$
$5.62 = -\log[H_3O^+]$
$-5.62 = (-6 + 0.38) = \log[H_3O^+]$
$[H_3O^+] = 2.4 \times 10^{-6}$

C. pH $= \log \dfrac{1}{[H_3O^+]}$
$5.62 = \log \dfrac{1}{[H_3O^+]}$
$= \log 1 - \log[H_3O^+]$
$= 0 - \log [H_3O^+] = -\log [H_3O^+]$, etc., as in B

4. What is the pH of a 0.1 N solution of NH_4OH if it is 1.31 per cent ionized?

A. NOTE.—At this point we may introduce a new term, pOH, which is a term expressing the hydroxide-ion concentration in the same way that pH expresses hydronium-ion concentration. It is easily obtained by subtracting the pH from 14. (See Table 1.) Therefore:

pOH $= 14 - $ pH
or pH $= 14 - $ pOH

This problem is readily solved by attacking it as a pH problem, but solving for pOH instead and then finally subtracting the pOH from 14 to get the pH.

0.1 N $\times 1.31\% = 0.00131$ N (with respect to OH^-)
$[OH^-] = 1.31 \times 10^{-3} = 1 \times 10^{(-3 +0.12)} = 1 \times 10^{-2.88}$
$\therefore$ pOH $= 2.88$
pH $= 14 - 2.88 = 11.12$

B. $[OH^-] = 0.1 N \times 1.31\% = 0.00131 N$
and, since $[H_3O^+] [OH^-] = 10^{-14}$

$$[H_3O^+] = \frac{10^{-14}}{[OH^-]} = \frac{10^{-14}}{0.00131}$$

$pH = -(\log 10^{-14} - \log 0.00131)$
$\log 10^{-14} = -14 = 6-20$
$\log 0.00131 = 7.12 - 10$
$pH = -[6-20-(7.12-10)] = 11.12$

C. $0.1 N \times 1.31\% = 0.00131 N$, the OH-ion concentration.
$10^{-14} \div 0.00131 = 7.63 \times 10^{-12} N$, the H_3O^+ concentration.

$$pH = \log \frac{1}{7.63 \times 10^{-12}} = 11.12$$

On examination of Table 1 it is observed that each pH unit has a hydrogen ion concentration 10 times that of the next unit. In other words, a solution of pH 4 is 10 times more acid than a solution of pH 5 and 1000 times stronger than one of pH 7. However, a breakdown of the intervening acid strengths between pH 4 and pH 5 expresses the relationship of hydrogen ion concentrations in moles of $[H^+]$ per liter to pH units. This, it is noted is not linear or $[H^+]$ concentration of 0.00005 is not equal to pH 4.5.

H^+ moles/L.	pH
0.00001	5.0
0.00002	4.69
0.00003	4.52
0.00004	4.39
0.00005	4.30
0.00006	4.22
0.00007	4.15
0.00008	4.09
0.00009	4.04
0.0001	4.0

Determination of pH.—There are three methods commonly used for the determination of the hydronium-ion concentration: (1) colorimetric, (2) potentiometric, and (3) chemical.

(1) The *colorimetric* method utilizes reagents called indicators. Indicators (see U.S.P. XII, p. 1067) are usually weak organic acids or bases in which the undissociated molecule has one color, and the anion or cation produced by dissociation has another color. This may be illustrated by considering the ionization of a typical weak acid, bromophenol blue, which exhibits a yellow color in the acid form, and a blue color in the basic form. Representing bromophenol blue by the general formula (HInd) for an indicator acid we have:

$$HInd + H_2O \rightleftarrows H_3O^+ + Ind^-$$
Acid form   Basic form

or

$$\text{Yellow molecules} + H_2O \rightleftarrows H_3O^+ + \text{Blue Anions.}$$

The law of mass action when applied to the first equation[1] gives us:

$$\frac{[H_3O^+]\,[Ind^-]}{[HInd]\,[H_2O]} = K;\quad \frac{[H_3O^+]\,[Ind^-]}{[HInd]} = K\,[H_2O];\quad \frac{[H_3O^+]\,[Ind^-]}{[HInd]} = K_1$$

or

$$\frac{[H_3O^+]}{K_1} = \frac{[HInd]}{[Ind^-]} = \frac{[\text{Yellow Molecules}]}{[\text{Blue Anions}]}$$

From the above mathematical expression it is apparent that since K_1 is constant, the variation of $[H_3O^+]$ changes the ratio of yellow molecules to blue anions. If the $[H_3O^+]$ becomes smaller, then the ratio of yellow molecules to blue anions must change so that we have relatively more blue anions than yellow molecules. The reverse would be true if the $[H_3O^+]$ becomes larger. The qualities desired in an indicator are: that there be a sharp contrast between the two colors and that the color change be effected by a small change of pH. There is a sufficient number of indicators to cover the whole range of hydrogen-ion concentration, with a satisfactory amount of overlapping and duplication.

The following table gives a number of the more common indicators, together with their respective ranges of pH and color changes.

Indicator	Range of pH and Color Changes
Meta cresol-purple	1.2 (red) to 2.8 (yellow)
Hellige orange	2.6 (red) to 4.2 (yellow)
Bromophenol blue	3.0 (yellow) to 4.6 (blue)
Methyl orange	3.1 (red) to 4.4 (yellow)
Bromocresol green	4.0 (yellow) to 5.6 (blue)
Methyl red	4.2 (red) to 6.3 (yellow)
Chlorophenol red and bromocresol purple	5.2 (green) to 6.8 (purple)
Bromothymol blue	6.0 (yellow) to 7.6 (blue)
Phenol red	6.8 (yellow) to 8.4 (red)
Cresol red	7.2 (yellow) to 8.8 (red)
Thymol blue	8.0 (yellow) to 9.6 (blue)
Phenolphthalein	8.3 (colorless) to 10.0 (red)
Thymolphthalein	9.4 (colorless) to 10.6 (blue)
Nitro yellow	10.0 (faint yellow) to 11.6 (deep yellow)
Violet	12.0 (purple) to 13.6 (blue)

The technique of measuring pH by the colorimetric method (U.S.P. XVII, p. 914) involves matching the colors of the unknown solution treated with a proper indicator, to the colors of solutions of known pH treated with the same indicator. When the solution of which the pH is to be measured is colored, the color must be duplicated in the comparison solutions of known pH. This is accomplished by putting an equal volume of the solution in the line of the light passing through the standard colors.

---

[1] Since H_2O is very nearly constant in these solutions, it may be incorporated into the constant K to give a new constant K_1.

Various apparatus have been produced commercially to facilitate the colorimetric measurement of pH. Two of these are the LaMotte comparator and the Hellige comparator. The colorimetric method of measuring pH is widely used in industry. For convenience, the colorimetric method of determining hydrogen-ion concentration has been adopted for pharmacopeial purposes and is to be employed where pigments and proteins present in the solution do not vitiate its use.

(2) The *electrometric or potentiometric method* (U.S.P. XVII, p. 914) is based upon the measurement of the voltage developed between special electrodes when immersed in the solution. The difference in potential is measured with a potentiometer and since this difference is directly dependent upon the presence of H_3O^+ in the solution, it is equivalent to determining the concentration of H_3O^+. The voltmeter, or its equivalent, is frequently graduated to read directly in pH on instruments designed specifically for this purpose. The electrometric method is preferred by the U.S.P. because of its accuracy, rapidity, and because it can be used in turbid and jelly-like solutions and in solutions containing pigments and proteins. It can also be used, with the aid of relays, to control a chemical reaction in which the pH must be carefully established and maintained.

(3) The *chemical method* for measuring hydrogen-ion concentration is only of scientific interest and is not used practically as a method for determining pH. One means of determining pH chemically is to compare the rate of inversion of sucrose with the rate at which an acid of known hydrogen-ion concentration inverts the sucrose under the same conditions.

In addition to the three well-defined, exact methods of pH determination, there is a less exact but more practical variation of the colorimetric method in which strips of paper are impregnated with an indicator. Merely dipping the paper in the unknown solution produces a color on the paper which can be compared with charts supplied by the manufacturer. These are of value to diabetic patients for testing the actual acidity of the urine, and also to the chemist and pharmacist. Examples of these papers are the "Nitrazine" paper (Squibb), "pHydrion" paper (Central Scientific Co.), "Alkacid Test Ribbon" (Fisher Scientific Co.), "Accutint" paper (E. H. Sargent and Co.), "Special pH paper" (Paul Frank, N.Y.), "Universal pH Indicator Paper" (Braun-Knecht-Heimann Co.) and "Oxyphen" paper (J. Einstein Co.).

Buffers.—The importance of controlling the pH in solutions has been recognized for a long time. Unfortunately, the pH of a solution, even when carefully adjusted, will not remain at that point indefinitely because of extraneous factors such as alkali in the glass from which cheap bottles are made, and gases such as CO_2, Cl_2 and NH_3 in the air. To remedy this situation, use is made of *buffer mixtures*.

Acids

Buffers may be considered as pairs of chemical compounds which control a change in pH of solutions. The recognition of the importance of hydrogen-ion concentration (pH) in physiological processes, in stability of pharmaceuticals, in therapeutic effect and in comfort of the patient is firmly established in the profession of pharmacy. Methods of controlling changes in pH are important in connection with collyria, oral penicillin, milk of magnesia, vitamin preparations, alkaloidal solutions, and parenteral solutions, to point out only a few.

A buffer mixture (or *buffer pair*) is usually a solution composed of a weak acid and a salt of the weak acid or a weak base and its salt. The latter is not widely used because of greater sensitivity to temperature changes (NH_4OH/NH_4Cl). A buffered solution will resist any great change in the pH which might be caused by the addition of small amounts of acids or bases. A solution with an adjusted pH is considered more important than one adjusted to osmotic pressure.

Literally, the term "buffer" means to deaden a shock or bear the brunt of a collision. In a pharmaceutical sense it is used to designate a combination of chemicals in a particular proportion which when dissolved in a solution will produce and maintain a desired hydrogen ion concentration. Maintenance of a particular hydrogen ion concentration is of prime importance in pharmaceuticals since the stability of the preparation may depend upon this one factor. It can readily be seen from Table 7 that a variation in the hydrogen ion concentration will cause a change in the hydroxide ion concentration since the product of the two concentrations remains constant. These variations in hydrogen ion concentration can be caused by dust particles, alkali in glass, carbon dioxide in the air, oxidation, and the introduction of medicinal agents. The ability of buffers to prevent a change in pH is, of course, not complete, but they will remove a majority of any hydrogen ions (H^+) or hydroxide ions (OH^-) which may by various means become added to a buffered solution. The method by which a buffer functions is dependent upon the removal of hydrogen ions (H^+) by their combining with an anion to form a very slightly ionized weak acid or by the removal of hydroxide ions as water.

As an example, a typical acetic acid-sodium acetate buffer mixture will clearly show the mechanism of buffering. Upon the addition of HCl to a buffer of this composition we have the introduction of potentially enough hydronium ions to change the pH tremendously. However, in the buffer, acetate ions exist (furnished by the sodium acetate) which are strong bases and are capable of combining with the hydronium ions to form relatively non-ionized acetic acid molecules. This effectively removes the acidic hydronium ions and prevents them from exerting their activity. In effect, a "strong" acid has been converted to a "weak" acid according to the following equation:

$$H_3O^+ + CH_3COO^- \rightleftarrows CH_3COOH + H_2O$$

or written molecularly,

$$HCl + CH_3COONa \rightleftarrows CH_3COOH + NaCl$$

Addition of an alkali, such as NaOH, to this buffer mixture sets up a different chain of events to take care of the excess hydroxide ions. The acetic acid in the buffer mixture, while not greatly ionized, furnishes enough hydronium ions to combine with the added hydroxide ion to form water, which is practically non-ionized insofar as affecting the pH is concerned. This is illustrated by the following reactions:

$$CH_3COOH + H_2O \rightleftarrows CH_3COO^- + H_3O^+$$

$$H_3O^+ + OH^- \rightleftarrows H_2O + H_2O$$

or written molecularly,

$$CH_3COOH + NaOH \rightleftarrows CH_3COONa + H_2O$$

The buffers listed by the U.S.P. XVII are presumably designed to reproduce a given pH for analytical purposes rather than to provide a desirable solution for dispensing drugs. The sodium hydroxide used will contain unknown amounts of barium ions and the use of potassium chloride, potassium acid phthalate and potassium biphosphate introduce the undesirable potassium ions.

Buffer systems in common use are:

	pH Range
Feldman's Buffer	7 –8.2
Gifford's Buffer	6 –7.8
Atkins and Pantin Buffer . . .	7.6–11.0
Sørensen Phosphate Buffer . .	4.5–8.0

In 1915 Palitzsch introduced a series of borate buffers that were modified by Feldman in 1937 for better pharmaceutical application. The original pH values given for Feldman's Buffer have been found in error by several workers. Table 8 gives the corrected Feldman's Buffer as it is currently used.

Equations representing how Feldman's Buffer may function are given for the acid buffer (1, 2, 3, 4) and the alkaline buffer (5, 6, 7, 8).

Acid Buffer:

(1) $H_3BO_3 \rightleftarrows H^+ + H_2BO_3^-$
    slightly
    ionized
    Assume now that sodium hydroxide is added:

(2) $H_3BO_3 + NaOH \rightarrow NaH_2BO_3 + H_2O$

(3) $NaH_2BO_3 \rightarrow NaBO_2 + H_2O$

(4) $2NaBO_2 + 2H_3BO_3 \rightarrow Na_2B_4O_7 + 3H_2O$

Alkaline Buffer:

(5) $Na_2B_4O_7 \rightleftarrows 2Na^+ + B_4O_7^=$
highly
ionized

Assume now that hydrochloric acid is added:

(6) $HCl \rightleftarrows H^+ + Cl^-$

(7) $2H^+ + B_4O_7^= \rightleftarrows H_2B_4O_7$
slightly
ionized

(8) $H_2B_4O_7 + 3H_2O \rightleftarrows 2HBO_2 + 2H_3BO_3$

TABLE 8.—REVISED FELDMAN'S BUFFER MIXTURES

Feldman's Acid Buffer Solution		*Feldman's Alkaline Buffer Solution*	
Boric acid, U.S.P.	12.4 Gm.	Sodium borate (10H₂O),	
Sodium chloride, U.S.P.	2.9 Gm.	U.S.P.	19.07 Gm.
Distilled water, q.s.	1000.0 ml.	Distilled water, q.s.	1000.0 ml.

pH of Mixture	Ml. Acid Buffer	Ml. Alkaline Buffer
7.0	95.0	5.0
7.1	94.0	6.0
7.2	93.0	7.0
7.3	91.0	9.0
7.4	89.0	11.0
7.5	87.0	13.0
7.6	85.0	15.0
7.7	82.0	18.0
7.8	80.0	20.0
7.9	76.0	24.0
8.0	73.0	27.0
8.1	69.0	31.0
8.2	65.0	35.0

Atkins and Pantin introduced perhaps the best buffer system (Table 9) but for some reason it has not become popular. The sodium borate ($Na_2B_4O_7.10H_2O$) was replaced by the more stable sodium carbonate ($Na_2CO_3.H_2O$) and sodium chloride was added to approach a more isotonic finished solution.

This buffer system is useful in the alkaline range for contact lens solutions, pH 7.8 to pH 8.4, as a solvent for soluble fluorescein (pH 8.4) and as an alkaline buffer for most collyria. The solution contains sodium chloride as does Feldman's buffers.

Compensation for added hydrogen ions or hydroxide ions to an Atkins and Pantin buffer may be better understood by first observing what happens when the buffer pairs are mixed (9, 10, 11).

(9) $Na_2CO_3 + 2H_2O \rightleftarrows 2NaOH + H_2CO_3$
highly   highly   slightly
ionized   ionized ionized

9

The sodium hydroxide formed will react with boric acid present (10, 11):

(10) $H_3BO_3 + NaOH \rightleftarrows NaBO_2 + 2H_2O$

(11) $2NaBO_2 + 2H_3BO_3 \rightleftarrows Na_2B_4O_7 + 3H_2O$

It is apparent that in an Atkins and Pantin buffer the same chemicals utilized by Feldman, $Na_2B_4O_7$ and H_3BO_3 are actually the buffers. Added hydroxide ions are removed as slightly ionized water (2, 3, 4). The hydrogen ions are removed as slightly ionized metaboric and boric acids (7, 8). This is an excellent borate buffer.

TABLE 9.—ATKINS AND PANTIN ALKALINE BUFFER

Acid Buffer Solution

Boric Acid U.S.P. 12.4 Gm. (0.2 M)
Sodium Chloride U.S.P. 7.5 Gm.
Purified Water U.S.P., q.s. 1000.0 ml.

Alkaline Buffer Solution

Sodium Carbonate U.S.P. 24.8 Gm. (0.2 M)
Purified Water U.S.P., q.s. 1000.0 ml.

pH of Mixture	Ml. Acid Buffer	Ml. Alkaline Buffer
7.6	93.8	6.2
7.8	91.7	8.3
8.0	88.8	11.2
8.2	85.0	15.0
8.4	80.7	19.3
8.6	75.7	24.3
8.8	69.5	30.5
9.0	63.0	37.0
9.2	56.4	43.6
9.4	49.7	50.3
9.6	42.9	57.1
9.8	36.0	64.0
10.0	29.1	70.9
10.2	22.1	77.9
10.4	15.4	84.6
10.6	9.8	90.2
10.8	5.7	94.3
11.0	3.5	96.5

Gifford's buffer was introduced in 1933 and has likewise undergone revision. This buffer system is a slight modification of the Atkins and Pantin buffer system having only replaced potassium chloride for sodium chloride and arranged the volumes on a basis of 30 ml. (see Table 10). Actually, too much potassium chloride is present in that Gifford's Buffer is hypertonic.

The chemistry of Gifford's Buffer is the same as that shown for Atkins and Pantin buffer. In reality they all depend upon sodium borate ($Na_2B_4O_7$) and boric acid (H_3BO_3). This buffer mixture is prone to slow decomposition with an increase in alkalinity during the first six months. It is most unstable below a pH of 8 with a tendency to lose carbon dioxide and become more alkaline. Recommendations are that it be stored in hard glass containers under refrigeration.

TABLE 10.—REVISED GIFFORD'S BUFFER MIXTURES

Gifford's Acid Buffer Solution

Boric Acid U.S.P.	12.4 Gm.
Potassium Chloride U.S.P.	7.4 Gm.
Purified Water U.S.P., q.s.	1000.0 ml.

Gifford's Alkaline Buffer Solution

Sodium Carbonate U.S.P.	24.8 Gm
Purified Water U.S.P., q.s.	1000.0 ml.

Proportions to be Mixed

pH of Mixture*	pH Values† of Hind and Goyan	ml. Acid Buffer	ml. Alkaline Buffer	
5.0	4.66	30.0	0.00	Acid Buffer No. 1
6.0	5.99	30.0	0.05	Acid Buffer No. 2
6.2	6.24	30.0	0.10	
6.4		30.0	0.15	
6.6		30.0	0.20	
6.7	6.62	30.0	0.25	
6.8		30.0	0.35	
6.9		30.0	0.46	
6.95	6.91	30.0	0.50	
7.0		30.0	0.60	
7.1		30.0	0.74	
7.2	7.23	30.0	1.00	
7.3		30.0	1.14	
7.4		30.0	1.40	Normal Lachrymal Fluid
7.5		30.0	1.69	
(7.6)	7.42	30.0	1.50	
7.6		30.0	2.02	Alkaline Buffer No. 1
7.7		30.0	2.40	
(7.8)	7.58	30.0	2.00	
7.8		30.0	2.85	
8.2	7.81	30.0	3.00	
8.4	7.91	30.0	4.00	
9.0	8.47	30.0	8.00	Alkaline Buffer No. 2

* Gifford's values
† Hind, H. W. and Goyan, F. M., J. Amer. Pharm. Assoc., Sci. Ed., **36**, 33 (1947)

Borate buffers have a buffer range of from pH 5 to 11. They are unsatisfactory below a pH of 7 and function best between pH 7 to 11 with greatest buffer capacity at about pH 9. Because a solution of pH 8.5 or over is rarely used therapeutically, the Gifford and Feldman tables have not been extended. Even though a borate buffer is not too efficient in an acid pH range, they are used with zinc and silver salts at pH 6. These metal ions are incompatible with Sørensen phosphate buffer. All borate buffers are suitable for ophthalmic, nasal, and external application, but, of course, not for solutions to be used parenterally.

The Sørensen phosphate buffer system covers a range of pH 5.8 to pH 8 and has greatest buffer capacity at pH 6.7. It is a valuable buffer system for ophthalmic drugs, as the ions present are normally found in the eye and the pH range includes the isohydric[1] point of tears (pH 7.4). The disadvantages of the phosphate system include incompatibility with salts of silver, zinc, aluminum, calcium, etc., and the lack of bactericidal properties which allow mold growth.

[1] "Isohydric" connotes a solution having the same pH as another liquid or fluid with which it is compared.

The addition of Zephiran Chloride or Phemerol Chloride in a concentration of 1:50,000 will prevent mold growth and will not interfere with buffer properties. Phenylmercuric nitrate (.05%) may also be used.

TABLE 11.—MODIFIED PHOSPHATE BUFFER SYSTEM (SØRENSEN) ADJUSTED TO
BE ISOTONIC TO PHYSIOLOGICAL SALINE

| M/15 Sodium Acid Phosphate | Sodium Acid Phosphate, U.S.P. | 9.2 Gm. |
| | Purified Water, q.s. | 1000.0 ml. |

| M/15 Disodium Phosphate | Disodium Phosphate U.S.P. | 17.86 Gm. |
| | Purified Water, q.s. | 1000.0 ml. |

pH	Acid Buffer NaH_2PO_4, ml.	Alkaline Buffer Na_2HPO_4, ml.	Grams of Sodium Chloride per 100 ml. to Render Isotonic
5.91	90.0	10.0	0.52
6.24	80.0	20.0	0.51
6.47	70.0	30.0	0.50
6.64	60.0	40.0	0.49
6.81	50.0	50.0	0.48
6.98	40.0	60.0	0.46
7.17	30.0	70.0	0.45
7.38	20.0	80.0	0.44
7.73	10.0	90.0	0.43
8.04	5.0	95.0	0.42

Buffers are used in numerous ways in pharmaceuticals. Milk of Magnesia is stabilized with citric acid which depends upon buffer action. Sodium bicarbonate, sodium acetate, or sodium citrate are employed with sulfonamides. Penicillin preparations commonly contain sodium citrate, calcium carbonate, or aluminum hydroxide. Note the use of sodium bicarbonate in Diluted Sodium Hypochlorite Solution N.F. XII as a buffer to maintain a pH of 9 to 10. Also observe use of boric acid in Aluminum Subacetate Solution U.S.P. XVII and Aluminum Acetate Solution U.S.P. XVII. Most antacid preparations depend upon a buffer action such as magnesium trisilicate, tribasic magnesium phosphate, tribasic calcium phosphate, sodium citrate, etc.

The importance of pH adjustment of lotions and ointments has been pointed out by several workers. The "acid mantle" of the skin is recorded as being from pH 4.2 to 5.6 but more recent findings place it between pH 3.5 to 4.5. Many pathogenic bacteria and fungi are sensitive to acids and thrive in a slightly alkaline environment. When a skin abrasion occurs, a pH 7.4 occurs due to presence of blood. External preparations probably should be adjusted to acid pH values for best therapeutic results. The buffer mixtures in the U.S.P. XVII, are satisfactory for this purpose. A proprietary product, Iodex, is buffered to pH 3.6. Boric Acid Ointment N.F. XI would be expected to create an area of pH 5, thus inhibiting growth of most bacteria and fungi, yet it is not a disinfectant. Guth presents a number of ointment bases and suitable buffers for dermatological preparations. The products, Acid Mantle Creme and Lotion (Dome), are designed to restore normal skin acidity.

The adjustment and stabilization of pH in solutions is of widespread importance in many fields of work. In pharmacy the close control of pH in many pharmaceutical preparations is of utmost concern. The stability of preparations such as tinctures of aconite and digitalis, fluidextract of ergot, and others is dependent upon adjustment of the pH to a relatively acidic reading, because the deterioration of these preparations is greatly accelerated under alkaline conditions. Aqueous and dilute alcoholic solutions of most of the vitamin B group, particularly thiamine hydrochloride, are sensitive to a pH over 5 and for maximum stability should have a pH ranging from 3.5 to 4.5. Solutions of alkaloidal salts should be kept on the acid side of the pH scale to prevent precipitation of the free alkaloid. Maintenance of a good coloration in many galenical preparations is dependent upon the control of pH. In therapy with mandelates and methenamine as urinary antiseptics an acidity of pH 4.8 and 5.2, respectively, is necessary. Usually sodium biphosphate, ammonium chloride, or ammonium nitrate is used. It is important to note that certain drugs used in prescription work may be unstable in either acidic or alkaline media.

Some of the medicinal agents affected by pH are compiled under "Effect of pH on Individual Drugs" in the Appendix.

The adjustment of pH in prescriptions may be carried out by the following practical method.[1]

Practical Adjustment of pH. — "*Step I.* — The prescription ingredients are combined and the preparation is brought to within ½ to 1 fluid ounce of the desired volume. Using an indicator paper of wide pH range, the approximate pH value of the mixture is determined by moistening the paper with a drop of the preparation and comparing the resulting color with the standards provided. This step serves to indicate whether acid or alkali will be needed for the adjustment and to show approximately how far the pH of the mixture is from the desired range.

Step II. — Small pieces of indicator paper, especially suitable for showing differences of pH over a narrow range of pH, then are placed on a pill tile or other convenient surface. Let it be assumed, for example, that the desired pH is to be approximately 4, with an upper limit of 5 and a lower limit of 3. A drop of each of three standard buffer solutions is placed on individual pieces of the indi-

[1] Wyss, A. P., The Importance of pH in Prescriptions, Merck Report, p. 16, April, 1945.

cator paper—one buffer solution representing the upper limit of the desired pH range (pH 5), one the lower limit (pH 3), and one the median value (pH 4). The colors thus produced will serve as guides in adjusting the pH of the finished prescription.

Step III.—Dilute hydrochloric acid or sodium hydroxide of known strength is added in measured small amounts to exactly 10 ml. of the prescribed mixture as the case requires. Each addition is followed by thorough mixing and testing on fresh portions of indicator paper until the color obtained shows the pH of the sample to compare favorably with that produced by the specified standard buffer solution (pH 4). From the amount of acid (or alkali) required for the 10 ml. portion of the prescribed mixture, the volume needed for the remainder of the prescription may be calculated.

Step IV.—The calculated volume of acid (or alkali) is combined with the rest of the mixture, the above portion which was subjected to the preliminary adjustment is added, and sufficient vehicle is used to yield the final volume. The completed preparation is mixed thoroughly and subjected to a final check of the pH value; if satisfactory, the product is packaged properly and labeled, with complete instructions to the patient concerning proper conditions of storage and use."

OFFICAL INORGANIC ACIDS

BORIC ACID

Boric Acid, U.S.P. XVII

Formula, H_3BO_3.   Molecular weight, 61.83

History.—In 1702, William Homberg obtained boric acid by heating borax with copperas. Later he prepared it by the action of sulfuric acid upon borax. Until Gay-Lussac and Thenard identified it in 1804 as being an oxygen compound of boron, it was known as Sal Sedativum Hombergi.

Occurrence.—Free boric acid is found in sea water, certain plants and in nearly all fruits. It is likewise found in some volcanic steam jets, notably those in the Tuscany Marshes and the Lipari Islands. It is also present in the natural waters of these regions. By far its largest natural source is in the combined form as, for example, $Na_2B_4O_7 \cdot 4H_2O$ (rasorite or kernite); $Na_2B_4O_7 \cdot 10H_2O$ (borax); $CaB_4O_7 \cdot 4H_2O$ (borocalcite); $H_3BO_3 \cdot Na_2B_4O_7 \cdot 2CaB_4O_7 \cdot 18H_2O$ (tincal); and $Ca_2B_6O_{11} \cdot 5H_2O$ (colemanite). The natural supplies of these minerals occur largely in California.

Physical Properties.—Boric acid is found on the market in three forms: transparent, colorless, odorless, pearly scales having a smooth feel; six-sided triclinic crystals; and a white, odorless, rather bulky powder which is unctuous to the touch. It has a density of 1.46. All forms are stable in air. The scale and crystalline forms are most suitable for preparing aqueous solutions, because the powder tends to float on top of the water. However, the powder (prepared by precipitation) is very useful in dusting powders and ointments because of the difficulty in powdering the slippery scales and crystals.

At 25° C., 1 Gm. of boric acid is soluble in 18 ml. of water, in 18 ml. of alcohol, and in 4 ml. of glycerin. One Gm. is soluble in 4 ml. of boiling water and in 6 ml. of boiling alcohol. The addition of HCl decreases its solubility in water. It volatilizes appreciably from aqueous and alcoholic solutions at 60° C. and above.

Only the alkali borates are soluble in water, and their solutions are strongly basic in reaction. The borates of other metals quickly undergo hydrolysis and thus the insoluble hydroxide forms.

Chemical Properties.—Orthoboric acid is a weak acid, its dissociation for the first hydrogen at 25° C. being $K_1 = 6.4 \times 10^{-10}$.

Since dissociation is so slight for the first stage, even the primary salts of boric acid are hydrolyzed and tertiary salts cannot be prepared from aqueous solution. Aqueous solutions impart a claret color to litmus paper. It is a tribasic acid, as shown by its esterification to ethyl orthoborate, the vapor density of which corresponds to a molecular formula $B(OC_2H_5)_3$. Boric acid cannot be titrated accurately with standard alkali because it is such a weak acid. However, when dissolved in a glycerin solution (official assay) it behaves as a strong monobasic acid which can readily be titrated with standard alkali using phenophthalein as an indicator. The following reaction is thought to take place to account for the monobasicity of boric acid in glycerin (1).[1]

(1)

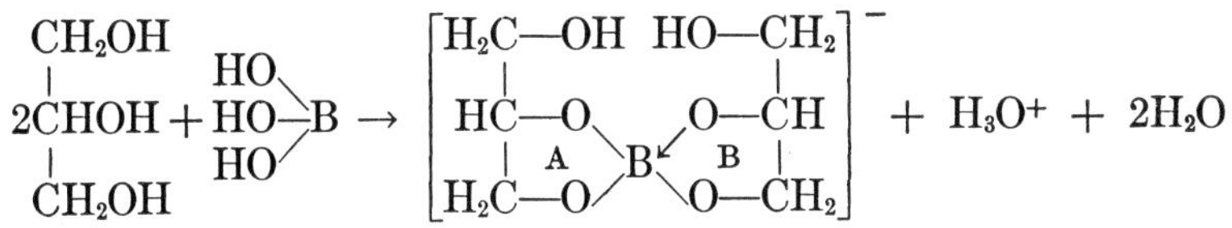

Glycerin   Glyceroboric acid

[1] This formulation expresses the currently accepted reaction that takes place between glycerin and boric acid. The arrow indicates a semi-polar bond. The desire of boron to obey the octet rule and borrow another pair of electrons results in a dynamic resonating system of 3 covalent bonds and 1 semi-polar bond. Additional weight is lent to this reaction by the fact that 2 organically stable 5-membered rings (A and B) are formed.

It is also often misrepresented as follows (2):

$$
\begin{array}{ll}
\text{CH}_2\text{OH} & \text{CH}_2\text{OH} \\
| & | \\
\text{(2) CHOH + HO} & \text{CH—O} \qquad\qquad + 2\text{H}_2\text{O} \\
| \qquad\qquad\qquad \searrow & | \qquad\qquad \searrow \\
\text{CH}_2\text{OH} \qquad \text{B—OH} \rightarrow & \qquad\qquad \text{B—OH} \\
\qquad\qquad \nearrow & | \qquad\qquad \nearrow \\
\qquad \text{HO} & \text{H}_2\text{C——O}
\end{array}
$$

Glyceroboric
acid

In an analogous manner boric acid enters into combination with other polyhydroxy organic compounds such as glycols and mannitol.

When orthoboric acid is heated at 100° C. or slightly above, it is converted to metaboric acid by loss of a molecule of water (3). Manufacturers who make boric acid tablets often heat the orthoboric acid to obtain a partial conversion to metaboric acid. Tablets made in this way disintegrate more readily than would otherwise be the case.

$$\text{(3) } H_3BO_3 \xrightarrow[100°\,C.]{\Delta} HBO_2 + H_2O$$

Ortho-   Meta-
boric acid   boric acid

Further heating to approximately 160° C. results in the formation of tetraboric acid (4).

$$\text{(4) } 4HBO_2 \xrightarrow[160°\,C.]{\Delta} H_2B_4O_7 + H_2O$$

Still further heating converts the residue to boron trioxide, a glassy-appearing solid (5).

$$\text{(5) } H_2B_4O_7 \xrightarrow[\text{strong heat}]{\Delta} 2B_2O_3 + H_2O$$

On account of the nonvolatitity of the oxide, it will displace most acids from salts when fused with them.

The borates are salts of neither H_3BO_3 or HBO_2 but mainly of $H_2B_4O_7$. A solution of boric acid contains only a minute amount of $H_2B_4O_7$ but when neutralized with base and concentrated the more stable crystalline salts, $M_2B_4O_7$, form. However, due to the method of preparation, sodium metaborate will crystallize with a molecule of H_2O_2 and $3H_2O$ to form the so-called Sodium Perborate N.F. XII.

Official Tests for Identity.—1. An aqueous solution of boric acid will color turmeric paper a brownish-red color. The color is slightly intensified by prior acidification with hydrochloric acid. After drying, the brownish-red color is more pronounced and upon moistening with ammonia T.S. it becomes greenish-black.

2. Boric acid mixed with methanol and the mass ignited, burns with a green-bordered flame.

Commercial Manufacture.—Orthoboric acid is obtained commercially from (1) the decomposition of certain naturally occurring borates and (2) from volcanic steam jets.

1. Most of the world's supply of boric acid is prepared from the naturally occurring deposits of colemanite, rasorite, borax, etc. For example, colemanite is reduced to a powder, mixed with boiling water, and the suspension is then treated with sulfur dioxide gas to liberate boric acid (6) (see preparation of sodium borate).

$$(6)\ Ca_2B_6O_{11}.5H_2O + 2SO_2 + 4H_2O \rightarrow 2CaSO_3 + 6H_3BO_3$$

When the solution is cooled, the boric acid crystallizes out.

Borax, when treated with HCl, liberates a high grade of medicinal boric acid (7).

$$(7)\ Na_2B_4O_7.10H_2O + 2HCl \rightarrow 4H_3BO_3 + 2NaCl + 5H_2O$$

The use of HCl, a volatile acid, has superseded that of H_2SO_4 because residual traces of HCl will not remain on the crystal surfaces when they are dried, whereas H_2SO_4, a non-volatile acid, is less easily removed.

2. Although the foregoing procedures account for much of the world's supply of boric acid, a significant amount of *natural* boric acid is obtained from certain volcanic areas in Tuscany and the Lipari Islands. In these areas, volcanic steam jets (soffioni) issue from the ground carrying a small amount of vaporized boric acid together with some other gases. These jets are passed into natural or artificially constructed pools of water (lagoni) which become highly charged with boric acid. The water from these pools is then concentrated (utilizing the heat of the steam jets) to obtain the crystalline boric acid. More recently, artificial soffioni have been bored to increase production.

Pharmacology of Boric Acid and Borate.—The only boron compounds of interest medicinally are boric acid, sodium borate, sodium perborate and preparations derived from them. Their only current usefulness lies in their limited antiseptic properties. The use of borates as food preservatives has been discouraged because of a possible cumulative toxic effect. It is generally conceded that boric acid and sodium borate cannot kill bacteria but that a more or less sterile condition can be maintained once sterility has been established by other methods. However, in view of its low value as an antiseptic, and because of its demonstrated toxic nature when taken internally (orally or parenterally) it has been suggested that boric acid be deleted entirely from medicinal use. The toxicity of boric acid has been a subject of investigation in view of its once general acceptance in burn treatment. It has been definitely established that absorption of boric acid reaching toxic levels can be obtained by applying the ointment to large denuded areas. There is also the possibility of absorption from the intact skin although most authorities discount this route as being of importance in toxicity. Irrigation of cavities with the saturated solution results in almost complete absorption of the acid. The evidence points to the fact that the toxicity of boric acid is apparent only when small doses are given over a long period of time rather than following the administration of a single large dose. The fatal dose of boric acid in adults is somewhat more than 15 to 20 Gm., and in an infant about 5 to 6 Gm. The principal symptoms of poisoning are depression of the circulation, vomiting and diarrhea, followed by shock and coma. Most cases of poisoning are associated with a scarlatiniform rash giving the patient the appearance of a "boiled lobster." Boric acid accumulates principally in the brain, liver, and body fat, with the greatest amount in the brain and the least amount in the body fat. It is the gray matter of the cerebrum and the spinal cord that have the greatest content of boron following death.

Uses.—*Boric Acid*, U.S.P. XVII contains not less than 99.5 per cent of H_3BO_3 calculated on the dried basis. An older synonym is Boracic Acid. Boric acid is used in solution, as a dusting powder, or incorporated in ointment bases, to allay inflammation and for its mild antiseptic properties. Application of its antiseptic properties is found in N.F. *Antiseptic Solution*. To maintain pH at about 6 it has been used as a buffer in *Epinephrine Bitartrate Ophthalmic Solution* N.F. XI where it also contributed to isotonicity. The buffer property is also used in *Aluminum Acetate* and *Aluminum Subacetate Solutions*.

It is a pharmaceutic necessity for *Compound Iodochlorhydroxyquin Power* to aid in establishing a vaginal pH close to normal.

Boric Acid Ointment depends in part on its pH (5.1) for the antiseptic action. A commercial product is Borofax Ointment.

Boric Acid Solution is available for external use. It is used mainly as an eye wash when diluted with an equal volume of water which produces almost an isotonic solution. Because it is a saturated solution boric acid tends to crystallize out with a slight drop in temperature. For this reason some manufacturers supply a solution containing only about 3.5 per cent boric acid.

Boroglycerin Glycerite ($C_3H_5BO_3$) N.F. XI is formed by the splitting out of three moles of water from the reaction of equimolar amounts of glycerin and boric acid at 140° to 150° C. It has found use as a suppository base.

HYDRIODIC ACID AND HYDROGEN IODIDE

Diluted Hydriodic Acid, N.F. XII

Formula, HI.   Molecular Weight, 127.91

History and Occurrence.—Clement and Desormes identified hydrogen iodide in 1813. During the same year it was investigated by Gay-Lussac. The acid was introduced into medicine by Dr. Buchanan, Junior Surgeon of the Glasgow Infirmary, primarily as a less irritant means of administering iodine. In his own words "It appeared to me, however, that it would be well to save the stomach the labor of preparing hydriodic acid, by giving, for the purposes of medicine, not free iodine, but the hydriodic acid itself."[1] Very small amounts of hydrogen iodide have been found in volcanic gases.

Physical Properties.—Hydrogen iodide is a colorless gas having a penetrating odor. It fumes strongly upon exposure to air and is readily liquefied at $0°$ C. under a pressure of 4 atmospheres. Liquid hydrogen iodide boils at $-35.1°$ C., and has a density at $25°$ C. of 5.23 g./liter. When further cooled, it becomes a solid which melts at $-50.8°$ C. Both gaseous and liquefied hydrogen iodide are nonconductors of electricity. It is exceedingly soluble in water. One volume of H_2O at $10°$ C. and 760 mm. pressure dissolves 425 volumes of HI, giving a 70 per cent solution. At $127°$ C., a 57 per cent solution distils without decomposition.

The N.F. XII Diluted Hydriodic Acid, containing 9.5 to 10.5 Gm. HI per 100 ml., is a colorless or not more than a pale yellow, odorless, aqueous liquid, having a specific gravity of about 1.100 ($25°$ C.). Decomposition of the diluted acid is retarded by the presence of about 0.8 Gm. of hypophosphorous acid per 100 ml.

Chemical Properties.—Hydrogen iodide (gaseous HI) is the least stable of the hydrogen halides, decomposing into H_2 and I_2 at elevated temperatures (1).

(1) $2HI \rightleftarrows H_2 + I_2$

It burns readily with O_2 to liberate I_2 and H_2O (2).

(2) $4HI + O_2 \rightleftarrows 2H_2O + 2I_2$

Hydriodic acid (aqueous solution of HI) behaves in most respects like hydrochloric and hydrobromic acids (*i.e.*, as a strong acid), but is the least stable of the hydrohalide acids. Hydriodic acid unites with all metallic oxides and hydroxides (except Cr_2O_3) to form iodides. Aqueous solutions are colorless when freshly prepared, but assume a brown color on standing because of the liberation of

[1] Am. J. Pharm., **3**, 175-6 (1838).

free iodine (2). Hydriodic acid readily reacts with Cl_2 and Br_2 to liberate I_2 (3) (4).

(3) $2I^- + X_2 \rightarrow 2X^- + I_2$ (X = Cl or Br)

or written molecularly

(4) $2HI + X_2 \rightarrow 2HX + I_2$

Hydriodic acid is a powerful reducing agent and has been used for that purpose by organic chemists. Also, many oxidizing agents such as ferric ions, peroxides, sulfuric acid and hydrosulfuric acid (H_2S) will liberate iodine from iodides.

Most iodides are soluble except those of silver, bismuth, lead, mercury(ous–ic) and copper(ous).

Because iodides are precipitated by silver ion, the official assay utilizes the reaction. An excess of 0.1 N silver nitrate solution is added to the hydriodic acid sample resulting in precipitation of silver iodide (5).

(5) $HI + AgNO_3 \rightarrow AgI \downarrow + HNO_3$

The excess silver nitrate solution is determined by titration with 0.1 N ammonium thiocyanate solution (6) using ferric ammonium sulfate T.S. as indicator (7).

(6) $AgNO_3 + NH_4SCN \rightarrow AgSCN \downarrow + NH_4NO_3$

(7) $6NH_4SCN + 2FeNH_4(SO_4)_2 \rightarrow 2Fe(SCN)_3 + 4(NH_4)_2SO_4$

Official Tests for Identity.—1. When chlorine water is added drop by drop to an aqueous solution of hydrogen iodide or a soluble iodide, the solution is colored yellow to red, due to liberated iodine (8). When this solution is shaken with chloroform, the latter is colored violet. The iodine thus liberated gives a blue color with starch T.S.

(8) $2HI + Cl_2 \rightarrow 2HCl + I_2$

2. Silver nitrate test solution produces a yellow, curdy precipitate of silver iodide (9) which is insoluble in nitric acid and in ammonia T.S.

(9) $HI + AgNO_3 \rightarrow AgI \downarrow + HNO_3$

Commercial Manufacture.—Hydrogen iodide may be prepared by the direct union of its elements in the presence of a catalyst. This process involves the passing of hydrogen and iodine vapors over heated platinum black (10).

(10) $H_2 + I_2 \rightleftharpoons 2HI$

The union takes place slowly and, since the reaction is a decidedly reversible one, always remains incomplete. The product obtained in this manner is impure and unsatisfactory from a medicinal standpoint.

Hydrogen iodide cannot be prepared by the action of sulfuric acid on an iodide because it is very unstable, parting with its hydrogen with ease, and reducing the sulfuric acid. The primary product of the reduction is H_2S (11). As soon as the temperature has been raised sufficiently by the heat of reaction, nearly all of the hydrogen iodide is oxidized. Sulfur is frequently precipitated, due to a secondary reaction between the hydrogen sulfide and the sulfuric acid (12), and between the sulfur dioxide so formed and the excess of hydrogen sulfide present (13).

(11) $H_2SO_4 + 8HI \rightarrow H_2S \uparrow + 4H_2O + 4I_2$

(12) $H_2S + H_2SO_4 \rightarrow SO_2 \uparrow + 2H_2O + S \downarrow$

(13) $SO_2 + 2H_2S \rightarrow 2H_2O + 3S \downarrow$

Hydrogen iodide may be prepared by the action of hydrogen sulfide upon iodine in aqueous suspension (14).

(14) $H_2S + I_2 \rightarrow 2HI + S \downarrow$

The precipitated sulfur is filtered off and the liquid concentrated to about 57 per cent of HI by distilling off the water.

Hydrogen iodide is usually made by mixing amorphous (red) phosphorus and a large excess of iodine and allowing water to drop slowly upon them (15). The reaction starts easily and the gaseous hydrogen iodide is freed from iodine vapors by passing the gas through a tube containing amorphous phosphorus.

(15) $PI_3 + 3H_2O \rightarrow 3HI + P(OH)_3$

Pharmacological Action of Iodide Ion.—Other than the external antiseptic action of iodine, the internal use of iodine and iodides is an interesting subject. Reference has already been made to the fact that elemental iodine (as in Lugol's solution) accomplishes systemic effects only because the iodine is converted to iodide ion in the gastrointestinal tract. Therefore, it is only logical to utilize the iodides themselves rather than solutions containing free iodine. One of the most rapidly absorbed iodides is that of sodium, with potassium iodide running a close second. Other iodides used include calcium, ferrous, ammonium and the acid, hydriodic acid. Some well-known organic iodine-containing products are Amend's Solution, Calcium Iodobehenate, Organidin, Oridine, and Iodized Oil. The iodide ion, following absorption, appears to distribute itself more or less uniformly in the extracellular fluid. Elimination appears to be principally via the urine. The only place in the body where any special affinity for the iodide ion seems to exist is in the thyroid follicle cells, and furthermore, the only use for the iodide ion in the body economy seems to be as a source of iodine for the synthesis of triiodothyronine and thyroxin.

The usual daily requirement of iodine for an average man is approximately 200 micrograms. Lack of sufficient iodine in the diet results in enlargement of the thyroid gland and "simple" or colloid goiter. Adequate iodine in the diet in iodine deficient areas is easily insured by the use of iodized table salt containing 0.01 per cent potassium iodide.

There are two principal categories into which the further pharmacological discussion of iodides may be placed: (1) its relationship with the thyroid gland, and (2) its general therapeutic uses.

1. Iodine is an essential constituent of the thyroid hormone, being present in the amino acids, thyroxin and triiodothyronine. In the normal utilization of iodine for the synthesis of these amino acids it may be considered as being in the iodide form which is then oxidized to iodine for incorporation into tyrosine to form mono-iodotyrosine and diiodotyrosine. These are then coupled to form the triiodo- and tetraiodothyronines (*i.e.*, the amino acids). The oxidation step from iodide to iodine is not well understood and, by many, is thought to involve a peroxidase system. That the iodine (as iodide) is incorporated into the thyroid gland only to form the amino acids has been shown by tracer studies with radioactive iodine. In comparing goitrous glands with normal glands it is always found that there is a lesser iodine and amino acid content in the former. The size of the thyroid gland has been shown to be, in general, inversely proportional to the iodine content of the gland. Also it has been well established that the iodine content of the thyroid gland is roughly proportional to the iodine intake. When iodine is administered its uptake is governed by three principal factors: (1) character of the local thyroid tissue, because abnormal adenomatous thyroid tissue has a slower uptake of iodide and a lower content of iodine than the normal tissue, (2) blood level of inorganic iodide because a high level keeps the iodine at a high level in the colloid, thus using up only a small part of the administered iodide. Paradoxically, the administration of excessive amounts of iodide will inhibit the conversion of the element into the iodinated amino acids provided other factors do not enter into the picture, (3) thyrotrophin (a hormone secreted by the anterior pituitary) level in the blood because the thyrotrophin content has a direct bearing on the complete conversion of iodine to the iodinated amino acids. Thyrotrophin also controls the release of thyroid hormone to the circulation because in its absence none is released. Actually, the amount of thyroid hormone released is a reflection of the true state of the thyroid gland, mere storage of the thyroid hormone in the colloid not being truly indicative. In this connection it is interesting to note that the effect of such antithyroid

drugs as propylthiouracil, etc., is not to inhibit iodine uptake but rather to block the enzyme system that iodinates the amino acids. The actual nature of the thyroid hormone itself has not been determined. It is known that the hormone is not thyroglobulin but it is, nevertheless, a protein combination of some kind. Indeed, thyroid hormone has been induced in such ordinary proteins as casein and plasma protein by *in vitro* treatment with iodine.

2. Reference has already been made to the significant use of iodides in the prevention of colloid goiter. Other than this, iodide has been used therapeutically as an ameliorating agent in hyperthyroidism; as a fibrolytic agent in syphilis, leprosy, sporotrichosis, blastomycosis, and actinomycosis; as an expectorant and, finally as an "alterative."

In *hyperthyroidism* it is well established that in virtually all cases a moderate drop in metabolic level can be demonstrated following iodide therapy. About 6 mg. per day is the optimal dosage. The effect is not upon the systemic action of the thyroid hormone but appears to be brought about by a slower release of hormone. The slower release of thyroid hormone takes place even though the follicular colloid becomes more highly iodinated. A secondary result of iodide medication in hyperthyroidism is the involution of the gland. This characteristic is not possessed by propylthiouracil and makes iodide therapy an extremely invaluable adjunct to therapy by propylthiouracil as well as in preparation for thyroidectomy. It has been demonstrated that administration of propylthiouracil, although controlling the formation and release of thyroid hormone, will not bring about involution of the gland as does iodide and may possibly bring on hyperplasia. On the other hand, although administered iodide relieves the symptoms of hyperthyroidism, the effect is n ot permanent and in time the symptoms return, often in an exaggerated form.

As a *fibrolytic agent,* iodides in large doses often cause striking recessions of the gummatous formations in late secondary and tertiary syphilitic infections, although it is becoming increasingly difficult to find cases that have progressed to these stages in this day of antibiotics. The iodide, apparently, has no curative properties nor does it influence resistance in any way. In actinomycosis and the other fungous infections beneficial results are often brought about with relatively small doses, although in blastomycosis large doses are the rule.

As *expectorants* the iodides have had a long medical history, having been used in asthma, chronic bronchitis and in the late stages of acute bronchitis. Actually, although they are still popular today, it has not been demonstrated conclusively that they are effective in changing either the character or the amount of the sputum. Allergists, in particular, feel that there is a definite liquefaction of tenacious mucus associated with the aftermath of an asthmatic attack. The effect may possibly be ascribed to reflex action from the saline taste of salivary secretions, the iodide ion appearing promptly in these secretions following administration.

The *alterative* use of iodides, once popular, has become a casualty because of more detailed pharmacological knowledge and more critical clinical evaluation.

Administration of iodides in amounts which exceed a certain level in the body often brings about certain irritative phenomena to the skin and mucous membranes. This is termed "iodism" and is exhibited by rashes, headache, conjunctivitis, laryngitis, and the like. For this reason iodides should not be given in cases of acne. However, when skin infections require "opening up," such as seborrhea, iodides are indicated. Gastrointestinal effects are characterized by nausea, vomiting and diarrhea. Discontinuation of the medication together with forcing of fluids is indicated in such cases. Administration of sodium chloride may also aid in the more rapid elimination of iodide.

A contraindication to iodide therapy is tuberculosis which appears to flare up even in dormant cases. Likewise, adenoma of the thyroid gland is cause for not administering iodides due to the possibility of hyperthyroidism.

Uses.—*Diluted Hydriodic Acid*, N.F. XII, is a solution containing in each 100 ml., not less than 9.5 Gm. and not more than 10.5 Gm. of HI, and not less than 600 mg. and not more than 1 Gm. of HPH_2O_2. This official form of HI is provided as a pharmaceutic necessity for preparing Hydriodic Acid Syrup, the dosage form.

Hydriodic Acid Syrup, N.F. XII, is made by diluting Diluted Hydriodic Acid with purified water and dissolving sucrose in the liquid by agitation (note that HPH_2O_2 is present). The product is filtered. The brown color which develops in the syrup on long standing is not necessarily iodine, but may be due to caramelization of the levulose resulting from acid hydrolysis of the sucrose used in the syrup. It should not be dispensed if brown or amber in color. This syrup is the most commonly administered form of hydriodic acid, and is much used for the expectorant effect of the iodide ion. A similar commercial product is Hyodin. Organic forms of HI include the marketed forms known as Glyco-HI, and Iod-Ethamine. Usual dose—5 ml.

HYDROCHLORIC ACID AND HYDROGEN CHLORIDE

Hydrochloric Acid, U.S.P. XVII

Formula, HCl. Molecular Weight, 36.46

History.—Hydrochloric acid was first obtained by J. R. Glauber in 1648. In 1772, Priestley isolated it in the gaseous condition and thought it was an oxyacid. In 1810, Sir H. Davy showed that it contained only hydrogen and chlorine.

Occurrence.—Hydrogen chloride is found in the fumes issuing from active volcanoes in South America and Mexico. When secreted into the stomach, pure human gastric juice contains from 0.4 to 0.5 per cent of free HCl. This appreciable concentration, however, does not usually persist for any length of time, as the acid is neutralized by the saliva, the mucus, and the return flow of the contents of the duodenum to about 0.15 to 0.2 per cent of HCl. While the mechanism of gastric HCl formation has not been fully and conclusively determined definite progress has been made toward this objective. The locus of formation has been suggested as being the parietal cells of the stomach (those lining the stomach wall). A postulated mechanism involves a proposed separation of hydrogen ions arising from the reduction of pyridine nucleotide (by some carbohydrate intermediate) from hydroxide ions which arise from the reaction of reduced cytochrome oxidase with oxygen. An essential feature of the proposed mechanism is that the enzymes of the oxidation-reduction systems in the parietal cells are arranged in successive strata in order to effect the separation of hydrogen ions and hydroxide ions. Having effected a separation of the hydrogen and hydroxide ions by the above proposed method the hydrogen ions diffuse through the cell wall into the gastric lumen together with the chloride ion which passively accompanies the elaborated hydrogen ion. The hydroxide ion is converted to bicarbonate and is elaborated at the vascular border of the cell into the venous drainage of the stomach together with accompanying sodium ion. Hydrochloric acid is necessary to the principal digestive function of the gastric juice, *e.g.*, its action upon protein. In Nature, large quantities of chlorides occur in sea water and in mineral deposits. Sodium chloride is the source of all commercial hydrochloric acid in one way or another.

Physical Properties.—Hydrogen chloride is a colorless gas having an acrid irritating odor and an acid taste. The density of the gas is 1.2681 (air = 1) and hence it is about 25 per cent heavier than air. One liter weighs 1.6394 Gm. On account of its high critical temperature (52° C.) it can be liquefied by pressure alone. As a liquid (b. p. −5.8° C.) as well as in the gaseous state, it is a nonconductor of electricity. Solid hydrogen chloride melts at −111° C. Its heat of solution is 17,400 (calories per 1 formula-weight of hydrogen chloride in unlimited water).

Hydrogen chloride is very soluble in water. Five hundred and three volumes of the gas dissolve in 1 volume of water at 0° C. (760 mm. pressure) and 460 volumes of the gas dissolve in 1 volume of water at 20° C. (760 mm. pressure). In aqueous solution (18° C.) it is ionized to the extent of 92 per cent in tenth-normal solution and conducts electricity readily. When a saturated solution of hydrogen chloride (43.4 per cent of HCl) is distilled at normal barometric pressure, the gas is driven off until a concentration of 20.24 per cent hydrogen chloride with a constant boiling-point of

10

110° C. is obtained. Hydrochloric acid of this strength distils unchanged, the water vapor carrying over hydrogen chloride in the same proportion as it exists in the liquid.

Chemical Properties.—Dry hydrogen chloride is quite inactive. It does not react with any of the non-metals (sulfur, phosphorus, etc.). Some of the active metals decompose it, forming hydrogen and the chloride of the metal (1).

$$(1)\ 2Na + 2HCl \rightarrow 2NaCl + H_2 \uparrow$$

Hydrogen chloride combines directly with ammonia to form ammonium chloride (2).

$$(2)\ NH_3 + HCl \rightarrow NH_4Cl$$

The chemical properties of aqueous solutions of HCl are typical of those of all strong acids. The hydrogen in the acid is displaced by all metals preceding hydrogen in the electromotive series (3).

$$(3)\ Zn + 2HCl \rightarrow ZnCl_2 + H_2 \uparrow$$

Hydrochloric acid reacts readily with most oxides (4) and hydroxides (5) of the metals to form water and the chloride of the metal.

$$(4)\ Fe_2O_3 + 6HCl \rightarrow 2FeCl_3 + 3H_2O$$
$$(5)\ NaOH + HCl \rightarrow NaCl + H_2O$$

These are known as *neutralization* reactions. The reaction of HCl with sulfites (6) to form SO_2 (7) and with carbonates (8) to form CO_2 (9) is still another type of neutralization reaction.

$$(6)\ Na_2SO_3 + 2HCl \rightarrow 2NaCl + H_2SO_3 \text{ (unstable)}$$
$$(7)\ H_2SO_3 \rightarrow H_2O + SO_2 \uparrow$$
$$(8)\ Na_2CO_3 + 2HCl \rightarrow 2NaCl + H_2CO_3 \text{ (unstable)}$$
$$(9)\ H_2CO_3 \rightarrow H_2O + CO_2 \uparrow$$

Because it contains the chloride ion, the acid will precipitate from aqueous solution the water-insoluble chlorides of certain metals, namely Ag, Pb and Hg(ous) (10).

$$(10)\ AgNO_3 + HCl \rightarrow AgCl \downarrow + HNO_3$$

Hydrochloric acid is oxidized by strong oxidizing agents (*e.g.,* $KMnO_4$, MnO_2, etc.), liberating chlorine (11, 12).

$$(11)\ 4HCl + MnO_2 \rightarrow MnCl_2 + Cl_2 \uparrow + 2H_2O$$
$$(12)\ 16HCl + 2KMnO_4 \rightarrow 2MnCl_2 + 2KCl + 5Cl_2 \uparrow + 8H_2O$$

Hydrochloric acid is assayed by titrating a weighed sample with 1 N sodium hydroxide (13) using methyl red as an indicator.

$$(13)\ HCl + NaOH \rightarrow NaCl + H_2O$$

Tests for Identity.—1. When Hydrochloric Acid is added to potassium permanganate, chlorine is evolved (12).

2. Hydrochloric acid or its soluble salts precipitate a white, curdy silver chloride from solutions of silver nitrate (10). The precipitate is insoluble in nitric acid. Silver chloride is soluble in ammonia solutions as diammino-silver chloride $Ag(NH_3)_2Cl$ (14) (see ammonia).

(14) $AgCl + 2NH_3 \rightarrow Ag(NH_3)_2Cl$

Commercial Manufacture.—Hydrogen chloride may be made (1) from salt with sulfuric acid, (2) by burning electrolytic chlorine directly in excess hydrogen, and (3) as a by-product in the chlorination of hydrocarbons.

1. The manufacture of hydrochloric acid from salt and sulfuric acid may be depicted as taking place in two steps (15, 16).

(15) $NaCl + H_2SO_4 \rightarrow NaHSO_4 + HCl$
(16) $NaHSO_4 + NaCl \rightarrow Na_2SO_4$ (salt cake) $+ HCl$

Formerly, the salt cake was used in the manufacture of sodium carbonate by the Le Blanc Process, but since the advent of the Solvay Ammonia-Soda Process for manufacturing sodium carbonate the use of salt cake has diminished greatly and consequently the production of hydrochloric acid by this method has decreased. The chief use of salt cake today is in the manufacture of glass.

The hydrogen chloride obtained by the first reaction (15) is called "pan acid" and is purer and easier to condense than the "roaster acid" obtained by the second reaction (16). Consequently, the "pan acid" is used principally in the manufacture of the finer grades of hydrochloric acid, whereas the "roaster acid" yields the muriatic acids of commerce. *Muriatic acid* (Latin, *muria*, brine) is a yellow liquid containing a number of impurities, *e.g.*, chlorine, arsenous and sulfurous acids, iron, etc. The color is thought to be due to ferric chloride and yellow organic coloring materials. It contains approximately 35 to 38 per cent HCl.[1]

2. A large proportion of the hydrochloric acid manufactured today is made by the burning of electrolytic chlorine in excess hydrogen (17) using quartz bunsen burners, or in some commercial installations hydrogen is burned in an atmosphere of chlorine.

(17) $H_2 + Cl_2 \rightarrow 2HCl$

The product is 100 per cent HCl which when dissolved in water in stoneware absorbing systems produces a water-white acid of great purity.

This method has attained prominence because of the extensive manufacture of caustic soda by the electrolytic method in which the by-products are H_2 and Cl_2.

[1] For a more detailed discussion of this method of manufacture see the 3rd edition of this textbook.

3. Because of the large scale chlorination of hydrocarbons, such as benzene (18) and pentane, considerable quantities of by-product HCl are obtained.

(18) C_6H_6 (benzene) $+ Cl_2 \rightarrow C_6H_5Cl + HCl$

Essentially, for every mole of Cl_2 used, a mole of HCl is formed. The amount of HCl obtained in this way often becomes a problem to the manufacturer, and cases are on record where the manufacturer pays to have the hydrochloric acid removed from the premises.

Pharmacological Action of the Chloride Ion.—The chloride ion has practically no pharmacological action. Chloride ions, together with sodium ions, are necessary for the osmotic functions which they perform. The extracellular fluid of the body contains about 0.17 per cent of dissociated sodium chloride. This concentration is maintained through the agency of the skin and urine, which either give off or retain sodium chloride, depending upon the increase or decrease of its intake.

Acidosis may be caused by an excess of the chloride ion in the body. (See ammonium chloride.) Chloride salts of this type are known as the acid-producing diuretics.

Uses.—*Hydrochloric Acid*, U.S.P. XVII, contains not less than 35 per cent and not more than 38 per cent, by weight, of HCl. It is a colorless, fuming liquid with a pungent odor. The odor and fumes disappear when the acid is diluted with 2 volumes of water. It has a specific gravity of about 1.18 at 25° C.

Diluted Hydrochloric Acid, N.F. XII, is an aqueous solution containing, in each 100 ml., not less than 9.5 Gm. and not more than 10.5 Gm. of HCl. It is prepared by mixing 234 ml. of Hydrochloric Acid with a sufficient quantity of Purified Water to make 1000 ml. Diluted Hydrochloric Acid, when further diluted with 25 to 50 volumes of water is administered in gastric achlorhydria (lack of hydrochloric acid in the gastric juices). The therapeutic dose usually given is not sufficient to cause the secretion of natural hydrochloric acid in the stomach, but it does appear to give some relief from the achlorhydria. Certain investigators feel that sufficient acid should be administered at each meal to cause the appearance of the free acid in the gastric juices. This necessitates a dose of approximately 10 ml. of the diluted acid in contrast to the usual dose of about 1 or 2 ml. In any event, the acid should be taken in a diluted form through a drinking tube to minimize the danger of its solvent action on the enamel of the teeth. To avoid this difficulty, preparations such as glutamic acid hydrochloride [$HOOC(CH_2)_2CH(NH_2)COOH \cdot HCl$] and betaine hydrochloride ($C_5H_{11}O_2N \cdot HCl$) have been advocated. These compounds are crystalline and may be administered in capsule form. They liberate HCl in the stomach, the glutamic acid or betaine residue being metabolized at the same time. Usual dose—5 ml, well diluted with water.

Aside from the medicinal application of Diluted Hydrochloric Acid that has been discussed above there are other uses that depend on the chemical properties of the acid. Among these the most important probably has been its usefulness in imparting an acidic reaction to menstrua used in the extraction of crude alkaloid-containing drugs as for example, *Ergot Fluidextract*, N.F. XI and *Nux Vomica Tincture*, N.F. XI. The extractions are facilitated by the conversion of the plant bases to the more water-soluble hydrochlorides. In other cases, the acid is used to adjust preparations to a desirable degree of acidity in order to impart maximum stability and solubility to the alkaloidal content. In *Pentobarbital Sodium Elixir*, use is made of the hydrogen ion concentration of the acid to convert Pentobarbital Sodium (pentobarbital not being conveniently available as the free acid) to pentobarbital. In the case of *Podophyllum Resin*, the acid is used to acidulate the precipitating medium in order to give a more complete precipitation.

HYPOPHOSPHOROUS ACID

Hypophosphorous Acid, N.F. XII

Formula, HPH_2O_2; Molecular Weight, 66.00

History and Occurrence.—Hypophosphorous acid was discovered in 1816 by Dulong. H. Rose investigated it more thoroughly in 1826. In 1874, Thompson obtained it in crystalline form. It does not occur in Nature.

Physical Properties.—At ordinary temperatures, pure hypophosphorous acid is a colorless, syrupy liquid having a specific gravity of 1.493 at 18.8° C. At 17.4° C. it becomes a white crystalline solid which melts at 26.5° C. It is soluble in water.

The official hypophosphorous acid is a colorless or slightly yellow, odorless liquid, containing not less than 30 per cent and not more than 32 per cent of HPH_2O_2. It has a specific gravity of about 1.130 at 25° C.

Chemical Properties.—The chemical properties of the acid may be considered as falling chiefly into the following categories: (1) acidic properties, (2) reducing properties and (3) decomposition of the acid.

1. The acid acts as a monobasic acid because only one of the three hydrogens present in the formula is ionizable (1).

(1) $HPH_2O_2 + H_2O \rightleftarrows H_3O^+ + PH_2O_2^-$

It may be neutralized with metal hydroxides or carbonates (2) to form the corresponding hypophosphite salt.

(2) $2HPH_2O_2 + Na_2CO_3 \rightarrow 2NaPH_2O_2 + H_2O + CO_2 \uparrow$

It is a sufficiently strong acid to react with some of the metals, such as zinc (3) and iron, to form hydrogen and the corresponding hypophosphite.

$$(3) \ Zn + 2HPH_2O_2 \rightarrow Zn(PH_2O_2)_2 + H_2 \uparrow$$

All salts of the acid are soluble in water except ferric hypophosphite.

2. Hypophosphorous acid is readily oxidized to form phosphoric acid and, therefore, acts as a powerful reducing agent. An example of its reducing action as applied to a pharmaceutical preparation has been cited under the discussion of hydriodic acid, in which preparation it acts to reduce any free iodine formed back to the iodide (4).

$$(4) \ HPH_2O_2 + 2I_2 + 2H_2O \rightarrow 4HI + H_3PO_4$$

Because of its reducing property, the acid has been used for the preservation of Diluted Hydriodic Acid and Ferrous Iodide Syrup, in which capacity it acts to reduce free iodine and ferric ion back to iodide and ferrous ion respectively.

When heated to 60° C. with a solution of $CuSO_4$, a reddish precipitate of impure cuprous hydride (Cu_2H_2) is formed (5). If the solution is boiled, the hydride decomposes to metallic copper and hydrogen.

$$(5) \ 2CuSO_4 + 2HPH_2O_2 + 4H_2O \rightarrow 2H_3PO_4 + Cu_2H_2 \downarrow + 2H_2SO_4 + H_2 \uparrow$$

Solutions of potassium permanganate are immediately decolorized through reduction with hypophosphorous acid (6).

$$(6) \ 5HPH_2O_2 + 4KMnO_4 + 6H_2SO_4 \rightarrow 2K_2SO_4 + 4MnSO_4 + 5H_3PO_4 + 6H_2O$$

The acid will form a white precipitate with mercuric chloride solutions (7), and in the presence of an excess of the acid the reduction causes the formation of free mercury (8). (See also silver salts.)

$$(7) \ HPH_2O_2 + 4HgCl_2 + 2H_2O \rightarrow H_3PO_4 + 2Hg_2Cl_2 \downarrow + 4HCl$$

$$(8) \ HPH_2O_2 + 2Hg_2Cl_2 + 2H_2O \rightarrow H_3PO_4 + 4Hg \downarrow + 4HCl$$

There are many other examples of reduction with hypophosphorous acid, but the above represent most of the important ones. One can readily see from the above reactions that any reducible substance (oxidizing agent) combined with the acid would constitute an incompatibility.

3. When concentrated hypophosphorous acid is heated between 130° and 140° C., it decomposes into phosphorous acid (H_3PO_3) and hydrogen phosphide (phosphine) (9).

$$(9) \ 3HPH_2O_2 \rightarrow PH_3 \uparrow + 2H_3PO_3$$

The phosphine is ignited on contact with air (10), because it is associated with the spontaneously inflammable phosphorus dihydride (PH_2 or P_2H_4) which forms simultaneously in small amounts. Pure phosphine does not ignite on contact with air.

(10) $2PH_3 + 4O_2 \rightarrow 2HPO_3 + 2H_2O$

Hypophosphorous Acid is assayed by titrating a weighed sample with 1 N sodium hydroxide (11) using methyl red as an indicator.

(11) $HPH_2O_2 + NaOH \rightarrow NaPH_2O_2 + H_2O$

Official Tests for Identity.—1. It responds to all the tests for *Hypophosphite*:

(a) When heated it liberates spontaneously inflammable phosphine (9) (10).

(b) It yields a white precipitate with mercuric chloride T.S. (7). This precipitate becomes gray with an excess of hypophosphorous acid because mercurous salt is easily reduced to free mercury (8).

(c) It gives a red precipitate of Cu_2H_2 when warmed with copper sulfate T.S. (5).

Commercial Methods of Manufacture.—Hypophosphorous acid is made commercially in three ways:

1. By decomposing boiling aqueous solutions of calcium hypophosphite with oxalic acid (12), filtering off the insoluble calcium oxalate and concentrating the acid filtrate in vacuum.

(12) $Ca(PH_2O_2)_2 + H_2C_2O_4 . 2H_2O \rightarrow CaC_2O_4 . H_2O \downarrow + 2HPH_2O_2 + H_2O$

2. By mixing a concentrated aqueous solution of potassium hypophosphite with a hydro-alcoholic solution of tartaric acid (13), allowing the mixture to stand at 5° C. for twenty-four hours, separating the insoluble potassium bitartrate, washing it with diluted alcohol and concentrating the filtrate.

(13) $KPH_2O_2 + H_2C_4H_4O_6 \rightarrow HPH_2O_2 + KHC_4H_4O_6 \downarrow$

3. By gently heating white phosphorus in an open dish with baryta water until hydrogen phosphide (PH_3—very poisonous) ceases to be evolved (14). The excess of barium ion is precipitated by passing in carbon dioxide (15). After filtering, the liquid is evaporated until the barium hypophosphite crystallizes out. This is dissolved in water and decomposed with the theoretical amount of sulfuric acid (16). The mixture is filtered and the filtrate evaporated in an open dish, care being taken not to heat the liquid over 110° C. Upon cooling, white crystalline hypophosphorous acid separates out.

(14) $8P + 3Ba(OH)_2 + 6H_2O \rightarrow 3Ba(PH_2O_2)_2 + 2PH_3 \uparrow$

(15) $Ba(OH)_2 + CO_2 \rightarrow BaCO_3 \downarrow + H_2O$

(16) $Ba(PH_2O_2)_2 + H_2SO_4 \rightarrow BaSO_4 \downarrow + 2HPH_2O_2$

The N.F. gives appropriate tests for barium, oxalates, heavy metals, and arsenic (from sulfuric acid) because of the above methods of manufacture.

Pharmacology of the Hypophosphites.—The hypophosphites were first used in 1855 by Churchill who used the salts to treat tuberculosis. He somehow assumed that there would be an interference with oxidation and a beneficial effect on organic phosphorus. On this basis for almost one hundred years, hypophosphites were used in tonics. All hypophosphites are ineffective and none are recognized officially.

Uses.—*Hypophosphorous Acid*, N.F. XII, should contain not less than 30 per cent and not more than 32 per cent of HPH_2O_2. It is a powerful reducing agent, and hence is used in medicinal preparations to retard oxidation and resulting decomposition of various ingredients, *e.g.*, hydriodic acid in *Hydriodic Acid Syrup*, N.F. XII; and ferrous iodide in *Ferrous Iodide Syrup*, N.F. XI. The acid itself is rarely administered internally.

PHOSPHORIC ACID (ORTHO)

Phosphoric Acid, N.F. XII

Formula, H_3PO_4; Molecular Weight, 98.00

History.—This principal acid of phosphorus was discovered in 1746 by Andreas Sigismund Marggraf, who observed that this then unknown substance produced peculiar yellow precipitates with silver nitrate and, when calcined with charcoal, yielded elemental phosphorus. In 1833, Thomas Graham published the results of his masterly investigations of the acids of phosphorus in which he pointed out the differences between the ortho-, pyro-, and metaphosphoric acids (see Appendix).

Occurrence.—Uncombined orthophosphoric acid does not occur in Nature. However, its calcium, aluminum, and iron salts are abundantly found in the minerals *apatite* ($3Ca_3[PO_4]_2.CaF_2$) and *phosphorite* ($Ca_3[PO_4]_2$). The latter is known as "phosphate rock" and occurs as large deposits in Florida, Tennessee, etc. It is the largest source of phosphates for fertilizers. Phosphates occur also in the blood, bone and urine. The slag from steel and iron furnaces contains appreciable quantities of recoverable phosphates. Phosphates are always found in fertile soil and are essential to the development of fruits and seeds.

Physical Properties.—When a solution of orthophosphoric acid is evaporated in a vacuum over sulfuric acid, transparent, hard, six-sided, rhombic crystals result. These crystals are very deliquescent in air, have a specific gravity of 1.834 at 18.2° C. and melt at

Acids

42.3° C. When crystallized from water, the product is a hydrated form, $2H_3PO_4.H_2O$. Orthophosphoric acid is very soluble in water and in alcohol. The official concentrated solution contains 85 to 88 per cent H_3PO_4 and is a colorless and odorless syrupy liquid. Its specific gravity is about 1.71 at 25° C. Diluted Phosphoric Acid containing from 9.5 to 10.5 Gm. of H_3PO_4 in 100 ml. of solution, specific gravity about 1.057, is also official. It is a clear, colorless, and odorless solution.

Chemical Properties.—Orthophosphoric acid is a triprotic (tertiary) acid, and consequently ionizes in three steps (1, 2, 3).[1]

(1) $H_3PO_4 + H_2O \rightleftarrows H_3O^+ + H_2PO_4^-$ $K_1 = 7.5 \times 10^{-3}$

(2) $H_2PO_4^- + H_2O \rightleftarrows H_3O^+ + HPO_4^=$ $K_2 = 6.2 \times 10^{-8}$

(3) $HPO_4^= + H_2O \rightleftarrows H_3O^+ + PO_4^{\equiv}$ $K_3 = 4.8 \times 10^{-13}$

One can see from the ionization constants (K_1, K_2, K_3) that the ionization of the acid takes place in the same manner as any other polyprotic acid, namely each successive ionization step takes place to a lesser extent than the preceding. Actually, the ionization produces very little phosphate ion ($PO_4^{\equiv}$). The acid forms three sodium salts which show very nicely the three possible anions: (1) primary sodium orthophosphate (NaH_2PO_4), (2) secondary sodium orthophosphate (Na_2HPO_4), (3) tertiary sodium orthophosphate (Na_3PO_4). When an aqueous solution of orthophosphoric acid is titrated with sodium hydroxide solution using methyl orange as the indicator the color changes when the salt NaH_2PO_4 has formed (pH 3.1 to 4.4). When it is titrated using phenolphthalein as the indicator the color changes when the compound Na_2HPO_4 has formed (pH 8.3 to 10). The use of trinitrobenzene as an indicator shows the conversion to Na_3PO_4 (pH 12). In conformity with the results in the titrations, it is found that when the primary sodium phosphate is dissolved in water it reacts acidic (will effervesce carbonate), the secondary phosphate reacts slightly alkaline, and the tertiary phosphate is exceedingly alkaline. To explain the resultant acidity or alkalinity of the various sodium phosphates, the extent of ionization and hydrolysis of each anion must be considered. Primary sodium phosphate (NaH_2PO_4) ionizes according to the following equation (4).

(4) $NaH_2PO_4 \rightleftarrows Na^+ + H_2PO_4^-$

Sodium ion is so weak as a cation acid that its reaction with water (5) may be disregarded wherever it occurs. In the case of the di-

(5) $Na^+ + 2H_2O \rightleftarrows NaOH + H_3O^+$

[1] There is a disagreement in most textbooks as to the exact values but, in general and relatively speaking, they agree. These figures are from Handbook of Chemistry (Lange).

hydrogen phosphate ion the situation is different. It being amphiprotic, this ion can either ionize or hydrolyze (6) (7).

(6) $H_2PO_4^- + H_2O \rightleftarrows H_3O^+ + HPO_4^=$ (ionization reaction)

(7) $H_2PO_4^- + H_2O \rightleftarrows H_3PO_4 + OH^-$ (hydrolysis equation)

Actually, both reactions take place but the ionization reaction occurs to a greater extent than the hydrolysis reaction and the net result is an *acidic* solution (see sodium biphosphate).

Secondary sodium phosphate (Na_2HPO_4) ionizes according to the following equation (8).

(8) $Na_2HPO_4 \rightleftarrows 2Na^+ + HPO_4^=$

Again, the $HPO_4^=$ ionizes and hydrolyzes, but in this case the hydrolysis reaction (10) progresses to a greater extent than the ionization (9) with a resultant *alkalinity* in the solution (see Sorenson buffer).

(9) $HPO_4^= + H_2O \rightleftarrows H_3O^+ + PO_4^{\equiv}$ (ionization reaction).

(10) $HPO_4^= + H_2O \rightleftarrows H_2PO_4^- + OH^-$ (hydrolysis reaction).

Finally, tertiary sodium phosphate, if it exists in solution at all, will ionize in the following manner (11). The phosphate ion is

(11) $Na_3PO_4 \rightleftarrows 3Na^+ + PO_4^{\equiv}$

unable to ionize because it is lacking in hydrogen, but it does hydrolyze readily to yield a strong alkaline solution (12).

(12) $PO_4^{\equiv} + H_2O \rightleftarrows HPO_4^= + OH^-$

The phosphates of the alkali metals (and ammonium) and the dihydrogen phosphates of the alkaline earth metals are the only water-soluble phosphates. Under neutral conditions the alkaline earth metals and magnesium precipitate as the acid phosphates (13).

(13) $Na_2HPO_4 + MCl_2 \rightarrow MHPO_4 \downarrow + 2NaCl$ (M = Ca, Sr, Ba and Mg).

However, when an excess of ammonia is used in the above reaction, only the normal phosphate precipitates (14). To explain this

(14) $2Na_2HPO_4 + 3MCl_2 + 2NH_4OH \rightarrow M_3(PO_4)_2 \downarrow + 4NaCl + 2NH_4Cl + 2H_2O$

difference in reaction it is well to recall that, although the $HPO_4^=$ ion readily hydrolyzes to give some $H_2PO_4^-$ and OH^- (10), and that it also gives by ionization (9) some H_3O^+ and $PO_4^{\equiv}$, the greatest amount of ion by far is in the form of $HPO_4^=$. Thus, one would expect to get the $MHPO_4$ type of precipitate because the amount of phosphate ($PO_4^{\equiv}$) is too small to exceed the solubility product for the normal salt. On the other hand, when the solution is ammoniacal, the common ion effect brought about by added hydroxide ions represses the hydrolysis equation (10), and at the same time the added hydroxide ions promote the ionization reaction by using up the elaborated hydronium ions (15).

$$\text{(15)} \quad HPO_4^= + OH^- \rightleftarrows PO_4^\equiv + H_2O$$

By thus increasing the $PO_4^\equiv$ concentration the solubility product of the $M_3(PO_4)_2$ phosphate is exceeded and precipitation of the normal phosphate occurs.

In analytical determinations a special type of reaction is utilized especially with magnesium ion. As previously indicated, in a neutral solution the addition of secondary phosphate precipitates magnesium ion as $MgHPO_4$. However, addition of secondary phosphate ion to magnesia mixture T.S. (containing $MgCl_2$, NH_4Cl, and ammonia water) results in a precipitate of $MgNH_4PO_4 . 6H_2O$ (16). In this

$$\text{(16)} \quad Mg^{++} + NH_4^+ + PO_4^\equiv + 6H_2O \rightarrow MgNH_4PO_4 . 6H_2O \downarrow$$

case, the ammonium ions contributed by the ammonium chloride repress the ionization of ammonium hydroxide by a common ion effect thus effectively decreasing the concentration of hydroxide ion that would normally precipitate some of the magnesium as $Mg(OH)_2$. The ammonium hydroxide nevertheless supplies sufficient hydroxide ions to repress hydrolysis of $HPO_4^=$ to $H_2PO_4^-$ and at the same time promotes formation of $PO_4^\equiv$ by the reaction given in (15). Thus, the solubility product of $MgNH_4PO_4$ is exceeded and as a result its precipitation occurs as the hexahydrate. Acidification of this precipitate permits formation of the dihydrogen phosphate which is soluble and the precipitate is thus solubilized.

Aluminum and ferric salts are precipitated directly as the normal phosphates, $AlPO_4$ and $FePO_4$ respectively in the presence of secondary phosphate. Presumably, the great insolubility and very low solubility products of these precipitates result in a continuous removal of $PO_4^\equiv$ as the normal salts, thereby continuously disturbing the equilibrium until all of the phosphate ion is removed as the insoluble salt. The same sequence of events is responsible in the official test for identity for the precipitation of silver phosphate in which a solution of the secondary phosphate (obtained by neutralizing phosphoric acid with sodium hydroxide using phenolphthalein as an indicator) is treated with silver nitrate. Because of the low solubility product of Ag_3PO_4 it precipitates as the normal salt rather than as an intermediate acid salt. The precipitate is soluble in nitric acid because the hydronium ions from the nitric acid combine with the hydroxide ions obtained by hydrolysis of phosphate ion elaborated by the precipitate. This disturbs the equilibrium and causes more silver phosphate to ionize and the procedure continues until the precipitate dissolves completely. The silver phosphate precipitate is also soluble in ammonia, but by a different mechanism. In this case the silver ions resulting from the slight ionization of silver phosphate are taken up as the relatively non-ionized silver-diammino complex (17) which process disturbs the equilibrium and causes more silver ions to be ionized and again the process continues until the precipitate is dissolved.

(17) $Ag^+ + 2NH_3 \rightleftarrows [Ag(NH_3)_2]^+$

Orthophosphoric acid, when heated to 200° C. loses a mole of water to form pyrophosphoric acid (18) which for purposes of study may be considered to be an *inter*molecular dehydration.

$$(18)\ 2HO{-}\!\!\!\overset{HO}{\underset{HO}{\diagdown}}\!\!\!P{\rightarrow}O \overset{\Delta}{\rightarrow} O{\leftarrow}\overset{\overset{\displaystyle HO}{|}}{\underset{\underset{\displaystyle HO}{|}}{P}}{-}O{-}\overset{\overset{\displaystyle OH}{|}}{\underset{\underset{\displaystyle OH}{|}}{P}}{\rightarrow}O + H_2O$$

When heated to about 300° C., the pyrophosphoric acid is converted to metaphosphoric acid (19).

(19) $H_4P_2O_7 \overset{\Delta}{\rightarrow} 2HPO_3 + H_2O$

However, to simplify the presentation and to fix it more firmly in the student's mind it is convenient to consider that when ortho-phosphoric acid is heated to 300° C. (neglect the formation of pyro-phosphoric acid) an *intra*molecular dehydration takes place (20).

$$(20)\ \boxed{\overset{HO}{\underset{HO}{H{\mid}O}}}{\diagup}\!\!P{\rightarrow}O \rightarrow HO{-}\overset{\overset{\displaystyle O}{||}}{P}{\rightarrow}O + H_2O$$

Metaphosphoric acid constitutes the "glacial phosphoric acid" of commerce. It is usually sold in the form of sticks or pellets, the metaphosphoric acid having been hardened by the addition of small amounts of sodium metaphosphate ($NaPO_3$). Because solutions of this acid slowly change to H_3PO_4 (21) they are impossible to keep and, therefore, are no longer officially recognized.

(21) $HPO_3 + H_2O \rightarrow H_3PO_4$

It is of interest to note that phosphoric acid has no oxidizing properties, thus enabling its use wherever a non-oxidizing acid is required (*e.g.*, to prepare HBr from NaBr, where H_2SO_4 is unsatisfactory because of its oxidizing action).

Phosphoric Acid is assayed by titrating a weighed sample with 1 N sodium hydroxide using phenolphthalein as an indicator. When a solution of phosphoric acid is titrated with sodium hydroxide the indicator changes color when two of the three replaceable hydrogens are taken up by sodium hydroxide to form disodium hydrogen phosphate (22). Immediately upon forming, of course, the disodium

$$(22) \ H_3PO_4 + 2NaOH \rightarrow Na_2HPO_4 + 2H_2O$$

salt ionizes in the usual manner (8). The $HPO_4^=$ ion hydrolyzes as previously indicated (10) yielding hydroxide ions which are in sufficient concentration to cause phenolphthalein to change color before all of the phosphoric acid is neutralized. To repress the hydrolysis use is made of sodium chloride. This supplies an excess of Na^+ causing the ionization process to be reversed by common ion effect and thus effectively reducing the OH^- concentration.

Official Tests for Identity.—1. Orthophosphoric acid responds to all general tests for acids.

2. When phosphoric acid is carefully neutralized with potassium hydroxide test solution and a solution of silver nitrate added, a characteristic yellow precipitate of silver phosphate results (23, 24, 25). The precipitate is soluble in ammonium hydroxide and in nitric acid.

$$(23) \ 3H_3O^+ + PO_4^{\equiv} + 2OH^- \rightarrow HPO_4^= + 5H_2O \text{ (neutralization).}$$

$$(24) \ HPO_4^= + H_2O \rightleftarrows H_3O^+ + PO_4^{\equiv}$$

$$(25) \ PO_4^{\equiv} + 3Ag^+ \rightleftarrows Ag_3PO_4 \downarrow$$

Free orthophosphoric acid forms no precipitate with a solution of silver nitrate.

3. Orthophosphoric acid produces a canary yellow colored precipitate when digested at 40° C. with ammonium molybdate solution (nitric acid solution) (26). The precipitate of ammonium phosphomolybdate is insoluble in acids but readily soluble in ammonia water (27) and sodium hydroxide T.S.

$$(26) \ 12(NH_4)_2MoO_4 + H_3PO_4 + 21HNO_3$$
$$\rightarrow (NH_4)_3PO_4.12MoO_3 \downarrow + 21NH_4NO_3 + 12H_2O$$

$$(27) \ (NH_4)_3PO_4.12MoO_3 + 23OH^- \rightarrow 3NH_4^+ + HPO_4^= + 12MoO_4^= + 11H_2O$$

4. If 3 ml. of the phosphoric acid dilution is rendered alkaline with ammonia water and magnesium sulfate test solution added, a white crystalline precipitate of magnesium ammonium phosphate is produced (28).

$$(28) \ PO_4^{\equiv} + Mg^{++} + NH_4^+ + 6H_2O \rightarrow MgNH_4PO_4.6H_2O \downarrow$$

If the dried precipitate of magnesium ammonium phosphate is heated, magnesium pyrophosphate results (29).

$$(29) \ 2MgNH_4PO_4.6H_2O \xrightarrow{\Delta} Mg_2P_2O_7 + 2NH_3 \uparrow + 13H_2O \uparrow$$

5. When a precipitate of magnesium ammonium phosphate is dissolved in diluted acetic acid and silver nitrate test solution added, a yellow precipitate of silver phosphate is formed (distinction from metaphosphoric or pyrophosphoric acid).

Commercial Manufacture.—Orthophosphoric acid is now prepared by (1) the "wet process" and (2) the pyrolytic or thermal methods.

1. Ground phosphate rock or bone ash (principally $Ca_3(PO_4)_2$) is treated with sulfuric acid (30) and filtered to remove calcium sulfate and other insoluble materials. The filtrate of dilute phosphoric acid is then concentrated in simple evaporators to about 50 per cent H_3PO_4 (31). The acid made by this process is not of food grade or pharmaceutical purity unless it is put through a relatively costly purification process. This is used as a constituent of mixed fertilizers.

$$(30)\ Ca_3(PO_4)_2 + 3H_2SO_4 \rightarrow 2H_3PO_4 + 3CaSO_4$$
$$(31)\ Ca_3(PO_4)_2 + 4H_3PO_4 \rightleftarrows 3CaH_4(PO_4)_2$$

2. The greatest advances in phosphoric acid manufacture in the chemical industry have been through the development of the thermal methods. The thermal process consists in smelting phosphate rock with coke and silica at high temperatures (32). A continuous evolution of phosphorus vapor and carbon monoxide issues from the furnace, and they are either burned to produce P_2O_5 (33) and CO_2 (34) or else, more recently, the elemental phosphorus is condensed as such. When P_2O_5 is the product, it is dissolved in water to form phosphoric acid (35).

$$(32)\ Ca_3(PO_4)_2 + 3SiO_2 + 5C + heat \rightarrow 3CaSiO_3 + 5CO\uparrow + 2P\uparrow$$
$$(33)\ 4P + 5O_2\ (air) \rightarrow 2P_2O_5$$
$$(34)\ 2CO + O_2\ (air) \rightarrow 2CO_2$$
$$(35)\ P_2O_5 + 3H_2O \rightarrow 2H_3PO_4$$

Most of the acid used in chemical manufacturing is prepared by the electric furnace, and is obtainable in the standard concentrations of industrial phosphoric acid, namely, 50, 75 and 85 per cent. Acid of greater strength than 100 per cent is also prepared and is analogous to fuming sulfuric acid or fuming nitric acid.

Pharmacology of the Phosphate Ion.—Phosphates are highly important to the body. The average person does not require added phosphate in the diet to provide for his requirements because as a rule the diet supplies the necessary amount of phosphate ion. In addition, it is doubtful whether simple phosphate administration would serve to correct any condition serious enough to derange the phosphate balance in the body. Among the roles that phosphate plays in the body economy may be mentioned: (1) action as one of the buffer systems for maintaining acid-base balance, (2) integral part in the metabolism of carbohydrates, (3) combination with calcium to form calcium phosphate for bone formation, (4) regulation of calcium metabolism and level in the blood.

The maintenance of acid-base balance by the phosphate buffer system of $Na_2HPO_4:NaH_2PO_4$ is not as important as the $NaHCO_3:H_2CO_3$ system, but nevertheless still plays a significant role in the regulation of body pH. It is especially adapted to taking care of acidic substances and, although slow, it is probably the most efficient because it guards the alkali reserve. The probable mechanism is by transformation of disodium phosphate by the kidney to the monosodium form with the consequent saving of 1 equivalent of alkali for the body (36). The buffer mixture is said to be com-

(36) $Na_2HPO_4 + H_3O^+ \rightleftarrows NaH_2PO_4 + H_2O + Na^+$

posed of approximately 80 per cent of the disodium salt and 20 per cent of the monosodium salt.

A discussion of the role of phosphates in the intermediary metabolism of carbohydrates is beyond the scope of this text. Suffice it to say, however, that the phosphate residue is utilized in the phosphorylation of simple monohexoses to render them capable of being oxidized and transformed by enzymatic processes into a utilizable form of energy. Likewise, the discussion of bone formation, regulation of calcium metabolism and calcium blood level should be treated in texts on physiological chemistry and biochemistry (see, pharmacological action of calcium ion). There is a very close inverse relationship between the level of calcium and that of phosphate in the blood. Observations show that when blood calcium is high, the phosphate value is low and vice versa. This is probably due to an ionic equilibrium existing between the various phosphate salts of calcium, namely, $Ca(H_2PO_4)_2$, $CaHPO_4$ and $Ca_3(PO_4)_2$. Excessive intake of phosphate tends to drive the equilibrium to the formation of insoluble normal calcium phosphate which deposits in the bones. On the other hand, administration of salts that reduce the calcium content of the blood, e.g., oxalates or fluorides, or of acidifying salts tends to cause reversion of bone calcium phosphate to the more soluble calcium phosphates with a consequent rise in phosphate value as contrasted to a low calcium value.

Some years ago, in connection with leg cramps occurring in pregnant women it was recognized that phosphates are preferentially absorbed to calcium and thus establish a calcium deficiency. Treatment of leg cramps due to a lack of calcium has created a demand for phosphorus-free calcium pharmaceuticals.

Because inorganic phosphates administered orally are only slowly absorbed from the alimentary canal, large doses will act as saline cathartics of the osmotic type (see uses of sodium phosphate). Phosphates although slowly absorbed are best absorbed from an acid condition in the bowels, whereas alkaline conditions and conditions in which excess calcium is present in the intestines will retard the absorption of phosphate. The phosphate ion that is absorbed has little or no physiological action and is excreted mainly in the urine. Because phosphate is somewhat absorbed the administration of substantial amounts of sodium biphosphate will result in an acid urine, and it is used for this purpose (see uses of sodium biphosphate).

Uses.—*Phosphoric Acid*, N.F. XII, should contain not less than 85 per cent and not more than 88 per cent of H_3PO_4. It is used to a very limited extent (hydrochloric acid is better) in medicine as a tonic and stimulant to the gastric mucous membranes. It aids proteolytic enzymes in the formation of peptones. It was a constituent of *Glycerinated Gentian Elixir*, N.F. XI.

Phosphoric Acid in a diluted form is used in the treatment of lead poisoning because it lowers the pH of the blood, promoting (1) decalcification of the bones and (2) the associated excretion of lead from the bones at the same time. It is particularly well suited for this type of lead-poisoning treatment (deleading the body) because at the same time that it brings about a beneficial acidosis it also furnishes the lead-solubilizing phosphate ion. In a solution with an acid pH the lead tends to form a soluble lead phosphate salt rather than remaining as insoluble tertiary lead phosphate.

Diluted Phosphoric Acid, N.F. XII, should contain, in each 100 ml., not less than 9.5 Gm. and not more than 10.5 Gm. of H_3PO_4. It is prepared by mixing 69 ml. of Phosphoric Acid with sufficient Purified Water to make 1000 ml. Diluted Phosphoric Acid is given in doses of from 0.1 to 1 ml., largely diluted with water for the purposes discussed under *Phosphoric Acid*. No official dose is given.

Important Non-offical Acids

Nitric Acid, N.F.X, HNO_3, is mentioned in the "De Inventione Veritatis" ascribed to Geber in the eighth century. It was made by calcining a mixture of niter, alum and blue vitriol. Nitric acid was described by Albert le Grand in the thirteenth century, and later by Raimon Lull. The latter obtained it by heating potassium nitrate and clay, and he called the product "eau forte" (strong water). The character of nitric acid was not determined until the eighteenth century, when A. L. Lavoisier (1776) proved that it contained oxygen. In 1784 H. Cavendish determined its constitution and showed that it could be made by electrical discharges through moist air. About 1684 Glauber devised the process of distillation of niter with concentrated sulfuric acid. Since about 1930, the Ostwald process of ammonia oxidation has become the most important method of manufacture.

This acid exists to a slight extent in some waters, the air (after a thunderstorm) and in the humus of the soil. In combination with sodium, potassium, ammonium, magnesium and calcium, nitric acid occurs widely distributed in Nature. When animal or vegetable matter decomposes, ammonia and other nitrogenous products result. Through the agency of nitrifying bacteria, these products of putrefaction are oxidized to nitric acid, which in turn reacts with the mineral constituents of the soil to form nitrates. These nitrates occur in immense deposits (some being 5 feet thick, 2 miles wide, and 220 miles long) containing from 20 to 60 per cent of sodium nitrate in rainless desert regions of Peru and Chilean Bolivia. Smaller deposits of potassium nitrate, or Bengal saltpeter, occur in Spain, the trans-Caspian region, India, Iran and other oriental countries.

Hydrogen nitrate (anhydrous HNO_3 or 100 per cent) is a colorless, mobile, strongly fuming liquid. It has a specific gravity of 1.502 at $\frac{20}{4}$° and boils at 86° C. At this temperature it begins to decompose into water, oxygen and nitrogen dioxide (1).

$$\text{(1)}\quad 4HNO_3 \xrightarrow{\ 86°C.\ } 4NO_2\uparrow + 2H_2O + O_2\uparrow$$

Hydrogen nitrate may be converted to a solid with a melting-point of −42° C. Concentrated nitric acid forms a constant boiling mixture with water. This mixture boils at 121.6° C. (251° F.), contains 67 to 71 per cent weight to weight of HNO_3, and has a specific gravity of 1.41 at 25° C. An azeotropic mixture is formed of water and nitric acid that makes it quite difficult to obtain higher than 68 per cent acid. It is exceedingly hygroscopic and corrosive. On mixing nitric acid with water there is a rise in temperature and a contraction in volume. It is miscible in all proportions with water. All salts of nitric acid (nitrates) are soluble in water. Fuming nitric acid is any nitric acid over 86 per cent weight to weight of HNO_3 that contains oxides of nitrogen. Red fuming nitric acid is a high-strength acid containing 10 to 15 per cent of oxides of nitrogen.

The chemical properties of nitric acid may conveniently be classified in three groups: (1) acidic properties, (2) oxidizing properties, (3) nitrating properties.

1. Hydrogen nitrate, when dissolved in water, is highly ionized, and is therefore a strong acid (2).

$$\text{(2)}\quad HNO_3 + H_2O \rightarrow H_3O^+ + NO_3^-$$

Because of this property it neutralizes bases just as does any other substance capable of forming hydronium ions (3).

$$\text{(3)}\quad OH^- + H_3O^+ \rightarrow 2H_2O$$

11

Whenever it can exhibit its property of reacting with a metal oxide to form the nitrate without effecting an oxidation it is again apparent that its activity is that of an acid (4).

(4) $ZnO + 2HNO_3 \rightarrow Zn(NO_3)_2 + H_2O$

2. Nitric acid acts as an oxidizing agent on both metals and non-metals in many cases, even in *very dilute solutions*. Although there is little argument about its oxidizing abilities it is a little known fact that the oxidizing action in most cases is the result of the enhancing action of small amounts of nitrous acid which are usually present (by action of heat and sunlight on HNO_3). It attacks all common metals except gold and platinum under favorable conditions. The manner in which it reacts with metals is greatly influenced by the concentration of the acid, and also by the position of the metal in the electromotive series with respect to hydrogen. For example, when copper (below hydrogen in the electromotive series) is dissolved in *concentrated* nitric acid the main by-product is NO_2 (5).

(5) $Cu + 4HNO_3 \rightarrow Cu(NO_3)_2 + 2H_2O + 2NO_2 \uparrow$

However, the *dilute* acid gives as the main by-product nitric oxide (NO) (6).

(6) $3Cu + 8HNO_3 \rightarrow 3Cu(NO_3)_2 + 2NO \uparrow + 4H_2O$

It is not surprising that the above reactions take place because if NO did form in the first reaction (5) it would necessarily bubble through concentrated acid on its way out of solution and would very likely be oxidized to NO_2 (7).

(7) $NO + 2HNO_3 \rightarrow 3NO_2 \uparrow + H_2O$

If one adds equation (7) to equation (6) it is readily apparent that equation (5) results.

On the other hand, if zinc (above H in the electromotive series) is treated with *concentrated* acid it yields ammonia combined as ammonium nitrate (8) (see also copper and iron).

(8) $4Zn + 10HNO_3 \rightarrow 4Zn(NO_3)_2 + 3H_2O + NH_4NO_3$

The *dilute* acid with zinc yields principally nitrous oxide (N_2O) (9).

(9) $4Zn + 10HNO_3 \rightarrow 4Zn(NO_3)_2 + 5H_2O + N_2O \uparrow$

These reactions may be explained by the fact that hydrogen would be formed by any acid reacting on a metal above hydrogen in the electromotive series (10).

(10) $Zn + 2HNO_3 \rightarrow Zn(NO_3)_2 + H_2 \uparrow$

However, this hydrogen is a strong reducing agent and is in contact with nitric acid (a strong oxidizing agent) thus effecting a more or less complete reduction of the nitric acid, yielding in one case NH_3 (11), and in the other N_2O (12).

(11) $2HNO_3 + 4H_2 \rightarrow NH_4NO_3 + 3H_2O$

(12) $2HNO_3 + 4H_2 \rightarrow N_2O \uparrow + 5H_2O$

If equation (11) is added to equation (10) the result is equation (8), illustrating the action of concentrated nitric acid on Zn. Likewise, if equation (12) be added to equation (10), the result is equation (9), which expresses the reaction of dilute nitric acid on Zn.

Non-metals are also readily attacked by nitric acid as illustrated by these typical equations (13, 14).

(13) $S + 2HNO_3 \rightarrow H_2SO_4 + 2NO \uparrow$

(14) $3P + 5HNO_3 + 2H_2O \rightarrow 3H_3PO_4 + 5NO \uparrow$

3. Nitric acid is utilized extensively as a nitrating agent for organic compounds, usually in the form of "mixed acid" (nitric acid and sulfuric acid mixed in varying proportions at the acid plant for any specific nitrating job). It is used to nitrate toluene in the preparation of trinitrotoluene (TNT). The purpose of the sulfuric acid in "mixed acid" is to bind the water formed in the nitrating reaction, thus preventing dilution of the nitric acid. The group $-NO_2$ is a *nitro group*. Nitric acid stains woolen fabrics and animal tissues yellow because substances high in protein, *e.g.*, egg albumen, skin, hair, silk, etc., are acted upon by nitric acid, forming a yellow nitro compound known as *xanthoprotein*.

Nitric acid is assayed by titrating a weighed sample with 1 N sodium hydroxide using methyl red as an indicator (15).

(15) $HNO_3 + NaOH \rightarrow NaNO_3 + H_2O$

Nitric acid responds to the several tests for nitrates. Perhaps the most common is the so-called "brown-ring test" which is carried out as follows.

Mix the diluted nitric acid or solution of a nitrate with an equal volume of concentrated sulfuric acid and allow to cool. Now add a concentrated solution of ferrous sulfate in such a way that the two liquids do not mix. In the presence of nitric acid or a nitrate, a purple ring, changing to brown, will form at the junction of the two liquids (16, 17).

(16) $6FeSO_4 + 2HNO_3 + 3H_2SO_4 \rightarrow 2NO + 3Fe_2(SO_4)_3 + 4H_2O$

(17) $FeSO_4 + NO \rightarrow FeSO_4 \cdot NO$

This test is commonly known as the "brown ring" test. The composition of the brown material ($FeSO_4 \cdot NO$) is not known with certainty and equation (17), therefore, is not necessarily an accurate representation of what takes place.

Nitric acid may be prepared commercially by (1) treatment of Chile saltpeter with sulfuric acid or (2) by the oxidation of ammonia.

1. Until about 1930, a great proportion of nitric acid production was based on this method. At the present time the oxidation of ammonia accounts for almost all of the nitric acid produced. Chile saltpeter ($NaNO_3$) is treated with sulfuric acid (a non-volatile acid) forming hydrogen nitrate (18).

(18) $NaNO_3 + H_2SO_4 \rightarrow NaHSO_4 + HNO_3$

2. As previously pointed out, approximately 90 per cent of the world production of nitric acid is by the ammonia oxidation process. The ammonia is prepared on a large scale through the Haber Process or some modification of it (19). The oxidation of the ammonia is accomplished by the *Ostwald Process*, in which ammonia is mixed with air (21 per cent of O_2), the mixture heated and rapidly passed through a fine wire gauze of activated platinum raised to a glowing heat. Better than 95 per cent of the ammonia is oxidized to NO, and then to NO_2 (20, 21), which is absorbed by water to form nitric acid (22).

(19) $N_2 + 3H_2 \rightarrow 2NH_3$
(20) $4NH_3 + 5O_2 \rightarrow 4NO + 6H_2O$
(21) $2NO + O_2 \rightarrow 2NO_2$
(22) $3NO_2 + H_2O \rightarrow 2HNO_3 + NO$

The only disadvantage of this method is that due to an azeotropic mixture it produces nitric acid of only 61 to 65 per cent concentrations, whereas for many industrial operations an acid of 98 to 99 per cent concentration is required. However, methods have been devised to concentrate the dilute acid to any specified concentration by mixing with sulfuric acid and collecting the nearly pure HNO_3. Nitric acid is used in the manufacture of sulfuric acid (*q.v.*), coal-tar dyes, explosives, nitrates, etc. It was used as an oxidizing agent in the manufacture of pharmaceutical preparations (Ferric Sulfate Solution, Mercuric Nitrate Ointment, etc.), and externally to destroy chancres, warts, and phagedenic ulcers (rapidly spreading and sloughing ulcers). It is rarely, if ever, prescribed for internal use, although nitric acid is a suitable substitute for hydrochloric acid in gastric achlorhydria.

Nitric acid is a highly corrosive liquid. In contact with the skin, mucous membranes, eyes, gastrointestinal tract or respiratory mucosa in liquid form (as a spray or splash) or as a vapor, the acid penetrates the tissues, causing destruction proportionate to the concentration of the solution or vapor and the duration of contact. It is imperative that the acid be removed from the skin or other surface by copious flushing with water to prevent damage.

The corrosive properties of nitric acid are not the only dangers, since the gases evolved (nitrous fumes) from spillage on heavy metals or organic materials are also exceedingly toxic. Since the gaseous oxides may cause little or no discomfort *at the time of inhalation*, the victim may proceed about his ordinary work for a few hours until the damage to the lung tissue becomes apparent. Untreated cases frequently terminate fatally as a result of severe pulmonary congestion (edema), *i.e.*, from suffocation.

It is used as a nitrating agent in *Pyroxylin*, as a source of nitrate ion in *Bismuth Magma* and, formerly, as an oxidizing agent in the preparation of *Ferric Subsulfate Solution.*

Pharmacology of the Nitrate Ion.—The nitrate ion does not enjoy the therapeutic usage that certain other anions do, *e.g.*, iodide, bromide, etc. It has no specific action in the body. However, it is used in relatively large doses as the potassium and ammonium salts for a diuretic effect. The ammonium salt is an acid-producing salt by virtue of the fact that the ammonium ion is converted to urea and the acid portion of the molecule (which may be pictured as transient nitric acid in the blood) serves to lower the alkaline reserve thus inducing acidosis. On the other hand potassium nitrate is a neutral salt but according to some investigators is the most potent diuretic of all the salts. Its action is probably by upsetting the ionic balance of the blood and tissue fluids.

As is true with any of the diuretic salts, renal insufficiency is a definite contraindication to their use because without renal excretion they accumulate in the body. Also, these salts tend to be irritating to the stomach in the large doses necessary for diuretic action. This is best overcome by the administration of enteric coated tablets.

The administration of certain nitrates, *e.g.*, bismuth subnitrate, is attended by the formation of nitrites due to the action of intestinal bacteria. As a source of nitrites for therapeutic use this procedure is probably not the best.

The burning of nitrates together with stramonium or belladonna is said to result in the formation of nitrites in the smoke which is inhaled for the relief of asthma. This usage is of doubtful value.

Sulfuric Acid, N.F. X, H_2SO_4, was known to the alchemists in 1440. Basil Valentine prepared an acid, which he called "oil of vitriol," by heating anhydrous copperas to a high temperature and dissolving the evolved gas in water. Joshua Ward (1685–1761) prepared the same substance by deflagrating a mixture of sodium nitrate and sulfur in large, glass bell jars, absorbing the gases in water and concentrating the solution. Dr. John Roebuck (1718–1794) replaced the glass jars with leaden ones. In 1777, Lavoisier showed that this acid contained sulfur and oxygen, and in 1795 Richter determined its composition. Sulfuric acid in the free state is rarely found in Nature, but it occurs widely distributed in combination with calcium, magnesium, etc.

Hydrogen sulfate (100 per cent pure) is a colorless, odorless, hygroscopic liquid of oily consistency, having a specific gravity of 1.834 at 15° C. It freezes to a colorless, crystalline mass melting at 10.5° C.

The N.F. X described Sulfuric Acid as a colorless, odorless liquid of oily consistency containing not less than 94 per cent and not more than 98 per cent of H_2SO_4. When strongly heated the acid is vaporized giving off dense, white fumes of SO_3. It dissolves in both water and alcohol with the evolution of much heat.

The usual reagent grade of sulfuric acid contains not less than 95.5 per cent H_2SO_4 and has a specific gravity of not less than 1.84 at 15.56° C. (60° F.).

Even at the boiling-point of water, sulfuric acid is not volatilized and therefore is classed as a *non-volatile* acid.

The chemical properties of sulfuric acid may be considered as follows: (1) stability, (2) hydration, (3) acid properties, (4) oxidizing properties, (5) sulfonating and sulfating properties, and (6) other properties.

1. When heated, pure H_2SO_4 is resolved into SO_3 and H_2O (1). The reaction is reversible.

$$(1) \quad H_2SO_4 \rightleftharpoons H_2O + SO_3$$

As the heat is slowly increased, pure H_2SO_4 loses increasing amounts of SO_3 and H_2O, but not in equimolecular amounts (more SO_3 is lost than H_2O). Eventually, at a temperature of 338° C. the H_2SO_4 distills over constantly, with about 30 per cent of the acid in the dissociated form (1). When the dissociated portion is cooled, it reunites to form a 98.33 per cent solution of H_2SO_4. However, when the temperature is increased to 420° C. the dissociation of H_2SO_4 into SO_3 and H_2O is practically complete.

When H_2SO_4 is suddenly raised to red heat, it is completely decomposed into H_2O, SO_2 and O_2 (2).

$$(2) \quad 2H_2SO_4 \overset{\Delta}{\rightarrow} 2H_2O \uparrow + 2SO_2 \uparrow + O_2 \uparrow$$

2. Sulfuric acid should *always be added to water* whenever solutions (dilutions) of it are to be made. This precaution should also be observed with other diluents because the amount of heat generated when the two are mixed may cause splashing of the acid. It is believed that the reason for the development of heat is a hydration reaction (3).

$$(3) \quad H_2SO_4 + nH_2O \rightarrow H_2SO_4 \cdot nH_2O$$

The reasons for the above supposition are (1) that a mixture of sulfuric acid and water occupies less volume than would be expected from a simple mixture of two unreacting liquids (in which the volume should be additive), and (2) several compounds of H_2SO_4

have been isolated, namely $H_2SO_4.SO_3$, $H_2SO_4.H_2O$, $H_2SO_4.2H_2O$ and $H_2SO_4.4H_2O$. There is some question as to the manner in which these compounds should be regarded, that is, whether they are hydrates of SO_3 or of H_2SO_4. The proponents of the first form infer, for example, that H_2SO_4 is simply a hydrate of SO_3 ($SO_3.H_2O$). If the hydrates are considered in this manner we have:

$$2SO_3.H_2O = H_2SO_4.SO_3.H_2O$$
$$SO_3.H_2O = H_2SO_4$$
$$SO_3.2H_2O = H_2SO_4.H_2O$$
etc.

The tendency for sulfuric acid to take up water is so great that it abstracts the elements of water from many compounds containing hydrogen and oxygen. A typical example is the charring of sugar (4).

$$(4)\ C_6H_{12}O_6 \rightarrow 6C + 6H_2O$$

Because of its affinity for water, care should be taken not to leave concentrated sulfuric acid exposed to the atmosphere for long periods of time because there is danger that it will take up enough moisture from the air to overflow the vessel in which it is stored.

3. Sulfuric acid, particularly in dilute aqueous solutions, behaves as a strong diprotic acid. It ionizes in two steps (5).

$$(5)\ H_2SO_4 + H_2O \rightarrow H_3O^+ + HSO_4^- \quad K_1 = 4 \times 10^{-1}\ (?)$$
$$HSO_4^- + H_2O \rightarrow H_3O^+ + SO_4^= \quad K_2 = 2 \times 10^{-2}$$

It is capable, through the hydronium ion, of dissolving metals *above* hydrogen in the electromotive series with the formation of hydrogen and the sulfate of the metal (6).

$$(6)\ Zn + H_2SO_4\ (dil.) \rightarrow ZnSO_4 + H_2 \uparrow$$

Although the reaction between dilute sulfuric acid and zinc can be construed |to be an oxidizing action (zinc to zinc ion [$Zn \rightarrow Zn^{++}$]), this is true of all acids (oxidizing and non-oxidizing) because of the hydronium-ion content. The rate of solution in an acid of a metal above hydrogen in the electromotive series is directly dependent upon the hydronium-ion concentration. Sulfuric acid is classed as a "strong" acid although it is not as strong as hydrochloric or nitric acid.

Sulfuric acid will also react in the ordinary manner with metal oxides, hydroxides, carbonates and sulfites.

4. *Hot* concentrated solutions of sulfuric acid exhibit an oxidizing action on metals, non-metals and many compounds.

The action on metals *above* hydrogen in the electromotive series has been described.

Metals *below* hydrogen also dissolve in sulfuric acid but sulfur dioxide (SO_2) is liberated instead of hydrogen (7).

(7) $Hg + 2H_2SO_4 \rightarrow HgSO_4 + SO_2 \uparrow + 2H_2O$

It is convenient to assume that the sulfuric acid first oxidizes the metal to the oxide (8) which then reacts with the sulfuric acid to give the sulfate (9). (See also copper.)

(8) $Hg + H_2SO_4 \rightarrow HgO + SO_2 \uparrow + H_2O$

(9) $HgO + H_2SO_4 \rightarrow HgSO_4 + H_2O$

The sum total of equations (8) and (9) is, of course, equation (7).

Non-metals are oxidized more or less readily by sulfuric acid, liberating sulfur dioxide in the process (10, 11).

(10) $2H_2SO_4 + S \rightarrow 3SO_2 \uparrow + 2H_2O$

(11) $2H_2SO_4 + C \rightarrow 2SO_2 \uparrow + CO_2 \uparrow + 2H_2O$

Among the compounds which are readily oxidized by sulfuric acid are the hydrogen halides (with the exception of HCl). It will be recalled that neither HBr nor HI could be prepared by the action of sulfuric acid on the corresponding sodium halide because the hydrogen halide formed is readily oxidized. This oxidation takes place at room temperature (12, 13). (See also preparation of HI.)

(12) $H_2SO_4 + 2HBr \rightarrow Br_2 + SO_2 \uparrow + 2H_2O$

(13) $H_2SO_4 + 8HI \rightarrow H_2S \uparrow + 4I_2 + 4H_2O$

5. Concentrated sulfuric acid is used as a *sulfonating* agent in many organic reactions, because it is capable of replacing a hydrogen attached to carbon (14).

(14) $R-\boxed{H} + \boxed{HO}-SO_3H \rightarrow R-SO_3H + H_2O$

$$R = \text{aromatic or aliphatic}$$

The process is called *sulfonation* and the product is a *sulfonic acid.* Sulfonations are also carried out with concentrated sulfuric acid to which has been added varying amounts of SO_3. These fortified acids are known as "oleums" or fuming sulfuric acids.

Sulfation is a characteristic reaction of sulfuric acid, forming monoalkyl sulfates and dialkyl sulfates. When the acid is added to an alcohol at room temperature a monoalkyl sulfate is usually formed (15).

(15) $R-\boxed{OH} + \boxed{H}O{\Large\diagdown}_{HO}{\diagup}SO_2 \rightarrow {RO\diagdown}_{HO}{\diagup}SO_2 + H_2O$

The dialkyl sulfates are formed by passing the alcohol and acid vapors over a suitable catalyst (16).

$$(16) \quad 2ROH + \begin{array}{c} HO \\ \diagdown \\ HO \diagup \end{array} SO_2 \rightarrow \begin{array}{c} RO \\ \diagdown \\ RO \diagup \end{array} SO_2 + 2H_2O$$

6. As previously stated, sulfur trioxide dissolves in concentrated sulfuric acid to form a somewhat viscous liquid, called "oleum" or fuming sulfuric acid (also Nordhausen acid). Fuming sulfuric acid may contain any specified amount of SO_3. When cooled, the fuming acid deposits crystals of disulfuric acid ($H_2S_2O_7$) which are thought to be formed according to the following reaction (17):

$$(17) \quad H_2SO_4 + SO_3 \rightleftarrows H_2S_2O_7$$

Of course, disulfuric acid may also be considered as $H_2SO_4 . SO_3$ or $H_2O . 2SO_3$.

Sulfuric acid forms two series of salts because of its two replaceable hydrogens. Thus, for example, we have an acid sodium sulfate ($NaHSO_4$) and a normal sodium sulfate (Na_2SO_4).

Most sulfates of the metals are soluble with the notable exception of Ba. Sr. and Pb. In addition, the Ca, Ag, and Hg(ous) salts are only somewhat soluble. A few will hydrolyze in aqueous solution to form basic salts (bismuth, antimony, and iron) but are stable in acid solution. The salts of sulfuric acid, sulfates, in solution have no oxidizing ability. In the dry state with strong reducing agents (carbon), oxidation occurs on heating.

Acid sulfates (bisulfates) are known for the alkali metals. Bisulfates of other metals are quite unusual.

Sulfuric Acid is assayed by the titration of a weighed sample diluted with water using 1 N sodium hydroxide to carry out the titration. Methyl red is used as an indicator.

The principal tests for identifying sulfates in general are: 1. If barium chloride T.S. is added to a dilute solution of sulfuric acid (or a soluble sulfate) a white precipitate of barium sulfate ($BaSO_4$) is formed (18).

$$(18) \quad H_2SO_4 + BaCl_2 \rightarrow BaSO_4 \downarrow + 2HCl$$

2. If dilute sulfuric acid (or a soluble sulfate) is treated with lead acetate T.S. a white precipitate forms (19) which is soluble in ammonium acetate T.S.

$$(19) \quad (CH_3COO)_2Pb + H_2SO_4 \rightarrow PbSO_4 \downarrow + 2CH_3COOH$$

3. Hydrochloric acid produces no precipitate with sulfates. This distinguishes them from thiosulfates which do give precipitates (20).

$$(20) \quad Na_2SO_4 + HCl \rightarrow \text{no reaction}$$

but

$$Na_2S_2O_3 + 2HCl \rightarrow S \downarrow + SO_2 \uparrow + 2NaCl + H_2O$$

Sulfuric acid is manufactured[1] by two methods: (1) the *lead chamber process*, and (2) the *contact* or *catalytic process*. In both processes sulfur (or of lesser importance, iron pyrites) is converted to SO_2 by oxidation. However, the manner in which the SO_2 is converted into sulfuric acid differs greatly in the two processes.

1. *The lead chamber process* is the older of the two processes, and it has been decreasing in importance from year to year. It derives its name from the fact that the reaction is carried out in large chambers constructed of sheet lead. Lead is not acted on by the concentrations of sulfuric acid obtained in the process. Most of the acid prepared by this process is utilized in the preparation of a fertilizer, superphosphate of calcium.

The process is in reality a catalytic process inasmuch as large volumes of sulfur dioxide, oxygen and water are induced to react to form sulfuric acid by a small quantity of nitrogen oxides. The over-all reaction may be visualized as (21):

$$(21) \quad SO_2 + \tfrac{1}{2}O_2 + H_2O \rightarrow H_2SO_4$$

There is some doubt as to the exact nature of the reactions taking place in the process but it is thought that the principal reactions taking place are:

In the gaseous phase, homogeneous (22):

$$(22) \quad 2NO + O_2 \rightarrow 2NO_2$$

On the gas-liquid interface (23)

$$(23) \quad SO_2 + H_2O \rightarrow H_2SO_3$$
$$H_2SO_3 + NO_2 \rightarrow H_2SO_3 \cdot NO_2 \text{ (nitrosulfuric acid)}$$
$$NO_2 \rightarrow NO + \tfrac{1}{2}O_2$$
$$2(H_2SO_3 \cdot NO_2) + \tfrac{1}{2}O_2 \rightarrow H_2O + 2(HSO_3 \cdot NO_2)$$
$$\text{nitrosyl sulfuric acid}$$
$$2(HSO_3 \cdot NO_2) + SO_2 + H_2O \rightleftarrows 2(H_2SO_3 \cdot NO_2) + H_2SO_4$$

In the liquid phase (24):

$$(24) \quad H_2SO_3 \cdot NO_2 \rightleftarrows H_2SO_4 + NO$$
$$2(HSO_3 \cdot NO_2) + H_2O \rightleftarrows H_2SO_4 + NO + NO_2$$
$$HSO_3 \cdot NO_2 + HNO_3 \rightleftarrows 2NO_2 + H_2SO_4$$

The principal drawback to this method of manufacture has been that the acid obtained is at best only 78 per cent H_2SO_4, whereas a much more concentrated acid is required for many operations. To obtain a concentrated acid from chamber acid it is necessary to carry out a concentration procedure. This is undesirable in that it increases the cost of the acid.

[1] For a comprehensive discussion of the manufacture of this important chemical see the A.C.S. Monograph No. 144 entitled "Manufacture of Sulfuric Acid," ed. by W. W. Durecker and J. R. West, Reinhold Pub. Corp., New York, 1959.

2. *The contact or catalytic process* is the most important method for preparing sulfuric acid today. Its great advantage lies in the fact that the process yields sulfuric acid of any desired concentration without the necessity of concentrating the acid. It is especially desirable to have a highly concentrated acid (*i.e.*, contact acid) for nitration procedures.

Essentially, the process depends on the oxidation of sulfur dioxide to sulfur trioxide by the use of a suitable catalyst (25).

$$(25)\ 2SO_2 + O_2 \rightarrow 2SO_3$$

The SO_3 which forms can then readily be converted to sulfuric acid.

The optimum temperature in the converter is about 450° C. The catalysts used are of various types. At the present time vanadium catalysts are used more than are platinum catalysts, although recently a highly effective platinized silica gel has been developed. The SO_3 which forms is absorbed in 97 per cent sulfuric acid because the SO_3 gas is obtained in a state which does not combine well with water. However, it does react smoothly with the 3 per cent of water in the 97 per cent acid to form more sulfuric acid (26).

$$(26)\ SO_3 + H_2O \rightarrow H_2SO_4$$

The acid which results is practically 100 per cent pure H_2SO_4 and may be diluted to give a weaker acid or more SO_3 may be passed into it to give the previously discussed "oleums" or fuming sulfuric acids.

Sulfuric acid was used in *Ferric Subsulfate Solution*, N.F. XI as a source of sulfate ion to maintain solubility of ingredients. In the preparation of *Pyroxylin*, U.S.P. XVII, it is a dehydrating agent.

Diluted Sulfuric Acid, N.F. X, contained, in each 100 ml., not less than 9.5 Gm. and not more than 10.5 Gm. of H_2SO_4. In a highly diluted form it had value in the treatment of achlorhydria since, in common with other inorganic acids, it activates pepsin. It is used little, if any, in present-day medicine.

Pharmacology of the Sulfate Ion.—The sulfates are not absorbed from the gastrointestinal tract when administered orally. This property enables oral administration without significant systemic effects, and also accounts for the use of various soluble sulfates as saline cathartics. Because the sulfates are not absorbed, their administration in hypertonic solution draws water into the lumen of the intestine. The bulk of the intestinal contents then provokes the intestines to peristalsis by reflex stimulation with consequent movement of the bowels. (See uses of sodium phosphate.)

Injection of sulfates as, for example, sodium sulfate brings about a copious diuresis. The diuretic action is believed to be due to the impermeability of the renal tubule cells to the sulfate ion, keeping the sulfate in the tubule and preserving its osmotic action. This diminishes the re-absorption of water from the tubule and thus promotes diuresis.

11

Solutions and Solubility Phenomena

HOMOGENEOUS systems may be characterized as those having a uniform composition throughout the entire system. They are contrasted to heterogeneous systems where the system is made up of matter in different states of aggregation (phases) which are separable from one another by definite physical boundaries.

Solutions are single phase systems that are composed of two or more chemical substances representing a homogeneous molecular dispersion. In general, the components of a solution retain their identity and, to a degree, their properties. Thus, a solution is properly termed a *homogeneous mixture* on the basis of this variability of composition. However, solutions are uniform in properties throughout the mixture because the dispersion of the solute molecules in the solvent as a result of kinetic energy is on a molecular scale and cannot be distinguished by the naked eye or even by a microscope. Although colloidal solutions contain small particles they cannot be termed true solutions because the particles are not of molecular dimensions.

The components of a solution are, of course, the *solute* and the *solvent*. By common usage, the component that establishes the phase of a solution may be termed the solvent, this usually being the one in largest concentration. However, in considering an alcohol-water solution such as Diluted Alcohol either one could be considered the solvent. Actually, there is no theoretical basis for distinguishing one component as the solute and the other as the solvent.

The three states of matter (gas, liquid and solid) may act as solvents for one or more of the same three states of matter. Normally, however, it is considered that a gas cannot dissolve anything else but another gas. On the other hand, liquids and solids may act as solvents for gases, liquids or solids. Liquid solutions of gases, other liquids, or solids are by far the most important to the pharmacist and, therefore, the other types of solutions will not be considered in this chapter. If they are of importance in some specific instance a discussion will be found at that point in the text.

Concentration.—The concentration of a solution may be expressed in a number of different ways depending on the convenience of the person or persons concerned with its use. Those commonly used are as follows:—

(1) *Molarity.*—The molarity of a solution expresses the number of *gram-molecular weights* (moles) of solute in 1000 ml. of the solution. This is synonymous with *formality* (gram-formula weights per liter).

(2) *Normality.*—The normality of a solution expresses the number of *gram-equivalent weights* of the solute in 1000 ml. of the solution. Usually, we are concerned with aqueous solutions of acids, bases and salts. The equivalent weight is defined as the weight of compound containing one equivalent of the element or radical in which we are interested. With respect to acids, the equivalent weight is the amount of acid which can furnish 1.008 Gm. of hydrogen ion and, with respect to bases, it is the amount of base that can furnish 17.008 Gm. of hydroxide ion. In salts it is necessary to determine which ion is to be considered. There is no problem with sodium chloride (NaCl) or sodium sulfate (Na_2SO_4) inasmuch as a gram-molecular weight of the former contains one equivalent of each ion and one-half of the gram-molecular weight of the latter contains one equivalent of each ion. However, a compound such as sodium acid sulfate ($NaHSO_4$) contains one equivalent each of sodium or hydrogen ion and two equivalents of sulfate ion per gram-molecular weight. Thus, if it is to be used for its sodium or for its hydrogen (as an acid) a gram-molecular weight is equal to the equivalent weight, but when used for its sulfate ion, the equivalent weight is one-half the gram-molecular weight.

Normality may also be applied to concentrations of oxidizing and reducing agents if we ascertain the oxidizing or reducing valence of the compound in question. For example, HNO_3 is reduced to NO when it acts as an oxidizer, a process involving a change from positive pentavalent nitrogen to positive divalent nitrogen. The oxidizing valence change is, therefore, *three* and the gram-molecular weight of HNO_3 divided by this valence change gives the gram-equivalent weight which is dissolved in enough water to give a liter of normal solution.

(3) *Molality.*—The molality of a solution expresses the number of moles of the solute in 1000 Gm. of the solvent.

(4) *Per Cent.*—Per cent means "parts per hundred parts." Aside from the analytical aspects of pharmacy, the per cent designation is the most important to pharmacists. Although the chemist traditionally considers per cent to be reserved primarily for the expression of a weight in weight concentration, the pharmacist finds three official interpretations of per cent. The U.S.P. XVII (p. 12) expresses it as follows:

"Percentage Solutions in Compounding Prescriptions.—Percentage concentrations of solutions are expressed as follows:
Per cent weight in weight—(w/w) expresses the number of Gm. of a constituent in 100 Gm. of solution.
Per cent weight in volume—(w/v) expresses the number of Gm. of a constituent in 100 ml. of solution, and is used in prescription practice regardless of whether water or another liquid is the solvent.

Per cent volume in volume—(v/v) expresses the number of ml. of a constituent in 100 ml. of solution.

The term *per cent* used in prescriptions without qualification means, for mixtures of solids, per cent weight in weight; for solutions or suspensions of solids in liquids, per cent weight in volume; for solutions of liquids in liquids, per cent volume in volume; and for solutions of gases in liquids, per cent weight in volume. For example, a 1 per cent solution is prepared by dissolving 1 Gm. of a solid or 1 ml. of a liquid in sufficient of the solvent to make 100 ml. of the solution. A solution of approximately the same strength may be prepared by by dissolving 4.5 grains of a solid or 4.8 minims of a liquid in sufficient of the solvent to make 1 fluidounce of the solution.

In dispensing prescriptions, slight changes in volume owing to variations in room temperature may be disregarded."

(5) *Saturated.*—A saturated solution is one which has dissolved all of the solute it is capable of holding at a given temperature, this temperature being 25° C. unless otherwise specified. As implied by the fact that a solution can be saturated with a chemical, the constituents of a solution are not always miscible in all proportions to form a homogeneous mixture. Thus, if potassium iodide is dissolved in water to the limit of its solubility, any excess of potassium iodide forms a separate and distinct phase from the solution phase. At this point of maximum solubility the salt crystallizes back onto the surface of the solid phase at the same rate as salt is being dissolved into the solution phase. Increasing the amount of solid phase increases the surface for dissolution but also increases the surface area onto which the salt from the solution can crystallize and the total amount of salt in solution is not increased. This state of affairs is termed an *equilibrium* and the solution is said to be *saturated* with respect to the *solute*. The concentration of salt in this solution is termed the *solubility* of the salt at that temperature.

Solubility.—The solubility of a salt is expressed in many ways. The official compendia have adopted a system of stating the amount of solvent necessary to dissolve 1 Gm. of the substance in question (at 25° C.). This actually is used as a purity criterion for the compound in question. Whenever the exact solubility of a pharmaceutically important compound is not known or designated, the following descriptive terms (U.S.P. XVII, p. 8) are helpful to the pharmacist.

Descriptive Term	Parts of Solvents for 1 Part of Solute
Very soluble	Less than 1
Freely soluble	From 1 to 10
Soluble	From 10 to 30
Sparingly soluble	From 30 to 100
Slightly soluble	From 100 to 1000
Very slightly soluble	From 1000 to 10,000
Practically insoluble, or insoluble	More than 10,000

Often, the chemist prefers to express solubility in terms of the number of grams solute in 100 Gm. of solvent. By plotting the solubility of a salt over a temperature range a *solubility curve* can be constructed showing graphically the amount of a salt in equilibrium with the saturated solution at different temperatures. Figure 4 illustrates a composite of such a solubility graph for a number of inorganic salts. If a curve rises steeply on the graph it is an indication that a rise in temperature has a pronounced effect on solubility but if a curve is flat, with little or no rise, it indicates that a rise in temperature has little or no effect on solubility. In some

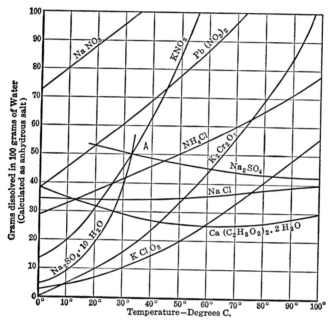

FIG. 4.—Typical Solubility Curves.
(From *General Chemistry* by H. G. Deming, courtesy of John W. Wiley & Sons Inc.)

cases the curve will decline rather than rise indicating a decreasing solubility with rising temperature. In other cases the curve will have a break in it, as with sodium sulfate, indicating that the hydrate has reverted to the anhydrous salt or to a lower hydrate. Depending on whether the solubility of a substance increases or decreases with rising temperature, the substance may be said to possess a *positive* or *negative temperature coefficient of solubility*. The use of solubility curves for the preparation of chemicals is well illustrated by the preparation of potassium nitrate (*q.v.*).

Heat of Solution.—Almost invariably, a heat change will be noted when a solute is dissolved and, in some cases, it is of considerable magnitude. The heat change may be with liberation of heat (*exothermic*) or with absorption of heat (*endothermic*). This heat change is termed the *heat of solution* and is dependent on the amounts and nature of the solute and solvent. Another heat effect is noted also when concentrated solutions are diluted with more solvent, namely the *heat of dilution*, which may be either exothermic or endothermic and, in some cases, may be opposite the heat of solution. The experimental determination of the true direction of the heat of solution is carried out by adding solute to an almost saturated solution which eliminates concentration changes. Heat is usually absorbed when a crystalline salt goes into solution because a considerable amount of energy is required to separate the ions away from one another. If energy is not furnished by some other source, the heat energy necessary for the solution process is extracted from the solution mixture and it often becomes very cold. Barring chemical interactions between the solute and solvent, the heat of solution of a solid is approximately equal to the heat of fusion of the solid and the solid may be thought of as "melting" into the solvent. In a similar fashion, the heat liberated by a gas upon going into solution (without chemical interaction) is roughly the same as the heat of condensation of the gas to its liquid form and, again, we can regard the gas as having liquefied in the solution process. In most cases, the process of solution is not without interactions between solvent and solute with the consequent liberation of relatively large quantities of heat energy. This quite frequently offsets the heat absorption in whole or in part. Indeed, this energy release plays an integral part in the solution process.

There is a quantitative relationship between the heat of solution and the temperature coefficient of solubility of a substance. If the heat of solution is exothermic, the solubility of the substance decreases with a temperature increase and, if it is endothermic, the solubility will increase. This is in accord with LeChatelier's Principle which states that *any equilibrium tends to shift in the direction that will neutralize the effect of any stress applied to it.* Considering a system where a solute and its solution are in equilibrium at a given temperature (saturated solution in contact with excess solute) and then consider what happens if the temperature is increased. The stress applied is heat to raise the temperature and the shift of equilibrium will be such as to restore the original temperature as nearly as possible. Salts having negative heats of solution will tend to go into solution whereas those with positive heats of solution will tend to deposit from solution. The process of solution in the former case uses up heat and is reasonable if one recalls the analogy to "melting" of the solid previously cited. In accord with this reasoning is the fact that, in the absence of chemical or other interactions, the mixing of liquids produces no heat effect comparable to the heat of solution because no phase changes are involved. As a corollary to the above statements it may be stated that the process of crystallization is usually accompanied by the liberation of heat because of the change of phase from liquid to solid.

Factors Affecting Solubility.—Some of these factors have already been discussed in the preceding pages but a brief summary will not be out of order.

(1) *Temperature.*—The effect of an increase in temperature has already been treated. Generally speaking, a temperature increase will cause an increase in solubility unless the solute is in some complex form due to interaction with the solvent. In the latter case, an increase in temperature can reasonably cause a lessening of the stability of the complex and lead to decreased solubility. The relationship of the heat of solution and the temperature coefficient of solubility has also been cited and shown to be related to the Le-Chatelier Principle.

The main exception to the above general statement that solubility increases with the temperature is in the case of gases, where the increase causes a drop in solubility. The thermal agitation induced in the gaseous atoms and molecules overcomes the weak cohesive forces which account for their solubility. The least polar gases are the ones most readily expelled, followed by the gases that enter into reaction with the solvent (*e.g.*, water). This is in accord with the Law of Henry in that the partial pressure of a gas over the solution determines its solubility. The partial pressure over a boiling solution is further diminished toward zero by the vapors of solvent carrying away the solute molecules from the surface of the solution. However, it is not accurate to say that all gases can be expelled completely from a solution by boiling because we need only look to the constant boiling acids (*e.g.*, hydrochloric acid) to find exceptions. In the case of hydrochloric acid it is found that a saturated or near saturated solution (*e.g.*, concentrated hydrochloric acid) will lose HCl faster than it will water molecules when it is heated to boiling but only until it reaches a certain concentration which is approximately 20 per cent (w/w). At this point the two species of molecules present (HCl and H_2O) leave the solution at the same rate and the concentration of the boiling liquid remains unchanged. The same phenomenon is true when a very dilute solution of hydrochloric acid is boiled, in that water molecules escape faster than HCl molecules until the point of equal escape is reached. The concentration at which this happens depends on the barometric pressure and the mixture is termed a *constant boiling solution.*

(2) *Pressure.*—In the case of gases the solubility in liquid solvents is especially influenced by the partial pressure of the gas over the solution. As the pressure increases at a given temperature, the solubility of the gas increases linearly. This behavior of gases is expressed by *Henry's Law* which states that *the solubility of a gas in a liquid is directly proportional to its partial pressure above the liquid.* The behavior of gases in this respect is a consequence of the low concentration of molecules at the lower pressures and the relatively higher concentration under greater pressures. Again, in ac-

12

cord with the Principle of LeChatelier, the stress upon the system is relieved by the gas going into solution ("liquefying"). This is not true of liquids and solids because they are relatively incompressible and the constituent molecules or ions are already in a closely packed system. Henry's Law holds for slightly soluble gases such as N_2, H_2, CO, O_2 and the inert gases and is independent of the number of gases involved. Gases that react with water to some extent as, for example, CO_2 and SO_2, are moderately soluble and also exhibit an increased solubility with increasing pressure but do not conform to the Law of Henry as well as do the slightly soluble gases. The apparent deviation from Henry's Law is probably due in large measure to the chemical reaction with the solvent. In some cases it may seem to violate the law but this is due to the relative magnitudes of these two factors. Although the solubility of all gases is not the same in all solvents, it has been noted that almost invariably the order of solubility is the same in the various solvents.

(3) *Particle Size.*—Usually we do not consider that particle size has any particular effect on the solubility of a substance although we recognize that it plays an important role in the *rate* of solution. Thus, coarse particles of a solute do not have as much surface area exposed per unit weight to the action of a solvent as do finer particles of the same substance. In this respect, agitation of a mixture of undissolved solute and the solvent serves also to increase the rate of solution by preventing local accumulations of highly concentrated solution around the undissolved particles. Therefore, the rate of solution of any solute can be speeded up considerably by a combination of comminution of the solute and agitation. However, it was shown by Hulett that, with slightly soluble substances ($CaSO_4$, $BaSO_4$, etc.), the size of particle has a definite bearing on the actual solubility. Thus, for example, he found that finely divided calcium sulfate had a materially higher solubility (2.5 Gm. per liter) than ordinary calcium sulfate (2.0 Gm. per liter). This phenomenon is useful to the chemist, particularly if both varieties are in contact with a solution as in the analytical procedures employing precipitation of $BaSO_4$. If the precipitated mixture is allowed to digest, the solution becomes supersaturated with respect to the larger particles and material separates then as larger crystals at the expense of the smaller ones, making for easier filtration. Likewise, it probably accounts for the considerably greater physiological effect of certain finely divided materials (*e.g.*, antiseptic effect of colloidal calomel or silver chloride) over the usual sized particles. Nevertheless, the crystals of commonly used materials are sufficiently large that the phenomenon is believed to be relatively unimportant.

(4) *Electrostatic Forces.*—The general statement that "like dissolves like" is a good empirical guide. In effect it depends on the specific character of the solute and solvent. This, in turn, is de-

pendent on the kinds and magnitudes of attractive forces within the system. These are solute-solute, solvent-solvent, and solute-solvent attractions. To effect solution of a given solute, the attractive forces between the ions or molecules must be overcome as must the attractive forces between the solvent molecules. The preceding forces must, in soluble substances, be overcome by the solute-solvent attractive forces.

The attractive forces may all be classified as being of the electrostatic type and are responsible for holding atoms together in crystals, molecules and intermolecular complexes. It is often thought that electrostatic forces apply only to ionic forms because in these situations it is most evident, but it is also true that they apply equally well to dipoles and induced dipoles. In ionic compounds the charges exist because of more or less complete electron exchanges between the participating atoms. Dipoles are the result of a separation of charge within an unsymmetrical molecule and can be likened to small magnets with one portion being negatively charged and the other positively charged. In dipoles it may be said that the centers of electricity and mass do not coincide. The separation of charge within the molecule may be an inherent quality of a permanent nature or it may be an induced effect due to the proximity of another charged species. The former is a *permanent dipole* and the latter an *induced dipole*. The *dipole moment* expresses the extent to which this effect exists in a given molecule and is defined as the product of one of the charges and the distance between the two average centers of positive and negative electricity. A compound with a large dipole moment will usually have a large *dielectric constant*. This is to say that water molecules, for example, will tend to orient themselves and partially neutralize an applied field between two electrostatically charged plates of a condenser (water being the medium between the plates). If the attractive force between the two plates is set at 1 for air (or a vacuum) as the medium, then it will be only $\frac{1}{81}$ as much for water as the medium which is equivalent to saying that water has a dielectric constant of 81. If one likens the ions within ionic compounds to the charged plates of a condenser, it becomes clear why water exerts a diminishing effect on the attractive forces between the ions and aids in their solubilization. Thus, it is apparent that the attraction between two opposite electric charges is not only dependent on the size of the charge and the distance apart but also on the intervening medium.

The combinations of these attractive forces that are commonly recognized are as follows although they are not sharply distinguished from one another. Any one or more may be operative at one time.

(1) Ion-Ion
(2) Dipole-Dipole
(3) Induced Dipole-Induced Dipole (van der Waals')
(4) Ion-Dipole
(5) Ion-Induced Dipole
(6) Dipole-Induced Dipole

A. In *solutes*, the principal operative forces are the ion-ion, dipole-dipole, and induced dipole-induced dipole types. The ion-ion type is the strongest type of attractive force, the dipole-dipole next strongest and the induced dipole-induced dipole the weakest. Ion-ion forces are found in all salts, metal oxides and metal hydroxides. These substances are all considered to be completely ionic even in the solid state and exist in the solid form as *ionic crystal lattices*. They are not properly termed molecules because in the orderly arrangement in the crystal lattice it is not possible to designate ion pairs. The strong ionic forces in these compounds are reflected in their hardness and high melting points. The dipole-dipole attractive forces are not as strong and, as a result, the compounds wherein they exist (in conjunction with van der Waals' forces) are relatively soft and have low melting points when compared to the ionic compounds. Most organic compounds belong in this classification as well as some of the inorganic compounds (*e.g.*, boric acid). The bond types in these compounds are predominantly covalent but may possess some ionic character to account for the dipoles. However, even in molecules that have a zero dipole moment (*e.g.*, CCl_4) there is still a displacement of electrons in the carbon-chlorine bonds to give a *bond moment* that accounts for the ability of one molecule to attract other molecules so that the substance can exist in a liquid state. The induced dipole-induced dipole bond is the weakest of all and is sometimes termed the van der Waals' force or the van der Waals'-London force in recognition of the scientist who investigated its theoretical aspects. It diminishes rapidly with increasing distance between the molecules. It probably contributes, as previously indicated, in some small measure even in dipole-dipole interactions. Normally, gases such as H_2, Ne, N_2, etc., are considered as being symmetrical and electrically neutral and, thus, as having no attractive forces. However, the fact remains that some cohesive force must exist to account for the condensation of these gases even though they require very low temperatures and high pressures. Current opinion holds that these weak attractive (cohesive) forces are the result of temporary polarizations of the molecules by internal electronic oscillations which induce similar polarizations in neighboring molecules to set up mutual attractions.

B. In *solvents* the principal attractive forces between molecules are of the van der Waals' and dipole-dipole types. The van der Waals' type represents the main cohesive force in non-polar solvents such as benzene, carbon tetrachloride, cyclohexane, etc., none of which possess significant dipole moments. The dipole-dipole type is probably the most important of the two types in solvents. Water represents a solvent of pharmaceutical importance with a high dipole moment. The water molecule is known to exist in a "bent" shape (at an angle of $105°$) rather than in a linear form. This nonlinear form results in a dipole being set up with the negative charge residing preferentially at the oxygen end and the positive charge toward the two hydrogens. It is this dipolar character of water that largely accounts for its high dielectric constant and makes it an excellent solvent for many ionic substances and also for other dipolar materials. In addition, it can readily induce dipoles and thus bring about interactions with normally non-polar substances. Water exists in a transiently organized state in that the dipoles tend to align themselves by means of *hydrogen bonds*. The hydrogen bonds can be looked upon as being a consequence of the strong attraction by oxygen of the electron pair being shared by the hydrogen and oxygen which leaves the hydrogen with a character somewhat similar to a proton which can then attract the oxygen of a neighboring water molecule. The fact that water molecules have this tendency to form hydrogen bonds leads to an abnormally high boiling point and freezing point. This tendency for *association* is not found in H_2S, H_2Se or H_2Te.

C. *Solute-solvent* relationships, in terms of attractive forces, are largely responsible for the process of solution. The preceding paragraphs have described the attractive forces to be found in the pure solute and the pure solvent. It now remains to determine the types that are found in the solute-solvent combinations. They may be classified into five general types: 1) induced dipole-induced dipole, 2) induced dipole-dipole, 3) dipole-dipole, 4) dipole-ion, and 5) induced dipole-ion.

(1) The first class of induced dipole forces is of importance in the solubility of non-polar substances in other non-polar substances. Examples of this category are the solubility of the hydrocarbon naphthalene in the hydrocarbon benzene, and the complete miscibility of most of the liquid hydrocarbons. They are not of importance in the inorganic field, but play an important role among organic compounds.

(2) The dipole-induced dipole interaction is most prominent in the solubility of the inert gases (He, Ne, etc.) in a polar solvent such as water. The dipole character of the water is sufficient to induce a dipole in the otherwise non-polar atoms of these gases. The effect is more accentuated than with the mutually induced dipoles between two atoms of the gases because of the more polar character of the water molecule.

(3) Dipole-dipole attractions are of considerable magnitude when compared to the two types that have already been discussed. This type of attraction leads to association of dipole molecules, *e.g.*, water, alcohols, and the other dipolar substances. Most of these may be characterized as hydrogen bonds between the two participating molecular species, as for example, the dipole-dipole bonds formed between water and an alcohol:

$$
\begin{array}{cccc}
\text{H---O} & + & \text{H---O} & \rightarrow & \text{H---O} \text{----} \text{H---O} \\
| & & | & & | \qquad\qquad | \\
\text{R} & & \text{H} & & \text{R} \qquad\qquad \text{H}
\end{array}
\quad
\begin{array}{l}
\text{[or more realistically,} \\
\text{}^{+}\text{(ROH)}^{-}\ {}^{+}\text{(H}_2\text{O)}^{-}_{\overline{x}}\text{]}
\end{array}
$$

In a similar fashion, the formation of water-ammonia dipole bonds creates the familiar ammonium hydroxide (prior to ionization):

$$
\begin{array}{l}
\text{H} \\
\ \ \backslash \\
\text{H---N} \ + \ \text{H---O} \rightarrow \text{H---N} \text{----} \text{H---O} \qquad \text{[or better,} \\
\ \ / \qquad\qquad | \qquad / \qquad\qquad\qquad | \qquad\quad {}^{-}\text{(NH}_3\text{)}^{+}\ {}^{-}\text{(OH}_2\text{)}^{+}_{\overline{x}}\text{]} \\
\text{H} \qquad\qquad \text{H} \quad \text{H} \qquad\qquad \text{H}
\end{array}
$$

To summarize the interactions in this important group it can be said that dipole-dipole attractions account for the solubility of most carbonyl-containing organic compounds (acids, esters, aldehydes, ketones, etc.), amines, organic hydroxy compounds (alcohols, sugars, etc.), inorganic hydroxy compounds (*e.g.*, boric acid) and other dipole molecules. These effects in solubilizing the above types of compounds are predicated on the assumption that the organic or hydrocarbon portion of the molecule does not badly overshadow the polar characteristics. If the hydrocarbon characteristics prevail, solubility in polar solvents is not a predominant characteristic. However, as a general rule, it may be expected that polar groupings

$(-\text{NH}_2, -\text{OH}, \ \ \diagdown \!\!\!\! \diagup \ \text{C}=\text{O, etc.})$ in low molecular weight compounds

will exert a pronounced effect toward solubility in polar solvents.

(4) Insofar as inorganic chemicals are concerned, perhaps the most important category is the dipole-ion attraction. It is here that the common solute-solvent interactions of salts, metal oxides and metal hydroxides are classified. Although these do not represent by any means all inorganic compounds, they do represent many of the pharmaceutically important ones. One may picture the process of solution in this group as being a *solvation* of the ions by the dipolar solvent molecules, that is, a clustering of solvent molecules around the solute ions through electrostatic forces. When water is the solvent the process is termed *hydration*. In most cases, the cation is the most strongly solvated because of the stronger nuclear charge.

Some of the important considerations in these dipole-ion interactions are:—

(*a*) The dielectric constant and dipole moment of the solvent and the size of its molecule.

(*b*) The charge on the ion.

(*c*) The size of the ion.

(a) The effect of solvents with a high dielectric constant in reducing the attractive forces between oppositely charged ions has already been discussed (see Factors Affecting Solubility). It is also reasonable to expect greater interaction between a given ion and a solvent molecule with a high dipole moment than one with a lower one. The size of the dipole solvent molecule also has a bearing on its solvating ability. Water molecules, being small, permit a closer packing around the ions and, thus, are able to exert a greater solvating effect than would a larger dipole molecule. On this basis it is not sufficient for a solvating dipole to have only a high dipole moment. It should also be small in size, which accounts in part for the exceptional solvating abilities of water, methyl alcohol, and ethyl alcohol. The solvating process can be pictured as one where the solvating dipole wedges itself between the oppositely charged ions to reduce the interionic attractive forces. This permits other dipoles to attach themselves to the ion which eventually is carried away from the attractive force of the other ions with a more or less complete "shell" of water molecules (or other dipoles) bound to it by the dipole-ion attractive forces.

(b) Many of the polyvalent cations form very stable hydrates (e.g., Al^{+++}, Be^{++}, Mg^{++}, Fe^{++}, Ni^{++}, etc.), indicating a strong attraction for the water dipole. Although univalent cations also exert this attraction, the effect is strongest with the bivalent and trivalent cations as evidenced by the fact that they often carry a shell of water molecules into the ionic crystal lattices in the solid state. Thus, aluminum (q.v.) holds six water molecules and beryllium holds four water molecules in crystalline salts. These water molecules usually arrange themselves in a suitable geometric arrangement as, for example, in aluminum salts where the water molecules are at the corners of a circumscribed octahedron or in the beryllium salts where the water molecules are at the corners of a regular tetrahedron. Where the cation size is small (e.g., Al, Mg, Be, etc.) the water molecules can fit rather easily into the spaces in the crystal lattice but as the size increases and approaches the size of the anion it becomes more difficult to fit the water molecules into the crystal pattern. The salts which already have water in the crystal lattice are, in a manner of speaking, already partially "solubilized" and, frequently, are rather easily soluble. The number of water molecules primarily attached to an ion is a function of the size and geometry of the cation and is designated as its *coordination number*. It might be expected that the highly positive character of a polyvalent cation would cause such strong interionic forces that compounds of this type would be insoluble. While this is true, especially in combinations of polyvalent cations with polyvalent anions (e.g., $AlPO_4$, MgO, etc.), this effect is partially offset by the solvation process if it is possible for the dipole molecules to get between the ions. The solvation process is more evident in combinations of monovalent ions and, to a lesser extent, polyvalent ions with monovalent ions. A few general rules can be stated on the basis of the above statements:—

(*1*) If *both* the cation and anion of an ionic compound are monovalent, the attractive forces are usually easy to overcome and, as a rule, these compounds are quite soluble. The silver halides are an exception, possibly due to the somewhat covalent character of the bonding.

(*2*) If only *one* of the two ions in an ionic compound is univalent it is still the general case that the compounds are water-soluble if the cation is an alkali metal or ammonium or if the anion is nitrate, acetate or an oxy-halogen ion.

(*3*) If *both* the cation and anion are bivalent or trivalent, the compound will usually be insoluble because of the strength of the ionic bond. There are, however, numerous exceptions to this rule if one considers the high water solubilities of aluminum sulfate, zinc sulfate, ferric sulfate, etc. Most of these, it may be noted, have hydrated cations so that the process of "solution" may be considered as being partially in effect even in the crystal form.

(*c*) The smaller ions exert a stronger attractive force on dipoles than do the ions of larger diameter. This, in turn, reflects the energy of hydration (*i.e.*, for water), with the greater affinity being responsible for greater energy release. Thus, the energies of hydration of the alkali metal ions are in the order $Li^+ > Na^+ > K^+$ and the relative ion sizes are $K^+ > Na^+ > Li^+$. A similar arrangement can be made for the alkaline earth metal ions. In some of the salts of the above cations (*e.g.*, chlorides and sulfates), the solubilities tend to parallel the energies of hydration. However, among the alkali metals, if the series is extended to rubidium and cesium salts, the solubilities will again begin to increase. This may be ascribed to the increasing ionic radius with a concomitant lessening of electrostatic attraction. In fact, the majority of salts of the alkali metals increase in relative solubility in progressing from lithium to cesium, leading to the conclusion that the ionic radius plays a more important role in solubility than does the hydration energy. Among the alkaline earth metals, however, one finds (with the notable exception of the hydroxides) a conformity to the parallelism between hydration energy and solubility. It has already been stated that the smaller cations form quite stable hydrates in comparison to the larger ones, the number of water molecules depending on the coordination number. The coordination of dipoles is not unique to water dipoles as evidenced in the formation of $Cu(NH_3)_4^{++}$, $Ag(NH_3)_2^+$, etc. The smaller cations can exert a strong enough attractive effect on the oxygen of hydroxide ions so that they actually acquire acidic character in addition to their basic properties. Examples of this are to be found in the hydroxides of zinc, aluminum, tin, etc. These are classified as amphoteric compounds.

The above discussions have dealt with ionic compounds in the main but the actual decision as to whether a solute is really completely ionic is not as simple as one might surmise. Between such a compound as sodium chloride (ionic) and chlorine (covalent bonding) there can exist a gradation of ionic character of the bond. The per cent of ionic character of the bond may be determined on the basis of the relative electronegativities (electron affinities) of the participating atoms. The concept of electronegativity has already been considered under the discussion of the Chemical Bond (p. 8). However, it might be well to point out that elements of groups that are far apart in the Periodic Table will tend to have widely differing electronegativities, whereas elements in groups that are close together in the Periodic Table will have similar electronegativities. In general, electronegativities increase in going from the left to the right and from the bottom to the top of the Periodic Table. It is customary to regard the 50 per cent point of ionic character as being the dividing line between ionic compounds and covalent ones. Compounds whose component atoms are bonded by forces which are neither purely ionic or purely covalent are described as polar-ionic or polar-covalent. In general, it can be said that there is a parallelism between the per cent ionic character of a compound on the basis of electronegativities and its solubility in polar solvents. However, it is not safe to say that the extent of ionization of a compound, when dissolved, will be directly correlated with the above per cent ionic character. In the ionization process it must be remembered that *ions* are being formed, rather than atoms, and that the electronegativities have been derived from bond energies. Thus, we find that the relative strengths of the hydrogen halide acids in aqueous solution is $HI > HBr > HCl > HF$, whereas the per cent ionic character is directly opposite. In the case of HI, it can be rationalized that the weakness of the bond is due to the larger interatomic distance (1.7 Å) when compared, for instance, to HF (1.0 Å).

(5) The solubility effects associated with the ion-induced dipole attractive force are probably due to inductive effects. As an example, the solubility of iodine in aqueous iodide solutions can be considered as an induction of a dipole in the normally non-polar iodine by the iodide ion. It can best be pictured by visually considering the effects that would result from the enclosure of an extra pair of electrons in the outer shell of iodine. Iodine is unique in this respect.

PROPERTIES OF SOLUTIONS

Colligative Properties.—The *colligative properties* of solutions are those which are independent of the *kinds* of molecules in solution but which are dependent on the *number* of molecules (or particles) present. Thus, provided a molecule does not ionize (*i.e.*, is a non-electrolyte), it is equally effective in imparting these properties to a solution in comparison to another non-electrolyte, without consideration of size, structure or components of the two molecules. The colligative properties of solutions are:—

(a) Freezing point   (c) Vapor pressure
(b) Boiling point   (d) Osmotic pressure

(a) *Freezing Point.*—In general, the presence of a solute (non-electrolyte) in a solution (*e.g.*, aqueous) depresses the freezing point of the solution directly in proportion to the amount of solute. The freezing point of the solution is depressed because energy must be utilized to offset the ion-dipole attractions between the water dipoles and the solute ions. Until these attractions are compensated the formation of water crystals is inhibited. The depression varies in different solvents but is characteristic of the solvent for any given solute. It is usually expressed as the *molal freezing point depression constant* which is derived from the depression of freezing point imparted to a solvent by dissolving one gram-molecular weight of the substance in 1000 Gm. of the solvent. The constant for water is 1.86° (*i.e.*, freezing point of water is −1.86° C.). It is useful for determining molecular weights of non-electrolytes. Ionizable substances, however, depress the freezing point to a greater degree than a non-electrolyte of identical molecular weight. Inasmuch as this is due to the additional particles formed by ionization and, if the molecular weight and ionization equation is known, it is then possible to assign a degree of dissociation for the solute. Actually, because we know that salts are practically entirely ionized even in the solid state, the indication of a degree of dissociation is only an indication of an apparent state of affairs. Indeed, measurement of the degree of dissociation by different methods will often give variant results. One of the principal factors causing deviations from the true state of affairs is the mutual effects that ions have upon one another in solution, particularly in concentrated solutions.

(b) *Boiling Point.*—The boiling point of a solution is raised by the presence of a solute. The solute molecules limit the escape area (surface of the solution) of the more volatile solvent molecules and, thus, it requires greater thermal agitation to permit them to escape at the same rate as they did from the pure solvent. The quantitative aspects with respect to non-electrolytes are similar to those for freezing point depression although, obviously, the constants are different. For water, the *molal boiling point elevation* by a non-electrolyte is 0.52° C.

(c) *Vapor Pressure.*—The vapor pressure of a solution is inversely proportional to the mole fraction of solvent in the solution. This lowering of vapor pressure in connection with a dissolved solute is known as *Raoult's Law* and, in many respects, is related to the boiling point elevation. Indeed, boiling point elevation, freezing point depression and osmotic pressure can all be related to the vapor pressure and the calculations based upon these properties are derivable from Raoult's Law.

(d) *Osmotic Pressure.*—Water has a remarkable property of being able to pass readily through certain membranes such as parchment whereas most solutes dissolved in water are not able to traverse the barrier. Membranes with a selectivity of this type are termed *semi-permeable membranes.* The movement of water molecules through the semi-permeable membrane is termed *osmosis* and is also observed to exist between two solutions of differing concentrations separated by a membrane. Thus we note a movement of water molecules from the less concentrated (where the concentration of H_2O is greater) to the more concentrated solution until equilibrium is reached when both solutions contain the same concentration of water molecules. The *osmotic pressure* is the pressure exerted by the solvent coming in through a membrane separating pure solvent and solution. It may be measured by determining the pressure necessary to be applied to the solution to prevent the solvent from passing through the membrane. Osmotic pressure usually does not depend on the kind of membrane but, in dilute solutions, is proportional to the concentration and absolute temperature. The osmotic pressure may be as high as several atmospheres for moderately concentrated solutions. It is obvious that this phenomenon is extremely important in pharmacy and medicine when one considers the many functions of the human body dependent on it, the mechanism of saline cathartics and osmotic diuretics, etc.

Homogeneous Equilibria.—In contrast to systems where two or more phases participate, there are systems where all reactions take place in the same phase. Examples of this are certain chemical reactions of dissolved solutes (where no precipitation or gas evolution occurs) and interactions of gases. These are *homogeneous equilibria.* The term equilibrium implies that a dynamic situation exists where there is, so to speak, forward and backward movement or equal and opposing movements of ions or molecules. An example of a homogeneous equilibrium is the solution of chlorine in water (1) or ammonia in water (2). On the other hand, a *heterogeneous* equilibrium

(1) $Cl_2 + H_2O \rightleftharpoons HCl + HOCl$
(2) $NH_3 + H_2O \rightleftharpoons NH_4^+ + OH^-$

would be illustrated by the dissociation of $CaCO_3$ to CaO and CO_2 (3)

(3) $CaCO_3 \rightleftharpoons CaO + CO_2$

where, at equilibrium, $CaCO_3$ forms as fast as it dissociates but we have solid phases represented by $CaCO_3$ and CaO and the gaseous phase by CO_2.

Guldberg and Waage, in 1864, presented their well-known *Law of Mass Action* which states essentially that *the speed (rate or velocity) of a chemical reaction is proportional to the concentrations of the reacting substances.* This is the fundamental law of chemical kinetics and equilibrium and relates the effect of concentration to the reaction rate. In general, given the equation (4) representing an equilibrium between two reactants it is noted that the velocity of the forward reaction between A and B and the reverse reaction between C and D is given by the expression (5) where k_1 and k_2 are the *rate constants* (the rate at unit concentration). The initial concentrations of A and B are high at the beginning of the reaction and, consequently,

$$(4) \quad aA + bB \underset{v_2}{\overset{v_1}{\rightleftarrows}} cC + dD$$

$$(5) \quad velocity_1 = v_1 = k_1 [A]^a[B]^b$$
$$ velocity_2 = v_2 = k_2 [C]^c[D]^d$$

the rate is high but diminishes as the reaction proceeds. Likewise, the reverse reaction of C with D is slow at the beginning of the reaction but the velocity increases apace as the reaction of A with B progresses. Finally, a state of equilibrium is reached when $v_1 = v_2$ and where,

$$k_1 [A]^a[B]^b = k_2 [C]^c[D]^d \text{ and, therefore,}$$
$$k_1/k_2 = K = [C]^c[D]^d/[A]^a[B]^b$$

Thus, the equilibrium constant K of the reaction is defined as the ratio of the rate constants. By convention the products of a reaction are used as the numerator expression and the reactants as the denominator. This is a measure of the extent to which the equilibrium reaction proceeds to the right. If it is numerically large, one should anticipate a high equilibrium yield of the products and, if it is low, the reverse should be true. These considerations are summed up as the *Law of Chemical Equilibrium; "When a reversible reaction has reached an equilibrium at a given temperature, the product of the molar concentrations of the reaction products, divided by the product of the molar concentrations of the reactants will be a constant, provided the concentrations are raised to a power equal to the number of moles taking part in the reaction."*

The temperature at which an equilibrium takes place is important because reactions either absorb or evolve heat. If a reaction liberates heat in progressing to the right the indication would be that carrying it out at a low temperature would promote better yields. This is true except where the low temperature so affects the velocity of the reaction that it takes too long to reach equilibrium. Such is the case with the reaction of SO_2 and O_2 to form SO_3 but, with the use of a platinum catalyst, the reaction is speeded up at moderate temperatures to where it is commercially feasible. On the other hand, a reaction that absorbs heat can be promoted by using higher temperatures. It will be recalled (see Factors Affecting Solubility) that solubility phenomena obey the same rules and the function of the LeChatelier principle was illustrated. The principle is equally applicable here. Catalysts affect the velocities of both forward and reverse reactions to exactly the same degree. Their principal value lies in their ability to bring a given reaction to equilibrium in a much shorter period of time than would otherwise be possible.

The effect of pressure is only evident where there is a change in volume of the reaction. Thus, it is of great importance in gaseous reactions but of relatively minor importance in connection with liquids and solids. If no change in volume is encountered, changes in pressure do not affect the reaction, whereas, if the products have a lesser volume than the starting materials, the reaction will shift to the right to relieve the increased pressure. Consider the reaction:

$$2SO_2 + O_2 \rightleftarrows 2SO_3$$

It will be noted that there is a total of three molecules of SO_2 and O_2 on the left hand side of the equation and only two molecules of SO_3 on the right hand side. Thus, the reaction will tend to shift to the right to offset any added pressure.

As we have previously noted, many of our important reactions involve equilibrium reactions. The mass action equation is particularly useful for weak electrolytes (*i.e.*, those not highly ionized) but is not usually applied to strong electrolytes because they are considered to be completely ionized in solution. In the case of strong electrolytes the concentration of ions, if high, is not an accurate representation because the activity coefficients are not equal to unity. However, when low concentrations of ions are encountered the activity coefficient approaches unity and the use of concentrations in the mass action equation is again reasonable. Nevertheless, the ions from strong electrolytes may enter into other equilibria. Weak electrolytes do not have high ion concentrations and exist largely in the non-ionized form and, thus, are particularly susceptible to treatment by the mass action law. Among these weak electrolytes, a particularly interesting group is the weak acid and base category. The calculation of ion concentrations in solutions of these weak electrolytes is well covered in the usual qualitative inorganic chemistry textbooks and, in addition, we have reviewed the calculations pertinent to determination of hydrogen ion concentrations which are of particular interest to pharmacists. For the above reasons we will not here review the calculations of ion concentrations or equilibrium constants. However, it is well to consider some of the general factors associated with equilibria of this kind.

The *common ion effect* is an important consideration in the determination of ion concentrations. In general, if two compounds in solution have an identical ion, this ion is said to be the *common ion*. For example a solution of acetic acid and sodium acetate has the acetate ion as a common ion. The addition of sodium acetate (considered to be completely ionized) to the acetic acid solution has raised the concentration of acetate ion much higher than the concentration provided by the acetic acid alone (6) and, on the basis of

$$(6) \quad CH_3COOH + H_2O \rightleftarrows H_3O^+ + CH_3COO^-$$

LeChatelier's principle has caused the equilibrium to shift to the left with a consequent decrease in H_3O^+ concentration. This effect is known as the *common ion effect*. The importance of this in the mass action expression has been illustrated in the case of indicators.

Another important consideration is the *neutralization effect* in which a solution of a strong electrolyte has added to it an ion that can form a weak electrolyte with one of the ions. This weak electrolyte formation is particularly well illustrated by the conventional neutralization reaction of acids and bases in which hydroxide and hydronium ions unite to form relatively non-ionized water molecules. The use of acetate ion in a buffer mixture (see Buffers) illustrates its ability to take up hydronium ions from a highly acidic solution and convert them to relatively non-ionized acetic acid. Indeed, acetate ion is almost as effective as hydroxide ion. The addition of ammonium chloride to a sodium hydroxide solution illustrates the effective reduction of the hydroxide ion concentration by the formation of relatively non-ionized water molecules (7) as a result of the high basicity of OH^- as compared to NH_3.

$$(7) \quad NH_4^+ + OH^- \rightleftarrows NH_3 + H_2O$$

The process of *hydrolysis* in solutions of electrolytes is essentially a protolytic reaction between ions of a salt and water. The transfer of a proton from an acid to a base (forming a new acid and base) is often called a *protolysis* (see also p. 104). Water, of course, contains both the acid ion H_3O^+ and the basic ion OH^- and, therefore, it is to be expected that if it is used as a solvent for a salt which has an ion that can act as an acid or a base to any extent, it will react with one of the ions in water. Thus, when sodium acetate is dissolved in water, the acetate ion being a rather strong base, will react with water to capture protons to form non-ionized acetic acid. In this way, hydroxide ions accumulate because the sodium ion has no acidic or basic character to speak of. As the acetate ion takes up protons it causes the ionization of more water and, hence, more OH^- is formed. The extent of hydrolysis is determined by the dissociation constant of the acid as well as the concentration. Probably the best equation (8) we can write for this hydrolysis is:—

$$(8) \quad H_2O + CH_3COO- \rightleftarrows CH_3COOH + OH^-$$

A similar process can be proposed for the hydrolyses which result in acidic solutions. Ammonium chloride, for example, is hydrolyzed (9) by proton transfer from the ammonium ion to the water molecule resulting in H_3O^+. The chloride ion has little or no tendency to capture any of the ions available from water. Whenever the

(9) $H_2O + NH_4^+ \rightleftarrows NH_3 + H_3O^+$

salt in solution has two ions that have a tendency to combine with the ions of water the net result will depend on which one proceeds the greatest extent. Considering ammonium acetate, one can predict that both non-ionized acetic acid as well as NH_3 will form and, in this case, the solution resulting will be nearly neutral. Another example of hydrolysis is the type where a more or less stable complex forms. This is illustrated by the strong acidity of aluminum sulfate or chloride solutions. The reason for the acidity is due to the strong hydrolysis of the aluminum ion which shows a strong tendency to hydrate and to complex itself in a manner involving OH^- ions. This type of hydrolysis is discussed in more detail in the Appendix. In some cases there is more than one factor operating to promote the hydrolysis. For example, a solution of sodium sulfide is very basic and has a strong odor of hydrogen sulfide. The sulfide ion is a rather strong base and the protolytic reaction with water takes place readily (10). The fact that hydrogen sulfide is volatile

(10) $S^= + H_2O \rightleftarrows OH^- + HS^-$
$HS^- + H_2O \rightleftarrows OH^- + H_2S$

leads to its escape from the solution and this promotes still further hydrolysis of the sulfide ion. If the solution is boiled, the hydrogen sulfide can virtually all be expelled and a solution of sodium hydroxide will be the net result.

Heterogeneous Equilibria.—This type of equilibrium and its distinction from homogeneous equilibria has been described previously (p. 175). The mass action law applies equally well to heterogeneous equilibria as to the homogeneous type that we have discussed.

Although there are many types of heterogeneous equilibria that could be cited, perhaps the one of greatest importance to the pharmacist is that dealing with the *solubility product principle*. It may be noted that the mixing of equal volumes of 0.1M solutions of barium chloride and sodium sulfate will result in an immediate precipitation (11) and, shortly, the establishment of an equilibrium

(11) $BaCl_2 + Na_2SO_4 \rightleftarrows BaSO_4 \downarrow + 2NaCl$

between the solid $BaSO_4$ and the two ions (Ba^{++} and $SO_4^=$) resulting from ionization (12). Thus, an equilibrium constant expression (13)

(12) $BaSO_4 \rightleftarrows Ba^{++} + SO_4^=$
(13) $K = [Ba^{++}][SO_4^=]$

can be written for the saturated solution of barium sulfate. Complete ionization of the salt is assumed in the solution phase because of the salt character of $BaSO_4$. The solid $BaSO_4$ is not customarily included in the equilibrium expression because it is constant and its activity may be considered as unity. The ion product, constant for any given temperature, is given the name of *solubility product*. Different authors use different symbols (*e.g.*, *s*, SP, $K_{s.p.}$, etc.) for this constant. We shall use $K_{s.p.}$.

The solubility product principle can then be restated as follows:— *"At a given temperature the product of the molar concentrations of the ions in a saturated solution of a slightly soluble salt is a constant, the concentrations being raised to a power corresponding to the occurrence of the ion in the ionization equation."* The principle is of value in determining whether precipitation will occur or whether precipitates will dissolve under given conditions. Whenever two or more ions are present in the same solution and can form a slightly soluble salt under conditions where the $K_{s.p.}$ of the salt is exceeded, precipitation of that salt is to be expected until the constant is satisfied. Given an equilibrium condition in a saturated solution of a difficultly soluble salt such as AgCl in contact with solid AgCl it is found that

$$[Ag^+] \, [Cl^-] \; = \; K_{s.p.}$$

However, if additional silver ion is added to the saturated solution it increases the total silver ion concentration and, in order to maintain the constant, the chloride ion concentration must decrease. On the other hand, addition of a small excess of chloride ion produces a similar imbalance of the equilibrium and, in order to maintain the equilibrium constant, the silver ion concentration decreases. Both procedures result in the further precipitation of AgCl. The situation upon addition of either ion in excess of that required to satisfy the $K_{s.p.}$ represents a momentary imbalance (14) that is

$$(14) \quad [Ag^+] \, [Cl^-] \; > K_{s.p.}$$

quickly corrected by the precipitation of AgCl. As we noted earlier this is known as the common-ion effect.

In a similar manner, if one can remove one of the ions in some way, a momentary imbalance in the other direction is brought about (15).

$$(15) \quad [Ag^+] \, [Cl^-] \; < K_{s.p.}$$

In order to correct this situation more AgCl goes into solution to satisfy the constant. An example of this is the dissolution of AgCl by addition of ammonia, a process where the Ag^+ combines by co-ordination with $2NH_3$ (16) to form the complex $[Ag(NH_3)_2]^+$ which

$$(16) \quad Ag^+ \; + \; 2NH_3 \; \rightleftarrows \; [Ag(NH_3)_2]^+$$

is soluble in excess NH_3. This complex is much less ionized than AgCl and so serves to act as a means for removing one of the ions in the equilibrium expression (*i.e.*, Ag^+).

It is well to note that, although excess chloride ion in small amounts will force more AgCl out of solution by common ion effect, the addition of a large excess of chloride ion may cause an increase in the solubility of the AgCl. This increase is brought about by what is known as the *complex-ion effect*. In the case of AgCl, the silver ions in solution combine with chloride ion to form a soluble complex (17) which effectively reduces the silver ion concentration

$$(17)\ Ag^+ + 2Cl^- \rightleftarrows [AgCl_2]^-$$

and requires dissolution of AgCl to satisfy the constant.

We shall not carry out calculations of the ion concentrations because they are well treated in most textbooks dealing with qualitative and quantitative chemistry. Suffice it to say, however, that if the solubility of a slightly soluble salt is known, the concentration of each ion can be calculated readily and if the solubility product constant is known the solubility is determined with equal ease. Variations on these basic calculations due to added common ions enlarge the scope of its application.

One other consideration should be mentioned in connection with these slightly soluble salts, namely the *salt effect*. It is an established fact that equilibrium constants, when expressed in terms of ion concentrations, do not remain constant in solutions of varying ionic concentration. Usually, the addition of an electrolyte not possessing ions in common with the solute, causes a small increase in the solubility of the precipitated salt as well as a small increase in the $K_{s.p.}$. The difficulty lies in the fact that, when the total ion concentration becomes high (with or without a common ion), the molar concentrations no longer can be assumed to be representative of the activities of the ions.

Other heterogeneous equilibria of interest to the pharmacist are the relationships of salt hydrates. These have been discussed elsewhere (see Appendix—Water) but a few words in this connection are not out of place. The familiar efflorescence of salts such as $Na_2CO_3 \cdot 10H_2O$, $CuSO_4 \cdot 5H_2O$ are examples of heterogeneous equilibria. Hydration is a reversible process and at any given temperature a hydrate will tend to establish an equilibrium with the water vapor in contact with it. Hydrates are known to have certain vapor pressures depending on the temperature although many of these hydrates are remarkably stable to loss of the water of hydration even in quite dry atmospheres. All hydrates, however, will lose their water when heated because the process of water loss is an endothermic one and the equilibrium aqueous vapor pressure (of the hydrate) will increase with the temperature. Most hydrates, when admixed with a small amount of a lower hydrate, will establish an equilibrium

13

aqueous vapor pressure. The mixture of $CuSO_4 \cdot 5H_2O$ and $CuSO_4 \cdot 3H_2O$ is representative (18). The vapor pressure exerted by the

$$(18) \quad CuSO_4 \cdot 5H_2O \rightleftarrows CuSO_4 \cdot 3H_2O + 2H_2O$$

mixture will correspond to that of the pentahydrate. Increase in the vapor pressure causes formation of more pentahydrate and decrease in vapor pressure brings about more conversion to the trihydrate.

THE ALKALI METALS

Introduction. — The principal metals comprising this group (Group I of the Periodic Table) are lithium, sodium, potassium, rubidium, cesium and more recently francium. The last named, francium, will not be further discussed. The compounds of the atomic group or radical, ammonium, are discussed after those of potassium to which they show the greatest resemblance.

PROPERTIES OF THE ALKALI METALS

Properties	Lithium	Sodium	Potassium	Rubidium	Cesium
Atomic Number	3	11	19	37	55
Atomic weight	6.939	22.9898	39.102	85.47	132.905
Isotopes	6, 7	23	39, 40,41	85, 87	133
Electrons	2–1	2–8–1	2–8–8–1	2–8–18–8–1	2–8–18–18–8–1
Density	0.534	0.97	0.862	1.525	1.873
Melting point	180°	97.7°	63.65°	39°	28.5°
Boiling point	1336°	883°	774°	696°	705°
Oxidation states	0, +1	0, +1	0, +1	0, +1	0, +1
Radius (covalent) (Angstroms)	1.23	1.57	2.03	2.16	2.35
Radius (ionic) (Angstroms)	0.60	0.95	1.33	1.48	1.69
Ionization potential (volts)	5.36	5.12	4.32	4.16	3.87
Oxidation potential (volts)	+3.02	+2.71	+2.92	+2.93	+3.02
Hydration energy (Kg.Cal./Gm. mole ion).	136	114	94	——	——
Flame color	Red	Yellow	Violet	Red	Blue

An inspection of the above table of properties indicates a number of regularities in the variation of properties which is indicative of the fact that these Group I metals are among the least complicated in the Periodic Table. They have, in common, one valence electron outside of a well-shielded kernel, the kernel representing the atom within the valence shell, *i.e.*, the nucleus and inner electrons. This electron is capable of easy removal, with the relative difficulty of removal decreasing as the atomic radius increases. This, of course, is to be expected as a consequence of the increased distance of the electron from the central nuclear charge and is further reflected by

(183)

the decreasing ionization potentials when progressing from lithium to cesium. The removal of another electron, however, presents quite a different picture. The energy required to remove a second electron from the sodium ion, for example, which has an inert gas (neon) configuration is approximately ten times that required to remove the first electron. A rough approximation of the relative volumes occupied by the valence electron as compared to the kernel may be arrived at by comparing the atomic radii with the ionic radii. Once again using sodium as an example, a simple approximation of the relative volumes of the atom as against the ion reveals the surprising fact that the kernel occupies roughly $\frac{1}{5}$ of the volume of the atom whereas the valence electron occupies $\frac{4}{5}$ of the volume. It is, therefore, not too surprising that this somewhat voluminous and loosely held electron is so easily removed to form monovalent ions. The above picture also accounts for the low ionization potential and for the fact that compounds of the alkali metals are predominantly in an ionic form in the solid state. Another way of expressing the "looseness" of the valence electron is to say that the alkali metals have pronounced *electropositive character* (tendency to go to an electropositive state). In general, the electropositive character lessens as one proceeds from left to right in the periods of the Periodic Table and increases in progressing downward in any particular group.

The ionic crystal forms of all of the alkali metal halides, except some cesium salts (chloride, bromide and iodide), have the familiar sodium chloride type of arrangement in which each particle is surrounded by six others with opposite charge. The cesium chloride ionic arrangement has eight chloride ions surrounding each cesium ion and is found in binary compounds where the cation and anion do not differ greatly in size. However, this is not the usual state, as revealed by reference to a table of ionic radii. As the radius ratio of positive to negative ions progresses from 1/1 to 0.73/1, the negative ions finally touch one another and further reduction of the cation size results in the oppositely charged ions no longer touching one another, causing a less stable crystal state. The sodium chloride arrangement, with six anions around the cation, once again permits contact between the cation and anions and results in a more stable crystal form. Still further change of the ratio to 0.41/1 once again brings the anions into contact, but still just in contact with the cation. Further reduction of the cation size brings about a less stable arrangement and the preferred form then becomes the more stable zinc blende structure where four anions surround the cation. However, the latter crystal form is not found among the alkali metal halides. The changes from one type of crystal arrangement to another are not as precise as the above statements might imply, the reason for this being that they are based on strictly geometrical reasoning without taking into account ion deformations due to electrostatic effects, etc.

The alkali metals form white solid hydrides quite readily when heated in hydrogen gas. They are among the most stable of the metallic hydrides and exist in an ionic lattice form (sodium chloride arrangement) consisting of sodium ions and hydride (H^-) ions. Only lithium reacts readily with nitrogen, even at room temperature, to form the nitride (Li_3N), which decomposes with water to ammonia and the hydroxide. The alkali metals have a high affinity for oxygen and readily form the ordinary oxides as well as the higher oxides with both the affinity and the tendency for higher oxide formation increasing with atomic weight. They also react vigorously with water to form hydrogen gas and the metallic hydroxide. All of the alkali metals bring about this facile reduction of water with the activity increasing as the atomic weight increases and, for this reason, must be stored under kerosene, coated with paraffin or protected in some other fashion. Although lithium has a low activity (as compared to other alkali metals) in contact with water, much of this can be attributed to the fact that it is the only one that does not melt below the boiling point of water. When a metal melts in the hot aqueous solution it has an opportunity to expose a continually new surface to the action of the water. The oxidation potential, given in the table, measures the extent to which each metal forms its hydrated ion in aqueous solution (also a measure of its action as a reducing agent.) It may be noted that the oxidation potential should increase with a decreasing ionization potential and, indeed, this is so with the exception of lithium which deviation is probably due to the strong hydration of the ion on account of its small size. The oxidation potential of lithium is approximately that of cesium and it is a better reducing agent than the latter because of the strong hydration effect. Because the oxidation potential is not as simple an effect as one might surmise but is in reality a composite of several energy considerations further consideration in this text will not be attempted.[1]

The alkali metal hydroxides are all alkaline in aqueous solution with the alkalinity naturally increasing as the ionic radius increases. In a similar way, the alkalinity of the alkali metal hydroxides is greater than that of the alkaline earth metal hydroxides (Group II) which, in turn, is greater than the Group III hydroxides. Thus, a generalization can be made that the alkalinity of metallic hydroxides increases from right to left and from top to bottom of the Periodic Table which, in effect, states that the greater the radius of the cation the greater will be the tendency for alkalinity.

Virtually all salts of the alkali metals are water-soluble (see p. 172) and, as a consequence, incompatibilities arising because of them are rare with most incompatibilities being ascribed to the anions. The general rule is that the salts of alkali metals are more soluble than

[1] The interested reader will find a discussion in Gould, E. S., "Inorganic Reactions and Structures," p. 98, pub. by Henry Holt and Co., New York, 1955.

the salts of any other periodic group. According to Sidgwick[1] there is a rather simple generalization concerning the order of solubilities of alkali metal salts. Briefly, he notes that when the anions are derived from strong acids, the lower atomic weight alkali metals form the most soluble salts but with anions from weak acids the opposite is true. These solubility generalizations can be rationalized on the basis that with weak acids the hydrogen must be held rather firmly and, because the lithium ion is small in size, it too will be held strongly in the solid state. On the other hand, the anions of strong acids are usually rather large and it is well-known that the stability of crystals is lowered somewhat by large discrepancies in the relative sizes of the cation and anion.

Generally speaking, the alkali metals do not form complexes although a few are known. If one includes the hydrated and ammoniated ions as complexes then these solvated forms represent perhaps the most common types that will be encountered. The degree of solvation of the ions is not precisely known but is known to diminish in going from lithium to cesium as indicated by the increase in mobility of the ions with increasing ionic radius. Although the smaller cations have a stronger tendency to hydrate, the number of dipoles that can be held is limited so that Li^+ can hold 4, Na^+ and K^+ can hold 6 and Rb^+ and Cs^+ can hold 8. However, the potential coordinating capacities of K^+, Rb^+ and Cs^+ are rarely, if ever, realized. The tendency for alkali metal ion hydration to carry over to the solid salts is, for all practical purposes, limited to lithium and sodium. Although potassium salts may possess some water of hydration this may be ascribed to anion water and, indeed, there is a parallelism between several potassium and ammonium (which cannot hold cation water) salts insofar as comparative hydrates are concerned. The above statements also hold for ammoniates (solid compounds of salts with ammonia or amines).

In conclusion, reference should be made to the behavior of the alkali metals with liquid ammonia. If oxidizing impurities are rigidly excluded all of the alkali metals will dissolve in this solvent with the formation of a blue solution. The nature of the process is still obscure. The blue solution can be evaporated to eventually recover the unchanged metal. However, in the presence of catalytic amounts of oxidizing agents, ammonia will rapidly react with the metals to form the alkali amides (MNH_2). The rapidity of reaction is correlated with increasing atomic weight (*i.e.*, Cs > Rb > K- > Na > Li).

[1] Sidgwick, N. V., "The Chemical Elements and Their Compounds," p. 95, pub. by Clarendon Press, Oxford, 1950.

12

Lithium and Lithium Compounds

LITHIUM

Symbol, Li. Valence, 1. Atomic Weight, 6.939; Atomic Number, 3

History and Occurrence.—In 1817 J. A. Arfwedson discovered lithium in a silicate known as *petalite*. The free metal was first isolated by Bunsen and Matthiessen in 1855. The name *lithium* was derived from the Greek word, λιθos, meaning *a stone*, and the element was so named because it was believed to be present only in stones. Also, it was thought that the salts of lithium assisted in dissolving "stones" in the kidneys, gall bladder, etc.

This element does not occur free in Nature. In combination it is found widely diffused. Traces of lithium salts are found in some mineral waters (Mur Springs at Baden-Baden), in soils and in the ashes of many plants, especially in those of tobacco, sugar beet, tea, coffee and sugar cane. It is found in a few minerals, *e.g.*, *spodumene* (LiAl[SiO$_3$]$_2$), *lepidolite* or *lithium mica* (KLi-[AlOH,F]$_2$Al[SiO$_3$]$_3$), *amblygonite* (Li[AlF]PO$_4$), and *triphyllite* (Li[FeMn]PO$_4$). One of the largest sources of spodumene (the most plentiful of the lithium-bearing ores) is the Black Hills of South Dakota. A new source of lithium has been found in Searles Lake and was developed during World War II. This source is now supplying a substantial part of the lithium used in this country.

Physical Properties.—Lithium is the lightest of all the metals. It is preserved by coating with petrolatum. Its density at 20° C. is 0.534. It has a silvery-white luster and, though harder than sodium or potassium, it is softer than lead, calcium and strontium. Its toughness permits it to be drawn into wire or rolled into sheets. Lithium melts at 180° C. and does not vaporize at red heat. It boils at 1336° C. All lithium salts (not the metal) color a flame crimson red and give a characteristic red line together with a less brilliant orange line in the spectrum.

Chemical Properties.—Lithium ignites in air at 200° C. and burns quietly with a very intense, white light. It decomposes water more slowly than sodium. The metal unites vigorously with oxygen (Li$_2$O), hydrogen (LiH), and nitrogen (Li$_3$N) to form stable compounds. The lithium salts differ markedly in some respects from other alkali metal salts. As an outstanding example the lithium soaps are not water-soluble as are the soaps of sodium and potassium. Indeed, they are quite water-repellent and have, by virtue of this property, enabled the preparation of soaps (lithium stearate particularly) useful as lubricating greases.

Other lithium salts that would be expected to be soluble on the basis of comparison with sodium salts, but which actually are only slightly soluble, are the carbonate, orthoarsenate, fluoride, and phosphate.

Tests for Identity of Lithium Ion.—1. A small quantity of a lithium salt moistened with hydrochloric acid imparts a crimson color to the non-luminous flame of a Bunsen burner.

2. Lithium salts in solution, made alkaline with sodium hydroxide, yield with sodium carbonate T.S. a white precipitate on boiling (1) (2).

(1) $Li^+ + NaOH \rightleftarrows LiOH + Na^+$

(2) $2LiOH + Na_2CO_3 \rightarrow Li_2CO_3 \downarrow + 2NaOH$

The Li_2CO_3 is soluble in a solution of ammonium chloride.

3. Solutions of lithium salts are not precipitated by diluted sulfuric acid or soluble sulfates. This test is necessary to avoid confusion with strontium which also gives a crimson color with the flame test, but gives a precipitate of $SrSO_4$ with soluble sulfates.

Commercial Manufacture.—Lithium may be obtained by electrolyzing (1) fused lithium chloride, (2) a fused mixture of lithium chloride and potassium chloride, or (3) the chloride in solution in pyridine. The very deliquescent lithium chloride is obtained by fusing lithium minerals with barium chloride. The cooled "melt" is lixiviated with water and the resulting solution filtered and evaporated to dryness. The residue is then extracted with a mixture of absolute alcohol and ether, which dissolves the lithium chloride but not the chlorides of sodium and potassium. The alcohol-ether mixture is recovered and the residue of lithium chloride thoroughly dried. It is from this fused salt that the metal is obtained by electrolysis. The electrolytic process is similar to that used for obtaining sodium from sodium chloride (see p. 193).

Pharmacological Action of the Lithium Ion.[1]—The lithium ion behaves systemically very much like the potassium ion. It is depressant to the nerve centers and to the circulation. The ion has a diuretic action but has no advantages over potassium ion and may have some disadvantages. The lithium ion is said to be somewhat less toxic to the heart than potassium ion. It stimulates the vagus and a gastro-enteritis may be produced by continual administration of even small doses.

---

[1] For a thorough review of the biology and pharmacology of the lithium ion the reader should consult the review by M. Schou, Pharmacological Reviews, **9**, 17 (1957).

The introduction of lithium salts into medicine was on the basis of the observed water solubility of lithium urate. This was due to an observation by Lipowitz in 1841 that lithium carbonate was a much better solvent for uric acid than sodium carbonate. The implication was that administration of lithium salts would solubilize the known deposits of uric acid in gouty conditions. However, inasmuch as the body contains a good supply of sodium, potassium, and ammonium ions it is no more possible for a soluble lithium urate to form than it is for soluble sodium oxalate to form in the presence of calcium ion. The irrationality of using lithium salts in this condition has long been recognized and all salts formerly official have lost their status. Indeed, lithium bromide, used only for its bromide ion content and last recognized in N.F. XI, has also been deleted.

An interesting therapeutic usage of lithium salts, pr ncipally abroad, has been in mental hospitals for the treatment o i mania.[1] Under controlled conditions, the use of the carbonate or cit rate salts in a dosage of 40 to 60 millequivalents per day initially and with reduction to one-half this dose in the maintenance phase have been quite encouraging. Although barbiturates and tranquilizers have been used for the same indication they are distinctively different from lithium salts in that the latter show no "drugged" effect, thus indicating a fairly specific lithium ion action in producing the calmative action.

The relatively toxic nature of lithium was strikingly brought into the limelight a few years ago when a number of deaths and injuries resulted from the use of lithium chloride as a salt-substitute for cardiac patients. At the time of the outbreak of the poisonings, lithium chloride was marketed as a constituent of Westsal, Foodsal, Salti-Salt, Milosal and Salnil for use in salt-free diets and also as a seasoning agent in salt-free bread. All of these preparations were recalled by the companies involved under direction of the Federal Security Agency's Food and Drug Administration.

The mechanism of lithium poisoning and its residual effects is somewhat obscure but it appears that there is a correlation between the success in limiting sodium ion intake and the severity of poisoning by ingested lithium ion. Lithium poisoning is seldom seen in patients on a normal sodium ion intake. Early symptoms of lithium poisoning are similar to those of the heart and kidney disease requiring the salt-free diet. These include weakness, drowsiness, loss of appetite, nausea, tremors and blurring of vision. Daily doses of 1 to 5 Gm. may bring on these effects, especially in patients on a restricted sodium intake. In mild cases it seems probable that withdrawal of the lithium brings about an early cessation of untoward action, and no continuing effect is believed to exist. Lithium may be stored briefly in the body but it is quite well established that it is eliminated by both kidneys and intestinal tract.

[1] See ref. by M. Schou on previous page.

Lithium Bromide, N.F. XI, $LiBr \cdot xH_2O$ occurs as a white, or pinkish-white granular powder, or in colorless prismatic crystals. It is odorless and has a sharp, slightly bitter taste. Its density is 3.446 and its melting-point 547° C. The salt is so very deliquescent that it goes into solution in its absorbed moisture.

One Gm. of Lithium Bromide is soluble in 0.6 ml. of water at 25° C. and in 0.4 ml. of boiling water. It is freely soluble in alcohol and it dissolves in ether.

At red heat the salt fuses and at higher temperatures it slowly sublimes without decomposition.

Lithium bromide gives the reactions of both the lithium ion (*q.v.*) and those of the bromide ion. It gives a precipitate of yellow silver bromide when treated with silver nitrate (1).

$$(1)\ LiBr + AgNO_3 \rightarrow AgBr \downarrow + LiNO_3$$

This precipitate is almost insoluble in an excess of ammonia water.

Addition of chlorine water to a solution of lithium bromide causes the liberation of bromine (2).

$$(2)\ 2LiBr + Cl_2 \rightarrow 2LiCl + Br_2$$

Lithium bromide may be prepared by treating lithium carbonate with a solution of ferrous bromide (4) obtained by treating an excess of iron wire with bromine (3). The lithium carbonate ordinarily is obtained by treating lithium chloride with ammonium carbonate which results in the precipitation of the relatively insoluble lithium carbonate. Lithium bromide is obtained in crystalline form from a highly concentrated solution by slowly evaporating it over sulfuric acid.

$$(3)\ Fe + Br_2 \rightarrow FeBr_2$$

$$(4)\ Li_2CO_3 + FeBr_2 \rightarrow 2LiBr + FeCO_3 \downarrow$$

This salt has been used as a sedative because of the central depressant properties of the bromide ion (see p. 214) and possesses the greatest concentration of bromide ion per unit weight of any of the alkali metal bromides. It is not usually used alone because of potential toxicity but is often found in combination with other bromides in such preparations as the formerly official Bromides Syrup. No average dose was given for this salt by the N.F. XI although the N.F. VIII gave 1 Gm. as the average dose. This lack of a specific dose for the salt probably indicates the uncertain status of its toxicity (see Pharmacological Action of Lithium).

13

Sodium and Sodium Compounds

SODIUM

Symbol, Na. Valence, 1. Atomic Weight, 22.9898; Atomic Number 11

History.—The metallic element sodium was discovered by Sir H. Davy in 1807 when he electrolyzed sodium hydroxide. Shortly afterward, Gay-Lussac and Thénard suggested a method whereby molten caustic soda could be decomposed by means of red hot iron. This method in turn was succeeded by Brunner's process of igniting sodium carbonate with charcoal. In 1886, Castner recommended the use of sodium hydroxide in place of sodium carbonate and thereby greatly lessened the cost of manufacture. Later, he advocated the use of iron carbide to replace charcoal and this process is still used. In 1890, Castner patented an electrolytic process by which most of the metallic sodium of commerce was made for a long time. In 1924, J. C. Downs patented the process by which metallic sodium is made today.

Occurrence.—Sodium, like the other chemical elements belonging to the group of alkali metals, is found abundantly and widely distributed in Nature, but always in combination. Sodium chloride forms more than two-thirds of the solids dissolved in sea water. It occurs also in the form of rock salt in the earth. Many compounds of sodium are constituents of spring water and, in combination, sodium is universally distributed in vegetable and animal organisms.

Soda felspar ($NaAlSi_3O_8$) is present in enormous quantities throughout the rocky crust of the earth. The decomposition of igneous rocks accounts for the presence of sodium compounds in all soils. Sodium carbonate is found widely distributed in Nature as the constituent of many mineral waters and as the principal saline component of natron or trona lakes. Sodium carbonate occurs as efflorescences in lower Egypt, China and Iran, and as a natural deposit in warm and dry districts of many countries, *e.g.*, Egypt, India, and also in California, Nevada and Wyoming. In the latter localities it is usually found mixed with sulfates, chlorides or borates. The crude alkaline crusts of carbonate occurring in Hungary are known as "Szekso." In Nature, sodium sulfate occurs as *thenardite* (Na_2SO_4—anhydrous) in Chile, and in rock salt deposits in Spain. Large deposits of sodium nitrate are found in the district of Atacama and the province of Tarapaca. A double fluoride of sodium and aluminum (Na_3AlF_6) called *cryolite* is extensively mined in Greenland and elsewhere.

Physical Properties.—Sodium is a soft metal having a silvery-white luster when freshly cut. At ordinary temperatures the metal has the consistency of wax and can be readily cut with a knife. It hardens on cooling. It has a density of 0.97, a melting-point of 97.7° C., and boils at 883° C., giving a green vapor which is a monatomic gas. Because of its marked tendency to lose an electron and pass from the elemental into the ionic state, sodium occurs high in the electromotive series of the metals.

Chemical Properties of Sodium and Sodium Ion.—*Sodium metal* is very active chemically. Because of this activity it is stored under an inert liquid such as kerosene to retard the action of air and moisture upon it or in air-tight containers. When exposed to the air, it rapidly becomes covered with a dull gray coating which is a mixture of hydroxide, oxide and carbonate of the metal. When heated in air, it burns with a bright yellow flame, forming sodium monoxide (Na_2O) and sodium peroxide (Na_2O_2). Sodium decomposes water with the formation of the hydroxide and the evolution of hydrogen (1), which inflames only when hot water is used.

$$(1)\ \ 2Na + 2H_2O \rightarrow 2NaOH + H_2 \uparrow$$

It also reacts with alcohols in an analogous manner (2).

$$(2)\ \ 2Na + 2ROH \rightarrow 2RONa + H_2 \uparrow$$

When dry ammonia gas is reacted with sodium metal, a compound known as sodium amide (or sodamide) is formed (3).

$$(3)\ \ 2Na + 2NH_3 \rightarrow 2NaNH_2 + H_2 \uparrow$$

The reaction is quite analogous to the reaction of sodium with water.

The element combines directly with most non-metallic elements, especially in the presence of a trace of moisture. Sodium forms an amalgam (an alloy of mercury with another metal), which is said to contain one or more compounds of the two elements, although the amalgam behaves chemically like a simple mixture of the two metals. When the amalgam contains more than a small amount of sodium, it is a solid and is frequently used instead of pure sodium as an active reducing agent because of the ease with which the interactions of the metal with aqueous or alcoholic solutions may be controlled. An amalgam containing 2 per cent of Na is a soft solid having a silvery luster. The reaction of the amalgam may be pictured as simply a reaction of sodium with water or alcohol, since sodium hydroxide (or a sodium alkoxide in the case of an alcohol) together with hydrogen is formed and mercury deposited.

Sodium ion does not form very many insoluble salts, but the few that are known deserve mention. Uric acid, for example, reacts with sodium ion to form two possible salts, the acid urate (4) and the normal urate (5).

(4) $H_2C_5H_2O_3N_4 + NaOH \rightarrow NaHC_5H_2O_3N_4\downarrow + H_2O$
$$\text{sol. in } H_2O = 1:1200 \text{ (cold)}$$

(5) $H_2C_5H_2O_3N_4 + 2NaOH \rightarrow Na_2C_5H_2O_3N_4\downarrow + 2H_2O$
$$\text{sol. in } H_2O = 1:75 \text{ (cold)}$$

Use has been made of the relative insolubility of the sodium urates together with other chemicals in the chemical demineralization of sea water for the emergency preparation of drinking water.

When a freshly prepared solution of potassium antimonate is added to a neutral or slightly alkaline (with KOH) solution of sodium chloride and the mixture allowed to stand for an hour, a white crystalline precipitate of disodium pyroantimonate (nearly insoluble in water) settles out (6).

(6) $2KH_2SbO_4 + 2Na^+ \rightarrow Na_2H_2Sb_2O_7 \downarrow + 2K^+ + H_2O$

There is a group of reagents which forms so-called *triple acetates* with sodium. Chief among these are zinc uranyl acetate, magnesium uranyl acetate and cobalt uranyl acetate. They have the property of forming relatively insoluble salts with sodium ion having, in general, the following composition:

$$3UO_2(C_2H_3O_2)_2 . M(C_2H_3O_2)_2 . NaC_2H_3O_2 . 6H_2O,$$
$$\text{where } M = \text{Zn, Mg or Co}$$

The zinc salt has been recommended as a reagent for the gravimetric determination of the sodium ion. However, it is said that the cobalt derivative is more suitable for qualitative testing because it is not interfered with by potassium ion.

Official Tests for Identity of Sodium Ion.—1. When sodium compounds are converted to the chloride or nitrate salt they will yield a golden-yellow precipitate with cobalt-uranyl acetate T.S. upon agitation. (See under Chemical Properties of Sodium and Sodium ion.)

2. Sodium compounds will impart an intense yellow color to a non-luminous flame. This test may be said to be almost too sensitive in that it is difficult to tell from the color and intensity of the flame whether significant amounts or mere traces of sodium are present.

Commercial Manufacture.—The method of production of metallic sodium has changed over the years. The most important old or new commercial methods, however, have been electrolytic in nature. The principal difference in the old and new methods is in the electrolyte used.

The older method, now almost obsolete, was the Castner electrolytic process which was used extensively until approximately 1925. Briefly, it depended upon the electrolysis of fused sodium hydroxide (caustic soda) to yield sodium metal and hydrogen at the cathode and oxygen at the anode.

In 1924, J. C. Downs patented the electrolytic process now in extensive use. It differs from the Castner process in that the less expensive sodium chloride is used as the electrolyte in place of sodium hydroxide (which must be manufactured from NaCl). Because the melting-point of NaCl (804° C.) approaches the boiling-point of metallic sodium (880° C.) the process at first encountered trouble because it was difficult to collect the sodium metal. High temperatures, such as those existing in the cell, caused the sodium metal to form a "fog" which was exceedingly difficult to condense. However, the addition of electrolytes which are unchanged by electrolysis to the fusion bath was found to bring the melting-point of the bath down to about 600° C. and this solved the problem.

The commercial handling of sodium is deserving of mention. It is no longer shipped under kerosene as is stated in some of the older texts on inorganic chemistry. Instead it is shipped either in airtight containers or is shipped solid in tank cars. The tank cars are loaded with the metal in a molten condition and the sodium is then allowed to solidify. When it arrives at its destination it is remelted by means of heated jackets and is piped into the plants in the liquid form. It is stored under either liquid or solid nitrogen in huge tanks.

Pharmacology of the Sodium Ion.—The sodium ion is almost devoid of any demonstrable drug or chemical effect upon the human body. This would be expected from the knowledge that sodium ion is normally present in the body fluids in relatively large amounts, and it would be unreasonable to expect pronounced drug effects by adding more sodium ion. However, the sodium ion is extremely important because of the *osmotic* effects it is capable of producing. The sodium ion is the predominant cation in the so-called *extracellular* fluid (that outside the cells, *i.e.*, in the circulation and surrounding the tissue cells), whereas the potassium ion is the predominant cation in the *intracellular* fluid (fluid inside the cells). It is well known that an osmotic gradient (with a consequent flow of water molecules) results when the concentration of water molecules on one side of a semipermeable membrane (permeable to water molecules but not to salts) exceeds the concentration on the other side. Therefore, in the body we have essentially a balanced system of electrolytes where sodium ions (associated with various anions, principally chloride and bicarbonate) exist on one side of a membrane (the cell wall) and potassium ions (also associated with several anions) exist on the other side. It is believed that it is the sodium ion which is unable to pass through the membrane rather than the potassium ion. In this way, an osmotic gradient is set up in one direction or another through the cell wall, depending on whether the sodium-ion concentration of the extracellular fluid is *hypotonic* or *hypertonic* to the electrolyte concentration of the cell contents (intracellular fluid). If the extracellular solution is hypotonic, water molecules flow into the cell, whereas if the solution is hypertonic water flows out of the cell and it becomes dehydrated. Needless to say, if the sodium-ion concentration is *isotonic* with the cell contents no osmotic gradient exists and, therefore, no flow of water molecules will take place. From the foregoing discussion, it is apparent that while the sodium ion has no specific action on the body tissue, its osmotic function is highly important with regard to the distribution of fluids in the body.

Disturbances causing an abnormal sodium content in the body fluids lead to several well-defined clinical symptoms. Among the common causes for such disturbances may be excessive vomiting, diarrhea or perspiration. A detailed discussion[1] of the alterations in blood sodium and consequent effects is not within the scope of this book. It should be pointed out, however, that the intelligent treatment of conditions arising from abnormal fluid distribution demands a knowledge of the osmotic phenomena bringing about the condition. For example, cardiac patients often display an edematous condition (excess fluid in the tissues). One might come to the conclusion that because sodium chloride is a diuretic, a good way to get rid of the extra fluid in the tissues would be to administer sodium chloride in sufficient amounts. However, in this case, it would be exactly contraindicated, since it would cause a hypertonic condition of the extracellular fluid. This, of course, would attract water from the intracellular fluid aggravating the edematous condition. For this reason, cardiac patients usually are on a low sodium chloride (or any sodium salt) diet. The achievement of a diet is not too easily accomplished. Patients accustomed to the use of salt feel rather strongly about being deprived of its use and numerous salt-free condiments have been devised as a result (*e.g.,* Neo-Curtasal, Co-Salt, Diasal, Gustamate, etc.). An ingenious approach to the control of the sodium level without severe dietary restriction of sodium intake has been through the use of the ion-exchange type of resin (see p. 41). In this case the resin is of the weakly acidic carboxylic acid cation exchange type first suggested by Dock[2] and which has been shown to effectively remove sodium in the gastrointestinal tract. Commercial products of this type are Carbo-Resin, Katonium, Natrinil and Resodex.

[1] Goodman and Gilman: *The Pharmacological Basis of Therapeutics,* p. 763, 1965.
[2] Dock. W., Tr. A. Am. Physicians, **59**, 282 (1946).

OFFICIAL COMPOUNDS OF SODIUM

SODIUM ACETATE

Sodium Acetate, N.F. XII

Formula, $CH_3COONa.3H_2O$.   Molecular Weight, 136.08

Physical Properties.—Sodium Acetate occurs as colorless, transparent monoclinic prisms, or as a granular, crystalline powder. It is odorless or has a faint acetous odor and has a cooling saline taste. When exposed to dry, warm air, the salt effloresces. Its density is 1.45.

One Gm. of Sodium Acetate is soluble in about 0.8 ml. of water and in about 19 ml. of alcohol, at 25° C. It is insoluble in ether.

Chemical Properties.—Sodium Acetate is a good catalyst for some of the acetylation reactions of organic chemistry. For this purpose it is used in the anhydrous condition as "fused sodium acetate." By carefully heating official sodium acetate in a casserole it is first observed to dissolve in its own water of crystallization, but with final evaporation of the water it solidifies. If the solid material is heated carefully to prevent charring it can be melted. This melt is then poured out on a clean surface and pulverized to obtain the product.

In the discussion of buffers (see p. 114) sodium acetate was used as an example. Its virtue in this capacity results from the hydrolysis due to the acetate ion (1).

$$(1)\quad CH_3COO^- + H_2O \rightleftarrows CH_3COOH + OH^-$$

It is, obviously, the member of the buffer pair (sodium acetate: acetic acid) that is capable of handling the addition of reasonable quantities of acid without major deviation in the pH. It cannot prevent changes in pH due to added hydroxide ions.

In general, the principal incompatibilities associated with acetates result from the alkalinity imparted by hydrolysis of the alkali metal acetates. Virtually all metal acetates are water-soluble.

By means of its ability to "tie up" the added hydronium ions, sodium acetate will react with excess sulfuric acid (2) to liberate acetic acid which may be detected (vinegar odor) by heating the

$$(2)\quad 2CH_3COONa + H_2SO_4 \rightarrow 2CH_3COOH + Na_2SO_4$$

solution. Also, when sodium acetate is warmed with sulfuric acid and ethyl alcohol, the acetic acid is esterified to form ethyl acetate (3).

$$(3)\quad CH_3COOH + C_2H_5OH \xrightarrow[\Delta]{H_2SO_4} CH_3COOC_2H_5 \uparrow + H_2O$$

Sodium Acetate is assayed by igniting a weighed sample in a crucible until the residue consists of sodium carbonate (4). This

$$(4)\ 2CH_3COONa.3H_2O + 4O_2 \rightarrow Na_2CO_3 + 9H_2O \uparrow + 3CO_2 \uparrow$$

residue is then treated with excess 0.5 N sulfuric acid and back titrated with 0.5 N sodium hydroxide using methyl orange as an indicator. Methyl orange is used as an indicator because its color change occurs well on the acid side of the pH scale (see p. 113).

Official Tests for Identity.—1. The salt responds to the "Official Tests for Identity of Sodium Ion" (p. 193).

2. When heated to about 58° C., the salt begins to liquefy, and at 120° C. it becomes hard and anhydrous. At higher temperatures it fuses and finally decomposes, emitting inflammable vapors and leaving a residue of sodium carbonate and carbon (4).
The residue gives positive tests for sodium, is alkaline to litmus paper and effervesces with acids.

3. Sodium Acetate gives all of the tests characteristic of *Acetates:*

(*a*) Acidification of Sodium Acetate or its solutions causes the evolution of an acetic acid (vinegar) odor, particularly if the mixture is warmed (2).

(*b*) If Sodium Acetate is warmed with sulfuric acid and ethyl alcohol the acid is esterified to form ethyl acetate which possesses a characteristic odor (3). The acid is formed first according to equation (2), and then the esterification takes place.

(*c*) Ferric chloride T.S. added to solutions of acetates causes the formation of a deep red color due to ferric acetate (5).[1] This color is destroyed by mineral acids.

$$(5)\ FeCl_3 + 3CH_3COONa \rightleftarrows (CH_3COO)_3Fe + 3NaCl$$

Commercial Manufacture.—Sodium acetate is made by neutralizing acetic acid with sodium carbonate or bicarbonate, filtering, and evaporating the resulting solution to crystallization (6).

$$(6)\ 2CH_3COOH + Na_2CO_3 \rightarrow 2CH_3COONa + H_2O + CO_2 \uparrow$$

or

$$CH_3COOH + NaHCO_3 \rightarrow CH_3COONa + H_2O + CO_2 \uparrow$$

Pharmacological Action of the Acetate Ion.—The acetate ion itself does not seem to possess any particular therapeutic virtue, except insofar as it is associated with a cation and functions as a means of introducing the cation into the body fluids. Thus, sodium acetate when orally administered is absorbed and easily oxidized in the tissues to sodium bicarbonate (7).

$$(7)\ CH_3COONa + 4(O) \xrightarrow[\text{oxidation}]{\text{tissue}} NaHCO_3 + H_2O + CO_2$$

---

[1] Some workers attribute the red color to the formation of colloidal Fe(OH)₃ from the readily hydrolyzable ferric acetate.

14

Its physiological action is reflected in the fact that it causes a hypertonic condition of the extracellular fluid. This "salt effect" results in a diuretic action, because the kidneys regulate the electrolyte concentration of the body fluids by excreting water and varying amounts of salts. Sodium acetate is, therefore, a diuretic. Sodium acetate is of particular value as a diuretic in the treatment of cystitis and diseases of the urinary tract associated with highly acid urine.

Uses.—*Sodium Acetate,* N.F. XII, when rendered anhydrous by overnight drying at 80° C. followed by drying for 4 hours at 120° C., contains not less than 99 per cent of CH_3COONa. It is used as a diuretic, urinary alkalizer and systemic antacid or alkalizer (7). It is usually administered in a dose of 1.5 Gm.

In approximately equimolecular amounts it is used also to solubilize the purine alkaloids as in *Theophylline Sodium Acetate.* This solubilization is often depicted as the formation of a double salt.

In order to fuse sodium acetate it requires about four times as much heat as is absorbed by an equal volume of water and, because this heat is very slowly evolved, the fused salt is used as a filler for foot warmers and many other types of thermophores.

SODIUM BICARBONATE

Sodium Bicarbonate, U.S.P. XVII

Formula, $NaHCO_3$; Molecular Weight, 84.01

Physical Properties.—Sodium Bicarbonate is a white, odorless, crystalline (monoclinic) powder. It is stable in dry air, but in moist air it slowly decomposes into sodium carbonate, carbon dioxide and water. It has a specific gravity of 2.206.

One Gm. of Sodium Bicarbonate is soluble in 10 ml. of water at 25° C. It is insoluble in alcohol.

Chemical Properties.—When heated, the salt loses water and carbon dioxide and is converted into the normal carbonate (1).

$$(1)\ 2NaHCO_3 \rightarrow Na_2CO_3 + H_2O \uparrow + CO_2 \uparrow$$

The above decomposition takes place whether the dry salt or a solution of it is heated. It accounts for one of the major difficulties in attempting to sterilize either the dry salt or solutions of it since the sodium carbonate solution which remains is much more alkaline than the bicarbonate solution and consequently would be dangerous to use parenterally. The British Pharmacopœia recognizes an injection of sodium bicarbonate which is a sterile solution of Sodium Bicarbonate in Water for Injection. It states that the solution can be sterilized by bacteriologic filtration or by autoclaving. The latter process is done by passing carbon dioxide through the solution for one minute and then placing the solution in gas-tight containers for the autoclaving process. After two hours of cooling at room temperature the solution is assayed in the conventional way to make sure that no decomposition has taken place. Another procedure that is sometimes used is to aseptically weigh reagent grade sodium bicarbonate into warm Sterile Water for Injection. Although there is a definite possibility of having a nonsterile solution as a result, this method has been used with few untoward results.

Sterilization of a sodium bicarbonate solution also may be effected by heating in an open vessel and then resaturating the cooled solution with sterile carbon dioxide.

Another characteristic reaction of bicarbonate (also carbonate) salts is that carbon dioxide is liberated when they are treated with acids (2). The liberated CO_2 bubbling through the liquid is termed

$$(2)\ NaHCO_3 + HA \rightarrow NaA + CO_2 \uparrow + H_2O\ (HA = any\ acid).$$

effervescence. Effervescent tablets and salts make use of the reaction of sodium bicarbonate with acids (usually organic acids, *e.g.*, tartaric acid, citric acid, etc.), because in the dry state the bicarbonate and acid do not react, whereas, when introduced into water a vigorous evolution of CO_2 takes place. However, it is well to remember that the reaction can take place in moist air and may account for incompatibilities in dry prescription mixtures of sodium bicarbonate with acetylsalicylic acid (aspirin) or other acidic substances.

Aqueous solutions of sodium bicarbonate are slightly alkaline (pH of about 8.2) as a result of hydrolysis of the bicarbonate ion (3).

$$(3)\ HCO_3^- + H_2O \rightleftarrows H_2CO_3 + OH^-$$

Of course, the bicarbonate ion ionizes (4) also to a slight extent, but the amount of ionization is so small as to be negligible.

$$(4)\ HCO_3^- + H_2O \rightleftarrows CO_3^= + H_3O^+$$

Sodium bicarbonate is so slightly alkaline that it fails to turn phenolphthalein red. This fact constitutes a distinguishing test between sodium bicarbonate and sodium carbonate, because the carbonate ion in the latter salt is so extensively ionized that the solution is quite alkaline (5) (pH is about 11.6).

$$(5)\ CO_3^= + H_2O \rightleftarrows HCO_3^- + OH^-$$

The bicarbonates of the alkali metals are all water-soluble. Other metallic bicarbonates are soluble to a limited extent and are usually so unstable that they decompose to the carbonates or hydrolyze to the hydroxides. An example of this is in the differentiation test between bicarbonate and carbonate using mercuric chloride T.S.

Addition of the reagent to a sodium bicarbonate solution gives no immediate precipitation, although in about one minute a reddish-brown residue begins to form in the bottom of the tube. It is assumed that mercuric bicarbonate forms as a transitory intermediate (6) but that part of the salt is quite rapidly hydrolyzed to mercuric hydroxide (7), which decomposes to give red mercuric oxide (8).

(6) $HgCl_2 + 2NaHCO_3 \rightarrow Hg(HCO_3)_2 + 2NaCl$
(7) $Hg(HCO_3)_2 \rightarrow Hg(OH)_2 \downarrow + 2CO_2 \uparrow$
(8) $Hg(OH)_2 \rightarrow HgO + H_2O$

In the case of sodium carbonate solutions the addition of the reagent causes the immediate formation of a reddish-brown precipitate. The composition of this precipitate is $HgCO_3.3HgO$. To explain its formation, it is assumed that the carbonate ion has hydrolyzed partly to yield hydroxide ions (5) which, with the mercuric ion, constitute the reactive ions. The mercuric ion will react normally with the carbonate to give $HgCO_3$ (9). The mercuric ion will also react with the hydroxide ions to give mercuric hydroxide (10) which is unstable and loses water to give red mercuric oxide (11).

(9) $Hg^{++} + CO_3^= \rightarrow HgCO_3 \downarrow$
(10) $Hg^{++} + 2OH^- \rightarrow Hg(OH)_2 \downarrow$
(11) $Hg(OH)_2 \rightarrow HgO + H_2O$

The completely balanced reaction would then be (12).

(12) $4Hg^{++} + CO_3^= + 6OH^- \rightarrow HgCO_3.3HgO \downarrow + 3H_2O$
        reddish-brown

Sodium Bicarbonate is assayed by titrating the weighed salt in aqueous solution with 1N sulfuric acid using methyl orange as an indicator (13).

(13) $2NaHCO_3 + H_2SO_4 \rightarrow Na_2SO_4 + 2H_2O + 2CO_2 \uparrow$

Official Tests for Identity.—1. The salt effervesces when treated with acids (2), and the CO_2 formed will cause precipitation of $CaCO_3$ when passed into lime water (contains $Ca(OH)_2$) (14).

(14) $Ca(OH)_2 + CO_2 \rightarrow CaCO_3 \downarrow + H_2O$

2. A cold aqueous solution of Sodium Bicarbonate, if pure, will not cause phenolphthalein to color red which serves to distinguish it from soluble carbonates (3, 5). Sodium carbonate, for example, colors phenolphthalein an intense red.

3. An aqueous solution responds to all the tests for *Sodium* ion (*q.v.*).

Commercial Manufacture.—Sodium bicarbonate is made by the Solvay Ammonia Soda Process which will be described in some detail under Sodium Carbonate (p. 219). When made by this process it does not meet the standards for medicinal or food grade sodium bicarbonate. To achieve a higher grade of purity, the more or less crude product from the Solvay process is heated to convert it to soda ash (anhydrous sodium carbonate) (1). The soda ash is then dissolved in water and treated in the cold with carbon dioxide (15) to reprecipitate the sodium bicarbonate which, when washed and dried, is of a high grade of purity.

(15) $Na_2CO_3 + CO_2 + H_2O \rightarrow 2NaHCO_3$

Pharmacological Action of the Bicarbonates.—Because sodium bicarbonate is the principal bicarbonate a discussion of its actions will serve as a guide to considerations of other bicarbonates. Sodium bicarbonate may be considered from the standpoint of two relationships: (1) its relationship to the body economy as a buffer component, (2) its therapeutic and miscellaneous uses.

1. The normal acid-base balance of the plasma is maintained by three mechanisms working together: the buffers of the body fluids and red blood cells; the pulmonary excretion of excess carbon dioxide; and the renal excretion of either acid or base, whichever is in excess.

Although there are other buffer systems in the plasma, e.g., (1) the sodium phosphate:sodium biphosphate system (see p. 147) and (2) the proteins, the $NaHCO_3:H_2CO_3$ buffer system is by far the most important. This buffer system involves an equilibrium between sodium bicarbonate and carbonic acid. At a given pH, the ratio of the concentrations of the two substances is constant. While the workings of the system are complex in detail, they are simple in principle. If an excess of *acid* is liberated in the body, it is neutralized by some of the sodium bicarbonate; the excess carbonic acid decomposes into water and carbon dioxide and the latter is excreted by the lungs until the normal ratio is achieved. If an excess of *alkali* arises in the body, it combines with carbonic acid to form bicarbonate, and more carbonic acid is formed from carbon dioxide and water to restore the balance. Since carbon dioxide is an end-product of the metabolism of all types of foodstuff, there is always an abundant supply upon which to draw. The situation may be represented as in Figure 5.

2. Sodium bicarbonate is used in medicine principally for its acid neutralizing properties. It is used (a) to combat gastric hyperacidity, (b) to combat systemic acidosis and (c) for miscellaneous uses.

(a) Because sodium bicarbonate is such a common household chemical it is considered by the layman as a rather innocuous

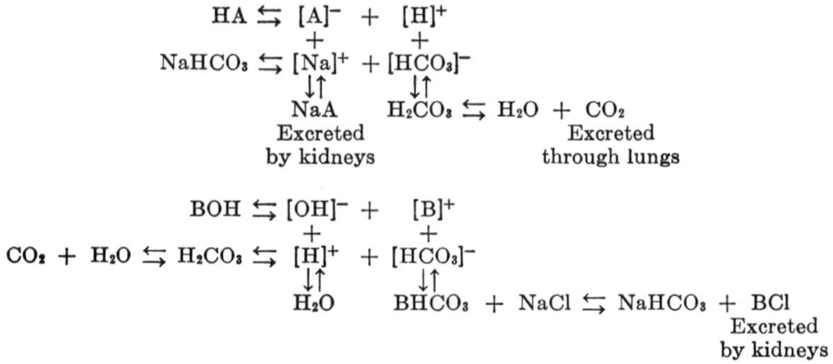

$$HA \leftrightarrows [A]^- + [H]^+$$
$$+ \qquad\qquad +$$
$$NaHCO_3 \leftrightarrows [Na]^+ + [HCO_3]^-$$
$$\downarrow\uparrow \qquad\qquad \downarrow\uparrow$$
$$NaA \qquad H_2CO_3 \leftrightarrows H_2O + CO_2$$
Excreted   Excreted
by kidneys   through lungs

$$BOH \leftrightarrows [OH]^- + [B]^+$$
$$+ \qquad\qquad +$$
$$CO_2 + H_2O \leftrightarrows H_2CO_3 \leftrightarrows [H]^+ + [HCO_3]^-$$
$$\downarrow\uparrow \qquad\qquad \downarrow\uparrow$$
$$H_2O \qquad BHCO_3 + NaCl \leftrightarrows NaHCO_3 + BCl$$
Excreted
by kidneys

Fig. 5.—Mechanism of bicarbonate: carbonic acid buffer system. "A" represents a radical of fixed (non-metabolizable) acid; "B," a radical of fixed base.

chemical and, in this way, has become quite popular for treating gastric hyperacidity and a multitude of other stomach ailments. It is common for the patient to attempt to treat "gas on the stomach" with sodium bicarbonate or an antacid powder containing it. Since the stomach is normally acid and thus reacts with carbonates or bicarbonates to liberate gaseous carbon dioxide, it is difficult to see where any benefit can be derived.

Of more serious consequence than the occasional use for gastric upset is its continued use in relatively large doses for the mitigation of the pains associated with peptic ulcer. The cause of the peptic ulcer is often traced back to the initial use of sodium bicarbonate, because sufficiently large doses of sodium bicarbonate will effectively neutralize all of the stomach acid and perhaps impart a slightly alkaline reaction to the gastric fluids. Since the stomach normally operates at an acid pH this obviously is an abnormal condition. Therefore, when the sodium bicarbonate has been eliminated, the stomach again secretes acid, but usually in larger amounts than were previously found in the stomach. This constitutes what is commonly known as "rebound acidity," and relief from the excess acidity is sought by again using sodium bicarbonate. In this way, a vicious cycle may be set up which can end in the formation of a peptic ulcer.

In spite of the misuses of sodium bicarbonate cited above, the drug is of established value in treating gastric hyperacidity, when used in controlled doses.

Oral administration of the drug also causes a lessening of the acidity of the urine or may even produce an alkalinization. This effect is of value during the administration of certain drugs to increase their effectiveness or lessen the possibility of their crystallizing in the kidneys or urinary tract. Notable among these drugs is sulfanilamide and its related drugs which, in an earlier day, were often prescribed with sodium bicarbonate for the purpose of preventing if possible the deposition of crystals of the conjugated sulfa drug in the kidney with consequent mechanical injury to that organ. It might be pointed out, however, that experience seems to indicate that large amounts of fluids ingested during the sulfa treatment are more apt to prevent this so-called "crystalluria" than is sodium bicarbonate. The administration of two or more sulfa drugs simultaneously has been quite effective, based on the principle that a given volume of liquid will hold more of the two (or more) than of any one. The development of sulfa drugs with better solubility characteristics has lessened the problem considerably. In addition to the use of sodium bicarbonate with drugs, it has been shown that changing the reaction of the urine alternately from acid to alkaline may have a beneficial effect in the treatment of certain types of urinary tract infections.

Occasionally, it is found that the simultaneous administration of sodium bicarbonate with other drugs inhibits the activity of the administered drug. Such a therapeutic incompatibility is found in the case of sodium bicarbonate and sodium salicylate which are often prescribed in equivalent amounts, the sodium bicarbonate being administered to alleviate the gastric discomfort attendant upon oral sodium salicylate administration. The investigators found that the administration of sodium bicarbonate and sodium salicylate simultaneously in equal amounts greatly retarded the rise in the serum salicylate level in contrast to sodium salicylate alone which rather quickly brings up the salicylate level. Furthermore, if a satisfactory salicylate level in the blood is reached by sodium salicylate alone, it was found that oral administration of sodium bicarbonate would markedly reduce the level. This has been related to an increased renal excretion in alkaline urine.

(b) Sodium bicarbonate is administered parenterally and orally to combat systemic acidosis. A dramatic use in this reference is in the treatment of methyl alcohol poisoning. Inasmuch as the metabolite of methyl alcohol is formic acid the intravenous use of large quantities of sodium bicarbonate is rational and credited with the saving of many lives. Its effect is mainly to increase the alkali reserve of the blood and to replace sodium ion in cases of clinical dehydration. Because it could easily be given in excessive amounts causing an alkalosis its intelligent use requires that the alkali reserve of the blood be determined before its administration. Inasmuch as it requires a laboratory analysis to determine the alkali reserve of the blood and because it is so difficult to sterilize sodium bicarbonate, several other sodium salts have been suggested as replacements, e.g., sodium lactate, sodium citrate, etc. These salts are claimed to be superior because the organic portion of the molecule is oxidized in the tissues to yield essentially sodium bicarbonate with the advantage that they can be sterilized and do not tend to cause alkalosis.

(c) When moistened with water, sodium bicarbonate is used as a local application for burns, insect bites, etc. It is also commonly used as a dentifrice although its taste does not lend itself to this purpose very well. One to 4 per cent solutions can be used as a cleansing lavage for mucous membranes.

Uses.—*Sodium Bicarbonate* (Baking Soda), U.S.P. XVII, "contains not less than 99 per cent of NaHCO₃, calculated on the dried basis." The principal medicinal applications of this salt have been discussed in conjunction with the "Pharmacological Action of Bicarbonates." The usual antacid dose is 2 Gm. up to four times a day with a range of 1 to 4 Gm.

Its usefulness as a pharmaceutical aid is to be observed in the many pharmaceutical preparations that make use of its chemical properties. As a source of sodium ion it is found in *Ascorbic Acid Injection* and *Phenolsulfonphthalein Injection*. Ascorbic Acid Injection is essentially a solution of sodium ascorbate. Although ascorbic acid itself is quite water-soluble it has been noted that the sodium salt, especially at a pH of 5 to 6, is much more stable than a solution of the acid with a pH of 2.5. However, more alkaline solutions of the sodium salt are prone to quick oxidation. In Phenolsulfonphthalein Injection the sodium bicarbonate (which changes to sodium carbonate when heated) is used to convert the water-insoluble phenolsulfonphthalein (Phenol Red) into the water-soluble sodium salt although sodium hydroxide can be used for the same purpose.

Its well-known use in providing carbonation of a solution by interaction with certain organic acids is to be noted in *Effervescent Sodium Phosphate* and *Seidlitz Powders*. The effect of carbonation is to improve palatability and also to promote faster gastric emptying time.

As a source of carbonate ions it was utilized in the preparation of *Saccharated Ferrous Carbonate* N.F. X and, as a buffering agent for holding down alkalinity, it is employed in *Diluted Sodium Hypochlorite Solution*.

SODIUM BIPHOSPHATE

Sodium Biphosphate, N.F. XII

Formula, NaH₂PO₄·H₂O; Molecular Weight, 137.99

Physical Properties.—Sodium Biphosphate occurs in the form of a white, crystalline powder or as colorless, transparent rhombic prisms. It is odorless and has an acid, saline taste. The salt is slightly deliquescent. It crystallizes in the rhombic system with 1 molecule of water, which it loses at 100° C. Sodium Biphosphate is very soluble in both cold and hot water, but is practically insoluble in alcohol.

Chemical Properties.—When the salt is heated to 240° C., it is converted into disodium dihydrogen pyrophosphate (1).

(1) $2NaH_2PO_4 \xrightarrow{\Delta} Na_2H_2P_2O_7 + H_2O$

When this salt ($Na_2H_2P_2O_7$) is heated to 240° C., it is changed into sodium metaphosphate (2) and modifications of sodium metaphosphate, such as $Na_2P_2O_6$, etc., the composition of the latter depending upon the conditions of heating.

(2) $Na_2H_2P_2O_7 \xrightarrow{\Delta} 2NaPO_3 + H_2O$

Although sodium biphosphate is a sodium salt of phosphoric acid, it is the result of replacing only one of the hydrogens of orthophosphoric acid with sodium and consequently exhibits acidic properties. The acidic properties are illustrated by the fact that solutions of the biphosphate will cause evolution of carbon dioxide from sodium bicarbonate or sodium carbonate (5).

The acidic properties can be largely attributed to the ionization of $H_2PO_4^-$ (4) which results from the ionization of sodium biphosphate (3).

(3) $NaH_2PO_4 \rightleftarrows Na^+ + H_2PO_4^-$

(4) $H_2PO_4^- + H_2O \rightleftarrows H_3O^+ + HPO_4^=$

The ionization in equation (4) takes place to approximately the same extent as the ionization of hypochlorous acid (HClO) or the ionization of the first hydrogen in carbonic acid. It is sufficiently acid to decolorize phenolphthalein but is not acidic enough to turn methyl orange yellow. Of course, the $HPO_4^=$ is also capable of ionizing but only to such a small extent that it is virtually negligible.

Because sodium biphosphate is essentially an acid it can be titrated and neutralized with sodium carbonate (5) or sodium hydroxide (6).

(5) $2NaH_2PO_4 + Na_2CO_3 \rightarrow 2Na_2HPO_4 + H_2O + CO_2 \uparrow$

(6) $NaH_2PO_4 + NaOH \rightarrow Na_2HPO_4 + H_2O$

The latter reaction (6) is the one involved in the titration of Sodium Biphosphate with 1N sodium hydroxide solution in the assay procedure. In the assay procedure sodium chloride is added to the solution being titrated for reasons explained earlier (see p. 145).

Official Tests for Identity.—1. Solutions of Sodium Biphosphate are acid to litmus paper and effervesce with sodium carbonate (5).

2. A 1 in 20 solution of Sodium Biphosphate responds to all of the official tests for *Sodium* ion (*q.v.*) and for *Phosphate* ion (*q.v.*).

Commercial Manufacture.—When orthophosphoric acid is added to a solution of secondary sodium orthophosphate and the solution evaporated, monohydrated sodium dihydrogen orthophosphate crystallizes out in rhombic prisms (7).

$$(7)\ Na_2HPO_4 + H_3PO_4 \rightarrow 2NaH_2PO_4$$

Uses.—*Sodium Biphosphate* (Sodium Dihydrogen Phosphate, Sodium Acid Phosphate), N.F. XII, contains an amount of NaH_2PO_4 equivalent to not less than 98 per cent and not more than 103 per cent of $NaH_2PO_4.H_2O$. This salt is administered internally to produce distinctly acid urine. It renders the urine acid because when absorbed it tends to disrupt the buffer system of phosphates in the blood. However, the kidneys excrete the excess phosphate as sodium acid phosphate which accounts for the urine acidity. The sodium biphosphate may be alternated with sodium bicarbonate for the purpose cited under Sodium Bicarbonate *i.e.*, to cause change of urine reaction from acid to alkaline or *vice versa*. Another important reason for the acidification of the urine is to "activate" certain antiseptic drugs, particularly methenamine. Methenamine itself is not antiseptic, but formaldehyde is liberated from it in acidic media. Formaldehyde, of course, is highly antiseptic and thus the methenamine combined with an acid urine acts as an antiseptic in the treatment of cystitis and other urinary tract infections. *Methenamine and Sodium Biphosphate Tablets* are a convenient way of administering sodium biphosphate with methenamine. However, the best time to administer the sodium biphosphate is midway between doses of methenamine.

Usual dose—0.6 Gm. four times a day ranging up to 1 Gm. Larger doses are apt to cause a cathartic action.

Technical grades of sodium biphosphate are used in some baking powders.

Sodium biphosphate with an effervescent alkaline buffer salt base for use as a laxative and cholagogue is marketed as Betaphos. Another mild saline laxative containing both sodium biphosphate and sodium phosphate is known as Phospho-Soda (Fleet).

SODIUM BISULFITE

Sodium Bisulfite, U.S.P. XVII

Formula, $NaHSO_3$; Molecular Weight, 104.06

Physical Properties.—Sodium Bisulfite occurs as a white, granular powder, or as white crystals. It has an odor of sulfur dioxide because it is somewhat unstable in air.

Chemical Properties.—The bisulfites as well as the sulfites are neutralized by the addition of acids to yield sulfurous acid (1)

which is essentially the same as a solution of sulfur dioxide in water
(2).

> (1) $NaHSO_3 + HCl \rightarrow NaCl + H_2SO_3$
> or $Na_2SO_3 + 2HCl \rightarrow 2NaCl + H_2SO_3$
> (2) $H_2SO_3 \rightleftarrows H_2O + SO_2 \uparrow$

If an acidified solution is boiled the sulfur dioxide is driven off as
a gas with a suffocating odor (2).

Perhaps the most important property of the bisulfites and sulfites
is their powerful reducing action which may be illustrated by the
following ionic equation (3). It is because of this facility for giving

> (3) $HSO_3^- + 3H_2O \rightarrow HSO_4^- + 2H_3O^+ + 2\epsilon$
> or $SO_3^= + 3H_2O \rightarrow SO_4^= + 2H_3O^+ + 2\epsilon$

up electrons and thereby acting as a reducing agent that it is able
to be oxidized in acid solution by such oxidizing agents as permanganate, dichromate, the halogens (4), hydrogen peroxide (5), hypochlorous acid, sodium hypochlorite, ferric salts, etc. It is for this
reducing action, and consequent protective action without formation

> (4) $H_2SO_3 + I_2 + H_2O \rightarrow 2HI + H_2SO_4$
> (5) $H_2SO_3 + H_2O_2 \rightarrow H_2SO_4 + H_2O$

of harmful by-products toward easily oxidizable medicinal compounds that it was introduced into the U.S.P. This is especially
true for solutions of alkaloidal salts that are usually acid because
bisulfite itself is acid.

All of the bisulfites are water-insoluble except the alkali metals
and to a less extent the alkaline earth elements. Similarly, most of
the sulfites are insoluble except for the alkali metal sulfites.

Sodium bisulfite is sufficiently acidic to cause effervescence with
sodium carbonate with formation of the sulfite (6).

> (6) $2NaHSO_3 + Na_2CO_3 \rightarrow 2Na_2SO_3 + H_2O + CO_2 \uparrow$

Much of the commercial sodium bisulfite is actually the metabisulfite which upon solution in water is immediately converted to
the bisulfite (7).

> (7) $Na_2S_2O_5 + H_2O \rightarrow 2NaHSO_3$

Sodium Bisulfite is assayed by residual titration with 0.1N
iodine (4). The procedure is to add an excess of standard iodine
solution to a weighed sample of the salt. The mixture is allowed to
stand for a few minutes and is then acidified and the excess iodine
determined by titration with standard thiosulfate solution (8) using
starch T.S. as an indicator. The equation for the over-all reaction
may be represented as shown (9).

> (8) $I_2 + 2Na_2S_2O_3 \rightarrow 2NaI + Na_2S_4O_6$
> (9) $NaHSO_3 + I_2 + H_2O \rightarrow NaHSO_4 + 2HI$

Sodium bisulfite has an interesting property in connection with organic compounds containing carbonyl groups ($>C = O$), especially aldehydes (and some ketones) (10). It is able to add to the carbonyl group to convert the organic compound to a stable water-soluble form suitable for injections.

$$(10) \quad >C = O + NaHSO_3 \rightarrow \quad \overset{\displaystyle OH}{\underset{\displaystyle SO_3Na}{C}} \quad \text{(water-soluble)}$$

Official Tests for Identity.—1. Solutions of Sodium Bisulfite respond to the tests for *Sodium* ion (*q.v.*).

2. A solution of Sodium Bisulfite will also respond to the test for *Sulfite* ion in that it will liberate colorless sulfur dioxide gas when treated with hydrochloric acid (1, 2). This gas has the odor of burning sulfur, and will blacken filter paper that has been moistened with mercurous nitrate T.S. due to the formation of free mercury (11).

$$(11) \quad Hg_2(NO_3)_2 + SO_2 + 2H_2O \rightarrow 2Hg \downarrow + H_2SO_4 + 2HNO_3$$

Commercial Manufacture.—Sodium bisulfite is usually made by passing sulfur dioxide into a solution of sodium carbonate until the solution is saturated (12, 13). It may be crystallized directly from

$$(12) \quad SO_2 + H_2O \rightleftarrows H_2SO_3$$
$$(13) \quad Na_2CO_3 + 2H_2SO_3 \rightarrow 2NaHSO_3 + H_2O + CO_2 \uparrow$$

the solution or it may be precipitated as a white powder with alcohol.

Uses.—*Sodium Bisulfite* (Sodium Hydrogen Sulfite, Sodium Acid Sulfite), U.S.P. XVII, "consists of sodium bisulfite ($NaHSO_3$) and sodium metabisulfite ($Na_2S_2O_5$) in varying proportions. It yields not less than 58.5 per cent and not more than 67.4 per cent of SO_2." This salt was introduced into the U.S.P. for the purpose of providing standards for a salt that is being used as a reducing agent (antioxidant) in certain easily oxidized preparations. Usually about 0.1 per cent is sufficient for most purposes although an amount equivalent to 0.2 per cent SO_2 is allowed officially. It is being used in epinephrine hydrochloride, phenylephrine hydrochloride, and ascorbic acid injections although the U.S.P. does not specifically permit its use.

Menadione Sodium Bisulfite is an example of the conversion of a practically water-insoluble organic compound to one that is very water-soluble without significant loss of activity.

Other uses for sodium bisulfite have been as an external application in parasitic skin diseases and internally (0.3 to 0.6 Gm. dose) for its effect as an antiseptic in gastric fermentation.

SODIUM BORATE

Sodium Borate, U.S.P. XVII

Formula, $Na_2B_4O_7.10H_2O$. Molecular Weight, 381.37

Physical Properties.—Sodium Borate occurs as colorless, odorless, transparent, monoclinic crystals. It has a sweetish, alkaline taste, and effloresces in warm, dry air. Its density is 1.694.

One Gm. of Sodium Borate is soluble in 16 ml. of water and in about 1 ml. of glycerin, at 25° C. One Gm. dissolves in about 1 ml. of boiling water. It is insoluble in alcohol.

Chemical Properties.—When sodium borate is heated, it loses part of its water of hydration and swells to a white, porous product. When the heat is increased to redness, the remainder of the water is expelled and the salt fuses to a colorless liquid, which on cooling forms a transparent mass known as *borax glass* or *bead*. If the formula for sodium tetraborate is written $(NaBO_2)_2.B_2O_3$ it will be noted that a considerable excess of boric anhydride (B_2O_3) is present. This may unite with basic oxides to form mixed metaborates (1). These usually have a characteristic color and are used in qualitative analysis to test for various cations.

$$(1)\ (NaBO_2)_2.B_2O_3 + CuO \rightarrow (NaBO_2)_2.Cu(BO_2)_2$$

An aqueous solution of sodium borate is distinctly alkaline to litmus paper and to phenolphthalein T.S. This is accounted for by the fact that the salt hydrolyzes into sodium metaborate and boric acid (2), and the former further hydrolyzes to sodium hydroxide and boric acid (3). Dilution increases the hydrolysis.

$$(2)\ Na_2B_4O_7 + 3H_2O \rightleftarrows 2NaBO_2 + 2H_3BO_3$$
$$(3)\ NaBO_2 + 2H_2O \rightleftarrows NaOH + H_3BO_3$$

Only the alkali borates are soluble in water, and their solutions are strongly basic in reaction. The borates of other metals quickly undergo hydrolysis and thus the insoluble hydroxide or oxide forms.

That the hydrolysis takes place as described above can be demonstrated by adding silver nitrate T.S. to a saturated solution of borax. White silver metaborate is precipitated (4). On the other hand, when silver nitrate T.S. is added to a *very dilute* solution of borax, silver oxide (black) is precipitated (5).

$$(4)\ NaBO_2 + AgNO_3 \rightarrow AgBO_2 \downarrow + NaNO_3$$
$$(5)\ 2NaOH + 2AgNO_3 \rightarrow Ag_2O \downarrow + 2NaNO_3 + H_2O$$

Based on the hydrolysis of sodium borate yielding boric acid, a potential incompatibility with sodium bicarbonate occurs when these two chemicals are present in solutions containing glycerin.

The resulting effervescence involved in the preparation of such solutions (15, 16) should be permitted to go to completion before bottling the product.

When acidified, aqueous solutions of sodium tetraborate will deposit crystals of boric acid (6).

$$(6) \quad Na_2B_4O_7 + H_2SO_4 + 5H_2O \rightarrow Na_2SO_4 + 4H_3BO_3 \downarrow$$

Most of the common metallic borates are insoluble in water, with the exception of the alkali metal borates. For example, calcium or barium nitrate will cause the formation of insoluble metaborates of the respective metals (7). These insoluble metaborates are soluble in hot, concentrated ammonium salt solutions (8).

$$(7) \quad Na_2B_4O_7 + Ca(NO_3)_2 + 3H_2O \rightarrow Ca(BO_2)_2 \downarrow + 2H_3BO_3 + 2NaNO_3$$

$$(8) \quad Ca(BO_2)_2 + 2NH_4Cl \rightarrow 2HBO_2 + CaCl_2 + 2NH_3 \uparrow$$

Of interest to the pharmacist is the incompatibility of Sodium Borate with soluble zinc salts to form insoluble basic zinc borate or zinc hydroxide as a consequence of the alkalinity due to hydrolysis of sodium borate. This can be avoided by using boric acid in place of the alkaline salt because the acid zinc borate forms which is quite water-soluble.

Because Sodium Borate is the salt of a strong base and a weak acid and gives an alkaline reaction when dissolved in water it is used as an important component of buffer mixtures (see p. 116).

Sodium Borate is assayed by directly titrating a weighed sample with 0.5 N hydrochloric acid with methyl red as an indicator. When sodium borate is treated with hydrochloric acid, sodium chloride and orthoboric acid are formed (9), the latter being indifferent to methyl red. Therefore, as soon as all of the borax is decomposed by the hydrochloric acid, a slight excess of the latter will give an acid reaction with the indicator.

$$(9) \quad Na_2B_4O_7.10H_2O + 2HCl \rightarrow 2NaCl + 4H_3BO_3 + 5H_2O$$

Official Tests for Identity.—1. Turmeric paper is colored reddish-brown by an acidulated (HCl) aqueous solution of sodium tetraborate. The color is intensified on drying. If the dried paper is moistened with ammonia T.S. the color changes to greenish-black. This is a general and quite sensitive test for borates.

2. When the salt is treated with sulfuric acid, methanol added, and the mixture ignited, it burns with a green-bordered flame. This is a general test for borates, and depends first upon the formation of boric acid according to equation (6), followed by the esterification of the boric acid with the methanol (10) to form trimethylborate which burns with a green flame.

3. It corresponds to all tests for the *Sodium ion* (*q.v.*).

$$(10) \quad H_3BO_3 + 3CH_3OH \rightarrow (CH_3)_3BO_3 + 3H_2O$$

Commercial Manufacture.—Much of the world supply of borax is manufactured by two American companies.

One of the companies uses the brine obtained from Searles Lake, which is a deposit of various salts with brine filling in the spaces between the crystals. The brine is pumped to the plant and concentrated to obtain deposits of the various chemicals. Potassium chloride is the first salt obtained. Since the mother liquor from it is nearly saturated with borax, cooling of the solution in a vacuum crystallizer yields crude borax. The crude borax, when recrystallized, constitutes commercial borax.

The other company has been working mainly with borax minerals. Until recently, this firm used *colemanite* ($Ca_2B_6O_{11}.5H_2O$) as its raw material. This mineral occurs in immense deposits in California (Death Valley). The mineral is mixed with sodium sulfate and heated to redness (11), but not to fusion, in a rotary furnace. After the mass has cooled, the borax is dissolved in water and allowed to crystallize.

$$(11)\ 2Ca_2B_6O_{11} + 3Na_2SO_4 \rightarrow 3CaSO_4 + CaO + 3Na_2B_4O_7$$

The mineral *borocalcite*, $CaB_4O_7.4H_2O$, is also converted into borax by this method (12).

$$(12)\ CaB_4O_7.4H_2O + Na_2SO_4 \rightarrow Na_2B_4O_7 + CaSO_4 + 4H_2O$$

The action of sodium carbonate upon colemanite forms borax, sodium hydroxide, and calcium carbonate (13).

$$(13)\ 2Ca_2B_6O_{11} + 4Na_2CO_3 + H_2O \rightarrow 3Na_2B_4O_7 + 2\ NaOH + 4CaCO_3$$

Recently, however, a large deposit of *rasorite* or *kernite* ($Na_2B_4O_7.4H_2O$) has been discovered in California and has replaced colemanite as the raw material. The rasorite is dissolved in water by heat and pressure, filtered, and a pure borax (14) crystallizes out.

$$(14)\ Na_2B_4O_7.4H_2O + 6H_2O \rightarrow Na_2B_4O_7.10H_2O$$

Pharmacological Action of the Borate Ion.—See p. 125.

Uses.—*Sodium Borate* (Borax, Sodium Tetraborate, Sodium Biborate, Sodium Pyroborate), U.S.P. XVII, "contains an amount of $Na_2B_4O_7$ equivalent to not less than 99 per cent and not more than 105 per cent of $Na_2B_4O_7.10H_2O$." This salt is not used *internally* to any extent because it has been shown to be of no value in the treatment of diseases such as cystitis or (with bromides) epilepsy. Although borax is a fair antiseptic, its use in food products as a preservative has been prohibited by the Food and Drug Administration on the grounds that it is too toxic for internal use.

Sodium borate is used *externally*, however, for (*a*) eye-washes in 1 to 2 per cent concentrations and (*b*) as wet dressings for wounds. It is claimed that its action is more bacteriostatic than bactericidal.

Borax is used for "softening" water. It is employed in making hard glass, glazes and enamels. Because it forms fusible salts with oxides of many metals, the calcined salt is used extensively as a flux in welding and soldering.

The function of the Sodium Borate in *Cold Cream,* its reason for official recognition, is not known with certainty, but it is believed to react with the free acids present in the white wax, principally cerotic acid. The sodium cerotate (a soap) so formed acts as an emulsifying agent giving a whiter and more homogenous product than would otherwise be obtained. It is replaceable by other alkaline substances or by certain soaps. Although the product is designated officially as "cold cream" it is actually not the commercial variety of cold cream.

N.F. Mouth Wash contains sodium borate, glycerin and potassium bicarbonate. The sodium borate forms boric acid when dissolved in water (2), and because boric acid reacts with glycerin to form a monobasic acid (see Boric Acid) the reactions which take place in manufacturing this preparation can probably be expressed by the following equations (15, 16):

$$(15)\ 2 \begin{matrix} CH_2OH \\ | \\ CHOH \\ | \\ CH_2OH \end{matrix} + \begin{matrix} HO \\ HO{-}B \\ HO \end{matrix} \rightarrow \left[\begin{matrix} CH_2OH & & CH_2OH \\ | & & | \\ CH{-}O & O{-}CH \\ | & B & | \\ CH_2{-}O & O{-}CH_2 \end{matrix} \right]^{-} H^{+} + 3H_2O$$

$$(16)\ \left[\begin{matrix} CH_2OH & & CH_2OH \\ | & & | \\ CH{-}O & O{-}CH \\ | & B & | \\ CH_2{-}O & O{-}CH_2 \end{matrix} \right]^{-} H^{+} + KHCO_3 \rightarrow \left[\begin{matrix} CH_2OH & & CH_2OH \\ | & & | \\ CH{-}O & O{-}CH \\ | & B & | \\ CH_2{-}O & O{-}CH_2 \end{matrix} \right]^{-} K^{+}$$

$$+ H_2O + CO_2 \uparrow$$

Compound Sodium Borate Solution, formerly official, contained sodium borate, sodium bicarbonate, liquefied phenol and glycerin. The reactions taking place here were probably the same as those taking place in N.F. Mouth Wash with the exception that sodium bicarbonate was used in place of potassium bicarbonate.

SODIUM BROMIDE

Sodium Bromide, N.F. XII

Formula, NaBr.   Molecular Weight, 102.90

Physical Properties.—Sodium Bromide occurs in colorless or white cubical crystals, or as a white, granular powder. It is odorless and has a saline, slightly bitter taste. Sodium Bromide slowly takes up moisture from the air without deliquescing. At temperatures below 30° C. the salt crystallizes with 2 molecules of water of hydration in the monoclinic system. At temperatures above 30° C., it forms anhydrous crystals belonging to the regular system. These facts probably account for its property of absorbing moisture from the air without deliquescing. Its specific gravity is about 3.014.

One Gm. of Sodium Bromide dissolves in 1.2 ml. of water and in 16 ml. of alcohol, at 25° C. One Gm. is soluble in 0.8 ml. of boiling water and in 11 ml. of boiling alcohol.

The salt melts at 768° C., and at higher temperatures is slowly volatilized with partial decomposition.

Chemical Properties.—Inasmuch as the chemistry of the sodium ion has been discussed (*q.v.*), it only remains to consider the chemistry of the bromide ion to clarify the chemistry of sodium bromide.

The bromide ion, in general, is easily oxidized by molecular chlorine (Cl_2) to free bromine (Br_2). This follows the general rule that halogens will displace other halogens of greater atomic weight from their binary salts (1). Other substances such as potassium permanganate, nitric acid and concentrated sulfuric acid will also oxidize bromides and liberate bromine.

(1) $2NaBr + Cl_2 \rightarrow 2NaCl + Br_2 \uparrow$

The bromide ion may be precipitated as an insoluble bromide by soluble salts of Ag, Hg(ous), Cu(ous) and Pb(ic). For example, sodium bromide solution will yield a precipitate of silver bromide with silver nitrate (2).

(2) $NaBr + AgNO_3 \rightarrow AgBr \downarrow + NaNO_3$

Sodium bromide is the salt of a strong acid and a strong base and, therefore, when in solution it is not appreciably hydrolyzed. This accounts for the fact that it is neutral or only slightly alkaline when in solution. The slight alkalinity may be accounted for by the fact that hydrobromic acid is weaker as an acid than sodium hydroxide is as a base. This slight alkalinity is sometimes held to be the cause of precipitation of alkaloids from concentrated solutions of sodium bromide.

15

The official assay involves the addition of excess standard silver nitrate solution to an aqueous solution of a weighed sample of sodium bromide. The excess silver nitrate is determined by residual titration with ammonium thiocyanate using ferric ammonium sulfate as an indicator.

Official Tests for Identity.—1. The salt responds to all of the tests for *Sodium* (*q.v.*).

2. It also responds to all of the tests for *Bromide* (*q.v.*).

Commercial Manufacture.—Most of the sodium bromide made commercially is prepared by adding a slight excess of bromine to a solution of sodium hydroxide to form a mixture of bromide and bromate (3).

$$(3)\ 6NaOH + 3Br_2 \rightarrow 5NaBr + NaBrO_3 + 3H_2O$$

The reaction mixture is evaporated to dryness and the solid residue is reduced with carbon to convert the sodium bromate to sodium bromide (4).

$$(4)\ NaBrO_3 + 3C \rightarrow NaBr + 3CO\uparrow$$

As will become increasingly apparent, this general method is used to advantage in the preparation of other bromides from bromine, and of iodides from iodine.

Searle's Lake brine is also a commercial source of sodium bromide, although the principal production scheme is built around the recovery of potassium chloride and borax.

Pharmacological Action of the Bromides.—Bromides were first introduced into medicine by Locock in 1853 for their antiepileptic effect. Their introduction into therapy was based on the theory that epilepsy might be caused by an over-abundance of amorousness and, since bromides were considered to be sex depressant, the depressant action should be therapeutically desirable. Although the hypothesis was incorrect, the fact was that bromides did produce a beneficial depression of the convulsions associated with epilepsy. Later, in 1864, Behrend utilized them in certain cases of sleeplessness. Since then the bromides have become a common item in the medical armamentarium. Early studies on bromides were done with potassium bromide and some confusion arose as to which portion of the salt contributed the sedative properties. This confusion was dispelled when it became apparent that other bromide salts had the same activity. Likewise, a depressant effect on the heart was noted with potassium bromide, but this was later shown to be due to the potassium content.

Administration of small doses (0.5 to 2 Gm.) of a bromide (*e.g.*, KBr) serves to cause a depression of the central nervous system. Larger doses (4 to 8 Gm.) depress all reflexes and cause a narcotic type of effect. The use of repeated small doses for a sedative effect depends on the above-mentioned depression of the central nervous system. The actual mechanism of sleep production is not known, but sleep is induced by diminishing the susceptibility of the patient to external stimuli.

Bromides have been a standard form of medication for epileptiform seizures but are slowly yielding to the newer hydantoin derivatives, e.g., diphenylhydantoin. Their usefulness in epilepsy depends on their ability to depress the motor areas of the brain, an effect brought about by large doses. Bromides do not have a clean-cut, highly selective action on the motor areas alone, but also depress the sensory functions to some extent. This makes it impossible to avoid some degree of sedation at all times if an effective level is to be maintained in an epileptic. This sedative action of bromides is responsible for the search among organic drugs for newer and more selective agents and such studies have led to the discovery of the usefulness of phenobarbital and the hydantoins.

Other than their usefulness in insomnia and epilepsy, the bromides find a field of usefulness in the treatment of various other nervous manifestations. Among these are reflex vomiting, anxiety states, worry, neurasthenia, sexual excitement, etc. These conditions often respond very well to the "calming" effect of bromides.

Bromides are rapidly absorbed and are excreted principally in the urine. Repeated doses tend to cause accumulation with a consequent replacement of chloride ion by the accumulated bromide ion. On the other hand, administration of sodium chloride tends to hasten the elimination of bromide. The distribution of the bromide ion in the body is virtually the same as that of the chloride ion, a fact that makes highly selective action by the bromides unlikely.

The use of bromides is attended by the possibility of *bromism* (poisoning by bromides). The occurrence of bromism is not infrequent in spite of the fact that cautions have been emphasized in both the medical and pharmaceutical journals. One of the reasons for this is the uncontrolled sale of bromide-containing proprietaries. Another reason is that physicians themselves are lax in keeping a careful watch on patients who are taking bromides over long periods of time. The early signs of bromide intoxication include insomnia and restlessness as well as dizziness, weakness, and headache. It is easy to see where physicians might be led to increase the dose in order to combat the very condition they are causing. A skin rash known as *bromide acne* often occurs with bromism but is not as common a finding as one would be led to believe from the older literature. *Bromide psychosis* (mental disease) may be induced also by long continued use of bromides. Death from bromides is rare, and the symptoms, as a rule, recede on discontinuation of the drug. However, treatment of bromism may be carried out by the administration of substantial doses of sodium chloride (6 Gm. daily in divided doses) or, where sodium intake is to be limited, ammonium chloride may be used instead.[1]

---

[1] See S. K. Sharpless in *The Pharmacological Basis of Therapeutics*, 3rd ed., ed. by Goodman and Gilman, Macmillan, New York, 1965, p. 130.

Uses.—*Sodium Bromide*, N.F. XII, when dried at 105° C. for four hours, contains not less than 99 per cent of NaBr. It is used solely for the effect of the bromide ion, namely, as a sedative due to its central depressant effect. The official usage is expressed in the formulations of *Three Bromides Elixir* (containing the bromides of Na, K and NH₄) and *Sodium Bromide Elixir* which provides a dosage form for the administration of Sodium Bromide alone. It has been recommended by some that Sodium Bromide be substituted for all other bromides inasmuch as it provides the action of the bromide ion in a relatively nontoxic form. Whether this suggestion is worthwhile is debatable. Usual dose—900 mg. daily.

SODIUM CARBONATE

Monohydrated Sodium Carbonate, U.S.P. XVII

Formula, $Na_2CO_3.H_2O$.   Molecular Weight, 124.00

Physical Properties.—Monohydrated Sodium Carbonate is a white, orthorhombic, crystalline or granular powder. It is odorless and has a strong alkaline taste. The salt absorbs a small amount of moisture from the air, but in warm, dry air at 50° C. or above it effloresces, becoming anhydrous at 100° C. Anhydrous sodium carbonate melts at 853° C., at which temperature it loses a small quantity of carbon dioxide. It is decomposed at very high temperatures.

One Gm. of Monohydrated Sodium Carbonate dissolves in 3 ml. of water and in 7 ml. of glycerin, at 25° C. One Gm. is soluble in 1.8 ml. of boiling water. It is insoluble in alcohol.

Chemical Properties.—The chemistry of sodium carbonate may be considered advantageously in three major divisions, namely, (*a*) hydrolysis reactions, (*b*) hydration and (*c*) other reactions.

(*a*) Sodium carbonate, when dissolved in water imparts a highly alkaline reaction to the water as evidenced by the fact that the pH of a molar solution is 11.6. This is due to the hydrolysis which takes place in aqueous solutions of it. The hydrolysis is due to the fact that the carbonate ion is a fairly strong base (see Lowry-Brönsted Concept of Acids and Bases, p. 103) (1).

$$(1) \quad CO_3^{=} + HOH \rightleftarrows HCO_3^{-} + OH^{-}$$

A further hydrolysis takes place (2) to a lesser extent wherein additional OH⁻ is formed.

$$(2) \quad HCO_3^{-} + HOH \rightleftarrows H_2CO_3 + OH^{-}$$

The accumulation of OH⁻ accounts for the alkalinity exhibited by the solution.

(b) Sodium carbonate is interesting from the standpoint that it forms at least 3 well-characterized hydrates besides the anhydrous salt. These are:

1. Monohydrate = $Na_2CO_3.H_2O$
2. Heptahydrate = $Na_2CO_3.7H_2O$
3. Dekahydrate = $Na_2CO_3.10H_2O$

At temperatures above 35° C. a saturated solution will deposit only the monohydrated form. If the hot saturated solution is allowed to cool in an atmosphere free of dust it is often possible to obtain the heptahydrate crystals. However, if the solution cools below 33° C. the dekahydrate forms because the heptahydrate is more soluble than the dekahydrate. It may be noted that the maximum solubility of sodium carbonate is at approximately 35° C.

Commercial anhydrous sodium carbonate is known as *soda ash*, whereas the dekahydrate is commonly known as *sal soda, washing soda,* or *soda crystals*. The dekahydrate is prone to *effloresce* under conditions of storage. *Efflorescence* is the term used to denote the loss of water of crystallization from a compound at room temperature. It is explained on the basis that every salt containing water of crystallization has a certain vapor pressure. If the vapor pressure exerted by the water of crystallization is greater than that exerted by the moisture in the air then the compound will lose water to the air until equilibrium has been established or until all available water is gone.

(c) Sodium carbonate enters into many reactions such as *neutralization, double decomposition, precipitation* and *saponification*.

Sodium carbonate, in solution or in the solid form, is capable of neutralizing acids with the formation of a salt, CO_2 and H_2O (3).

$$(3)\ Na_2CO_3 + 2HA \rightarrow 2NaA + H_2O + CO_2 \uparrow$$
$$(HA = any\ acid)$$

The reaction of sodium carbonate with acids is the basis of its official assay in which a weighed sample of sodium carbonate is dissolved in water and titrated with 1N sulfuric acid (4). It will be

$$(4)\ Na_2CO_3 + H_2SO_4 \rightarrow Na_2SO_4 + H_2O + CO_2 \uparrow$$

noted that the sodium carbonate in the equation (4) is anhydrous. This is so because the U.S.P. first directs that the monohydrated form be subjected to a heating process (105° for 4 hours) to determine its moisture content. This should not be less than 12 per cent or more than 15 per cent of the weight of the sample. This dehydrated sample is then used for the titration.

Cold solutions of sodium carbonate, when treated with carbon dioxide will form the bicarbonate (5), which may be regarded

as essentially a half neutralization of sodium carbonate with carbonic acid (formed by interaction of $CO_2 + H_2O \rightleftarrows H_2CO_3$).

(5) $Na_2CO_3 + CO_2 + H_2O \rightleftarrows 2NaHCO_3$

Sodium carbonate is used in qualitative analysis because of its
ability to decompose difficultly soluble precipitates such as $BaSO_4$,
$PbSO_4$, $CaSO_4$ and $SrSO_4$. For example, barium sulfate is decomposed (although with difficulty) by boiling or fusing it with sodium
carbonate (6).

(6) $BaSO_4 + Na_2CO_3 \rightleftarrows BaCO_3 \downarrow + Na_2SO_4$

Although $BaSO_4$ is difficult to decompose, the other sulfates mentioned are almost completely decomposed by this treatment.

Since the only normal carbonates which are freely soluble are
those of the alkali metals and ammonium, it is possible to use
sodium carbonate, for example, as a reagent to precipitate the
insoluble carbonates of the other metals. Thus, we find that silver
nitrate, and also barium chloride, form insoluble carbonates with
an aqueous solution of sodium carbonate. Although this might
seem to be the case with mercuric chloride, this does not occur,
inasmuch as mercuric chloride T.S. when added to an aqueous solution of the salt immediately gives a reddish-brown precipitate. For
a discussion of the mechanism of formation of this precipitate refer
to p. 200, equations (6) to (12).

Because sodium carbonate is alkaline in solution it is used to
some extent as a saponifying agent for fats and oils both in pharmaceutical practice and elsewhere. For example, a fat such as *stearin*,
which is a glyceryl ester of a fatty acid, will be hydrolyzed or
saponified by sodium carbonate (see also Sodium Hydroxide) to
yield glycerin and a soap (a metallic salt of a fatty acid; in this case
the sodium salt). This saponifying action of sodium carbonate has
led to the use of its preparations as detergents for removing grease
in many industrial operations. Often, however, the alkalinity
imparted by the sodium carbonate is too high. In these cases,
it is possible to obtain various admixtures of the sodium carbonate
with sodium bicarbonate which are less alkaline. One common
preparation of this type is *sodium sesquicarbonate*, $Na_2CO_3.Na-HCO_3.2H_2O$, also known as *urao* or *trona*.[1] It may be obtained naturally or by crystallizing a solution of equimolecular amounts of
carbonate and bicarbonate. The alkalinity of this product is intermediate between that of the carbonate and bicarbonate.

Official Tests for Identity.—1. A solution of Monohydrated Sodium
Carbonate (1 in 10) is strongly alkaline to litmus paper and to

---

[1] The formula of sodium sesquicarbonate is sometimes also given as $Na_2CO_3.Na-HCO_3.3H_2O$ a product obtained by heating a solution of sodium bicarbonate until sufficient CO_2 has been driven off, following which the product is crystallized.

phenolphthalein T.S. for the reasons cited under "Chemical Properties." This distinguishes it from sodium bicarbonate which either
does not color phenolphthalein or does so only slightly.

2. The salt responds to all of the tests for *Sodium* (*q.v.*).

3. The salt responds to all of the tests for *Carbonate*: Sodium
carbonate effervesces with acids (3) to liberate CO_2 which will cause
a precipitate of calcium carbonate if passed through lime water (7).

(7) $Ca(OH)_2 + CO_2 \rightarrow CaCO_3 \downarrow + H_2O$

Commercial Manufacture.—Sodium carbonate is or has been ob-
tained by the LeBlanc Process,[1] the Cryolite-Soda Process,[1] the
Solvay Process, and recovery from natural brine. The Solvay
Process is by far the most important.

Solvay Ammonia-soda Process.— In 1838, H. G. Dyar and
J. Hemming took out an English patent for making sodium carbonate by means of a reaction well known at that time (8 and 9).

(8) $NaCl + NH_4HCO_3 \rightarrow NaHCO_3 + NH_4Cl$

(9) $2NaHCO_3 + heat \rightarrow Na_2CO_3 + CO_2 \uparrow + H_2O \uparrow$

In 1863, Ernest Solvay, a Belgian, began to develop a commercial
method for making sodium carbonate from sodium chloride, ammonia, and carbon dioxide. Although unfamiliar with most of the
previous work that had been done upon it, he overcame the mechanical difficulties and made it a commercial success in 1873. Since that
time it has been growing in importance until at present most of the
world's supply of soda is made by the Solvay process.

In brief, the process consists in passing carbon dioxide, which
has been prepared either by burning limestone using coke or by
calcining sodium bicarbonate (10) (13), into ammonium hydroxide
to form ammonium bicarbonate (11). When the latter is mixed with
a solution of sodium chloride, sodium bicarbonate is precipitated and
ammonium chloride remains in solution (12). The sodium bicarbonate is collected and then calcined and the evolved carbon dioxide
is cooled and used over again (13). The ammonium chloride is
treated with milk of lime (14) and the evolved ammonia is led back
into the system (15). The solution of calcium chloride so formed
is usually run to waste or evaporated for commercial uses.

(10) $CaCO_3 \rightarrow CaO + CO_2 \uparrow$

(11) $NH_4OH + CO_2 \rightleftarrows NH_4HCO_3$

(12) $NaCl + NH_4HCO_3 \rightleftarrows NaHCO_3 \downarrow + NH_4Cl$

(13) $2NaHCO_3 \rightleftarrows H_2O + CO_2 \uparrow + Na_2CO_3$

(14) $CaO + H_2O \rightleftarrows Ca(OH)_2$

(15) $Ca(OH)_2 + 2NH_4Cl \rightleftarrows CaCl_2 + 2NH_3 \uparrow + 2H_2O$

[1] A more detailed discussion will be found in the 5th edition of this textbook.

In the actual process, the number of required steps is less than the foregoing equations would indicate, because the sodium chloride solution (brine) is first saturated with ammonia and then carbon dioxide passed through the mixture (11) and (12). At a lowered temperature sodium bicarbonate separates out. It will be noted that the reaction (12) between the sodium chloride and ammonium bicarbonate is a reversible one. Therefore, the reaction can never go to completion, although it can be driven in the desired direction by having an excess of sodium chloride present.

Although the reactions involved in the Solvay Process are usually represented as above, there is another mechanism whereby the end-product may be reached. In brief, it can be pointed out that the supposition of ammonium bicarbonate as an intermediate is irrational because (a) ammonium bicarbonate is just as sparingly soluble as sodium bicarbonate in the mother liquors and would itself be precipitated, and (b) such a reaction would be endothermal, whereas the actual reaction is exothermal. The suggested mechanism is as follows (16, 17, 18):

(16) $2NH_3 + CO_2 + H_2O \rightleftarrows (NH_4)_2CO_3$

(17) $(NH_4)_2CO_3 + 2NaCl \rightleftarrows Na_2CO_3 + 2NH_4Cl$

(18) $Na_2CO_3 + CO_2 + H_2O \rightleftarrows 2NaHCO_3 \downarrow$

Pharmacological Action of Carbonates.—The pharmacological action of bicarbonates has already been discussed.

It should be pointed out that the carbonates, in general, are usually active antacids. Among these are the alkali metal carbonates, ammonium carbonate, the alkaline earth carbonates, magnesium carbonate, etc. A notable exception is bismuth subcarbonate which actually has no antacid value but which does have a mechanical coating action that affords some relief. Some of the carbonates mentioned above are too strongly alkaline and, therefore, do not find much use in antacid therapy. Among these are the alkali metal carbonates. Others provide toxic ions when they function as antacids, an outstanding example of which is barium carbonate. The most useful antacids are the alkali metal bicarbonates, calcium carbonate, and magnesium carbonate.

In this connection it is well to point out that antacids may be placed in two general groups: (1) systemic antacids, and (2) nonsystemic antacids.

1. Among the systemic alkalizers perhaps the most important is sodium bicarbonate, although all of the soluble carbonates may be considered to fulfill the requirements of this type of antacid. The reason for classifying these compounds as systemic alkalizers is that by absorption (following neutralization of the gastric contents) from the gastro-intestinal tract they enter the blood and raise the level of the alkaline reserve. Having raised the alkaline reserve the body

acts to rid itself of the alkalinity and excretes the excess alkali renally, thus throwing a burden on the kidneys. One of the faults of the soluble bicarbonates and carbonates is that by neutralizing the gastric contents a temporary retardation or inhibition of the proteolytic activity of pepsin results. To avoid this, some workers prefer not to consider sodium bicarbonate, etc. as systemic alkalizers and instead reserve the term for alkali salts of organic acids such as citrates, lactates, malates, etc. Under this classification the systemic alkalizers would be those alkali salts of organic acids that do not materially alter the acidity of the stomach but are easily absorbed into the system and are there completely oxidized to the metallic bicarbonates with the same sequence of events required to rid the body of the excess alkalinity as has been described previously for sodium bicarbonate. The principal salts that fall in this category are the sodium salts of citric acid, lactic acid, malic acid, and succinic acid. All organic acid salts are not effective in this capacity as is evident from the tartrates (*q.v.*) and glucuronates. Glucuronic acid, for example, is not metabolized and can be administered in sufficient amounts to cause acidity of the urine. However, in equimolar amounts, the sodium salts that are completely metabolized are just as effective as an equivalent amount of sodium bicarbonate.

2. The non-systemic alkalizers or antacids are those which do not alter the blood chemistry when administered orally. There is room for argument as to whether they are or are not completely inactive in this respect. However, on oral administration they simply neutralize the gastric contents by reacting with the free hydrochloric acid. In the intestinal tract the resulting chlorides are converted again to the carbonates (and possibly phosphates) and excreted via the feces, the chloride ion being reabsorbed from the intestinal mucosa into the blood. Representatives of this type of antacid are calcium and magnesium carbonate, calcium and magnesium phosphate, acid absorbent resins, and aluminum hydroxide and phosphate. There are many others.

Uses.—*Monohydrated Sodium Carbonate*, U.S.P. XVII, "contains not less than 99.5 per cent of Na_2CO_3, calculated on the anhydrous basis." This is the only official sodium carbonate, although the anhydrous form is required as a buffer in *Sodium Thiopental for Injection*. Sodium carbonate may be given internally for the same conditions for which sodium bicarbonate is employed. However, it is seldom used because of its marked alkalinity and irritating properties. Solutions of sodium carbonate are employed as lotions in certain skin diseases, such as scaly eruptions, psoriasis, etc. They tend to dissolve skin oils and also the horny matter on the skin surface thus softening the skin.

This salt is used more for its alkalinity in making various pharmaceutical preparations than it is in therapy. Together with sodium hydroxide it is used to dissolve water-insoluble *Nitromersol* by opening its anhydride ring to form the water-soluble sodium salt in *Nitromersol Solution.*

It may, of course, be used as a source of carbonate ion for the preparation of various carbonates as, for example, ferrous carbonate from ferrous sulfate.

SODIUM CHLORIDE[1]

Sodium Chloride, U.S.P. XVII

Formula, NaCl. Molecular Weight, 58.44

Physical Properties.—Sodium Chloride occurs in the form of colorless, transparent, cubical crystals, or as a white crystalline powder. When crystallized from dilute solutions it forms hollow quadratic pyramids. When saturated solutions of Sodium Chloride are cooled to $-10°$ C., large monoclinic tablets of $NaCl.2H_2O$ separate out. At $0°$ C. these tablets lose water and are converted into cubes. The salt is odorless, has a saline taste, and a specific gravity of 2.163. Usually it is slightly hygroscopic, due to the presence of small amounts of magnesium or calcium chloride.

Sodium Chloride is only slightly more soluble in boiling water than it is in cold water, 1 Gm. dissolving in 2.8 ml. of water at $25°$ C. and in 2.7 ml. of boiling water. One Gm. is soluble in 10 ml. of glycerin, at $25°$ C. It is slightly soluble in alcohol and insoluble in hydrochloric acid.

When heated somewhat above $100°$ C., the salt decrepitates because of the evaporation of the interstitial water enclosed by the small crystals. It fuses at about $804°$ C., boils at $1413°$ C., and at white heat slowly volatilizes with partial decomposition.

Chemical Properties.—Most of the chemical properties of sodium chloride, which are of importance pharmaceutically, may be attributed to the chloride ion.

Chlorides of almost all of the metals are water-soluble with the notable exception of AgCl, HgCl and $PbCl_2$. Therefore, solutions of sodium chloride will produce precipitates with soluble silver, mercurous, and lead salts (1).

(1) $NaCl + AgNO_3 \rightarrow AgCl \downarrow + NaNO_3$

Sodium chloride reacts readily with fixed acids such as sulfuric (2) and phosphoric acids to liberate hydrogen chloride. This, of course, is the basis for the preparation of hydrochloric acid from salt.

(2) $2NaCl + H_2SO_4 \rightarrow 2HCl + Na_2SO_4$

[1] For a complete treatise on sodium chloride sources, production, properties, and uses see the A.C.S. Monograph No. 145 entitled "Sodium Chloride" edited by D. W. Kaufmann, pub. by Reinhold Pub. Co., New York, N. Y., 1960.

Sodium chloride is rather easily oxidized to liberate free chlorine, the oxidation being carried out either *chemically* or *electrolytically*.

The chemical oxidation of sodium chloride may be illustrated by the addition of concentrated sulfuric acid and MnO_2 to the chloride (3) to liberate free chlorine.

$$(3)\ 2NaCl + MnO_2 + 2H_2SO_4 \rightarrow MnSO_4 + Na_2SO_4 + 2H_2O + Cl_2 \uparrow$$

The electrolytic oxidation of sodium chloride may be carried out on the anhydrous fused salt (see manufacture of sodium), or it may be carried out on an aqueous solution of sodium chloride (see manufacture of chlorine).

Sodium Chloride is assayed by adding an excess of a standard silver nitrate solution to an aqueous solution of a weighed sample. The excess of silver nitrate is determined by residual titration with standard ammonium thiocyanate solution using ferric ammonium sulfate as an indicator. A small amount of nitrobenzene is added to the titration mixture for the purpose of coating the precipitated silver chloride. This coating effectively decreases the solubility of the silver chloride, which otherwise would begin to react with the added ammonium thiocyanate to form silver thiocyanate because silver chloride is more soluble than is silver thiocyanate. If nitrobenzene is not used, more ammonium thiocyanate will be used for the residual titration before changing the indicator color than should actually be needed.

Official Tests for Identity.—1. A solution of Sodium Chloride gives all of the tests for *Sodium* (*q.v.*).

2. Sodium Chloride solutions also respond to all of the tests for *Chloride* (*q.v.*).

Commercial Manufacture.—Sodium chloride is found in all parts of the world either in the form of natural deposits, such as those of Stassfurt, Reichenhall, Cheshire, New York, Kansas, Colorado, Louisiana, Utah, California, Michigan and many other districts; or in solution in sea, lake, spring, or natural or made wells. It is an absolute necessity to man and beast; aiding in the absorption of albuminoid materials and, by dissociation, no doubt supplying the chloride ion for the hydrochloric acid of the gastric juice.

In Germany, Louisiana, and elsewhere, it is mined as rock salt. Shafts are sunk to the bed and long galleries, often a mile in length, are run out. The salt is undercut and blasted down with low-power dynamite. It is then crushed in roller mills and screened to obtain the various sizes. In one Colorado deposit the salt occurs in the form of a crust over an underground lake of brine. This is worked by removing the earth, cutting the crusted salt like ice, washing it in the brine, and then crushing, as previously described, in mills.

In other deposits, *e.g.*, those of New York, Ohio, Michigan, etc., the salt is found either mixed with clay or organic matter, or the locations of the beds are such as to make mining very impractical. In such places, wells are sunk, the salt dissolved in water, and the resulting brine pumped to the surface.

In California and in the hot countries around the Mediterranean basin, salt is obtained from sea-water (containing about 3 per cent sodium chloride) by concentrating it in very large, shallow ponds connected in series. The heat from the sun is sufficient to effect the evaporation of the water. At high tide the sea-water is allowed to flow into the first basin where the less soluble material and suspended matter (calcium carbonate, clay, gypsum, organic substances etc.) precipitate out. It then goes to the so-called crystallizing ponds, where it is evaporated to about 25° Baumé. Here the crystallized salt separates out. In the succeeding pans, the more soluble salts, *e.g.*, magnesium sulfate, magnesium chloride, sodium sulfate, potassium chloride, and varying quantities of potassium iodide and bromide (bittern) are obtained.

A limited amount of what is known as "solar salt" is marketed in the United States. Solar salt is the purest known (99.63%) variety of raw salt, and the one in use is obtained from the Bahamas and specifically from the salt beds on Greater Inagua Island. This salt is produced by hot tropical winds blowing across impounded sea water, the production depending on just the right conditions of sun and wind and being, therefore, seasonal.

In northern Russia, Norway, and other cold countries the sea-water is concentrated by freezing the water in basins and pumping out the residual liquid part which contains all of the salt.

All sodium chloride that has been obtained from its natural source in the form of brine must be purified. The methods in use are many, and depend largely upon the character of the impurities present in a particular brine. Calcium and magnesium salts are the usual impurities and may be removed by treating the brine with either soda ash and lime or soda ash and caustic soda, and allowing the precipitate to settle.

The purified brine is concentrated in long, narrow, steam heated, shallow pans known as "grainers." As the salt crystals form on the pan bottom, they are raked out automatically onto a sloping drain board on one end of the pan. Triple-effect vacuum pans are also used for concentrating and crystallizing the salt. A novel form of salt that has been termed "dendritic salt" is made by utilizing the vacuum crystallization technique with the added feature of adding a small amount of sodium ferrocyanide to the crystallizing mixture. The function of the additive is to adsorb to the faces of the forming salt crystals and to retard growth of the crystals on the faces and edges. Since growth can only take place at the corners of the crystals they result in a 3-dimensional branched or starlike product. A significant advantage is the low bulk density as compared to conventional salt forms.

The purest form of salt is now obtained by passing hydrogen chloride into a saturated solution of salt, and mechanically "fishing out" the crystals as they form. The crystals so obtained are centrifuged and dried. When highly soluble hydrogen chloride is passed into a saturated solution of sodium chloride it forms a concentrated solution of hydrochloric acid in which the sodium chloride is only slightly soluble. The slight solubility of sodium chloride in solutions saturated with hydrogen chloride is accounted for by the fact that hydrogen chloride, when dissolved in water, forms hydrates which, of course, reduce the amount of water available for dissolving sodium chloride. It is comparable to having removed an equivalent number of water molecules from the solution by evaporation, etc.

Uses.—*Sodium Chloride*, U.S.P. XVII, "contains not less than 99.5 per cent of NaCl, calculated on the dried basis. It contains no added substance." Sodium chloride exerts the effect of the chloride ion, as well as the effect of the sodium ion. It occurs in all of the fluids and nearly all of the tissues of the body. When introduced into the stomach in moderate amounts, it produces very little effect. However, a deficiency of sodium and chloride ions in the body results in the phenomenon of "salt hunger," as evidenced by metabolic disturbances, emaciation, etc.

Sodium chloride, in 20 per cent solution, has been used to some extent for the injection treatment of varicose veins of the lower extremities. The solution, in amounts up to 5 or 10 ml. is injected into the lumen of the vein to bring the concentrated solution into intimate contact with the wall of the vein.

Several years ago, a group of American surgeons advised the Public Health Service that in many cases, the oral use of a dilute solution of sodium chloride is just "as effective as blood plasma in the emergency treatment of shock from serious burns and other injuries." The treatment calls for making a solution by adding one level teaspoonful of sodium chloride and one-half teaspoonful of sodium bicarbonate to a quart of water. This solution is quite palatable and is used as the only drinking fluid during the first few days following injury. Several quarts of the solution should be taken orally each day, a quantity which is not too great in view of the thirst of patients following serious burn injury. This treatment for shock is so simple that it should be a part of the knowledge of every pharmacist as a public health measure in view of the current unsettled world conditions and the possibility of war with consequent widespread injury due to bombing attacks.

As an electrolyte replenisher the salt is officially recognized as *Sodium Chloride Tablets* and if fluid replenishment is also to be achieved *Sodium Chloride Injection*, *Ringer's Injection* and *Lactated*

Ringer's Injection are available. To replenish nutrients as well as electrolyte the U.S.P. recognizes *Dextrose and Sodium Chloride Injection* for parenteral use and the N.F. provides a monograph for *Sodium Chloride and Dextrose Tablets.* Tablets of sodium chloride, with or without dextrose, are popular for use during excessively hot weather to replace sodium chloride lost by perspiration. The addition of dextrose to the salt tablets is said to supply a quickly available source of energy. It has been suggested that the use of tablets of sodium chloride is inferior to the use of salted water (0.1 to 0.2 per cent) in that the tablets are more apt to cause nausea and vomiting through gastric irritation. One gram of sodium chloride dissolved in a quart of water makes an approximately 0.1 per cent solution which may be used for this purpose.

Numerous articles have appeared in pharmaceutical and medical journals about the importance of making ophthalmic solutions with the same osmotic pressure as that of the lacrimal fluid. A 0.9 per cent solution of sodium chloride is isotonic with both lacrimal fluids and blood. In preparing isotonic collyria the same concentration of sodium chloride is used as for any body fluid. In recent years the calculations for preparing isotonic solutions have been reduced to table form and the simplified methods have been given considerable publicity. (See Appendix for tables.) For application to tissues where an isotonic physiological salt solution is necessary the official compendia recognize *Ringer's Solution* and *Sodium Chloride Solution.*[1] The deleterious effects of single-salt solutions upon excised tissues were responsible for the production of so-called "balanced solutions." Sodium Chloride Injection, when injected into animals, is rapidly adjusted, insofar as the several ion concentrations are concerned, by exchange with the various tissues. This, however, does not take place with excised tissues and, therefore, the ion concentrations of blood plasma must be simulated as nearly as possible in order that the solutions can maintain the functions of the excised tissues. Ringer's Solution is one of these balanced solutions in which the calcium ion antagonizes the inhibitory effects of the potassium ion as well as the stimulant effects of the sodium ion.

Other official preparations where isotonicity is achieved either for application to mucous membranes or for injection, by the use of sodium chloride, are *Naphazoline Hydrochloride Solution, Phenolsulfonphthalein Injection, Picrotoxin Injection, Ephedrine Sulfate Solution* and *Racephedrine Hydrochloride Solution.*

---

[1] An interesting article by G. A. Moerke entitled "Physiological Saline without Weighings," J. Lab. and Clin. Med., **30**, 186 (1945) shows how it is possible to take advantage of the chemical principle peculiar to sodium chloride, namely its relatively constant solubility regardless of temperature, in preparing this solution. Dilution of 2.6 ml. of filtered saturated brine to 100 ml. produces a solution containing almost exactly 0.9 Gm. of sodium chloride per 100 ml. Sterilization of saturated brine by boiling or autoclaving does not affect the concentration because loss of water still leaves a saturated solution. The only necessity is to have a saturated solution of sodium chloride stored over a thick layer of excess salt in a stock bottle.

An example of its innocuous character when used in small amounts is its use as a filler in adjusting the potency of *Thyroid.*

The varied commercial uses of salt are illustrated by the fact that the U.S. alone uses several millions of tons yearly in the chemical and metallurgical industries.

SODIUM CITRATE

Sodium Citrate, U.S.P. XVII

$$\begin{array}{l} CH_2COONa \\ | \\ \text{Formula, } Na_3C_6H_5O_7; \ C(OH)COONa \\ | \\ CH_2COONa \end{array}$$

Molecular Weight, 258.07 (anhydrous)

Physical Properties.—Sodium Citrate occurs in colorless, monoclinic crystals or as a white, odorless, crystalline powder, having a cool, saline taste. Hydrates of the salt (usually the dihydrate) slowly effloresce on exposure to dry air.

One Gm. of the salt dissolves in 1.5 ml. of water at 25° C. and in 0.6 ml. of boiling water. It is insoluble in alcohol.

Chemical Properties.—When heated to 100° C., the dihydrate begins to lose water and at about 150° C. it becomes anhydrous. At red heat it carbonizes, emitting inflammable gases having a pungent, acrid odor, and finally leaves a residue of sodium carbonate (1).

(1) $2Na_3C_6H_5O_7.2H_2O + 9O_2 \overset{\Delta}{\to} 3Na_2CO_3 + 9CO_2\uparrow + 9H_2O\uparrow$

It is a salt of a strong base and a relatively weak acid and it hydrolyzes sufficiently to impart a slight alkalinity to its aqueous solutions.

Because sodium citrate in solution ionizes to liberate sodium and citrate ions, the salt may be used as a buffer against acids. The mechanism whereby this takes place is through the citrate ion, which will take up hydrogen (or hydronium) ions from highly ionized acids such as hydrochloric acid, to form relatively non-ionized citric acid. The following schematic diagram shows the reactions taking place.

$$\begin{array}{ccc} Na_3C_6H_5O_7 & \rightleftarrows \ 3Na^+ + & C_6H_5O_7^{\equiv} \\ & + & + \\ 3H_2O + 3HCl \rightleftarrows & 3Cl^- + & 3H_3O^+ \\ & \uparrow\downarrow & \uparrow\downarrow \\ & 3NaCl & H_3C_6H_5O_7 + 3H_2O \end{array}$$

When taken orally, sodium citrate is converted into sodium bicarbonate, thus functioning as a systemic alkalizer.

In addition to the official salt which may be anhydrous or, more commonly, the dihydrated sodium citrate ($Na_3C_6H_5O_7 \cdot 2H_2O$) there is another common hydrate ($Na_3C_6H_5O_7)_2 \cdot 11H_2O$. This salt also occurs as a well-crystallized compound, 1 Gm. of which is soluble in 1.1 ml. of water at 25° C. and 0.4 ml. of water at 100° C. It was official in U.S.P. VIII, but was deleted because of its pronounced tendency to effloresce.

Another important chemical property of the citrate ion is its sequestering action. The citrate ion possesses not only the salt-forming carboxyl group (—C⫽O, \O—H) but also an alcoholic hydroxyl group. This alcoholic hydroxyl group provides the property of sequestration. Cupric Citrate, U.S.P. XIII was an example.

The salt is slightly soluble yet does not yield many cupric ions in solution and is not precipitated by bases. Benedict's Solution utilizes cupric citrate in a sodium carbonate solution. In buffered solutions of zinc salts, sodium citrate is often used to maintain the zinc in alkaline solution. Calcium, magnesium and iron are also readily sequestered by citrates.

Ferric ions are very commonly sequestered with citrates (sodium citrate or citric acid). Perhaps they react in the following manner:

Tartaric acid or its salts also have a function similar to that of citrates. With ferric ions a soluble ferritartaric acid has been suggested as forming.

Perhaps, similar structures account for the compounds of antimony and bismuth with tartrate. A copper complex in Fehling's Solution is that of potassium sodium tartrate—copper utilizing the alcoholic hydroxyl groups of the tartrate ion.

Glycerin is known to dissolve calcium oxide or calcium hydroxide and to increase the solubility of the calcium ion. A 70 per cent glycerin solution dissolves 3.5 Gm. of calcium hydroxide per 100 ml. In the syrups of hypophosphites 30 per cent of glycerin is used. The hydroxyl groups of glycerin are considered to provide the sequestering property.

Sucrose exhibits a weak sequestering property that is utilized mostly with ferrous ions. Citrates will sequester ferric or ferrous ions so completely that they will not react with tannin, phosphates, hydroxides, etc., but sucrose is not this effective, only holding the ferrous ion sufficiently to resist oxidation. Precipitation as the carbonate, for example, readily takes place. The principle in the case of sucrose is thought to be similar to that of glycerin.

The commonly used sequestering agents in pharmacy, the pharmaceutical preparation and the sequestered ion, are given in the following table:

Sequestering Agent	Pharmaceutical Preparation	Sequestered Ion
Citrate ion	Anticoagulant Sodium Citrate Solution tion U.S.P.	calcium
	Anticoagulant Acid Citrate Dextrose Solution U.S.P.	calcium
	Benedict's Qualitative Reagent	cupric
	Ferrous Sulfate Syrup N.F.	ferrous
	Magnesium Citrate Solution N.F.	magnesium
	Normal Human Plasma, U.S.P.	calcium
	Tannic Acid Glycerite N.F.	ferric
Tartrate	Fehling's Qualitative Reagent	cupric
	Antimony Potassium Tartrate U.S.P.	antimony
Sucrose	Ferrous Sulfate Syrup N.F.	ferrous

Sodium Citrate is assayed by first drying the salt to determine its loss of weight which should not exceed 1 per cent for the anhydrous form. In the hydrated form the loss in weight is due to water of crystallization and should be not less than 10 per cent or more than 13 per cent. Following this, the salt is ignited to the carbonate (2). The residual carbonate is treated with an excess of 0.5 N sulfuric acid, and the residual acid determined by titration with a standard solution of sodium hydroxide using methyl orange as the indicator.

$$(2)\quad 2Na_3C_6H_5O_7 + 9O_2 \xrightarrow{\Delta} 3Na_2CO_3\uparrow + 9CO_2\uparrow + 5H_2O\uparrow$$

Official Tests for Identity.—1. A solution of Sodium Citrate (1 in 20) responds to the tests for *Sodium* (*q.v.*).

2. A 1 in 10 solution also responds to the tests for *Citrate*
(*a*) When an excess of calcium chloride T.S. is added to a cold, slightly acid solution of Sodium Citrate, no precipitate is produced. However, when the solution is alkalinized and heated, a white granular precipitate of calcium citrate settles out (3). The precipitate is insoluble in sodium hydroxide T.S., but dissolves immediately in diluted hydrochloric acid (4) due to formation of water-soluble citric acid and calcium chloride.

$$
(3)\quad
\begin{array}{c}
CH_2-COONa \\
| \\
2HO-C-COONa + 3CaCl_2 \rightarrow \\
| \\
CH_2-COONa
\end{array}
$$

Calcium citrate

$$ + 6NaCl $$

$$
(4)\quad \text{Calcium Citrate} + 6HCl \rightarrow
\begin{array}{c}
CH_2-COOH \\
| \\
2HO-C-COOH \\
| \\
CH_2-COOH
\end{array}
+ 3CaCl_2
$$

(*b*) If potassium permanganate T.S. is added to a hot solution of Sodium Citrate, to which has been added one-tenth of its volume of mercuric sulfate T.S. (Denigé's reagent), a white precipitate is produced (5, 6, 7). Tartrates do not give this precipitate. The equations for the reactions thought to take place are given below.

$$(5)\quad 2H_3C_6H_5O_7 + O_2(KMnO_4) \rightarrow 2C\!\!
\begin{array}{c}
\nearrow CH_2COOH \\
=\!O \\
\searrow CH_2COOH
\end{array}
\quad \text{(acetone-dicar-}$$

boxylic acid) $+ 2CO_2\uparrow + 2H_2O$

$$(6)\quad 2HgSO_4 + 2H_2O \rightarrow Hg_2(OH)_2SO_4 + H_2SO_4$$

(7)

$$\text{O} \diagdown \atop \text{O} \diagup \text{S} \diagup \text{O—Hg—OH} \atop \diagdown \text{O—Hg—OH} \quad + \quad \text{HOOC—CH}_2 \diagdown \atop \text{HOOC—CH}_2 \diagup \text{C} = \text{O} \rightarrow$$

$$\text{O} \diagdown \atop \text{O} \diagup \text{S} \diagup \text{O—Hg—O—C—CH}_2 \atop \diagdown \text{O—Hg—O—C—CH}_2 \quad \diagdown \atop \diagup \text{C} = \text{O} \downarrow$$

(white)

3. When ignited, Sodium Citrate behaves in the manner characteristic of almost all metallic salts of organic acids, in that it first chars and burns, and then upon continued heating yields a residue of sodium carbonate (1) which effervesces with acids, and imparts the yellow sodium color to a non-luminous flame.

Commercial Manufacture.—Sodium citrate is made by neutralizing a solution of citric acid with sodium carbonate or bicarbonate (8). When effervescence has ceased, the solution is evaporated to crystallization or, more frequently, the salt is granulated in the usual way.

(8) $3\text{NaHCO}_3 + \text{H}_3\text{C}_6\text{H}_5\text{O}_7.\text{H}_2\text{O} \rightarrow \text{Na}_3\text{C}_6\text{H}_5\text{O}_7.2\text{H}_2\text{O} + 3\text{CO}_2\uparrow + 2\text{H}_2\text{O}$

Pharmacological Action of Citrate Ion.—This ion has no specific pharmacological action. It is readily oxidized in the system to carbon dioxide and water. When alkali citrates are administered they are quickly absorbed into the system and are there oxidized by the tissues to an equivalent amount of sodium bicarbonate.

When added to shed-blood it prevents its coagulation by its sequestering action on the calcium ion in the blood which is necessary for coagulation. Whether it simply forms calcium citrate or a complex salt is not known. The evidence, however, points to a more complex salt than the simple citrate.

Uses.—*Sodium Citrate,* U.S.P. XVII, contains not less than 99 per cent of $\text{C}_6\text{H}_5\text{Na}_3\text{O}_7$ calculated on the anhydrous basis and is anhydrous or contains two molecules of water of hydration. The uses of sodium citrate may be considered under specific headings as follows:

(a) *Orally,* sodium citrate is ingested into the body and is oxidized in the tissues to sodium bicarbonate. This oxidation is not as rapid as that taking place with acetates. Its therapeutic value, orally, depends then on this alkalinization, and hence its use to relieve mild acidosis and also to promote a diuretic effect (see also Sodium Acetate). A non-official compound which is closely related to sodium citrate is disodium citrate which has an analogous action to and is said to have a more agreeable taste than the official salt. The usual dose is 1 Gm. four times a day with a range of from 1 to 3 Gm.

(b) *Parenterally*, sodium citrate is capable of shortening the coagulation time of the blood, although this seems entirely in contradiction to its anticoagulant action on blood *in vitro*.

(c) *In vitro*, when sodium citrate is added to freshly drawn blood it prevents the coagulation of blood over a relatively long period of time. This action, the basis for its official recognition, is probably due to the inactivation of blood calcium as an undissociated calcium complex (sequestration). This attribute is utilized in preparing *Normal Human Plasma*, and in making blood transfusions, wherein the blood is drawn into a flask containing a suitable amount of sodium citrate. For Normal Human Plasma blood is drawn into sterile bottles containing a dilute solution of sodium citrate, followed by centrifugation to remove cells. The drawn blood may then be kept for some time, or may be used immediately without danger of clotting. The citration of whole blood is usually carried out by using a 4 per cent sodium citrate solution, in the proportion of 50 ml. to 500 ml. of the donor's blood and it is necessary that citrated blood be stored at body temperature and be used as soon as possible. Two official solutions, *Anticoagulant Sodium Citrate Solution* and *Anticoagulant Acid Citrate Dextrose Solution*, are employed in citration procedures. The former is used primarily for blood fractionation procedures and the latter for storage of whole blood.

(d) *Pharmaceutically*, sodium citrate is often used to prevent discoloration of various preparations such as the glycerites of phenol and tannic acid by sequestering ions such as Fe^{+++}, etc. and making them non-reactive. Examples of this kind of usage are to be found in the table on p. 229. The sequestered ion is still available to the body after ingestion of the products designed for internal usage.

The unpleasant features connected with the parenteral administration (intramuscular) of penicillin have led to methods for protecting penicillin from the inactivating effects of the acid gastric juices (it is also inactivated by excess alkali). Among the more effective procedures is the use of trisodium citrate or disodium citrate as a buffer salt to cause formation of the weak acid, citric acid, in the stomach at the expense of the more highly acidic hydrochloric acid normally present. The better absorption of penicillin is reflected in the raised urinary levels of excreted penicillin. Anhydrous sodium citrate (4 to 5 per cent) is probably the best to use in *Buffered Potassium Penicillin G for Injection* to prevent decomposition of the water-sensitive penicillin, inasmuch as the dihydrate is prone to effloresce and in that way release its water of hydration.

SODIUM FLUORIDE

Sodium Fluoride, U.S.P. XVII

Formula, NaF. Molecular Weight, 41.99

Physical Properties.—Sodium Fluoride occurs as colorless and odorless crystals, or more commonly as a white powder. It has a specific gravity of 2.8. The compound is soluble to the extent of 1 Gm. in 25 ml. of water, but is insoluble in alcohol. Aqueous solutions of the salt tend to corrode glass bottles and should be stored in Pyrex ware. Solutions for dental use should be made with distilled water and stored in dark, Pyrex bottles. The period of storage should not exceed six months.

Chemical Properties.—One of the most important properties of sodium fluoride, from the pharmacist's standpoint, is that acidification of its solution produces hydrofluoric acid (1) which is poisonous. Hydrofluoric acid is a weak acid which at low temperatures tends to form polymers such as H_6F_6 and at higher temperatures exists as HF. Even though the acid is a weak one it tends, either as gas or solution, to attack tissues and causes painful, slow-healing burns.

Sodium fluoride is a salt formed from a weak acid and a strong base and, therefore, can reasonably be expected to hydrolyze in aqueous solution to yield an alkaline reaction (2). This also ac-

(1) $NaF + HCl \rightarrow NaCl + HF$

(2) $F^- + H_2O \rightleftarrows HF + OH^-$

counts for the corrosive effects of sodium fluoride solutions on ordinary glassware inasmuch as hydrofluoric acid is unique in its ability to attack glass.

The fluorides of the alkali metals (except lithium), ammonium and silver are all soluble in water whereas the fluorides of other metals are either slightly soluble or entirely insoluble.

The assay of sodium fluoride depends on its ability to form reasonably stable complexes with ferric ion of the type $FeF_6^=$. The procedure is to titrate a carefully neutralized solution of the salt in a strongly saline solution with a freshly prepared and standardized solution of ferric chloride using potassium thiocyanate as an indicator (3). The sodium chloride represses the ionization and re-

(3) $FeCl_3 + 6NaF \rightarrow Na_3FeF_6 + 3NaCl$

sultant hydrolysis of the sodium fluoride (a salt of a weak acid and a strong base) which could cause precipitation of ferric hydroxide. The red color of the ferric thiocyanate end-point, being soluble in alcohol and ether, is concentrated for observation by shaking the titration mixture with a small amount of an alcohol-ether mixture.

Official Tests for Identity.—1. The corrosive effect of hydrogen fluoride on glass to form gaseous SiF_4 (4) is the basis of the official test wherein the salt is treated in a hood with sulfuric acid using a platinum crucible with a glass plate placed over it. Etching of the glass provides a positive test.

(4) $SiO_2 + 4HF - SiF_4$ (gaseous) $+ 2H_2O$.

2. A 1 in 10 aqueous solution of the salt responds to the tests for *Sodium* (*q.v.*).

Commercial Manufacture.—Sodium fluoride may be made by the neutralization of hydrofluoric acid with sodium carbonate (5) or by the double decomposition of calcium fluoride with sodium carbonate (6).

(5) $2HF + Na_2CO_3 \rightarrow 2NaF + H_2O + CO_2 \uparrow$

(6) $CaF_2 + Na_2CO_3 \rightarrow 2NaF + CaCO_3 \downarrow$

Pharmacology of Fluoride Ion and the Fluorides.—The fluoride ion is notably toxic with the acute lethal dose being about 4 Gm. It is thought that this property is occasioned partly by the formation of insoluble calcium fluoride with the calcium of the blood and partly by its toxic action on enzymatic activity. Sodium fluoride is a general protoplasmic poison. It is also an excellent antiseptic, and as such has been used as a preservative and to prevent fermentation. Less toxic substances, however, are available.

Although fluoride has a reputation as a toxic substance, there is a body of evidence accumulating to suggest that it may be a key nutritional factor in the etiology of osteoporosis.[1] An extensive study was made by Dr. D. M. Hegsted recently who compared bone densities in an adult population of which part lived in an area with a high fluoride content in their drinking water and the balance in an area with a low fluoride content. The conclusion was that there was a significant correlation between reduced bone density in all female adult age groups and low fluoride intake. Age was likewise significant with the incidence of low bone density being greatest in the aged female. A more objective criterion of its relationship to osteoporosis was in the threefold higher incidence of collapsed vertebrae in low fluoride area females as against those in high fluoride areas. For unknown reasons there was a lesser variation in bone density in the male than in the female. In males, however, the same study noted that calcification of the aorta was 2 to 3 times more prevalent in all age groups when the subjects came from low fluoride areas. Speculation that it is desirable for the aging female to live in a high fluoride area to forestall osteoporotic developments and for the aging male to live in the same area for the

---

[1] Geriatric Focus, **6**, No. 4, 1, 1967 (pub. by Knoll Pharmaceutical Co., Orange, N.J.).

purpose of slowing down arteriosclerotic degeneration are probably unwarranted and the evidence at present is too meager. Nevertheless, there will undoubtedly be developments in this area in the near future. Unfortunately, there is no knowledge as to the relationship between fluoride intake for caries prevention as against osteoporotic prophylaxis and it would, indeed, be ironic if there was a significant difference since this would rule out fluoridation of drinking water as a means of controlling both.

Perhaps not unrelated to the foregoing observations on the possible relationship of fluoride intake to bone density is a relatively new use for fluoride in osteoporotic treatment. This use is based on the original findings of Rich et al.[1] who found that administration of sodium fluoride to patients with idiopathic osteoporosis or Paget's disease of bone would cause the retention of calcium together with reduction of fecal and renal calcium output. Rather heroic doses are given with one suggested dosage regimen being 1 mg. fluoride ion/kg. body weight/day.[2] Such dosage has been given over a period of a few years without fluoride toxicity being observed. The findings are experimental, however, and need clinical verification.

The mechanism of action of fluoride with respect to osteoporotic conditions is not known with certainty. However, studies have suggested that fluoride somehow reduces the interface of minute calcium phosphate crystals embedded in the hydrated protein matrix of bone. Since it is at this interface where bone mineral gives up calcium and phosphorus to the protein phase and, hence, to the rest of the body, it is reasonable to suppose that limitation of the exchange process will slow down calcium depletion and bone demineralization. It is known that the interface area decreases almost linearly with increasing fluoride content in bone.

Certain fluoride salts, notably sodium flouride and stannous fluoride, have assumed importance in dental practice for retarding or preventing dental caries. It has been well established that there is an inverse relationship between fluoride-containing drinking water and the incidence of dental caries in school age children. Children living in areas where fluoride occurs in significant amounts in the domestic water supply always have a markedly lower incidence of caries than those living in areas supplied with fluoride-free water. Inasmuch as fluorides are toxic, their addition to drinking water has been a delicate matter. Studies on the amount of fluoride in water in many parts of the country have shown that the decline in rate of caries levels off at about 1 to 1.5 parts per million (p.p.m.). For that reason, about 1 p.p.m. is believed to be the optimum figure. The U.S.P. specifies a concentration of 1.5 to 3 parts per million of sodium fluoride (equivalent to 0.7 to 1.3

[1] Rich, C., Ensinci, J. and P. Ivanovich, J. Clin. Invest., 43, 545 (1964).
[2] Private communication from Dr. Wallace Armstrong, Biochemistry Department, University of Minnesota, Medical School, Minneapolis, Minnesota.

parts per million of fluoride ion) in drinking water. Fluoride at this level has not been shown to be toxic or cumulative and may be considered non-hazardous. Higher levels of fluoride than 1 p.p.m. may cause mottling of the teeth, a dental imperfection noted early in connection with excess fluoride in drinking water. Although there is still opposition to the fluoridization of municipal water supplies it would seem that the sheer weight of favorable evidence concerning its effectiveness in dental caries prevention and the safeness of the procedures used for fluoridizing water supplies will eventually result in nationwide use. At the present time the U.S. Public Health service estimates that about 42 million people in the U.S. are using water containing 0.7 to 1.2 p.p.m. of fluoride from central water supplies. About 7 million of these are using naturally occurring supplies. Hammarlund[1] has reviewed the problem and advocates an active participation by pharmacists in educating the public to the advantages of fluoridization.

There is also evidence to show that topical application of fluoride solutions to the surfaces of the teeth may have a limited inhibiting effect on tooth decay in children. The usual procedure is to apply a 1 to 2 per cent solution to the surfaces of the teeth immediately after dental prophylaxis. Usually four applications are made during a period of 10 days. More recently, stannous fluoride solutions (*q.v.*) have found favor with dentists for the same purpose. It appears that the combination of stannous ion with fluoride ion is superior to fluoride ion associated with other ions (*e.g.*, sodium). Tests showing a superior ability in decreasing solubility of tooth enamel in organic acids, decreasing incidence of caries in animals and decreasing incidence of caries in humans have led to increased acceptance. The basic research necessary to show this superiority necessitated studies on the mechanism of tooth decay itself. Acid attack on tooth enamel via a sodium lactate-lactic acid buffer system based in bacterial coatings (plaques) on teeth seem to be very important. Decay seems to begin as a demineralization inside the enamel rather than on the surface as formerly thought. Apparently, diffusion of hydrogen ions and free lactic acid past the enamel surface into the immediate area behind it with consequent release of calcium and phosphate ions which diffuse outward is basic to the initial decay process. It is believed that a hard layer forms on SnF_2-treated teeth preventing acid diffusion. The layer is thought to consist of tin phosphates, calcium fluoride, tin oxide and other materials.

The use of fluoride tablets for oral consumption, usually containing calcium fluoride, has meager clinical evidence to support it. However, a few studies have indicated that daily supplements of 3 mg. of calcium fluoride may have an inhibiting effect on the development of caries.

[1] Hammarlund, E. R., J. Am. Pharm. Assoc., Pract. Ed., **16**, 22 (1955).

Until recently, dentifrices containing fluorides have not been well accepted. The incorporation of stannous fluoride (*q.v.*) into a well-known dentifrice, approved by the American Dental Association, has changed this picture markedly. Other forms of fluorides have not met with the same acceptance. Mouth washes containing fluorides are not at present accepted and until stability problems connected with solutions of stannous fluoride are solved there is not too much prospect of immediate acceptance.

Uses.—*Sodium Fluoride*, U.S.P. XVII, "contains not less than 98 per cent and not more than 101 per cent of NaF, calculated on the dried basis."

The principal uses of sodium fluoride concerning its dental usages have been discussed above.

Fluorine in the form of sodium fluoride or sodium silicofluoride is used in aqueous solution (1 per cent) as a spray to mothproof clothing. The spray is also effective against ants, roaches and other insects. In the form of a dusting powder (95 per cent NaF) it has long been used to combat chicken lice. Sodium fluoroacetate, commercially known as 1080, is being used as a very effective rodenticide.

SODIUM HYDROXIDE

Sodium Hydroxide, U.S.P. XVII

Formula, NaOH. Molecular Weight, 40.00

Physical Properties.—Sodium Hydroxide is obtainable in dry, hard, brittle, white or nearly white sticks, in fused masses, in small pellets, in flakes, and in other forms; all having a dense crystalline fracture and a specific gravity of 2.13. It is very deliquescent and rapidly absorbs moisture and carbon dioxide from the air. Sodium hydroxide and its solutions rapidly destroy organic tissues, hence great care is necessary in handling them.

In the cold (0° C. or below), concentrated solutions deposit various crystalline hydrates, whose compositions vary from $NaOH.H_2O$ to $NaOH.7H_2O$.

Sodium Hydroxide melts at 318° C. and volatilizes at higher temperatures. The vapors decompose between 1200° and 1250° C.

One Gm. of Sodium Hydroxide dissolves in 1 ml. of water at 25° C. with the evolution of heat. One Gm. is soluble in 0.3 ml. of boiling water. It is soluble in alcohol, in ether, and in glycerin.

Chemical Properties.—The chemical properties of sodium hydroxide are quite varied and although there is some overlapping it is considered advantageous to discuss them under the headings: (*a*) basic properties, (*b*) reaction with salts, (*c*) reaction with metals, (*d*) reaction with non-metals, and (*e*) saponifying properties.

(*a*) Because sodium hydroxide is so highly ionized when dissolved in water, it is one of the strongest bases (1).   As has been previously pointed out, the basic properties are entirely due to the hydroxide ion (see p. 106).   Because solutions of sodium hydroxide are so alkaline it is necessary to take precautions in the filtration, storage, etc. of these solutions.   Filtration should be through glass wool or asbestos, and the solution should be stored in hard glass bottles using stoppers made of rubber.   Glass stoppers are liable to "freeze" in the neck of the bottle.   The use of a little petrolatum on the glass stopper helps to prevent freezing.

(1) $NaOH \rightleftarrows Na^+ + OH^-$

Its excellent acid-neutralizing powers (2) are made use of in various ways, especially in alkalimetry and acidimetry.

(2) $NaOH + HCl \rightarrow NaCl + H_2O$

The marked ability of sodium hydroxide (as well as many other metallic hydroxides) to absorb CO_2 with the subsequent formation of the corresponding carbonate is well known.   This is a good example of its acid-neutralizing effect.   One may consider that CO_2 on dissolving in water forms carbonic acid (3), which in turn reacts readily with sodium hydroxide to form sodium carbonate (4).

(3) $H_2O + CO_2 \rightleftarrows H_2CO_3$

(4) $2NaOH + H_2CO_3 \rightleftarrows Na_2CO_3 + 2H_2O$

(*b*) Sodium hydroxide reacts with the salts of all metals in solution, precipitating practically all except those of the alkali metals and ammonium.

In the case of ammonium salts the product of the reaction is NH_3 (5).   This reaction is used as a test for ammonium ion and is carried out by heating the alkalinized solution.   The evolution of ammonia (detected by odor or moistened red litmus) is a positive test for presence of ammonium ion.

(5) $NH_4Cl + NaOH \rightarrow NH_3 \uparrow + H_2O + NaCl$

When non-volatile hydroxides are formed they precipitate from solution, as in the case of ferric hydroxide (6).

(6) $FeCl_3 + 3NaOH \rightarrow Fe(OH)_3 \downarrow + 3NaCl$

In some cases, an excess of sodium hydroxide will redissolve the precipitated hydroxide.   For example, aluminum hydroxide when freshly precipitated (7) will readily dissolve (8) in an excess of sodium hydroxide.

(7) $AlCl_3 + 3NaOH \rightarrow Al(OH)_3 \downarrow + 3NaCl$

(8) $Al(OH)_3 + NaOH \rightarrow NaAlO_2 + 2H_2O$

(*c*) Many metals are attacked either by aqueous solution of sodium hydroxide or by the fused material. Zinc (9) and aluminum (10) are typical examples of metals which react rather easily in this manner.

(9) $Zn + 2NaOH$ (fused) $\rightarrow Na_2ZnO_2 + H_2 \uparrow$

(10) $2Al + 2NaOH + 2H_2O \rightarrow 2NaAlO_2 + 3H_2 \uparrow$

(*d*) Among the non-metals which react with sodium hydroxide are boron (11), silicon (12), phosphorus (13), and chlorine (14).

(11) $2B + 2NaOH + 2H_2O \rightarrow 2NaBO_2 + 3H_2 \uparrow$

(12) $Si + 2NaOH + H_2O \rightarrow Na_2SiO_3 + 2H_2 \uparrow$

(13) $4P + 3NaOH + 3H_2O \rightarrow 3NaPH_2O_2 + PH_3 \uparrow$

(14) $Cl_2 + 2NaOH \rightarrow NaClO + NaCl + H_2O$

(*e*) Sodium hydroxide is used extensively because of its very effective saponifying power (see also sodium carbonate, p. 218). As previously pointed out, saponification of a fat or oil is the process of hydrolyzing it by means of an alkali, *e.g.*, sodium hydroxide (15) to glycerin and the sodium salt of the fatty acids.

$$\begin{array}{ll}
C_{17}H_{35}COO—CH_2 & CH_2OH \\
| & | \\
(15)\ C_{17}H_{35}COO—CH + 3NaOH \rightarrow 3C_{17}H_{35}COONa + CHOH \\
| & | \\
C_{17}H_{35}COO—CH_2 & CH_2OH \\
\text{Stearin (a fat)} & \text{Sodium stearate (a soap)} \quad \text{Glycerin}
\end{array}$$

Sodium hydroxide is assayed by titration of an aqueous solution of a weighed sample with sulfuric acid in a two-step procedure. The first titration makes use of phenolphthalein as an indicator and is essentially a titration of the sodium hydroxide in the sample. Addition of a few drops of methyl orange T.S. at this point and further titration with the standard sulfuric acid to the methyl orange end point determines the amount of sodium carbonate in the sample. This procedure is necessary because of the avidity with which even solid sodium hydroxide absorbs carbon dioxide from the air with consequent formation of the carbonate (4).

Official Test for Identity.—A solution of Sodium Hydroxide (1 in 25) responds to the tests for *Sodium* (*q.v.*).

Commercial Manufacture.—Sodium hydroxide, or caustic soda as it is more commonly known, is prepared commercially by either (1) the *chemical* method or (2) the *electrolytic* method. Approximately one-half of the caustic soda manufactured today is made by the chemical process and one-half by the electrolytic method. However, the electrolytic procedure has been gaining in popularity and if the present trend continues will in a large measure replace the chemical method.

1. The chemical method involves causticizing milk of lime. Essentially, the process requires the interaction of sodium carbonate with calcium hydroxide to give sodium hydroxide and insoluble calcium carbonate (16).

(16) $Ca(OH)_2 + Na_2CO_3 \rightarrow 2NaOH + CaCO_3 \downarrow$

The calcium hydroxide is obtained by "slaking" lime (CaO), $i.e.$, adding enough water to the lime to convert it to a dry calcium hydroxide (17).

(17) $CaO + H_2O \rightarrow Ca(OH)_2$

In practice, the dry slaked lime and soda ash (anhydrous Na_2CO_3) are stirred into water in which they react to form a caustic soda solution containing a suspension of insoluble calcium carbonate. The caustic soda liquor is obtained from this mixture by allowing the precipitate to settle and then decanting the clear liquid. Since the "mud" of calcium carbonate which has settled out has too much caustic soda adhering to it, it is washed and the washings used as the liquid to which slaked lime and soda ash are added. The caustic soda solution obtained by decantation is evaporated either to a 50 per cent solution in which form one-third to one-half of all caustic soda is sold and used, or it may be evaporated in iron pots to the solid form in which case it is obtained as a solid mass which may be crushed or made into flakes. If desired, the fused material may be cast in silver molds into the form of sticks or pellets, the latter being the usual form in which the pharmacist obtains it. The manner in which the small pellets are made is quite interesting. They are made in one of two ways: (1) by dropping the fused material in the same manner as "drop shot" is made, in which case the fused caustic flattens out into a hemisphere when it strikes the receiving plate; (2) by the use of depression plates, in which the fused material is poured on a plate provided with small hemispherical depressions and the excess scraped off. In this case also, the material is obtained as small hemispheres. The purpose in shaping it into pellets or sticks is to offer a comparatively small surface to atmospheric moisture and CO_2, thus minimizing caking, deliquescence and conversion of the product into sodium carbonate.

2. The electrolytic process has already been discussed in some detail (see p. 84) in connection with the manufacture of chlorine. However, it should be pointed out that two distinct types of electrolytic cells are used, $viz.$, (a) the diaphragm cell, and (b) the mercury cell.

(a) The diaphragm cells are so named because they have the anode and cathode separated by an asbestos diaphragm. Usually the anode is enclosed with a diaphragm. The purpose of the diaphragm is to prevent, insofar as possible, the interaction of sodium hydroxide (around cathode) and chlorine (evolved at anode).

If the products of electrolysis are not separated by a diaphragm the following reactions take place (18, 19, 20):

(18) $2NaOH + Cl_2 \rightarrow NaCl + NaClO + H_2O$

(19) $3NaClO \rightarrow 2NaCl + NaClO_3$

(20) $NaClO + H_2 \rightarrow NaCl + H_2O$

The cell liquor after electrolysis contains from 8 to 12 per cent of sodium hydroxide and about 15 per cent of sodium chloride. It is concentrated to 50 per cent NaOH in multiple-effect evaporators when most of the sodium chloride crystallizes out of solution. The caustic liquor is then handled in a manner analogous to that cited for the chemical process.

(b) The mercury cell differs radically from the diaphragm cell. In this type of cell mercury is used as a cathode and graphite as the anode. Metallic sodium is the primary cathode product (in contrast to the diaphragm cells) and is deposited on the mercury to form an amalgam. The amalgam (liquid) is conducted into a decomposition cell where it is made to react with water (21) to form sodium hydroxide and hydrogen. The amount of water used is such that a 50 per cent caustic soda solution is obtained, thus obviating the necessity of costly evaporation, which is one of the principal disadvantages of the diaphragm cell.

(21) $2Na + 2H_2O \rightarrow 2NaOH + H_2 \uparrow$

Uses.—*Sodium Hydroxide* (Caustic Soda), U.S.P. XVII, "contains not less than 95 per cent of total alkali, calculated as NaOH, including not more than 3 per cent of Na_2CO_3." Sodium hydroxide is so caustic that it finds little use in therapy. Indeed, the U.S.P. cautions: *Exercise great care in handling Sodium Hydroxide, as it rapidly destroys tissue.* However, it is used to some extent in the preparation of various pharmaceuticals. Much of the caustic soda produced commercially is used in the soap industry and also in numerous other ways.

As was the case with sodium carbonate, sodium hydroxide is valuable for the solubilization of such compounds as Nitromersol in *Nitromersol Solution* and *Tincture* as well as in *Phenolsulfonphthalein Injection.*

Soda Lime (Calx Sodica), U.S.P. XVII (p. 821).—Soda Lime is a mixture of calcium hydroxide and sodium or potassium hydroxide or both, intended for use in metabolism tests, anesthesia, and oxygen therapy. The U.S.P. states that it may contain an indicator which will not react with the common anesthetic gases, and which will change color when the absorption capacity of the soda lime for CO_2 is exhausted. The function of Soda Lime in a closed system (such as exists in metabolism tests, etc.) is to absorb the CO_2 which otherwise would accumulate in the system. The sodium hydroxide is capable of picking up carbon dioxide with avidity (3, 4), but its combining power is soon exhausted. However, at this point the calcium hydroxide appropriates the accumulated carbon dioxide (22) to form calcium carbonate and thereby relieves the sodium hydroxide. Thus we see a continuous cycle in which the sodium hydroxide is converted to sodium carbonate, but is then changed back to sodium hydroxide which is again capable of combining with CO_2.

$$(22)\ Na_2CO_3 + Ca(OH)_2 \rightarrow 2NaOH + CaCO_3$$

In hospitals, where the uncolored (*i.e.*, with no indicator) form of soda lime is used, it is customary to keep a record of the length of time that a charge of soda lime has been used. From past experience it is then possible to change the soda lime before its strength is exhausted. In the case of soda lime to which has been added an indicator, the color change of the indicator serves warning that it must be changed.

It is of interest to note that Soda Lime has been reduced from the monograph status that it enjoyed in U.S.P. XV to a listing under "Adjuncts and Clinical Reagents" in U.S.P. XVI and XVII. This in no way is intended to minimize its valuable function as a CO_2 absorbant.

Saponated Cresol Solution consists essentially of cresol dissolved in a soap, the soap being formed by the saponification (15) of any of several oils (corn, linseed, cottonseed, etc.) with potassium or sodium hydroxide. The official formula calls for potassium hydroxide, but permission is given to use sodium hydroxide in an equivalent amount if desired. In the event that a different strength alkali is used than that specified, an equivalent amount is to be calculated and used.

SODIUM HYPOCHLORITE

Sodium Hypochlorite Solution, N.F. XII
Diluted Sodium Hypochlorite Solution, N.F. XII

Formula, NaClO. Molecular Weight, 74.44

Physical Properties.—Sodium hypochlorite, like all of the hypochlorites, is very unstable and therefore is not ordinarily obtainable in solid form.* It is official only in the form of its solutions.

Chemical Properties.—In solution, sodium hypochlorite is decomposed by boiling and by nearly all acids (1).

---

*A highly unstable pentahydrate, m.p. 18° is obtainable under certain conditions and even an anhydrous form may be obtained by freeze drying in a vacuum over concentrated sulfuric acid. These are not used pharmaceutically and are mainly of academic interest to the pharmacist.

(1) $4NaClO + 4HCl \rightarrow 4NaCl + 2Cl_2 \uparrow + O_2 \uparrow + 2H_2O$

The U.S.P. XIV required that Diluted Sodium Hypochlorite Solution contain the present concentration of $NaClO$ required by the N.F. XII and, in addition, that it be equivalent to not less than 430 mg. and not more than 480 mg. of "available chlorine" per 100 ml. Obviously, $NaClO$ does not contain this much chlorine but it can be explained on the basis of liberation of one-half the chlorine from the accompanying sodium chloride when the solution is acidified (1a).

(1a) $NaClO + NaCl + 2CH_3COOH \rightarrow Cl_2 \uparrow + 2CH_3COONa + H_2O$

It is a very powerful oxidizing agent; this action being attributable to active oxygen formed upon decomposition (2). Some investigators, however, feel that it acts as free chlorine.

(2) $NaClO \rightarrow NaCl + O$ (active)

A solution of sodium hypochlorite will form a precipitate of silver chloride with solutions of silver nitrate (3).

(3) $3AgNO_3 + 3NaClO \rightarrow 2AgCl \downarrow + AgClO_3 + 3NaNO_3$
and $AgNO_3 + NaCl \rightarrow AgCl \downarrow + NaNO_3$

Sodium hypochlorite is readily changed, when warmed, to sodium chloride and sodium chlorate (4). This property is characteristic of all hypochlorites.

(4) $3NaClO \rightarrow 2NaCl + NaClO_3$

Sodium hypochlorite solutions will cause the formation of mercuric oxide and sodium chloride when shaken with metallic mercury (5).

(5) $Hg + NaClO \rightarrow HgO + NaCl$

This is in contrast to free hypochlorous acid which reacts to form a brown basic mercuric chloride with metallic mercury (6).

(6) $2Hg + 2HClO \rightarrow Hg_2Cl_2O + H_2O$

Solutions of potassium iodide liberate free iodine when treated with sodium hypochlorite (7).

(7) $2KI + NaClO + H_2O \rightarrow 2KOH + NaCl + I_2$

The official assay of sodium hypochlorite solution depends on its ability to liberate iodine (7) from potassium iodide due to its oxidizing action. A weighed sample of the solution of sodium hypochlorite is treated with potassium iodide and acetic acid and the liberated iodine is titrated with a standard solution of sodium thiosulfate.

Official Tests for Identity. —There are no official tests for sodium hypochlorite since it is a non-existent compound *per se*, but the tests given for the Sodium Hypochlorite Solution may be taken as a criterion for the compound itself.

1. The solution at first colors red litmus blue, and then decolorizes it. The blue coloration of the litmus is, of course, due to the fact that sodium hypochlorite is somewhat hydrolyzed in solution (8)

$$(8)\ ClO^- + H_2O \rightleftarrows OH^- + HClO$$

and thus exhibits an alkaline reaction. Hypochlorous acid is a weaker acid than even carbonic acid. The paper is bleached because of the oxidizing action of the solution.

2. The addition of diluted hydrochloric acid to sodium hypochlorite solution causes an evolution of chlorine (1).

3. The solution obtained in the above experiment responds to the flame test for *Sodium.*

Commercial Manufacture. —Perhaps the most common method for the preparation of solutions of sodium hypochlorite in use today is that of passing chlorine through sodium hydroxide (9).

$$(9)\ Cl_2 + 2NaOH \rightarrow NaCl + NaClO + H_2O$$

Some of the commercial products containing sodium hypochlorite are made by electrolyzing a solution of sodium chloride. The cells do not contain a diaphragm and hence the chlorine liberated at the anode contacts the sodium hydroxide produced around the cathode to form sodium hypochlorite (9). The cell contents are usually cooled with cold water circulated in specially constructed hard rubber tubing, as any marked rise in the temperature is conducive to undesirable sodium chlorate formation.

Pharmacological Action of Hypochlorites. —Hypochlorites are active germicides and because of their alkalinity are able to dissolve necrotic tissue and many bacteria. They are often used by continuous irrigation. One of their faults is that they not only dissolve necrotic tissue but also dissolve blood clots. Furthermore, because their antiseptic action seems to be due to chlorination of bacterial protein (see Chlorine, p. 86) they are somewhat rapidly inactivated by combination with tissue protein as well as with bacterial protein. This type of medication, while important, is giving way to less irritating and equally effective medications.

Uses. —1. *Sodium Hypochlorite Solution,* N.F. XII, "contains not less than 4 per cent and not more than 6 per cent, by weight, of NaClO." The N.F. cautions: *this solution is not suitable for application to wounds.* It is a clear, pale, greenish-yellow liquid having an odor of chlorine, and it is affected adversely by light. If *"Labarraque's Solution"* is desired, this solution diluted with an equal volume of water may be dispensed. The solution is used as an oxidizing and bleaching agent. Solutions ranging from 2 to 5 per cent in concentration are widely used as laundry bleaching agents, *e.g.*, Hilex, Hy-Lo, etc.

2. *Diluted Sodium Hypochlorite Solution* (Modified Dakin's Solution), N.F. XII, is "a solution of chlorine compounds of sodium containing, in each 100 ml., not less than 450 mg. and not more than 500 mg. of NaClO."

It is prepared from Sodium Hypochlorite Solution[1] by dilution with distilled water. Sodium bicarbonate is added in sufficient excess to prevent the solution from bringing about the red color with phenolphthalein which means that it must be a pH of 8.3 or less. The mechanism of the buffering action has been explained as being the result of the well-known reaction (10) of bicarbonate ion with

$$(10) \quad OH^- + HCO_3^- \rightleftarrows CO_3^= + H_2O$$

hydroxide ion resulting from hydrolysis of sodium hypochlorite to form the normal carbonate. The hydrolysis of the carbonate ion is repressed to the left by sufficient excess bicarbonate (11) to the

$$(11) \quad CO_3^= + H_2O \rightleftarrows OH^- + HCO_3^-$$

point where it fails to color phenolphthalein. The purpose in buffering this solution is to lower the alkalinity and thus make it more suitable for application to tissues. It is used as an antiseptic and irrigant for wounds.

SODIUM IODIDE

Sodium Iodide, U.S.P. XVII

Formula, NaI.   Molecular Weight, 149.89

Physical Properties.—Sodium Iodide occurs as a white crystalline powder or as colorless, odorless, cubical crystals. The salt cakes and then deliquesces in moist air and frequently decomposes with the liberation of iodine which gives the salt a brown tint. It has a density of 3.667 at 20° C. At temperatures below 30° C., monoclinic crystals with 2 molecules of water separate from aqueous solutions.

One Gm. of Sodium Iodide dissolves in 0.6 ml. of water, in about 2 ml. of alcohol, and in about 1 ml. of glycerin, at 25° C. One Gm. is soluble in 0.4 ml. of boiling water. Aqueous solutions frequently cause the precipitation of alkaloids from alkaloidal salts due to a slight alkalinity.

[1] A laundry bleach prepared by a reputable manufacturer under conditions assuring control of excessive alkalinity and containing 5% NaClO may be used as Sodium Hypochlorite Solution with the permission of the physician.

17

Sodium iodide melts at 651° C. At higher temperatures it slowly volatilizes with partial decomposition of the vapors.

Chemical Properties.—The chemical reactivity of sodium iodide may be considered from the standpoint of (1) precipitation reactions and (2) ease of oxidation to iodine.

1. Almost all of the iodides are soluble with the exception of silver, mercury (ous and ic), lead, copper (ous), and bismuth. When solutions containing these cations are reacted with solutions of sodium iodide a precipitate of the corresponding insoluble iodide will be formed. For example, silver nitrate precipitates AgI (1), mercuric chloride precipitates HgI_2 (2), etc.

(1) $AgNO_3 + NaI \rightarrow AgI \downarrow + NaNO_3$

(2) $HgCl_2 + 2NaI \rightarrow HgI_2 \downarrow + 2NaCl$

However, in the presence of an excess of sodium iodide (or other soluble iodide) mercuric and bismuth iodides are converted to soluble compounds (3).

(3) $HgI_2 + 2NaI \rightarrow Na_2HgI_4$

Silver, mercurous, lead or cuprous iodides are not solubilized.

2. Sodium iodide (in common with other soluble iodides) is easily oxidized by many reagents to yield iodine.

Chlorine water (also bromine water) will displace iodine from its binary compounds as previously shown (see p. 84). Sodium iodide is no exception (4).

(4) $2NaI + X_2 \rightarrow 2NaX + I_2$ (X = Cl or Br)

Hydrogen peroxide liberates iodine from an acidified (dil. H_2SO_4) solution of sodium iodide (5).

(5) $H_2O_2 + 2NaI + H_2SO_4 \rightarrow I_2 + 2H_2O + Na_2SO_4$

Ferric salts have sufficient oxidizing power to oxidize sodium iodide to iodine (6), although they are incapable of doing the same to solutions of bromides.

(6) $2FeCl_3 + 2NaI \rightarrow 2FeCl_2 + I_2 + 2NaCl$

There are numerous other oxidizing agents which are capable of forming iodine from sodium iodide, but the above suffices to illustrate this type of reaction.

Sodium Iodide is assayed by titrating a strongly acidulated aqueous solution of a weighed sample with potassium iodate solution, and having a little chloroform in the flask. The first reaction that takes place is the reduction of the potassium iodate by sodium iodide (7). In the strongly acid solution the addition of more

(7) $5NaI + KIO_3 + 6HCl \rightarrow 5NaCl + KCl + 3I_2 + 3H_2O$

potassium iodate oxidizes the iodine (in the chloroform solution) to iodine monochloride and the color disappears (8). The function of the chloroform is to dissolve the free iodine formed in the first

$$(8)\ 2I_2 + KIO_3 + 6HCl \rightarrow KCl + 5ICl + 3H_2O$$

reaction (7) and to help see the end point when the iodine finally is completely oxidized to ICl.

Official Tests for Identity.—1. The salt responds to all tests for *Sodium* (*q.v.*).

2. Solutions (1 in 20) of sodium iodide respond to all tests for *Iodide* (*q.v.*).

Commercial Manufacture.—Sodium iodide is manufactured by two processes which are analogous to those described in detail for the laboratory preparation of potassium bromide (*q.v.*). Briefly, these methods involve (1) the decomposition of ferrous iodide with sodium carbonate or (2) the action of iodine upon a solution of sodium hydroxide. (See sodium bromide.)

1. Iodine may be reacted with iron wire or filings to obtain ferrous iodide (9, 10) which is then decomposed with sodium carbonate (11).

$$(9)\ Fe + I_2 \rightarrow FeI_2$$
$$(10)\ 3FeI_2 + I_2 \rightarrow FeI_2.2FeI_3$$
$$(11)\ FeI_2.2FeI_3 + 4Na_2CO_3 \rightarrow 8NaI + FeO.Fe_2O_3 \downarrow + 4CO_2 \uparrow$$

The ferroso-ferric oxide is filtered out and the filtrate is concentrated to obtain the sodium iodide.

2. As in the analogous case of sodium bromide, iodine may be added to a solution of sodium hydroxide until a slight excess is present. This causes the formation of sodium iodide and sodium iodate (12). The sodium iodate is converted to iodide by reduction with carbon (13).

$$(12)\ 6NaOH + 3I_2 \rightarrow 5NaI + NaIO_3 + 3H_2O$$
$$(13)\ NaIO_3 + 3C \rightarrow NaI + 3CO \uparrow$$

Uses.—*Sodium Iodide*, U.S.P. XVII, contains not less than 99 per cent and not more than 101.5 per cent of NaI, calculated on the anhydrous basis. Therapeutically, sodium iodide has the action of the iodide ion. Sodium Iodide is usually administered orally as a source of iodine in a usual dose of 100 mg. three times a day and a usual dose range of 300 mg. to 1 Gm.

Sodium iodide appears to be of some value in the treatment of herpes zoster opthalmicus. Many cases have been treated successfully by administering sodium iodide intravenously in 2 Gm. doses. Two or three doses are usually sufficient. Intravenous administration is also used in very special cases for (*a*) severe paroxysms of asthma and (*b*) acute thyrotoxicosis with severe vomiting.

In pharmaceutical practice sodium iodide may be used to dissolve difficultly water-soluble substances, *e.g.*, iodine, by forming a water-soluble salt as in *Iodine Tincture, Iodine Ampuls* and *Iodine Solution*. Sodium iodide is said to be preferable to potassium iodide for application to tissues because it is better tolerated.

Some commercial preparations employing sodium iodide in combination with iodinated proteins are Iodolake-S (for nonspecific iodide therapy) and Protide (for liquefaction of mucous secretions).

SODIUM LACTATE

Sodium Lactate Injection, U.S.P. XVII

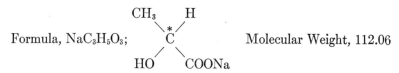

Formula, $NaC_3H_5O_3$;   Molecular Weight, 112.06

Physical Properties.—Sodium lactate occurs as a colorless or almost colorless, thick, odorless liquid. It is miscible with water and alcohol to give a neutral solution. In commerce it is available in admixture with water containing 70 to 80 per cent of sodium lactate.

Chemical Properties.—This salt is easily ignited to form sodium carbonate, CO_2 and water (1).

$$(1)\ 2NaC_3H_5O_3 + 6O_2 \overset{\Delta}{\rightarrow} Na_2CO_3 + 5CO_2 \uparrow + 5H_2O \uparrow$$

Because of the asymmetric carbon atom (*) in the lactic acid portion of the molecule there are two recognized forms of sodium lactate, namely sodium *d*-lactate and sodium *l*-lactate. However, the commercial salt is usually a racemic mixture consisting of equal parts of each of the above and may be termed sodium *r*-lactate. The *d*-lactate when administered intravenously is converted almost entirely to liver glycogen. The *l*-lactate is converted into sodium bicarbonate. In this way injection of the *r*-lactate is accompanied by both alkalinization ($NaHCO_3$) and antiketogenic effect (liver glycogen).

From a knowledge of lactate solubilities, the precipitation reactions of sodium lactate may be readily predicted. The lactates of the alkali metals are very soluble, those of the alkaline earth metals are only slightly soluble (*e.g.*, calcium lactate), and practically all others are insoluble.

Sodium lactate (as the injection) is assayed by first evaporating an accurately measured volume of sample to dryness and then carbonizing the residue to yield sodium carbonate (1). This is then treated with an excess of standard sulfuric acid, the residual amount of which is determined by titration with standard sodium hydroxide.

Official Tests for Identity.—1. Two ml. of sodium lactate solution is superimposed on 5 ml. of a 1:100 solution of catechol in sulfuric acid. A deep red color forms at the interface.

2. When solutions of lactates are acidified with sulfuric acid and then heated with potassium permanganate T.S. they liberate acetaldehyde which may be recognized by its odor (2).

$$(2)\ 10NaC_3H_5O_3 + 11H_2SO_4 + 4KMnO_4 \rightarrow 10CH_3CHO\uparrow + 2K_2SO_4 + 4MnSO_4 + 5Na_2SO_4 + 16H_2O + 10CO_2\uparrow$$

Commercial Manufacture.—Sodium lactate is made commercially by neutralizing dilute solutions of lactic acid with either sodium carbonate (3) or sodium hydroxide (4). A period of heating at an elevated temperature is required to insure complete opening of any of the anhydride (lactone) forms of the acid. The resulting solution should have an approximate pH of 7 (phenol red).

$$(3)\ 2HC_3H_5O_3 + Na_2CO_3 \rightarrow 2NaC_3H_5O_3 + H_2O + CO_2\uparrow$$

$$(4)\ HC_3H_5O_3 + NaOH \rightarrow NaC_3H_5O_3 + H_2O$$

The solution resulting from the neutralization is then concentrated to obtain sodium lactate as a 70 to 80 per cent solution. For therapeutic use sodium lactate solutions may be made up to a 1 molar concentration or a 20/6 molar concentration, these solutions then being the stock solutions from which 1/6 molar solution can be conveniently made by dilution with Water for Injection.

Pharmacological Action of the Lactate Ion.—The lactate ion is without specific effect in the body. For the most part it is a carrier of the sodium with which it is usually associated, and the final product in the body is largely sodium bicarbonate due to metabolism of the lactate portion. The most important lactates are sodium lactate, calcium lactate, and ferrous lactate, the last two salts being a convenient source of calcium and iron.

Uses.—Sodium lactate occurs in *Lactated Ringer's Injection* U.S.P. XVII, and in *Sodium Lactate Injection* U.S.P. XVII. In both cases the salt is antacid and antiketogenic and is officially designated as a fluid and electrolyte replenisher. The injection is usually marketed either as a 1 molar solution of the racemic form which must be diluted with 5 volumes of sterile distilled water or as a $\frac{1}{6}$ molar solution ready for use. A $\frac{1}{6}$ molar solution is approximately isotonic with body fluids. Injection of sodium lactate may be intravenously, intraperitoneally, or subcutaneously depending on the rapidity with which results are required. The function of sodium lactate, and incidentally the reason it is included in this text, is that the tissues oxidize it very readily to sodium bicarbonate with a resultant systemic alkalinizing effect. In the official form as an injection it serves as an effective fluid and electrolyte replenisher. The use of sodium lactate has certain advantages over the use of sodium bicarbonate in that it may be readily sterilized and does not produce a systemic alkalosis as readily as sodium bicarbonate. Furthermore, the salt is antiketogenic in that it corresponds to the effect obtained with dextrose solution, *i.e.*, glycogen deposition in the liver. To summarize, it may be said that sodium lactate can be used in all conditions where the systemic alkalinizing effect of sodium bicarbonate is desired to combat acidosis, *e.g.*, severe dehydration in diarrheas, diabetes mellitus, renal insufficiency, etc. The usual dose intravenously is one liter of a one-sixth molar solution with a dosage range of 500 ml. to two liters.

SODIUM NITRITE

Sodium Nitrite, U.S.P. XVII

Formula, $NaNO_2$. Molecular Weight, 69.00

Physical Properties.—Sodium Nitrite occurs in the form of (1) white or nearly white, opaque, fused masses or sticks, (2) colorless, transparent, hexagonal crystals, or (3) white or slightly yellow granular powder. It is odorless and has a mild, saline taste. It has a specific gravity of 2.168 at 20° C. When exposed to the atmosphere, it deliquesces and is slowly oxidized to sodium nitrate.

One Gm. of Sodium Nitrite dissolves in 1.5 ml. of water at 25° C. It is very soluble in boiling water but only sparingly soluble in alcohol.

When heated to 271° C. the salt melts, and at red heat it decomposes into oxygen, nitrogen, oxides of nitrogen, and sodium oxide.

Chemical Properties.—Aqueous solutions of sodium nitrite are alkaline because nitrous acid is a weak acid and its salts are appreciably hydrolyzed in solution.

All nitrites are easily decomposed by acidification with dilute sulfuric acid to yield nitric oxide which is readily oxidized by atmospheric oxygen to form NO_2 (1, 2, 3).

(1) $2NaNO_2 + H_2SO_4 \rightleftarrows Na_2SO_4 + 2HNO_2$

(2) $3HNO_2 \rightleftarrows H_2O + 2NO \uparrow + HNO_3$

(3) $2NO + O_2 \text{ (air)} \rightarrow 2NO_2 \uparrow \text{ (brown)}$

The reactions of the nitrites fall into two categories in which (1) the nitrite acts as a *reducing agent* and (2) the nitrite acts as an *oxidizing agent*.

1. When the nitrite acts as a reducing agent it itself is oxidized to the nitrate. Potassium permanganate, for example, is readily reduced when treated with sodium nitrite in acid solution (4).

(4) $2KMnO_4 + 5HNO_2 + 3H_2SO_4 \rightarrow 2MnSO_4 + 5HNO_3 + 3H_2O + K_2SO_4$

The chlorates (of the alkali metals) are likewise reduced by acidified solutions of the nitrite (5).

(5) $KClO_3 + 3HNO_2 \rightarrow 3HNO_3 + KCl$

2. The oxidizing action of the nitrites is accompanied by formation of nitric oxide (NO) or nitrogen. The oxidation of an acidified (acetic acid or dil. H_2SO_4) solution of potassium iodide to iodine illustrates the former (6).

(6) $2HNO_2 + 2KI + H_2SO_4 \rightarrow I_2 + 2NO \uparrow + 2H_2O + K_2SO_4$

The oxidation of ammonium chloride illustrates the latter (7).

(7) $NaNO_2 + NH_4Cl \rightarrow N_2 \uparrow + NaCl + 2H_2O$

Sodium nitrite is assayed by quantitatively oxidizing it to the nitrate by means of standard potassium permanganate solution (8).

(8) $5NaNO_2 + 2KMnO_4 + 3H_2SO_4 \rightarrow 5NaNO_3 + K_2SO_4$
$+ 2MnSO_4 + 3H_2O$

The excess permanganate is then removed by adding to it an excess of standard oxalic acid solution (9) which is then titrated with standard permanganate. The reason for titrating the excess of oxalic acid with permanganate instead of titrating the excess of permanganate directly with oxalic acid is because it is easier to detect the appearance of a color in a solution than the disappearance of a color.

(9) $5H_2C_2O_4.2H_2O + 3H_2SO_4 + 2KMnO_4 \rightarrow K_2SO_4 + 2MnSO_4$
$+ 18H_2O + 10CO_2 \uparrow$

Official Tests for Identity.—1. A solution of Sodium Nitrite responds to the tests for *Sodium (q.v.)*.

2. A solution of Sodium Nitrite also responds to the tests for *Nitrite:*

(*a*) When treated with mineral acids or acetic acid, nitrites yield brownish-red fumes of nitrogen dioxide (1, 2, 3).

(*b*) A few drops of potassium iodide T.S. added to an acidified solution of a nitrite liberates free iodine which responds to the starch test (turns starch blue) (6).

Commercial Manufacture.—1. Sodium nitrate is melted in iron pans and sheet lead added a little at a time (10). The temperature is kept between 450° and 500° C., to prevent the destruction of the iron pan. The fused mass is poured into water and any alkali developed during the reaction is neutralized with diluted sulfuric acid. Lead oxide settles to the bottom of the vat. The aqueous solution of sodium nitrite is sometimes treated with carbon dioxide to remove any dissolved lead, concentrated in open pans to a specific gravity of 1.47, and allowed to crystallize in special vessels. By this process approximately 93 per cent of the sodium nitrate is converted into sodium nitrite. A salt containing 98 per cent of sodium nitrite may be obtained by recrystallizing the product from hot water.

$$(10)\ NaNO_3 + Pb \rightarrow NaNO_2 + PbO$$

2. Sodium nitrite is also made by mixing a concentrated solution of sodium nitrate with quicklime. The mixture is heated and then air-free sulfur dioxide is passed through it (11). The precipitate is allowed to settle and the supernatant liquor filtered and concentrated to crystallization.

$$(11)\ NaNO_3 + CaO + SO_2 \rightarrow CaSO_4\downarrow + NaNO_2$$

3. When a mixture of sodium nitrate and sodium hydroxide is fused at 300° C. and anhydrous calcium sulfite added, the nitrate is reduced to the nitrite (12).

$$(12)\ NaNO_3 + CaSO_3 \rightarrow NaNO_2 + CaSO_4$$

4. Much sodium nitrite is also obtained by absorbing the NO gases, resulting from the catalytic oxidation of ammonia, in Na_2CO_3 (13).

$$(13)\ 2Na_2CO_3 + 4NO + O_2 \rightarrow 4NaNO_2 + 2CO_2\uparrow$$

Frequently, the crystallized sodium nitrite obtained by any one of the above processes is fused and the melt poured into stick or pencil-shaped moulds.

Pharmacological Action of the Nitrite Ion.—The principal action of the nitrites is that of relaxing smooth muscle, especially that in the smaller blood vessels. This action lowers the blood pressure markedly. Because of this action sodium nitrite has been used in a variety of diseases, of which angina pectoris is of particular importance. It requires from five to twenty minutes to obtain the nitrite effect from a dose of the drug but the activity lasts from one to two and a half hours. Because of its slow onset of action it is without value in the treatment of an acute attack. Because of its slowness in acting, other nitrites are in more common use for combating acute attacks of angina pectoris. Currently, *Nitroglycerin* U.S.P. XII and *Amyl Nitrite* N.F. XII represent the officially accepted compounds in this class with the former being used sublingually and the latter by inhalation to provide effective and speedy relief for anginal attacks. *Sodium Nitrite* U.S.P. is not officially recognized for this purpose (see below) because of its slow onset of action and long duration of action. Other nitrites and nitrates that have been used for this purpose are ethyl nitrite and erythrityl tetranitrate. The vasodilator effect of sodium nitrite would seem to suggest its use as a hypotensive in essential hypertension. This usage has not developed and its use is termed by some as "illogical and dangerous."

On the other hand, Sodium Nitrite has a well-defined use as an antidote in the treatment of cyanide poisoning. Its use is based on its ability, on intravenous injection, to cause the formation of *methemoglobin* (an oxidized hemoglobin). Although an excessive methemoglobinemia would prove toxic to the patient, in the case of cyanide poisoning the methemoglobin is an effective competitor for cyanide ion with cytochrome oxidase. The toxic action of cyanide ion is due to its combination with cytochrome oxidase to prevent the normal oxidative processes that take place in the body. By successfully competing with cytochrome oxidase for the cyanide ion and in the process being converted to cyanmethemoglobin the function of the oxidase is restored to normal. Although sodium nitrite alone is effective to a degree, the use of sodium thiosulfate (see p. 264) with sodium nitrite appears to be much more effective and, indeed, the effect is much greater than either agent alone or additively and, therefore, is an example of synergism. In the U.S. the usual treatment for cyanide poisoning is the rapid injection of Sodium Nitrite (1 Gm.) and Sodium Thiosulfate (10 Gm.) together with the administration of positive pressure oxygen (see p. 27).

Uses.—*Sodium Nitrite*, U.S.P. XVII, "contains not less than 97 per cent and not more than 101 per cent of $NaNO_2$, calculated on the dried basis. The use of sodium nitrite as a vasodilator has been discussed under "Pharmacological Action of the Nitrite Ion" (see above). The usual oral dose is 30 mg. three times a day, ranging up to 60 mg.

Numerous commercial combinations of sodium nitrite with other hypotensive agents are on the market. With sodium carbonate it is also used in the familiar Anti-Rust Tablets as a reducing agent.

SODIUM PERBORATE

Sodium Perborate, N.F. XII

Formula, $NaBO_3 \cdot 4H_2O$.   Molecular Weight, 153.86

Physical Properties.—Sodium Perborate occurs as white, crystalline granules or as a white powder. It crystallizes in transparent, colorless, monoclinic prisms. It is odorless and has a saline taste. The salt is stable in cool, dry air free from carbon dioxide. In warm (40° C.) or in moist air, it is decomposed with the evolution of oxygen. One Gm. is soluble in about 40 ml. of water.

A monohydrated form occurs as white flakes or as a white powder. It has no odor and has a slightly bitter taste. It is more stable than the tetrahydrate in that it is stable in dry air up to 60° C. and active decomposition does not occur until it is heated over 150° C. It may convert to the tetrahydrate in moist air (1). It is

(1) $NaBO_3 \cdot H_2O + 3H_2O \rightarrow NaBO_3 \cdot 4H_2O$

rapidly soluble in three or more times its weight of warm water, and a concentrated solution deposits crystals of the tetrahydrate if cooled below 60° C.

Chemical Properties.—Sodium perborate in aqueous solution slowly hydrolyzes at room temperature to form sodium metaborate and hydrogen peroxide (2) from which oxygen is slowly evolved. When the solution is warmed to 40° C., the oxygen is given off more rapidly.

$$(2) \; NaBO_3.4H_2O \rightleftarrows H_2O_2 + NaBO_2 + 3H_2O$$

Some investigators claim that the official formula does not accurately represent the constitution of this compound and contend that $NaBO_2.H_2O_2.3H_2O$ is the correct composition. This would explain the ease with which it is hydrolyzed yielding H_2O_2 (2). The same type of formula could be applied to the monohydrated form also, namely, that it be represented as sodium metaborate with peroxide of crystallization ($NaBO_2.H_2O_2$).

Solutions of either salt are alkaline in reaction. This is readily explained on the basis of its hydrolysis equations (3, 4).

$$(3) \; NaBO_3.4H_2O \rightleftarrows H_2O_2 + NaBO_2 + 3H_2O$$
$$(4) \; NaBO_2 + 2H_2O \rightleftarrows NaOH + H_3BO_3$$

The reactions of sodium perborate may be summarized as being a composite of those involving the sodium ion, hydroxide ion, boric acid, hydrogen peroxide and metaborate ion, all of which have been discussed previously.

Sodium perborate is assayed by directly titrating an acidulated solution of the weighed sample with potassium permanganate (5).

$$(5) \; 5H_2O_2 + 2KMnO_4 + 3H_2SO_4 \rightarrow 5O_2 \uparrow + K_2SO_4$$
$$+ \; 2MnSO_4 + 8H_2O$$

The end-point is indicated by the purple coloration of permanganate in excess.

Official Tests for Identity.—1. An aqueous solution gives an alkaline reaction to both litmus and phenolphthalein (3, 4).

2. The salt in solution gives the same test with turmeric paper as is obtained with borates (see p. 210).

3. Because hydrogen peroxide is obtained by the hydrolysis of the salt (1), the test for hydrogen peroxide (see p. 53) is used to detect it. This test is carried out by agitating a mixture of 1 ml. of an aqueous solution of the salt (1 in 50), 1 ml. of diluted sulfuric acid, a few drops of potassium dichromate T.S. and 2 ml. of ether. A blue color in the ether constitutes a positive test.

Commercial Manufacture.—Two of the methods used for the manufacture of sodium perborate are of German origin and differ only in the conditions under which boric acid and sodium peroxide react to form the salt.

1. Jaubert's method involves the mixing of boric acid and sodium peroxide and slowly adding it to cold water acidulated with either sulfuric or hydrochloric acids (6). The crystals that separate out are washed with alcohol and dried at 58° C.

$$(6) \quad H_3BO_3 + Na_2O_2 + HCl \rightarrow NaBO_3 + 2H_2O + NaCl$$

2. Another method which is said to yield better results is to add 150 kilos of sodium peroxide to 200 liters of cold water. A rise in temperature is prevented by the addition of ice. One hundred and fifty kilos of boric acid are then added and carbon dioxide passed into the liquid until 50 ml. of the filtered solution only reduces the permanganate in 5 to 10 ml. of an acidulated (H_2SO_4) fifth-normal solution of potassium permanganate. The reaction mixture is kept cold during the entire operation and the reaction is finally completed by saturating the mother liquors with sodium chloride (7).

$$(7) \quad 2H_3BO_3 + 2Na_2O_2 + CO_2 \rightarrow 2NaBO_3 + Na_2CO_3 + 3H_2O$$

3. Sodium perborate may be prepared by adding sodium hydroxide and twice the theoretical quantity of hydrogen peroxide to a saturated aqueous solution of borax (8).

$$(8) \quad Na_2B_4O_7 + 2NaOH + 4H_2O_2 \rightarrow 4NaBO_3 + 5H_2O$$

The monohydrated sodium perborate is obtained from solutions of sodium perborate by crystallizing at a temperature over 60° C.

Uses.—*Sodium Perborate*, N.F. XII "contains not less than 9 per cent of available oxygen, corresponding to about 86.5 per cent of $NaBO_3 \cdot 4H_2O$."[1] It is officially classed as an oxidant and local anti-infective. The use of this salt depends entirely upon its ability to form hydrogen peroxide upon hydrolysis (essentially nascent oxygen). Because of this formation of hydrogen peroxide it has been used extensively in the oral treatment of Vincent's angina. In this disease (commonly known as "trench mouth") sodium perborate is applied as a glycerin or water paste, and this may be supplemented by using a 2 per cent (saturated) solution as a mouth wash. It is widely used as a dentifrice either as such or in a 10 to 20 per cent mixture with other ingredients, although there is some danger of corrosion due to lodging of particles in the teeth with resultant hydrolysis (3, 4) to sodium hydroxide. It is occasionally used as a dusting powder.

An official preparation consisting of sodium perborate with saccharin and peppermint oil is known as *N.F. Aromatic Sodium Perborate*. The flavoring makes it pleasant for oral use.

[1] The official salt is considered to be a borate peroxyhydrate in contrast to very similar salts know as peroxyborates. The alkaline earth peroxyhydrates are often used in disinfectant powders and in dentifrices because of their low solubility.

SODIUM PHOSPHATE

Sodium Phosphate, N.F. XII

Formula, $Na_2HPO_4.7H_2O$. Molecular Weight, 268.07

Physical Properties.—Disodium hydrogen phosphate crystallizes from cold solutions in large, colorless, odorless, monoclinic prisms having 12 molecules of water of hydration. It also occurs as a colorless or white granular salt. It has a not unpleasant saline taste. The salt has a specific gravity of 1.524 at 16° C. and easily effloresces in air, losing 5 molecules of water. When crystallized from solutions above 35° C., it contains 7 molecules of water. This hydrate is the official form of the salt. It effloresces in warm, dry air.

One Gm. of Sodium Phosphate dissolves in 4 ml. of water at 25° C. It is very slightly soluble in alcohol.

Chemical Properties.—When the salt is heated to 40° C., it fuses to a colorless liquid. At 100° C. it becomes anhydrous and at about 300° C. it is converted into sodium pyrophosphate (2). It may be noted that when either the primary or secondary sodium phosphates are heated they lose water and are converted into sodium metaphosphate in the former instance (1) and into sodium pyrophosphate in the latter (2). Tertiary sodium phosphate is unchanged by heating because it does not contain any of the original hydrogen of orthophosphoric acid.

(1) $NaH_2PO_4 \xrightarrow{\Delta} NaPO_3 + H_2O$

(2) $2Na_2HPO_4 \xrightarrow{\Delta} Na_4P_2O_7 + H_2O$

An aqueous solution of disodium hydrogen phosphate is alkaline to litmus paper and to phenolphthalein test solution. As previously stated (p. 141), this is occasioned by hydrolysis, *i. e.*, the tendency of the hydrogen ion of the water to combine with the monohydrogen phosphate ion to form dihydrogen phosphate ion. The alkalinity, of course, is due to the presence of hydroxide ion (3).

(3) $HPO_4^= + H_2O \rightleftarrows H_2PO_4^- + OH^-$

Much of the chemistry of the phosphate ion has already been discussed (see p. 141), but it should be pointed out again that many of the incompatibilities of this salt which are not due to its alkalinity, are due to insoluble salt formation. Insoluble precipitates are readily formed with silver, barium (4), ferric (5), and lead salts (6).

(4) $Na_2HPO_4 + BaCl_2 \rightleftarrows 2NaCl + BaHPO_4 \downarrow$

(5) $Na_2HPO_4 + FeCl_3 \rightleftarrows FePO_4 \downarrow + 2NaCl + HCl$

(6) $2Na_2HPO_4 + 3Pb(CH_3COO)_2 \rightleftarrows Pb_3(PO_4)_2 \downarrow + 2CH_3COOH + 4CH_3COONa$

In reaction (4) the presence of ammonia will cause the formation of tertiary barium phosphate (7).

(7) $2Na_2HPO_4 + 3BaCl_2 + 2NH_3 \rightleftarrows Ba_3(PO_4)_2 \downarrow + 2NH_4$-Cl $+ 4NaCl$

The assay of sodium phosphate is carried out by treating an acid (nitric acid) solution of the weighed sample with an excess of ammonium molybdate T.S. (8). The precipitated phosphomolybdate

(8) $12(NH_4)_2MoO_4 + Na_2HPO_4 + 23HNO_3 \rightarrow (NH_4)_3PO_4$.-$12MoO_3 \downarrow + 21NH_4NO_3 + 2NaNO_3 + 12H_2O$

is then filtered from the solution and washed thoroughly. The washed precipitate is then dissolved in an excess of standard sodium hydroxide solution (9) and the excess of sodium hydroxide determined by titration with standard sulfuric acid using phenolphthalein as an indicator.

(9) $(NH_4)_3PO_4 . 12MoO_4 + 23NaOH \rightarrow 11Na_2MoO_4$
$+ NaNH_4HPO_4 + (NH_4)_2MoO_4 + 11H_2O$

Official Tests for Identity.—Aside from the fact that aqueous solutions of this salt are alkaline to phenolphthalein, its tests are exactly the same as those given for sodium biphosphate.

Commercial Manufacture.—Disodium hydrogen phosphate is manufactured by (1) neutralizing orthophosphoric acid with sodium carbonate and (2) from bone ash or phosphorite (q.v.).

1. Sodium carbonate does not affect the third hydrogen in phosphoric acid and, therefore, the result of interaction is disodium hydrogen phosphate (10).

(10) $H_3PO_4 + Na_2CO_3 \rightarrow Na_2HPO_4 + H_2O + CO_2 \uparrow$

The solution containing the salt is concentrated to crystallization at a specified temperature (see Physical Properties) to obtain either the heptahydrate or the hydrate containing 12 moles of water. The crystals are centrifuged, washed and dried. Care is taken to prevent efflorescence of the salt.

2. The salt is also prepared by first digesting bone ash or phosphorite for several days with diluted sulfuric acid (11). The resulting solution of phosphoric acid and primary calcium phosphate is then concentrated in order to completely separate the calcium sulfate, filtered, diluted, and sodium carbonate added until precipitation ceases (12). The filtered solution is concentrated and allowed to crystallize.

(11) $Ca_3(PO_4)_2 + 2H_2SO_4 \rightarrow CaH_4(PO_4)_2 + 2CaSO_4 \downarrow$

(12) $CaH_4(PO_4)_2 + Na_2CO_3 \rightarrow Na_2HPO_4 + CaHPO_4 \downarrow +$
$CO_2 \uparrow + H_2O$

Uses.—*Sodium Phosphate* (Disodium Hydrogen Phosphate), N.F. XII, "dried at 105° for 4 hours, contains not less than 98 per cent of Na_2HPO_4." This salt (the first phosphate salt commercially prepared) is used principally for its laxative properties. The administration of 2 to 4 Gm. of sodium phosphate in a glass of hot water an hour before breakfast usually results in a single soft stool within an hour. It belongs to the class of laxatives known as "saline laxatives." There are many schemes for classifying laxatives, but the following is easily understood. It divides the laxatives in the following way:

A. Bulk-increasing Laxatives:

    1. Cellulose and non-digestible polysaccharides (mucilages).
    2. Saline cathartics.
    3. Liquid petrolatum.

B. Irritant Cathartics:

    1. Vegetable acids and sulfur.
    2. Castor oil.
    3. Anthraquinone cathartics and phenolphthalein.
    4. Drastic purgatives.
    5. Mercurial purgatives.

Concerning *saline laxatives:* If a hypertonic solution of sodium chloride is in contact with the intestine it does not remain hypertonic long. The intestine, being permeable to both sodium ions and chloride ions, soon absorbs enough of the salt to render the solution isotonic and no purging takes place. If a solution of sodium sulfate is placed in the gut, a different condition exists. The intestine is permeable to sodium ions but not to sulfate ions. The sulfate ions (and enough positive ions to balance it) stay behind creating a hypertonic state. This can be alleviated only by the introduction of water from the blood and other tissues until the fluid inside the intestine is again isotonic. The increased pressure of this extra water, by virtue of its bulk, brings about catharsis. This is what happens when the physician prescribes a saline cathartic during edema; the water from the edematous area enters the gut to render its contents isotonic. Available laxative preparations are Clyserol, Enemol, and Phospho-Soda. There are also preparations for use as an enema.

Any simple inorganic compound can behave as a saline cathartic providing the intestine is impermeable to one or more of its ions. Compounds like magnesium sulfate, in which neither ion can penetrate the intestine in appreciable amounts, are very effective, although not necessarily more so, than compounds in which only one ion is not absorbed.

The frequent use of salines is inadvisable because it increases the possibility of dehydration.

Sodium phosphate may also be used as a supplementary source of phosphate either in simple phosphate deficiency or in the phosphorus deficiency accompanying diabetic acidosis. In the latter condition a low phosphorus level may be associated with poor utilization of carbohydrates, the role of phosphate in this connection being well-known.

Its use in the treatment of lead poisoning is of long standing and it has the virtue of being both effective and low in toxicity. The sodium phosphate may be used orally or intravenously.

It is also used in the adjustment of calcium-phosphorus ratios in prepared milk and ice cream. Its action is that of an emulsifier, tending to prevent agglomeration of solids, and insures a smooth, creamy consistency. Usual dose—4 Gm. (approximately 60 grains).

Among the official preparations utilizing sodium phosphate is *Dried Sodium Phosphate*. It is prepared by allowing the crystals of sodium phosphate to effloresce for several days in warm air at a temperature of from 25° to 30° C. The drying is continued in an oven, the temperature of which is gradually raised to 110° C. When the salt ceases to lose weight, it is powdered, sifted, and stored in well-closed containers. Too high a temperature at the beginning of the drying causes the salt to dissolve in its own water of hydration and it is then difficult to expel traces of water from the hard, caked residue left upon evaporation of this solution. Usual dose—2 Gm. (approximately 30 grains).

Dried Sodium Phosphate is used in the preparation of *Effervescent Sodium Phosphate* in which the palatability is improved by carbonation provided by the interaction of sodium bicarbonate with organic acids. In addition, it is probable that the effervescent mixture greatly shortens the gastric emptying time. The dried salt prevents moisture from the heptahydrate which might cause premature reaction of the carbonating ingredients in the dry state.

Another pharmaceutical form of sodium phosphate is as *Sodium Phosphate Solution* in which sodium phosphate or its dried form are permissible provided proper allowance is made for differences in water of crystallization. The presence of a small amount of sodium hydrogen citrate (formed when sodium phosphate and citric acid react) and glycerin tend to prevent crystallization. This preparation is used for the laxative properties of sodium phosphate.

SODIUM SULFATE

Sodium Sulfate, N.F. XII

Formula, $Na_2SO_4.10H_2O$. Molecular Weight, 322.19

Physical Properties.—Sodium Sulfate occurs in large, colorless, transparent, monoclinic crystals or smaller granular crystals, which are odorless and have a saline, bitter taste. Because the vapor pressure of the decahydrate is larger than the mean vapor tension of the moisture in the air, the crystals effloresce rapidly on exposure to air and become covered with a white powder of anhydrous sodium sulfate. The crystals have a specific gravity of 1.492 at 20° C.

One Gm. of Sodium Sulfate dissolves in about 8 ml. of water at 0° C., in 1.5 ml. of water at 25° C., in 0.28 ml. of water at 34° C. (temperature of greatest solubility) and in 0.42 ml. of water at 100° C. It is insoluble in alcohol but dissolves in glycerin.

At about 33° C. the salt melts in its water of hydration to form a supersaturated solution, and part of the anhydrous salt separates out. The anhydrous form of the salt may be obtained from a boiling concentrated solution of the salt. When the heating is continued at 100° C., all of the water (about 56 per cent) is driven off, and there remains an anhydrous sodium sulfate which fuses without decomposition at about 886° C.

Chemical Properties.—The principal chemical properties of sodium sulfate deal with the precipitation of the sulfate ion in the form of insoluble salts. Almost all sulfates are freely soluble, but there are several notable exceptions, namely $BaSO_4$, $CaSO_4$, $SrSO_4$ and $PbSO_4$. Addition of soluble salts of the above cations to solutions of Na_2SO_4 will cause precipitation of the corresponding sulfates.

The anhydrous salt readily hydrates itself to form the decahydrate, and for this reason is used as a drying agent for organic liquids such as ether, chloroform, etc.

Sodium sulfate is assayed by precipitating the sulfate ion in the form of barium sulfate (1). This is accomplished by treating a

$$(1) \quad Na_2SO_4 + BaCl_2 \rightarrow BaSO_4 \downarrow + 2NaCl$$

slightly acidified (with hydrochloric acid) hot solution of the sodium sulfate with excess barium chloride solution. The precipitated barium sulfate is permitted to digest for an hour to increase the crystal size for more easy filtration (see also p. 166).

Official Tests for Identity.—1. Solutions of sodium sulfate (1 in 20) respond to all tests for *Sodium* (*q.v.*).

2. Solutions of the salt also respond to all tests for *Sulfate* (*q.v.*).

Commercial Manufacture.—Sodium sulfate is found either with or without water of hydration in large saline deposits in Spain, Siberia, Sicily, Italy, Germany, North Dakota and Canada. It also occurs in many mineral waters (*q.v.*). The crystallized anhydrous salt is found in the form of *thenardite*, and the hydrous salt (Na_2SO_4.-$10H_2O$) occurs as *mirabilite* or Glauber's salt. It is found at Stassfurt in monoclinic crystals as *glauberite* ($Na_2SO_4.CaSO_4$).

Sodium sulfate is obtained by evaporating and cooling the mother liquors (which contain magnesium sulfate and sodium chloride) obtained in the recovery of sodium chloride from sea water (2). (See p. 224.)

$$(2) \quad MgSO_4 + 2NaCl + 10H_2O \rightarrow Na_2SO_4.10H_2O + MgCl_2$$

The mother liquors obtained by the treatment of carnallite or kieserite contain about 25 per cent of magnesium sulfate and 50 per cent of sodium chloride. At Stassfurt, these liquors are evaporated at a temperature of about 33° C. to a gravity of approximately 34° Baumé, and the sodium sulfate allowed to crystallize in large tanks during the cold winter nights. In this manner, large crystals containing 14 molecules of water of hydration are obtained.

Much of the sodium sulfate of commerce is obtained from the manufacture of hydrochloric acid (*q.v.*) and nitric acid (*q.v.*). Indeed, these methods of manufacturing the acids have probably survived because of the need for sodium sulfate in various industries.

Uses.—*Sodium Sulfate* (Glauber's Salt), N.F. XII, "dried at 105° for four hours, contains not less than 99 per cent of Na_2SO_4." Sodium sulfate is used therapeutically as a saline cathartic (see p. 258). Its usual dose for catharsis is 15 Gm. Although its taste and drastic action is a distinct disadvantage it is considered to be one of the most effective of the saline cathartics. Large quantities are used in veterinary practice as a cathartic. A less well-known action of sodium sulfate is as a diuretic. In this capacity it is administered intravenously as a 4 per cent solution and the resulting diuresis is believed to be due to the impermeability of the tubule cells to the salt, which therefore remains in the tubules and diminishes the reabsorption of water by its osmotic action. In adults the dosage ranges from 1 to 3 liters per day, intravenously.

SODIUM THIOSULFATE

Sodium Thiosulfate, U.S.P. XVII

Formula, $Na_2S_2O_3.5H_2O$. Molecular Weight, 248.18

Physical Properties.—Sodium Thiosulfate occurs in large, transparent, colorless, monoclinic prisms or as a coarse, crystalline powder. It is odorless and has a cooling, bitter taste. It has a specific gravity of 1.729 at 17° C. The salt is stable in air below 33° C., but effloresces in dry air above that temperature. It deliquesces in moist air.

One Gm. of sodium thiosulfate dissolves in 0.5 ml. of water at 25° C. Aqueous neutral or alkaline solutions of the salt decompose on boiling because of reduction to sulfide and oxidation to sulfate (1). In this case there is no formation of sulfur dioxide because the oxidation of the polysulfide salt does not take place in solution. It is insoluble in alcohol.

Chemical Properties.—At 56° C. the salt melts in its water of hydration and at 100° C. it becomes anhydrous. At 100° C. decomposition of the salt begins and at 220° C. it is completely converted into sulfur, sulfur dioxide, sodium sulfide and sodium sulfate (1, 2 and 3).

(1) $4Na_2S_2O_3 \overset{\Delta}{\to} 3Na_2SO_4 + Na_2S_5$

(2) $Na_2S_5 \overset{\Delta}{\to} Na_2S + 4S \downarrow$

(3) $Na_2S_5 + 4O_2 \overset{\Delta}{\to} Na_2S + 4SO_2 \uparrow$

Aqueous solutions are neutral or slightly alkaline (hydrolysis).

The addition of acids, *e.g.*, hydrochloric acid, to a solution of sodium thiosulfate liberates thiosulfuric acid (4) which instantly decomposes into sulfur, sulfur dioxide, and water (5).

(4) $Na_2S_2O_3 + 2HCl \rightleftarrows H_2S_2O_3 + 2NaCl$

(5) $H_2S_2O_3 \rightleftarrows S \downarrow + H_2SO_3 \rightleftarrows H_2O + SO_2 \uparrow$

Although the alkali thiosulfates are very soluble in water, most of the other thiosulfates are difficultly soluble and therefore addition of metallic cations other than the alkali cations may reasonably be expected to cause precipitation of the corresponding insoluble thiosulfate. For example, silver nitrate treated carefully with sodium thiosulfate will precipitate white silver thiosulfate (6), which quickly begins to hydrolyze to yield black silver sulfide (7). This

(6) $Na_2S_2O_3 + 2AgNO_3 \rightarrow Ag_2S_2O_3 \downarrow + 2NaNO_3$

(7) $Ag_2S_2O_3 + H_2O \rightarrow Ag_2S + H_2SO_4$

is especially so in strongly acid solutions (see also ammoniated mercury).

The principal chemical property exhibited by thiosulfates in general is that of reduction. The pronounced reducing power of sodium thiosulfate on halogens, for example, is shown by the effect on iodine (8). Solutions of iodine are colored, but the addition of

(8) $2Na_2S_2O_3 + I_2$ (colored) $\rightarrow 2NaI$ (colorless) $+ Na_2S_4O_6$
(colorless)   (colorless)

sodium thiosulfate causes immediate decolorization by the formation of colorless sodium iodide and sodium tetrathionate. The reaction is so clean-cut that use is made of it in quantitative analysis for determining amounts of iodine in unknown samples. Likewise, sodium thiosulfate is used to remove traces of chlorine from bleaching operations utilizing chlorine. It is also used in stills when preparing distilled water to remove the chlorine.

The reducing action is also shown by the reduction of ferric salts to the corresponding ferrous form (9, 10). Upon the addition of a drop or two of ferric chloride T.S. to a solution of sodium thiosulfate, a dark violet color is formed and then quickly disappears. The fugitive violet color has not been adequately explained, some suggesting that it may be due to formation of ferric thiosulfate and still others that it is due to the formation of ferric sulfite, $Fe_2(SO_3)_3$. The ferric sulfite is said to be formed by a reaction between ferric chloride and sulfurous acid (11), the latter having been developed by the action of some free hydrochloric acid in the ferric chloride test solution upon the sodium thiosulfate (12). The ferric sulfite (red color) would soon be reduced to ferrous sulfite with the subsequent disappearance of the color (13).

(9) $2FeCl_3 + 2Na_2S_2O_3 \rightarrow 2FeCl_2 + 2NaCl + Na_2S_4O_6$ (neutral solution)

(10) $2FeCl_3 + Na_2S_2O_3 + H_2O \rightarrow 2FeCl_2 + 2NaCl + H_2SO_4 +$ S $\downarrow$ (acid solution)

(11) $3H_2SO_3 + 2FeCl_3 \rightleftarrows Fe_2(SO_3)_3 + 6HCl$

(12) $Na_2S_2O_3 + 2HCl \rightleftarrows 2NaCl + H_2SO_3 + S \downarrow$

(13) $Fe_2(SO_3)_3 \rightarrow FeSO_3 + FeS_2O_6$

Sodium thiosulfate is assayed by directly titrating an aqueous solution of a weighed sample with a standard iodine solution using starch T.S. as an indicator.

Official Tests for Identity.—1. Solutions of Sodium Thiosulfate (1 in 20) respond to all tests for *Sodium* (*q.v.*).

2. Solutions of the salt also respond to all tests for *Thiosulfate*:

(*a*) Upon the addition of hydrochloric acid, a white precipitate of sulfur is formed. This changes to the yellow form of sulfur and sulfur dioxide (4, 5) is liberated.

(*b*) Addition of ferric chloride T.S. causes the formation of a dark violet color which quickly disappears (11, 12, 13).

(*c*) Iodine solutions are quickly decolorized by means of sodium thiosulfate (8).

Commercial Manufacture.—1. Soda ash (crude sodium carbonate) is dissolved in hot water and the solution (26° Baumé) is allowed to flow down over hardwood sticks contained in an absorption tower, where it meets an ascending current of gas weak in sulfur dioxide. The soda ash absorbs all of the sulfur dioxide and then flows down a second tower in which it contacts gases coming directly from the sulfur burner and hence rich in sulfur dioxide (14).

(14) $Na_2CO_3 + H_2O + 2SO_2 \rightarrow 2NaHSO_3 + CO_2 \uparrow$

The bisulfite liquor is then treated with soda ash to change it into neutral sodium sulfite (15) and this is heated with powdered brimstone in a brick-lined cast iron vessel that is provided with a stirrer (16). The resulting solution of sodium thiosulfate is concentrated, allowed to settle, and run into lead-lined crystallizers to cool and crystallize. After several days the crystals are transferred to centrifugals, washed free from mother liquor by a short spraying with water, and screened to size.

(15) $2NaHSO_3 + Na_2CO_3 \rightarrow 2Na_2SO_3 + H_2O + CO_2 \uparrow$

(16) $Na_2SO_3 + S \rightarrow Na_2S_2O_3$

2. The more important of the two commercial processes makes use of by-product sulfide liquors, which contain about 8 per cent of sodium sulfide (Na_2S) and 6 per cent of sodium carbonate (Na_2CO_3). When these liquors are rapidly circulated through a tower filled with wooden shelves, they meet an ascending current of sulfur dioxide, obtained from any one of the usual sources (17). After the liquors have absorbed a sufficient amount of the gas, they are filter-pressed, and concentrated in a steel boiler. The crystallization, etc., is carried out as described in the process immediately preceding.

$$(17)\ 2Na_2S + Na_2CO_3 + 4SO_2 \rightarrow 3Na_2S_2O_3 + CO_2 \uparrow$$

Pharmacological Action of Thiosulfate.—Thiosulfates were originally introduced into medicine as a means of applying the sulfide ion to the skin, the purpose being to exploit the known parasiticidal action of sulfides. This use is illogical and the thiosulfates are without value in this respect. However, in 10 per cent concentration as a footbath it is said to be useful in controlling "athlete's foot." This use is generally held to be inadequate and of doubtful value even when the feet are immersed for long periods.

An important therapeutic use of thiosulfates is as an antidotal treatment for arsenical and heavy metal poisoning, although this usage is without sound experimental basis. If, indeed, it does have a beneficial effect in the dermatitis resulting from arsphenamine and other arsenicals, the mechanism of action is unknown.

They are of definite value in the treatment of cyanide poisoning but are used as a follow-up treatment to other more quickly acting antidotes (see sodium nitrite). The antidotal action of thiosulfate in cyanide poisoning is believed to be based on the conversion of cyanide ion to the much less toxic thiocyanate ion under the influence of the enzyme rhodanase (formerly known as rhodanese) (18, 19).

$$(18)\quad E{\overset{S}{\underset{S}{\big|}}} + S\text{---}SO_3^{=} \longrightarrow E{\overset{S\text{---}S\text{---}SO_3^{-}}{\underset{S^{-}}{}}}$$

$$\text{Rhodanase} \qquad\qquad \text{Rhodanase-thiosulfate complex}$$

$$(19)\quad E{\overset{S\text{---}S\text{---}SO_3^{-}}{\underset{S^{-}}{}}} + CN^{-} \longrightarrow E{\overset{S}{\underset{S}{\big|}}} + SO_3^{=} + SCN^{-}$$

Ingestion of rather large doses orally will cause a cathartic action.

Uses.—*Sodium Thiosulfate* (Sodium Hyposulfite), U.S.P. XVII, "contains not less than 99 per cent of $Na_2S_2O_3$, calculated on the anhydrous basis." The common name of this compound, "sodium hyposulfite" is a misnomer. Sodium hyposulfite is really $Na_2S_2O_4$ (also sodium hydrosulfite). However, through common usage, the term is still used for sodium thiosulfate and is sometimes shortened to "hypo." Sodium thiosulfate is infrequently used as a cathartic and as an antiseptic wash to combat ringworm and other parasitic skin diseases. Dermatologists frequently prescribe it with acids (see reactions 4 and 5). Official recognition is based on its use as an antidote in cyanide poisoning (see injection form below). Usual dose—1 Gm. intravenously as an antidote in cyanide poisoning in the form of a 5 to 10 per cent solution with a range of 500 mg. to 2 Gm. Larger doses, however, may be used in combination with sodium nitrite (see p. 253).

The N.F. notes that if *Potassium Iodide Solution* is not to be used immediately it is desirable to add 0.5 Gm. of sodium thiosulfate per liter of finished solution. The function of the sodium thiosulfate in this case would, of course, be to reduce to the iodide any free iodine that might form in the solution.

Sodium Thiosulfate Injection is used for the intravenous injection of sodium thiosulfate in the treatment of arsenical (arsphenamine), cyanide, lead, bismuth and mercury poisoning. It is marketed in 5 or 10 per cent concentrations in 10 ml. ampuls. From 0.5 to 2 Gm. is given daily until symptoms are relieved, although as much as 6 Gm. of the salt on three successive days has been advocated in mercury poisoning.

NON-OFFICIAL SODIUM COMPOUNDS

Sodium Hypophosphite, N.F.X, $NaPH_2O_2.H_2O$, occurs in the form of small, colorless, transparent, rectangular plates, having a pearl luster, or as a white granular powder. It is odorless and has a saline taste. The salt deliquesces in moist air.

One Gm. of the salt dissolves in about 1 ml. of water at 45° C., or in about 0.20 ml. of boiling water. It is soluble in alcohol and freely soluble in glycerin at 25° C., and in boiling alcohol. It is slightly soluble in dehydrated alcohol.

When the salt is heated it loses its water of hydration (1). Upon further heating, it is decomposed into inflammable phosphine (2), and sodium pyrophosphate is left as a residue.

(1) $NaPH_2O_2.H_2O \xrightarrow{\Delta} NaPH_2O_2 + H_2O \uparrow$

(2) $4NaPH_2O_2 \xrightarrow{\Delta} Na_4P_2O_7 + H_2O \uparrow + 2PH_3 \uparrow$ (inflammable)

The principal chemical property of hypophosphites is evidenced in their remarkable reducing power. This has been discussed already under Hypophosphorous Acid (see p. 138).

Sodium hypophosphite is usually prepared by the decomposition of calcium hypophosphite with sodium carbonate (3), or by the less common method of boiling phosphorus with sodium hydroxide (4).

(3) $Ca(PH_2O_2)_2 + Na_2CO_3 \rightarrow 2NaPH_2O_2 + CaCO_3 \downarrow$

(4) $6NaOH + 8P + 6H_2O \rightarrow 6NaPH_2O_2 + 2PH_3 \uparrow$

N.F.X cautioned that care should be exercised in compounding sodium hypophosphite with other substances, especially nitrates, chlorates and other oxidizing agents. Because of its marked reducing properties, an explosion could result on intimate mixing with oxidizing agents.

The original therapeutic use of hypophosphites as nerve tonics is irrational. The usual oral dose, however, is 0.5 Gm. of which most passes through the body unchanged.

Exsiccated Sodium Sulfite, N.F.X, Na_2SO_3, occurs as a white, odorless powder. It has a cooling, saline, sulfurous taste. It undergoes oxidation in air.

One Gm. is soluble in about 4 ml. of water at 25° C. It is sparingly soluble in alcohol.

Aqueous solutions of the salt are alkaline to litmus paper and to phenolphthalein because of hydrolysis. This is in contrast to the acidity imparted to aqueous solutions by sodium bisulfite. The two salts are both reducing agents and may be used for this action in preserving solutions of differing pH. In other words, those solutions that are normally acidic in nature, such as solutions of the alkaloidal salts would find sodium bisulfite to be the preferable salt because it would not entail the possibility of precipitating the free bases. On the other hand, use of sodium bisulfite in an alkaline solution would be similar to starting initially with the normal sulfite.

When an aqueous solution of the salt is acidulated with sulfuric or hydrochloric acid it liberates sulfur dioxide (1).

(1) $Na_2SO_3 + H_2SO_4 \rightarrow Na_2SO_4 + H_2SO_3$
$H_2SO_3 \rightarrow H_2O + SO_2 \uparrow$

The principal chemical property associated with sulfites is the marked reducing action, a property that may be used to good advantage in preserving some easily oxidized pharmaceuticals. For example, the N.F. XII uses this salt as a reducing agent in *Tannic Acid Glycerite* to prevent oxidative changes in the tannic acid. It is rather surprising to note that it is used in this official preparation when the salt itself no longer enjoys official status.

This salt is prepared by saturating a solution of sodium carbonate with SO_2 (2) and then adding a quantity of sodium carbonate, previously dissolved in water, equal to that originally used (3). Evaporation of the solution provides crystals which are exsiccated in the usual way.

(2) $Na_2CO_3 + 2SO_2 + H_2O \rightarrow 2NaHSO_3 + CO_2 \uparrow$

(3) $2NaHSO_3 + Na_2CO_3 \rightarrow 2Na_2SO_3 + CO_2 \uparrow + H_2O$

As indicated above, the principal pharmaceutical value of this salt is as a reducing agent useful for preservation of easily oxidized pharmaceuticals. A 10 per cent solution has been used for the treatment of ringworm and other parasitic skin diseases.

Sodium Thiocyanate, N.F.X., NaSCN, is obtained as small, colorless, hygroscopic crystals, or as a white powder which is affected by light. It has a cooling, saline taste.

One Gm. of sodium thiocyanate is soluble in about 0.7 ml. of water or in about 4 ml. of alcohol at 25° C.

Thiocyanates in general are decomposed by the addition of approximately 35 per cent sulfuric acid to aqueous solutions, although the addition of more dilute (5 per cent) sulfuric acid is without effect.

The addition of certain metallic cations, namely Ag^+, Hg^{++}, Cu^{++}, Au^{+++} and Pb^{++}, to solutions of thiocyanates causes the precipitation of the corresponding insoluble thiocyanate.

Addition of ferric salts to solutions of thiocyanates causes the formation of a blood-red color which has been variously ascribed to the formation of $Fe(SCN)_3$, $Fe(SCN)_6^{\equiv}$ and $Fe(SCN)^{++}$. The latter postulation, based on dilution experiments and experiments on the migration of ions in an electric field, seems to explain the facts most satisfactorily (1). The addition of hydrochloric acid to the solution does not affect the color but, in fact, favors it by suppressing hydrolysis of the Fe^{+++} which indirectly increases the ferric-ion concentration.

$$(1) \quad Fe^{+++} + SCN^- \rightleftarrows Fe(SCN)^{++}$$

About the only useful pharmacological action of the thiocyanates (Na and K) is their ability to reduce the blood pressure, probably by relaxing the arterial tone in a manner similar to the nitrites (see sodium nitrite). The mechanism of blood pressure reduction is, however, by no means certain. They are quickly absorbed from the gastrointestinal tract and are distributed throughout the tissues in a manner similar to the chlorides. Thiocyanates cause an irritative phenomenon similar to that of iodides on mucous membranes and skin. The thiocyanate ion is not metabolized by the body and is excreted unchanged, principally by the kidneys. The thiocyanates are not without toxic properties and a careful check on blood levels should be maintained for safe use.

This drug has been used in the treatment of arterial hypertension but its use has been superseded by far more safe and effective drugs in recent years. Its use had to be safeguarded by a close control of the thiocyanate level in the blood (8 to 12 mg. per 100 ml. was considered safe and effective). Elderly people did not tolerate the drug very well. Weakness and fatigue were commonly experienced in the early stages of thiocyanate therapy, occurring in many cases prior to any relief of the hypertension. Usual dose—0.3 Gm. (approximately 5 grains).

14

Potassium and Potassium Compounds

POTASSIUM

Symbol, K. Valence, 1. Atomic Weight, 39.102; Atomic Number, 19.

History.—Some compounds of potassium have been known since the earliest times. In 1807, Sir Humphrey Davy isolated the element from potash (a residue composed primarily of potassium carbonate which was left after the evaporation of a solution obtained by leaching ashes and which was considered to be elemental in character) by placing a piece of it on a platinum plate which formed the negative pole of a series of electric batteries, and touching the substance with a platinum wire connected to the positive pole. An energetic action took place and minute, metallic globules of potassium were formed on the plate. Some of these globules burst into flame and others merely tarnished. In 1808 Gay-Lussac and Thénard obtained the metal by passing molten potash through a clay tube containing iron turnings heated to white heat. The researches by Gay-Lussac and Thénard (1811) established potassium as a metallic element.

Occurrence.—Potassium is never found free in Nature but, in combination, the metal is widely and abundantly distributed. Potassium compounds are present in sea water and comprise 2.6 per cent of the earth's crust. Potassiferous silicates, *e.g.*, *orthoclase* (felspar) ($KAlSi_3O_8$), potash mica, etc., occur universally but are not used commercially as sources of potassium. Silicates containing potassium are present in almost all rocks and their disintegration provides the soluble potassium salts found in all fertile soils. These salts are assimilated by plants and converted into the potassium salts of such organic acids as oxalic, tartaric, succinic, etc., which, when the plants are burned, are converted into potassium carbonate. This salt was one of the first known basic compounds and was used in soap making as well as in the early pharmaceuticals such as Fowler's Solution (bicarbonate) and ferrous carbonate preparations. Potash forms over 90 per cent of the total alkali in the ashes of most plants. Enormous deposits of various potassium-containing minerals are located at Stassfurt, Germany and near Carlsbad, N. M. These deposits, in addition to sodium chloride, contain *sylvite* (KCl); *carnallite* (KCl.MgCl$_2$.6H$_2$O); *kainite* (K$_2$SO$_4$.MgSO$_4$.MgCl$_2$.6H$_2$O); *polyhalite* (MgSO$_4$.K$_2$SO$_4$.-2CaSO$_4$.2H$_2$O); and other minerals of minor value. These minerals are of industrial importance because of their solubility in water and the ease with which they can be worked chemically.

At present the potassium needs of the United States are obtained from Searles Lake at Trona, California, where it occurs as KCl and K$_2$SO$_4$, and from mines in New Mexico and Texas, where it occurs as polyhalite.

Physical Properties.—When newly cut, potassium is a silver-white metal. The color changes rapidly to a grayish-white having a bluish tinge. It is slightly softer than sodium and has lower boiling- and melting-points. The metal dissolves in liquid ammonia, forming a blue solution. Upon exposure to the atmosphere potassium immediately forms a film of oxide. At ordinary temperatures the metal is of waxy consistency and may be kneaded with the fingers and cut with a dull knife. At temperatures below 0° C. it is quite hard and brittle. It has a density of 0.862, a melting-point of 63.65° C. and boils at 774° C. emitting a green vapor containing monatomic molecules. Potassium has been crystallized in bluish-green quadratic octahedra.

Chemical Properties of Potassium and Potassium Ion.—When *potassium metal* is heated in air it fuses and then inflames, producing a mixture of oxides (K$_2$O, K$_2$O$_2$, etc.). In behavior it resembles sodium very closely but it is a little more reactive. The element combines violently with sulfur, oxygen and the halogens. Potassium decomposes water with the evolution of hydrogen and the formation of the hydroxide (1).

$$(1) \quad 2K + 2H_2O \rightarrow 2KOH + H_2 \uparrow$$

The hydrogen immediately ignites and at the high temperature a part of the potassium is vaporized giving a violet color to the flame. Because of the ease with which potassium is oxidized and also because of its great affinity for water, the metal is kept under kerosene, petroleum benzin, benzene, liquid petrolatum or other liquids that are free from oxygen and are immiscible with water. Potassium also reacts with ethyl alcohol to form potassium ethoxide and hydrogen (2). In this case the hydrogen does not inflame.

$$(2) \quad 2K + 2C_2H_5OH \rightarrow 2C_2H_5OK + H_2 \uparrow$$

When hydrogen is passed over metallic potassium heated to 360° C., a white crystalline hydride (KH) is formed.

Potassium amide (KNH$_2$) is formed by passing ammonia over heated potassium whereby one-third of the hydrogen is replaced by potassium. Potassium has been shown to be slightly radioactive. It also has interesting photoelectric sensitivity because it emits electrons when exposed to light.

Potassium ion will form a precipitate by adding a drop of a solution of chloroplatinic acid (H_2PtCl_6) to 1 ml. of a neutral or acid solution (with hydrochloric acid) of the salt (3). The yellow crystalline precipitate of potassium chloroplatinate (K_2PtCl_6) so formed is almost insoluble in 80 per cent alcohol. This reaction is useful in determining potassium quantitatively. Small amounts of potassium may be detected by making the above test in the presence of alcohol on a slide and observing the crystals with a microscope.

(3) $PtCl_6^= + 2K^+ \rightarrow K_2PtCl_6 \downarrow$

Sodium perchlorate ($NaClO_4$) precipitates potassium perchlorate ($KClO_4$) (4) from solutions of potassium salts. It is only slightly soluble in water and nearly insoluble in 95 per cent alcohol.

(4) $NaClO_4 + K^+ \rightarrow KClO_4 \downarrow + Na^+$

If a neutral solution of a potassium salt is made slightly acid with acetic acid and then added to a solution of sodium cobaltinitrite, $[Na_3Co(NO_2)_6]$ T.S. (U. S. P. XVII, p. 1079), a double salt of potassium sodium cobaltinitrite, $K_2NaCo(NO_2)_6.H_2O$, is precipitated (5). In concentrated solutions the precipitate is formed immediately but in weak solutions the mixture must be allowed to stand for some time. Potassium cobaltinitrite is practically insoluble in water (1 to 11,000 at 15° C.) and completely insoluble in alcohol.

(5) $Na^+ + 2K^+ + [Co(NO_2)_6]^\equiv + H_2O \rightarrow K_2Na[Co(NO_2)_6].$-
$ H_2O \downarrow$ (yellow)

Picric acid, $C_6H_2(NO_2)_3OH$, or sodium picrate, precipitate yellow crystalline potassium picrate, $C_6H_2(NO_2)_3OK$, from a solution of a potassium salt. Potassium picrate has a solubility of about 0.5% in water.

If a solution of a soluble potassium salt is treated with a solution of fluosilicic acid, sparingly soluble potassium silicofluoride is formed (6)

(6) $2KCl + H_2SiF_6 \rightarrow K_2SiF_6 \downarrow + 2HCl$

Sodium bitartrate precipitates granular crystalline potassium hydrogen tartrate ($KHC_4H_4O_6$) from concentrated solutions of potassium salts (7). The precipitate is soluble in ammonia T.S., in alkali hydroxides or carbonates and is insoluble in alcohol. Agitation, alcohol, or a little glacial acetic acid increases the speed of the precipitation.

(7) $NaHC_4H_4O_6 + K^+ \rightarrow KHC_4H_4O_6 \downarrow + Na^+$

Potassium and most potassium salts impart a violet color to a non-luminous flame. If sodium is also present, the yellow sodium flame obscures the violet color unless a blue glass or preferably a saturated solution of potassium chrome alum is interposed between the flame and the eye.

All of the official potassium salts are freely soluble in water with the exception of potassium bitartrate, and potassium permanganate. Potassium permanganate is soluble to the extent of about 6 per cent while potassium bitartrate is soluble only to the extent of 0.6 per cent. Normal salts of potassium, when in solution, are either neutral or basic.   Exceptions are the acid salts such as bisulfite, bisulfate, bitartrate, and dihydrogen phosphate.

Official Tests for Identity.—1. Potassium compounds impart a violet color to a non-luminous flame (*q.v.*).

2. Sodium bitartrate T.S. produces a white, crystalline precipitate (7) (*q.v.*) (U.S.P. XVII, p. 880).

Commercial Manufacture.—Potassium metal has been prepared commercially by several methods.   (*a*) Brunner's process, which consists in the reduction of potassium carbonate with charcoal (8).

$$(8)\ K_2CO_3 + 2C \rightarrow 2K + 3CO \uparrow$$

(*b*) The reduction of caustic potash with iron carbide (9).

$$(9)\ 6KOH + 2FeC_2 \rightarrow 6K + 2Fe + 2CO \uparrow + 2CO_2 \uparrow + 3H_2 \uparrow$$

(*c*) Castner's process, which consists of electrolyzing potassium hydroxide (10).

$$(10)\ 2KOH \rightarrow 2K + H_2 \text{ (cathode) } \uparrow + O_2 \text{ (anode) } \uparrow$$

(*d*) At present, nearly all of the metal is obtained by the electrolysis of potassium chloride.   Potassium chloride fuses at 772° C. and since potassium boils at 760° C., considerable trouble was first encountered.   A mixture of potassium chloride, potassium fluoride and barium chloride was found suitable.   The Downs cell is used for the electrolysis.   (See Sodium, p. 193.)

Pharmacological Action of Potassium Ion.—The potassium ion is the predominating ion within the cell and is necessary for cell growth and function.   It is present in intracellular fluids in contrast to the sodium ion that is present in extracellular fluids.   Potassium ion administered orally or by injection is rapidly absorbed.   The kidney removes the excess potassium ions from the blood so quickly that at any one time there is slight change in blood concentration (0.3 Gm. per 1000 ml.).   It was in 1882 that Dr. Ringer pointed out the necessity of potassium ions in solutions used to maintain life in animal tissues.

A potassium deficiency[1] (less than 14 mg./100 ml. serum) may occur by diarrhea, intravenous infusion of solutions lacking in potassium, burns, hemorrhage, diabetic coma, vomiting, etc.   Another cause of hypopotassemia has arisen as a consequence of the widespread use of the very effective thiazide type diuretics.   Symp-

---

[1] For an interesting paper on potassium deficiency see "The Clinician Views Potassium Deficit" by W. D. Snively, Jr. and R. L. Westerman, Minnesota Medicine, **48**, 713, 1965.

toms are a general weakness and depression of the heart. Developments observed are flaccid and feeble muscles, low blood-pressure, pounding pulse and loud systolic precordial murmurs in the heart beat. This condition may be treated with potassium chloride or acetate given orally (see dangers with enteric coated tablets, however, p. 281). Potassium chloride (1.14 per cent) intravenously or with equal parts of saline by hypodermoclysis is also used. Darrow's Solution (chlorides of potassium and sodium with sodium lactate) is very satisfactory, particularly in babies and diabetics.

The dangers associated with administration of potassium salts in overdose are more or less negligible if there is no renal incapacitation and the urinary output is normal. However, serum levels that reach 4 times the normal may be fatal. Treatment of hyperpotassemia involves intravenous injection of sodium chloride, calcium chloride, calcium gluconate, or dextrose. Cation-exchange resins, either orally or by enema, may also be of value.

There is some evidence that potassium ions are essential to the metabolism of carbohydrates. In diabetic coma they prevent hyperglycemia and should be an ingredient in parenterals used in treatment.

Potassium salts were introduced as diuretics by Thomas Willis in 1679. They are among the best and most effective of the osmotic diuretics. This is true because the potassium ion is very rapidly absorbed from the blood by the glomerulus and renal tubules. There is but slight change in blood concentration following dosage. Since the tubules of the kidney do not reabsorb all of the potassium ion, an osmotic gradient is established and a net loss of water, together with sodium ion, is experienced. The larger the dose, the greater the response. The following order of diuretic efficiency has been observed for potassium salts: nitrate > chloride > bicarbonate = acetate = citrate.

About 1935, potassium chloride was reported to be effective in treating cases of hay fever and asthma. Since that time a number of studies have been undertaken to confirm this action of potassium chloride and all have indicated that the salt has little or no beneficial effect.

OFFICIAL COMPOUNDS OF POTASSIUM

POTASSIUM ACETATE

Potassium Acetate, N.F. XII

Formula, CH_3COOK.   Molecular Weight, 98.15

Physical Properties.—Potassium Acetate occurs in the form of a white crystalline powder, or colorless, monoclinic crystals. When dry the salt is odorless but when slightly damp it has a faint acetous odor. It has a saline and slightly alkaline taste. It melts at 292° C., and has a density of 1.8. It absorbs moisture very rapidly when exposed to the air (deliquescent) and hence must be kept in air-tight containers.

One Gm. of Potassium Acetate is soluble in 0.5 ml. of water and in 3 ml. of alcohol, at 25° C. One Gm. is soluble in about 0.2 ml. of boiling water. It is insoluble in ether.

Chemical Properties.—Potassium acetate fuses when heated and upon strong ignition, decomposes into volatile, inflammable vapors and leaves a residue of potassium carbonate containing particles of carbon (1) (see sodium acetate).

$$(1)\ 2CH_3COOK + 4O_2 \xrightarrow{\Delta} K_2CO_3 + 3H_2O + 3CO_2 \uparrow$$

The residue gives positive tests for potassium ion (*q. v.*), is alkaline to litmus paper and effervesces with acids (carbonate).

An aqueous solution of potassium acetate is alkaline to litmus. All of the acetates are soluble except the slightly soluble silver salt. Acetate salts are stable in solution and are oxidized by body tissues to bicarbonate.

Potassium Acetate is assayed in exactly the same manner as is sodium acetate (see p. 197).

Official Tests for Identity.—1. Potassium Acetate responds to all tests for *Acetate*. (See Sodium Acetate, p. 197.)

2. Potassium Acetate also responds to the test for *Potassium* (*q.v.*).

Commercial Manufacture.—Potassium acetate is made by adding potassium carbonate or bicarbonate to acetic acid until effervescence ceases, evaporating the solution to dryness, fusing the residue, and allowing the mass to solidify. While still warm it is quickly powdered and bottled. Anhydrous potassium acetate is now commercially available in fused masses. When crystalline flakes are desired, the solution of potassium acetate is stirred continuously during the concentration and the resulting crystalline mass centrifuged in a current of dry warm air. For the neutralization of the acetic acid, potassium bicarbonate is preferred to the carbonate on account of its greater purity. If potassium carbonate is used, it is usually necessary to filter the solution of potassium acetate from insoluble matter before concentrating it. The insoluble material is usually silica which is sometimes present as silicates in potassium carbonate.

Uses.—*Potassium Acetate*, N.F. XII when dried at 150° for two hours, contains not less than 99 per cent of CH_3COOK. The acetate of potassium is used mainly as a diuretic and urinary alkalizer. The acetate portion has no specific action. However, it does act by changing the physical properties of the body fluids and by functioning as an alkali after absorption. Also, the acetate ion functions as an antacid in the stomach by combining with hydrogen ions to form slightly ionized acetic acid. (See Sodium Acetate.) Like the alkali salts of most organic acids (except tartaric acid), it is decomposed in the body tissues with the formation of potassium bicarbonate (3).

$$(3)\ CH_3COOK + 2O_2 \rightarrow KHCO_3 + H_2O + CO_2 \uparrow$$

This reaction takes place very quickly and completely. This action as a systemic alkalizer is the same as that of carbonates and bicarbonates except that the pH of the gastric juice is changed to a lesser extent. Because of its deliquescent property, potassium acetate is seldom prescribed in the dry state but usually in solution. A moisture absorbent such as starch, magnesium oxide, or magnesium carbonate is a necessary aid in preparing dry preparations of potassium acetate. Usual dose—1 Gm.

POTASSIUM BICARBONATE

Potassium Bicarbonate, U.S.P. XVII

Formula, $KHCO_3$;   Molecular Weight, 100.12

History.—Potassium bicarbonate was first prepared by mixing saturated solutions of potassium carbonate and ammonium carbonate. Ammonium carbonate actually contains considerable bicarbonate which is available to the potassium ion. Since potassium bicarbonate is about one-third as soluble as the carbonate, it will crystallize first. Cartheuser discovered it in 1757. Cavendish is accredited with the process still used for its commercial manufacture.

Physical Properties.—Potassium Bicarbonate occurs in the form of white granules, a powder, or colorless, transparent, monoclinic prisms. It is odorless, and has a saline and slightly alkaline taste. It is stable in air. Any pronounced deliquescence is indicative of the presence of carbonate.

One Gm. of Potassium Bicarbonate is soluble in 2.8 ml. of water at 25° C. and in 2 ml. of water at 50° C. It is almost insoluble in alcohol. Its solutions are alkaline to litmus but not to phenolphthalein T.S. (pH less than 8.3) when freshly prepared. On standing the solution loses some carbon dioxide (particularly if agitated or warmed) and the alkalinity increases to the point where phenolphthalein T.S. will give a pink color.

Chemical Properties.—When heated at 100° C. the salt slowly loses carbon dioxide and water and forms the normal carbonate (1).

$$(1)\ 2KHCO_3 \xrightarrow{\Delta} K_2CO_3 + H_2O \uparrow + CO_2 \uparrow$$

This change is very rapid above 190° C.

When an aqueous solution of potassium bicarbonate is heated above 50° C., the salt loses carbon dioxide and water and, when the solution is boiled, it is completely converted to carbonate. This property prevents the preparation of a sterile solution by means of heat.

The assay of Potassium Bicarbonate is by precisely the same procedure used for sodium bicarbonate.

Official Tests for Identity.—1. Potassium Bicarbonate gives all the tests for *Bicarbonate*. (See Sodium Bicarbonate.)

2. An aqueous solution of the salt responds to all tests for *Potassium* (*q.v.*).

Commercial Manufacture.—1. Potassium bicarbonate is made by passing carbon dioxide through a very cold, saturated aqueous solution of the normal carbonate until the gas is no longer absorbed (2).

$$(2) \quad K_2CO_3 + H_2O + CO_2 \rightleftarrows 2KHCO_3$$

During the operation any silicates present in the carbonate solution are converted to bicarbonates and silica. The latter is filtered off. When the filtrate is concentrated at a temperature not exceeding 60° C. and cooled, anhydrous crystals of the salt are deposited.

2. A method also used is to pass carbon dioxide over a mixture of potassium carbonate and powdered charcoal which has been moistened with water. The mass is then lixiviated with water, filtered and concentrated. Large, monoclinic crystals of potassium bicarbonate separate out. They are permanent in air.

3. Potassium bicarbonate is made to a very limited extent by a process analogous to the Solvay process (*q.v.*). Trimethylamine is used in place of ammonia because the hydrochloride of the former is much more soluble than ammonium chloride and therefore permits of greater solution concentration with a correspondingly larger yield of the bicarbonate. Potassium chloride is used in place of sodium chloride. The reaction taking place is represented below (3).

$$(3) \quad KCl + N(CH_3)_3 + H_2O + CO_2 \rightarrow KHCO_3 \downarrow + N(CH_3)_3 . HCl$$

Uses.—*Potassium Bicarbonate*, U.S.P. XVII, "contains not less than 99 per cent and not more than 101 per cent of $KHCO_3$, calculated on the dried basis." The salt has about the same neutralizing strength as sodium bicarbonate and is more soluble. It is sometimes used as an antacid for gastric hyperacidity and as a diuretic. Its use as an alkalizer with sulfa drugs has been both advocated and opposed. However, it may have a beneficial effect in cases when it is inadvisable to administer sodium ion by the use of sodium bicarbonate (*e.g.*, cardiac edemas) but where sulfa drugs are indicated. The infrequent medicinal use is probably due to the toxic effect of the potassium ion. It is used technically in the manufacture of baking powder, effervescent salts and as a source of CO_2. It is officially recognized as an electrolyte replenisher. Usual dose— 1 Gm. four times a day with a range of 500 mg. to 2 Gm.

The use of potassium bicarbonate in the preparation of *N.F. Mouth Wash* has been discussed under sodium borate.

As a carbonating agent it is employed in the preparation of *Magnesium Citrate Solution* where it is added to the finished acidic solution just prior to the capping procedure.

POTASSIUM BITARTRATE

Potassium Bitartrate, N.F. XII

Formula, $KHC_4H_4O_6$;
$$\begin{array}{l} CH(OH)COOK \\ | \\ CH(OH)COOH \end{array}$$
Molecular Weight, 188.18

Physical Properties.—Potassium Bitartrate occurs as colorless or slightly opaque, rhombic prisms, or as a white, crystalline powder, which is odorless, has a pleasant, acid taste, and is permanent in air. Its density is 1.955.

One Gm. of the salt is soluble in 165 ml. of water and in 8820 ml. of alcohol, at 25° C. One Gm. is soluble in 16 ml. of boiling water.

Potassium bitartrate is soluble in mineral acids, alkalies, and in alkali carbonates. The salt dissolves freely in solutions of boric acid and borax.

Chemical Properties.—A saturated aqueous solution of the salt is acid to litmus paper and exhibits the chemical characteristics of the potassium ion.

It chars when heated and gives off inflammable vapors having the odor of burning sugar. When further ignited at a higher temperature, there remains a white fused mass (1) which gives positive tests for potassium ion and carbonate ion (*q.v.*).

$$(1)\ 2KHC_4H_4O_6 + 5O_2 \overset{\Delta}{\rightarrow} K_2CO_3 + 5H_2O \uparrow + 7CO_2 \uparrow$$

The carbonate produced by reaction (1) is titrated with an acid in the quantitative determinations of tartrates. Tartrates when treated with concentrated sulfuric acid char and emit the odor of burning sugar.

Some of the common chemical reactions of the tartrate ion are as follows:

1. When silver nitrate test solution is added to a saturated aqueous solution of potassium bitartrate, previously made neutral with a solution of sodium hydroxide (2),

$$(2)\ KHC_4H_4O_6 + NaOH \rightarrow KNaC_4H_4O_6 + H_2O$$

a white precipitate is formed (3).

$$(3)\ KNaC_4H_4O_6 + 2AgNO_3 \rightarrow Ag_2C_4H_4O_6 \downarrow + KNO_3 \\ + NaNO_3 \qquad\qquad\qquad (white)$$

If this precipitate is dissolved in sufficient ammonia test solution (4)

$$(4)\ Ag_2C_4H_4O_6 + 6NH_4OH \rightarrow (NH_4)_2C_4H_4O_6 \\ + 2Ag(NH_3)_2OH + 4H_2O$$

and the solution warmed, the silver ammonia complex is reduced to free silver (5).

$$(5)\ 2Ag(NH_3)_2OH \rightarrow 2Ag\downarrow + 4NH_3\uparrow + H_2O_2$$
$$\text{(mirror)}$$

2. If the dry salt is treated with a few drops of 1 per cent resorcinol in hydrochloric acid and 3 ml. of sulfuric acid and slowly heated, a rose-red color is formed. This color is destroyed by the addition of water.

3. When a solution of a tartrate salt is acidified with acetic acid and a drop of ferrous sulfate T.S. and hydrogen peroxide T.S. are added, then upon the addition of an excess of sodium hydroxide T.S., a purplish-violet color develops.

The tartrate ion is a useful sequestering agent (see water and sodium citrate) due to the presence of two alcoholic hydroxyl groups in conjunction with the carboxyl groups. Ions of iron, bismuth, antimony and particularly copper (-ic) may be maintained in alkaline media with tartrate. Use is made of this property in the stabilization of cupric ions in Fehling's Solution.

The assay of Potassium Bitartrate is carried out by directly titrating a solution of a weighed sample with 1N sodium hydroxide (2) solution using phenolphthalein as an indicator.

Official Tests for Identity.—1. A solution of the salt is positive to all the tests for *Potassium*.

2. Potassium Bitartrate chars when heated (1).

3. Sodium cobaltinitrite T.S. forms an orange precipitate with solutions of Potassium Bitartrate (see eq. 5, p. 270).

4. A silver mirror is formed with silver nitrate T.S. and ammonia T.S. (2, 3, 4, 5).

Commercial Manufacture.—Potassium bitartrate occurs in many acidulous fruits. It is usually obtained from the juice of grapes. When grape juice in casks is allowed to undergo alcoholic fermentation, crystalline crusts of crude potassium bitartrate known as crude tartar or argol are deposited.

Argol is composed of potassium bitartrate, calcium tartrate, coloring materials, extractives, yeast, and other organic substances. The crude tartar is dissolved in boiling water, the solution filtered and then allowed to stand. Slightly colored crystals of potassium bitartrate containing from 5 to 15 per cent of calcium tartrate settle out. These crystals of tartar are boiled with water and most of the coloring matter precipitated by the addition of pipe clay or egg albumen. The solution is filtered through charcoal and crystallized. In order to obtain cream of tartar free from calcium salts, the crystals are dissolved in boiling water, 10 per cent of hydrochloric acid added and the solution stirred continuously while cooling. The crystals of potassium bitartrate are separated from the mother

19

liquor, washed with cold water and dried. An appreciable amount of the bitartrate, together with some tartaric acid, remains in the mother liquor and is frequently utilized in the manufacture of tartaric acid.

Large quantities of cream of tartar of such high purity as to be used medicinally are made by a method known as the "precipitation process." The crude argol from wine casks is dissolved in hot water and partially neutralized with sodium carbonate. The resulting solution is percolated through soda ash, contained in stone cylinders, and the resulting potassium and sodium tartrate purified by crystallization. The slightly colored crystals are than redissolved in water and decomposed by acetic acid into almost pure potassium bitartrate which settles out as a very fine precipitate and sodium acetate which remains in solution (6).

(6) $KNaC_4H_4O_6 . 4H_2O + CH_3COOH \rightarrow KHC_4H_4O_6 \downarrow + CH_3CO-ONa + 4H_2O$

Pharmacological Action of Tartrate Ion.—Absorption of the tartrate ion through the intestinal wall is negligible. It is also resistant to oxidation and is not converted into bicarbonate. The ion when retained in the intestine creates a hypertonic solution. Osmosis increases the water content of the bowel and laxative action results.

Tartrate ion-containing salts are members of the group of saline cathartics.

Uses.—*Potassium Bitartrate* (Cream of Tartar, Acid Potassium Tartrate), N.F. XII, when dried at 105° C. for three hours, contains not less than 99 per cent and not more than 101 per cent of $C_4H_5KO_6$.

This salt is recognized officially for its cathartic action. Usual dose—2 Gm.

Potassium bitartrate has been suggested to replace talc as a dusting powder in surgery. It is more bacteriostatic and more readily absorbed than talc. In the industries it is used as a reducer of CrO_3 in a mordant bath for wool dyeing; in mixtures of chalk and alum as a silver cleaner; for coloring metals; and in baking powders to raise the dough (7).

(7) $KHC_4H_4O_6 + NaHCO_3 \rightarrow KNaC_4H_4O_6 + H_2O + CO_2 \uparrow$

POTASSIUM BROMIDE

Potassium Bromide, N.F. XII

Formula, KBr.   Molecular Weight, 119.01

Physical Properties.—Potassium Bromide occurs as colorless, translucent, or white cubical crystals, or as a granular powder. It is odorless and has a sharp, saline taste. The salt is stable in air and has a specific gravity of 2.75.

One Gm. of the salt is soluble in 1.5 ml. of water, in 250 ml. of alcohol, or in 5 ml. of glycerin, at 25° C. It is soluble in 1 part of boiling water or in about 21 parts of boiling alcohol.

When Potassium Bromide is heated it decrepitates, and at about 730° C. it fuses without decomposing. At a bright red heat (about 1435° C.), it volatilizes.

Chemical Properties.—Aqueous solutions of potassium bromide are neutral or faintly alkaline to litmus paper. The bromide ion forms insoluble salts with silver, mercurous mercury, cuprous copper, bismuth, antimony and lead.

The assay of potassium bromide is carried out by exactly the same procedure as that used for sodium bromide.

Official Tests for Identity.—1. An aqueous solution of potassium bromide responds to all tests for *Potassium* (*q.v.*).

2. The tests and chemistry of the bromide ion are discussed with Sodium Bromide, p. 213.

Commercial Manufacture.—The bromides of the alkali metals are all prepared by the same process. (See Sodium Bromide, p. 214.)

Uses.—*Potassium Bromide*, N.F. XII, dried at 105° for four hours, contains not less than 99 per cent and not more than 101 per cent of KBr.

The bromide ion is responsible for the central depressant effect produced by potassium bromide (see p. 214). Potassium bromide is usually employed in cases of mental excitement and all conditions arising therefrom, *e.g.*, insomnia, nervousness, etc. It is of particular value in controlling the seizures of epilepsy. It is a good sedative but possesses no anodyne properties. Usual dose—1 Gm. daily.

Among the official preparations utilizing potassium bromide for its sedative effect are *Three Bromides Elixir* and *Tablets*.

POTASSIUM CHLORIDE

Potassium Chloride, U.S.P. XVII

Formula, KCl. Molecular Weight, 74.56

Physical Properties.—Potassium Chloride occurs in the form of colorless, elongated, prismatic, or cubical crystals, or as a white, granular powder. The salt is odorless and possesses a saline taste. It is permanent in air. It has a specific gravity of 1.988, and melts at 772° C. When heated it decrepitates, and upon prolonged heating at red heat it sublimes.

One Gm. of Potassium Chloride dissolves in 2.8 ml. of water at 25° C., or in about 2 ml. of boiling water. A 10 per cent aqueous solution of Potassium Chloride is neutral to litmus paper. It is insoluble in alcohol or ether.

Chemical Properties.—The chloride ion is responsible for the important chemical properties (see p. 222).

The assay of potassium chloride is carried out in exactly the same way as that of sodium chloride.

Official Tests for Identity.—1. A solution of Potassium Chloride gives all of the tests for *Potassium* (*q.v.*).

2. Potassium Chloride solutions also respond to all of the tests for *Chloride* (*q.v.*).

Commercial Manufacture.—The sources of potassium chloride are: (1) *carnallite*, (2) *sylvite*, and (3) a bed of solid salt of very complex composition found at Searles Lake.

1. *Carnallite* ($MgCl_2.KCl.6H_2O$) which contains potassium equivalent to 26 per cent K_2O, is found in extensive deposits in Stassfurt, Germany. In these deposits with carnallite (55 per cent) are found sodium chloride (25 per cent) and *kieserite* ($MgSO_4.H_2O$) (15 per cent). The removal of the potassium chloride is complicated by the presence of the other salts. A process of fractional crystallization is carried out whereby the raw salt deposit is ground up and treated with hot water. The hot solution is allowed to stand until the insoluble material settles, transferred to clean containers and then allowed to cool causing about 80 per cent of the potassium chloride to crystallize. The process is repeated using the mother liquor and wash water.

2. *Sylvite* is found in large deposits in Alsace-Lorraine and near Carlsbad, New Mexico. It is a mixture of sodium and potassium chlorides. Two methods are used to separate these chlorides: (*a*) Crystallization, and (*b*) Flotation.

(*a*) *Crystallization Process.*—The sylvite is crushed and extracted with hot water at the boiling point. The hot solution is filtered and cooled by flask evaporation in vacuum crystallizers. The rapid cooling by the removal of water tends to cause both potassium and sodium chloride to crystallize out. The sodium chloride is prevented from separating out by the simultaneous addition of water corresponding to the quantity evaporated off. This is due to the fact that sodium chloride has about the same solubility in cold water as in hot water whereas the cooled solution is filtered and the crystals of potassium chloride recovered. The mother liquor is reheated and used over, only this time it will dissolve just the potassium chloride from the sylvite since it is already saturated with sodium chloride.

(*b*) *Flotation Process.*—The chlorides of potassium and sodium exist in sylvite as a mechanical mixture and not as a double salt or as mixed crystals. When the crude ore is crushed to about 40 mesh, the crystalline form of both potassium and sodium chloride separate out. A special flotation agent has been found that carries off the sodium chloride in the froth and allows the potassium chloride to collect on the bottom of the apparatus.

3. Searles Lake is the location of a deposit of salts consisting of K, Na, Cl, CO_3, B_4O_7, PO_4, and other ions in small amounts. A brine is present that is pumped into evaporators and by a series of evaporations and fractional crystallizations the salts are separated.

Uses.—*Potassium Chloride,* U.S.P. XVII, "contains not less than 99 per cent of KCl, calculated on the dried basis." Potassium chloride has been known for a long time as an effective diuretic. It has also been used successfully in the treatment of Ménière's disease, myasthenia gravis, and familial periodic paralysis. It has also been suggested for the relief of allergic symptoms including urticaria, hay fever, asthma, sinusitis of allergic origin, and migraine but its value is doubtful.

As an electrolyte replenisher in hypopotassemia it is officially represented by *Potassium Chloride Injection* which is marketed as a 10 to 15 per cent (w/v) solution and as *Potassium Chloride Tablets* (usually 0.3 and 1 Gm.). The use of enteric coated tablets of potassium chloride with or without thiazide diuretics has been shown to be a cause of stenosis and ulcer of the small intestine.[1,2] The use of these coated tablets should be avoided since it is possible to use liquid preparations without exposing the patient to the risk associated with the tablets.

It also occurs as a pharmaceutic necessity in the fluid and electrolyte replenishers, *Lactated Potassic Saline Injection* and *Ringer's Injection* and *Solution.* Usual dose.—1 Gm. orally as *Potassium Chloride Tablets* up to 6 times a day and intravenously, 1000 ml. of a 0.3 per cent solution infused over a period of four hours. The usual oral dosage range is 1 to 6 Gm. and the intravenous range is 1 to 3 Gm.

POTASSIUM CITRATE

Potassium Citrate, N.F. XII

CH_2COOK
|
$C(OH)COOK.H_2O$
|
CH_2COOK

Formula, $K_3C_6H_5O_7.H_2O$; Molecular Weight, 324.42

Physical Properties.—Potassium Citrate occurs in colorless, prismatic crystals, or as a white, granular powder. It is odorless, and has a cooling, saline taste. It has a specific gravity of 1.906. The salt is deliquescent in moist air and, therefore, should be kept in air-tight containers.

[1] Morgenstern, L., Freilich, M. and Panish, J. F., J. Am. Med. Assoc., **191**, 637 (1965).
[2] Lawrason, F. D., Alpert, E., Mohr, F. L., and McMahon, F. G., J. Am. Med. Assoc., **191**, 641 (1965).

One Gm. of the salt dissolves in 1 ml. of water at 25° C. It is freely soluble in glycerin but almost insoluble in alcohol.

Chemical Properties.—When heated to 100° C., the salt begins to lose water and at about 200° C. it becomes anhydrous. The anhydrous salt has a density of 1.908 and crystallizes in the triclinic system. At higher temperatures it carbonizes and emits inflammable gases having a pungent, acrid odor. A residue of carbon and potassium carbonate remains (1).

$$(1)\ 2K_3C_6H_5O_7.H_2O + 9O_2 \overset{\triangle}{\to} 3K_2CO_3 + 9CO_2 \uparrow + 7H_2O \uparrow$$

An aqueous solution is alkaline to litmus paper.

Potassium citrate is assayed in a manner identical to that employed for the assay of sodium citrate (see p. 230).

Official Tests for Identity.—1. A solution of Potassium Citrate responds to the tests for *Potassium* (*q.v.*).

2. An aqueous solution also gives the tests for *Citrate* (*q.v.*).

Commercial Manufacture.—Potassium citrate is prepared by neutralizing a solution of citric acid with potassium carbonate or bicarbonate (2). The solution is evaporated either to crystallization or to dryness with constant stirring. The resulting granular mass obtained by the latter process is reduced to a uniform fine powder by trituration in a warm mortar.

$$(2)\ 3KHCO_3 + H_3C_6H_5O_7.H_2O \to K_3C_6H_5O_7.H_2O + 3CO_2 \uparrow + 3H_2O$$

Uses.—*Potassium Citrate*, N.F. XII, when rendered anhydrous by drying at 180° for 4 hours, contains not less than 99 per cent of $C_3H_5K_3O_7$. It contains not less than 3 per cent and not more than 6 per cent of water. The diuretic, expectorant and diaphoretic actions are greater than those of the other alkaline salts and the compounds of ammonia. This salt has a slight laxative action due to the salt action and to slow absorption. Any expectorant action is probably empirical since the intake of water is also beneficial. It functions as a systemic alkalinizing agent in the same manner as other alkali salts of organic acids. (See Sodium Acetate.) Usual dose—1 Gm.

POTASSIUM HYDROXIDE

Potassium Hydroxide, U.S.P. XVII

Formula, KOH.   Molecular Weight, 56.11

Physical Properties.—Potassium Hydroxide is obtainable in dry, hard, brittle, white or nearly white, sticks, in fused masses, in small pellets, in flakes, and in other forms that have a crystalline fracture and a density of 2.044. It is very deliquescent and rapidly absorbs both moisture and carbon dioxide from the air.

One Gm. of Potassium Hydroxide dissolves in 1 ml. of water, in about 3 ml. of alcohol, or in about 2.5 ml. of glycerin, at 25° C. One Gm. is soluble in 0.6 ml. of boiling water. It is very soluble in boiling alcohol.

At 360° C. the base fuses. At higher temperatures, it is appreciably volatilized.

Chemical Properties.—The chemical properties of potassium hydroxide are due entirely to its basic character and high degree of ionization. The chemical characteristics of potassium hydroxide are similar to those of sodium hydroxide. For reactions characteristic of the potassium ion, see p. 269.

The assay of potassium hydroxide is the same as that employed for the assay of sodium hydroxide.

Official Tests for Identity.—1. All solutions of Potassium Hydroxide, even when greatly diluted, are strongly alkaline to litmus paper, phenolphthalein test solution, etc.

2. It responds to all reactions for *Potassium* (*q.v.*).

Commercial Manufacture.—Potassium hydroxide is manufactured in two ways: (1) by causticizing potassium carbonate with milk of lime and (2) by the electrolysis of a solution of potassium chloride.

Process 1.—Attention has been called to the fact that potassium hydroxide is the principal commercial product of the reaction between calcium hydroxide and potassium carbonate (1).

$$(1)\ Ca(OH)_2 + K_2CO_3 \rightleftarrows 2KOH + CaCO_3 \downarrow$$

Process 2.—The electrolytic process is by far the simpler of the two for manufacturing potassium hydroxide. When a direct current is passed through a solution of potassium chloride in a diaphragm cell, chlorine is liberated at the anode and potassium hydroxide together with hydrogen is formed at the cathode. (See Sodium Hydroxide, p. 239.)

Uses.—*Potassium Hydroxide* (Caustic Potash), U.S.P. XVII, contains not less than 85 per cent of total alkali, calculated as KOH, including not more than 3.5 per cent of K_2CO_3.

Caution.—*Exercise great care in handling Potassium Hydroxide, as it rapidly destroys tissues.* Because of its escharotic properties it finds little use as such in therapeutics. The principal use is in chemical and pharmaceutical processes, particularly those in which the potassium ion is desired, and in preparations that were formulated many years ago. It is rarely used internally but to some extent externally as a cauterizing agent. In analytical chemistry it finds some use as an alkaline reagent. The saponification value (U.S.P. XVII, p. 873) of fatty substances depends upon this basic compound. Volumetric solutions, both aqueous and alcoholic of potassium hydroxide are widely used (U.S.P. XVII, p. 1081). A test solution in alcohol or water is also available (U.S.P. XVII, p. 1079).

The principal use of potassium hydroxide in official preparations is as a saponifying agent. To this end it is employed in the saponification of vegetable oils in the preparation of both *Medicinal Soft Soap* (U.S.P. XVI) and *Saponated Cresol Solution* to give potassium salts of the fatty acids, principally oleic acid.

Its use in *Soda Lime* as a carbon dioxide absorbent has already been discussed under sodium hydroxide.

It also finds use in *Aromatic Eriodictyon Syrup* where it solubilizes the bitter resin, eriodictyol.

POTASSIUM IODIDE

Potassium Iodide, U.S.P. XVII

Formula, KI. Molecular Weight, 166.01

Physical Properties.—Potassium Iodide occurs as large, transparent and colorless or white and somewhat opaque cubes, or as a white, granular powder. The salt is stable in dry air, but deliquesces slightly in moist air. It has a specific gravity of 3.123 and melts at 773° C., yielding a vapor of normal density. The salt decrepitates when heated.

One Gm. of the salt is soluble in 0.7 ml. of water, in 22 ml. of alcohol, and in 2 ml. of glycerin, at 25° C. One Gm. of it is soluble in 0.5 ml. of boiling water and in 8 ml. of boiling alcohol. When a quantity of potassium iodide is shaken in a test-tube with one-half its weight of water, there is a marked decrease in the temperature of the solution. The phenomenon of solution may be likened to a change in the physical state and hence, the conversion of "solid" potassium iodide into "liquid" potassium iodide through the agency of a solvent would conform to the laws governing such changes, and heat would be absorbed by the molecules of the solute from those of the solvent.

Chemical Properties.—Aqueous solutions of potassium iodide take up iodine, forming KI_3 (see p. 94), in equilibrium with dissolved iodine: $KI_3 \rightleftarrows KI + I_2$ (in solution). The potassium tri-iodide may be obtained by evaporating the solution over sulfuric acid when black, acicular, monoclinic crystals separate out. These crystals have a specific gravity of 3.498, are very deliquescent, melt at 45° C., and decompose at 100° C. into iodine and potassium iodide. The chemical properties of potassium iodide are due to the iodide ion.

The assay of Potassium Iodide is carried out in precisely the same manner as that for sodium iodide.

Official Tests for Identity.—1. An aqueous solution of Potassium Iodide is neutral or slightly alkaline to litmus.

2. The salt responds to all the reactions for *Potassium* (*q.v.*).

3. A solution of Potassium Iodide responds to all of the tests for *Iodide.* (See Hydriodic Acid.)

Commercial Manufacture.—Nearly all potassium iodide is prepared by adding a slight excess of iodine to a solution of potassium hydroxide to form a mixture of iodide and iodate which is then reduced completely to iodide through the use of carbon. (See Sodium Iodide.)

Uses.—*Potassium Iodide*, U.S.P. XVII, "contains not less than 99.0 per cent and not more than 101.5 per cent of KI, calculated on the dried basis." The uses of iodides in general have been discussed under hydriodic acid (*q.v.*).

Potassium iodide is the iodide of choice because it is quite stable in air (sodium iodide is deliquescent) and the potassium ion provides a diuretic action so often beneficial.

This salt is often added to sodium chloride (table salt) and community water supplies to supplement the diet. In solid preparations (such as animal feeds) calcium stearate is first intimately mixed with the potassium iodide to stabilize it. Each particle of iodide is coated with stearate to prevent oxidation. Potassium iodide is present in several reagent solutions such as Nessler's Solution, Wagner's Solution, Mayer's Solution, etc. Usual dose—0.3 Gm. up to four times a day with a range up to 2 Gm.

Potassium Iodide Solution, N.F. XII, "contains, in each 100 ml., not less than 97 Gm. and not more than 103 Gm. of KI." The use of hot water is necessary to insure a solution containing the required amount of potassium iodide. When prepared in a pharmacy the correct proportions are 30 Gm. of potassium iodide and water sufficient to make 30 ml. Since the dose is small and the solution may be used over a period of time the N.F. allows the addition of 0.5 Gm. of sodium thiosulfate (per 1000 ml.) which will reduce any liberated free iodine to sodium iodide.

Enteric coated tablets of potassium iodide have been marketed by some companies because of findings that old solutions of potassium iodide may be unsatisfactory.

POTASSIUM PERMANGANATE

Potassium Permanganate, U.S.P. XVII

Formula, $KMnO_4$;   Molecular Weight, 158.04

Physical Properties.—Potassium Permanganate occurs in the form of odorless, slender, dark purple monoclinic prisms, almost opaque by transmitted light and of a blue metallic luster by reflected light. The color is sometimes modified by a dark bronze-like appearance. It has a specific gravity of 2.703 and is stable in air. Solutions of Potassium Permanganate have a sweetish, astringent taste.

One Gm. of the salt is soluble in 15 ml. of water at 25° C. or in 3.5 ml. of boiling water. It is reduced by alcohol.

When potassium permanganate is heated it decrepitates, and at about 240° C. it decomposes into oxygen, potassium manganate, and manganese dioxide (1).

(1) $2KMnO_4 \triangleq K_2MnO_4 + MnO_2 + O_2 \uparrow$

Chemical Properties.—This salt is a very powerful oxidizing agent both in the dry state and in solution (2 and 3). Therefore, great care should be exercised in handling it, as dangerous explosions are liable to occur if it comes in contact with organic or other readily oxidizable material, *e.g.*, cork, charcoal, etc., especially in the dry state. When mixed with glycerin, a fire is produced.

(2) $2KMnO_4 + 3H_2SO_4 \rightarrow K_2SO_4 + 2MnSO_4 + 3H_2O + 5[O]$
(acid solution)

(3) $2KMnO_4 + H_2O \rightarrow 2MnO_2 \downarrow + 2KOH + 3[O]$ (alkaline or neutral solution)

Reaction (3) is the one of therapeutic importance since the salt is often used in aqueous solution on the skin.

The chemical properties are due to the presence of the permanganate ion which reacts as a strong oxidizing agent toward many easily oxidizable compounds (reducing agents).

Reducing agents that are oxidized by permanganate include hypophosphites, iodides, bromides, chlorides, ferrous salts, nitrites, sulfites, thiosulfates, peroxides, oxalates, sulfides, and arsenites.

Organic materials such as ethyl alcohol and charcoal generally are readily oxidized.

When, to a solution of potassium permanganate, HCl and H_2S (reducing agent) are added, it will be noted that the violet color disappears and sulfur (oxidized product) is precipitated. The permanganate ion has been reduced to manganous ion (4).

(4) $2KMnO_4 + 6HCl + 5H_2S \rightarrow 2MnCl_2 + 2KCl + 5S \downarrow + 8H_2O$

In neutral solution with 1 per cent permanganate the reaction is (5).

(5) $10KMnO_4 + 22H_2S \rightarrow 3K_2SO_4 + 10MnS \downarrow + 2K_2S_2O_3 + 22H_2O + 5S \downarrow$

When a 3 per cent solution of hydrogen peroxide is added to an aqueous solution of potassium permanganate previously acidulated with sulfuric acid, the color of the permanganate solution is discharged (6). (See Hydrogen Peroxide.)

(6) $2KMnO_4 + 3H_2SO_4 + 5H_2O_2 \rightarrow K_2SO_4 + 2MnSO_4 + 8H_2O + 5O_2 \uparrow$

An aqueous solution of the salt acidulated with sulfuric acid is decolorized by a solution of oxalic acid in hot solution (7) and by a solution of sodium bisulfite in cold solution (8).

(7) $5H_2C_2O_4.2H_2O + 2KMnO_4 + 3H_2SO_4 \rightarrow K_2SO_4 + 2MnSO_4$
$+ 18H_2O + 10CO_2 \uparrow$

(8) $5NaHSO_3 + 2KMnO_4 + 3H_2SO_4 \rightarrow K_2SO_4 + 2MnSO_4$
$+ 5NaHSO_4 + 3H_2O$

On heating potassium permanganate at 240° C., very pure oxygen is evolved, and a black powdery residue of potassium manganate and manganese dioxide (9) remains.

(9) $2KMnO_4 \overset{\triangle}{\rightarrow} K_2MnO_4 + MnO_2 + O_2 \uparrow$

When a little water is added to the residue, a dark green color is formed.

Chlorine is produced by the action of hydrochloric acid on potassium permanganate (10).

(10) $2KMnO_4 + 16HCl \rightarrow 2KCl + 2MnCl_2 + 8H_2O + 5Cl_2 \uparrow$

Alkaline or neutral solutions of potassium permanganate oxidize iodides to iodates (11).

(11) $2KMnO_4 + H_2O + KI \rightarrow 2MnO_2 \downarrow + 2KOH + KIO_3$

Iodine is liberated from potassium iodide by an acid solution of potassium permanganate (12).

(12) $2KMnO_4 + 10KI + 8H_2SO_4 \rightarrow 6K_2SO_4 + 2MnSO_4 +$
$5I_2 + 8H_2O$

Ferrous salts are readily oxidized to ferric salts (13) by potassium permanganate in acid solution.

(13) $2KMnO_4 + 10FeSO_4 + 8H_2SO_4 \rightarrow K_2SO_4 + 2MnSO_4 +$
$5Fe_2(SO_4)_3 + 8H_2O$

Nitrites are oxidized to nitrates by potassium permanganate in acid solution (14).

(14) $2KNO_2 + H_2SO_4 \rightarrow K_2SO_4 + 2HNO_2$
$2KMnO_4 + 5HNO_2 + 3H_2SO_4 \rightarrow K_2SO_4 + 2MnSO_4 +$
$3H_2O + 5HNO_3$

Sulfuric acid is formed when sulfur dioxide is oxidized with permanganate (15).

(15) $2KMnO_4 + 5SO_2 + 2H_2O \rightarrow K_2SO_4 + 2MnSO_4 + 2H_2SO_4$

The assay of Potassium Permanganate is carried out by treating an acidulated solution of a weighed sample with an excess of standard oxalic acid solution (7). The excess oxalic acid is then determined by residual titration with standard potassium permanganate solution.

Official Tests for Identity.—1. A concentrated aqueous solution of potassium permanganate is deep violet red in color. Very dilute solutions are pink colored.

2. Solutions of potassium permanganate acidified with sulfuric acid are decolorized by solutions of hydrogen peroxide (6), by sodium bisulfite T.S. (8) in the cold, and by hot oxalic acid T.S. (7).

Commercial Manufacture.—This salt is prepared by mixing a solution of potassium hydroxide (specific gravity, 1.44) with powdered manganese dioxide and potassium chlorate. The mixture is boiled, evaporated and the residue heated in iron pans until it has acquired a pasty consistency (16).

$$(16)\ 6KOH + 3MnO_2 + KClO_3 \rightarrow 3K_2MnO_4 + KCl + 3H_2O$$

The potassium manganate (green) thus obtained is boiled with a large quantity of water, and at the same time a current of chlorine (17) carbon dioxide (18, 19) or ozonized air is passed into the liquid until the potassium manganate is completely converted to permanganate. The MnO_2 formed is removed continuously in order to prevent its breaking down the permanganate formed. Manganese dioxide seems to have a catalytic effect on the decomposition of permanganates.

$$(17)\ 6K_2MnO_4 + 3Cl_2 \rightarrow 6KMnO_4 + 6KCl$$

or

$$(18)\ 3K_2MnO_4 + 2H_2O \rightarrow 2KMnO_4 + MnO_2 \downarrow + 4KOH$$

$$(19)\ 4KOH + 4CO_2 \rightarrow 4KHCO_3$$

The solution of potassium permanganate is drawn off from any precipitate of manganese dioxide, concentrated and crystallized. The crystals are then centrifuged and dried.

Pharmacological Action of Permanganate Ion.—Permanganates function almost exclusively as oxidizing agents and are perhaps the best ones used in therapy. Internally in mild concentrations there is no noticeable effect except that of oxidation which has been utilized as for intestinal antisepsis (worthless) and in certain types of poisoning due to phosphorus, oxalates, and alkaloids, etc.

Externally its solutions are frequently employed as an antiseptic in concentrations of from 1:500 to 1:15000 with 1:5000 being the strongest non-irritating strength. *E. typhosa* is reported to be killed in a dilution of 1:5000. Bacteria in general show a wide variation in their resistance to permanganate solutions.

Therapeutic application depends primarily on the reduction of permanganate in neutral media by protein-like substances (20).

$$\text{(20)} \quad 2KMnO_4 + H_2O \xrightarrow{\text{protein}} 2MnO_2 \downarrow + 2KOH + 3(O)$$
(brown)

The oxygen (O) is the effective agent. A decided disadvantage is the deposition of manganese dioxide which adheres very tenaciously to the skin.

Uses.—*Potassium Permanganate*, U.S.P. XVII, contains not less than 99 per cent of $KMnO_4$, calculated on the dried basis. *Caution.— Observe great care in handling Potassium Permanganate, as dangerous explosions occur if it is brought in contact with organic or other readily oxidizable substances, either in solution or in the dry state.*

A solution of the salt when in contact with organic matter, such as albumin or bacteria, at once liberates oxygen. The oxygen oxidizes the protein of the bacteria and kills them. The action of permanganate is of short duration and is limited to the skin and the surface of the mucous membranes. There is very little penetration of this oxidizing action; this makes potassium permanganate of less value than most other antiseptics. Solutions of potassium permanganate up to one per cent are stable for months. For practical purposes, filtration may be conducted through wetted filter paper or cotton without serious decomposition.

It is used in the treatment of urethritis and occasionally of gonorrhea. Solutions varying in strength from 1:5000 to 1:15,000 are employed for irrigating the urethra. Due to its oxidizing power it finds some use in Vincent's infection, epidermophytosis, athlete's foot, snake bite, poison ivy and as a chemical antidote in poisoning.

Concentrations of 1:100 to 1:10,000 are commonly used for a local oxidative anti-infective action.

Potassium Permanganate Tablets (60, 120 and 300 mg.) are a convenient form for making solutions.

POTASSIUM PHOSPHATE

Potassium Phosphate, N.F. XII

Formula, K_2HPO_4. Molecular Weight, 174.18

Physical Properties.—Potassium Phosphate occurs as a colorless or white, granular salt. The salt is deliquescent when exposed to moist air. One Gm. of the salt is soluble in 3 ml. of water but it is only slightly soluble in alcohol. Aqueous solutions are alkaline toward phenolphthalein T.S.

Chemical Properties.—When the salt is ignited it is converted to the pyrophosphate in a manner similar to sodium phosphate (see p. 256). Its incompatibilities are principally due to the phosphate ion and to the slight alkalinity of its aqueous solutions so that in most respects its chemistry is analogous to that of sodium phosphate.

It is assayed by a procedure that is exactly the same as that used for sodium phosphate.

Official Tests for Identity.—A solution of potassium phosphate responds to all tests for *Potassium* (*q.v.*) and *Phosphate* (*q.v.*). The slight alkalinity of its solution serves to distinguish it from both potassium biphosphate (acidic solutions) and tribasic potassium phosphate (markedly alkaline solutions).

Commercial Manufacture.—This salt may be made in the same way that sodium phosphate is prepared, *i.e.*, by the neutralization of orthophosphoric acid with potassium carbonate (1).

$$(1)\ H_3PO_4 + K_2CO_3 \rightarrow K_2HPO_4 + H_2O + CO_2\uparrow$$

Uses.—*Potassium Phosphate* (Dipotassium Hydrogen Phosphate), N.F. XII, dried at 105° C. for 4 hours, contains not less than 98 per cent of K_2HPO_4. It is employed as a saline cathartic in a usual dose of 4 Gm.

POTASSIUM SODIUM TARTRATE

Potassium Sodium Tartrate, N.F. XII

$$HO-\overset{\displaystyle H}{\underset{\displaystyle H}{\overset{|}{\underset{|}{C}}}}-COOK$$
$$HO-C-COONa \quad .4H_2O$$

Formula, $KNaC_4H_4O_6.4H_2O$;   Molecular Weight, 282.23

In 1672 Pierre Seignette, an apothecary of Rochelle, France, first prepared Potassium Sodium Tartrate. In allusion to its discoverer and his native town this compound is called either Sal Seignette or Rochelle Salt.

Physical Properties.—Potassium Sodium Tartrate occurs as a white, crystalline powder, or as large, colorless, transparent, rhombic prisms which effloresce slightly in warm, dry air. It is odorless, has a cooling, saline taste, and a specific gravity of 1.783.

One Gm. of the salt is soluble in 1 ml. of water at 25° C. It is practically insoluble in alcohol.

Potassium Sodium Tartrate melts at about 74° C. When the temperature is raised, it carbonizes and gives off inflammable vapors having the odor of burnt sugar. Finally, a residue of the carbonates of potassium and sodium remains (1).

$$(1)\ 2KNaC_4H_4O_6 + 5O_2 \overset{\Delta}{\rightarrow} K_2CO_3 + Na_2CO_3 + 4H_2O\uparrow + 6CO_2\uparrow$$

Equation (1) expresses the completed reaction but if there is not an ample supply of oxygen or if heating is insufficient, some black carbon particles will remain.

Chemical Properties.—Potassium Sodium Tartrate is a salt of strong bases and a weak organic acid. It possesses the characteristics of the alkali salts of organic acids. Aqueous solutions are slightly alkaline due to hydrolysis. It responds to the chemical properties of tartrates discussed with potassium bitartrate.

When an equal volume of acetic acid is added to a solution of the salt, a white crystalline precipitate results (2).

(2) $KNaC_4H_4O_6.4H_2O + CH_3COOH \rightarrow KHC_4H_4O_6 \downarrow + CH_3COONa + 4H_2O$

The assay of Potassium Sodium Tartrate is carried out by igniting a dried sample of the salt to the carbonate form (essentially a mixture of sodium and potassium carbonates). The residue is then treated with an excess of a standard sulfuric acid solution and the excess sulfuric acid determined by residual titration with sodium hydroxide using methyl orange T.S. as an indicator.

Official Tests for Identity.—1. The salt, when ignited (1), gives the odor of burnt sugar and leaves a residue of sodium and potassium carbonates that is alkaline to litmus and gives off carbon dioxide on acidification.

2. Acidification of an aqueous solution (1 in 20) of the salt results in a precipitate of potassium bitartrate (2).

3. A solution of the salt (1 in 10) gives the tests for *Tartrate*. (See Potassium Bitartrate.)

Commercial Manufacture.—Potassium Sodium Tartrate is prepared by neutralizing a solution of sodium carbonate with potassium bitartrate (3). The solution is boiled for a short time and an exact neutrality produced by the addition of either sodium carbonate or potassium bitartrate. The solution is then allowed to stand at 60° C. for a period of time to permit the complete evolution of carbon dioxide thus forcing the reaction to completion. It is filtered, concentrated and crystallized.

(3) $2KHC_4H_4O_6 + Na_2CO_3.H_2O + 6H_2O \rightarrow 2KNaC_4H_4O_6.4H_2O + CO_2 \uparrow$

Uses.—*Potassium Sodium Tartrate* (Rochelle Salt), N.F. XII dried at 150° C. for 3 hours, contains not less than 99 per cent of $KNaC_4H_4O_6$. The official salt contains 4 molecules of water of crystallization corresponding to not less than 21 per cent and not more than 26 per cent of water. Depending upon the dose, the action of Rochelle Salt ranges from a mild laxative to an active hydragogue. It is a saline laxative. A palatable form for oral administration is *Seidlitz Powders*. Usual dose—10 Gm.

Due to the presence of the two alcoholic hydroxyl groups, the tartrate ion possesses sequestering properties. This property is utilized in Fehling's Solution (see Copper Sulfate), antimony potassium tartrate, and bismuth potassium tartrate (see discussion of sequestering agents).

SULFURATED POTASH

Sulfurated Potash, U.S.P. XVII

This substance is not a true chemical compound. It is a mixture composed chiefly of potassium polysulfides and potassium thiosulfate. The U.S.P. requires that the mixture contain polysulfides equivalent to not less than 12.8 per cent of sulfur.

Physical Properties.—Sulfurated Potash occurs in irregular pieces having a liver-brown color when freshly made, changing to greenish-yellow and finally to gray through absorption of moisture, oxygen, and carbon dioxide of the air. It has an odor of hydrogen sulfide and a bitter, acrid, alkaline taste.

One Gm. of Sulfurated Potash is soluble in about 2 ml. of water (usually leaving a slight residue), forming a yellow-brown solution which is strongly alkaline and possesses a hydrogen sulfide odor. Alcohol will dissolve only the sulfides.

Chemical Properties.—On exposure to air the color change is thought to be due to oxidation since it occurs in the dark as well as in the light. An aqueous solution exhibits all the chemical properties of sulfides, thiosulfates, hydroxide ions, and potassium ions.

Official Tests for Identity.—1. A 1 in 10 solution of Sulfurated Potash is light brown in color and is alkaline to litmus as a result of extensive hydrolysis.

2. When an excess of acetic acid is added to an aqueous solution of Sulfurated Potash, hydrogen sulfide is evolved and sulfur is precipitated (1). The hydrogen sulfide may be recognized by its characteristic odor and by its blackening of moist lead acetate test paper.

(1) $K_2S_3 + 2CH_3COOH \rightarrow 2CH_3COOK + H_2S \uparrow + 2S \downarrow$

(2) $K_2S_2O_3 + 2CH_3COOH \rightarrow 2CH_3COOK + S \downarrow + SO_2 \uparrow + H_2O$

When sulfur reacts with a basic material there also is formed some thiosulfate salt. Thiosulfates are unstable in acid media (2) (See sodium thiosulfate).

3. If the solution obtained in (1) is filtered and an excess of sodium bitartrate test solution added to the filtrate, an abundant, white, crystalline precipitate will be produced (3).

(3) $CH_3COOK + NaHC_4H_4O_6 \rightarrow KHC_4H_4O_6 \downarrow + CH_3COONa$

Commercial Preparation.—Sublimed sulfur and potassium carbonate are gradually heated together (not over 185° C.) in a crucible until effervescence ceases (4). Then the heat is increased to dull redness or until perfect fusion results. The melt is poured upon a stone slab, covered to prevent access of air, and allowed to cool. The solid is broken into pieces and bottled immediately.

(4) $3K_2CO_3 + 8S \overset{\Delta}{\rightarrow} 2K_2S_3 + K_2S_2O_3 + 3CO_2 \uparrow$

When potassium carbonate and sulfur are fused together, a mixture of potassium polysulfides (K_2S_3, K_2S_4, K_2S_5) and potassium thiosulfate is produced and carbon dioxide is evolved. If the temperature of the reaction is not carefully controlled, potassium sulfate may be formed due to the decomposition of the thiosulfate (5) (over 300°C.).

(5) $4K_2S_2O_3 \rightarrow 3K_2SO_4 + K_2S_5$

It is of interest to note that the simple limit test for sulfide content in which 1 Gm. each of the product and of $CuSO_4 \cdot 5H_2O$ were reacted and the filtrate tested for copper ion to determine whether sufficient sulfide ion had been present to precipitate it completely has given way to a direct assay method. The new method precipitates *all* of the sulfide as CuS (6) which is then ignited to convert it to CuO, the weight of which gives an indication of the *actual* sulfide content. Nevertheless, the original limit of 12.8 per cent sulfide is still the official requirement.

(6) $Cu^{++} + S^= \longrightarrow CuS \downarrow$

Uses.—*Sulfurated Potash* (Potassa Sulfurata), U.S.P. XVII.— Other synonyms are *sulfurated potassa, liver of sulfur,* and *hepar sulfuris*. It is a mixture composed chiefly of potassium polysulfides and potassium thiosulfate and contains not less than 12.8 per cent of sulfur in combination as sulfide. Sulfurated potash is rarely used internally. Due to the liberation of hydrogen sulfide on contact with the skin, and the alkaline medium which it creates, the compound is used in solutions, lotions, ointments, etc. to treat parasitic diseases of the skin. A 10 per cent ointment has been used for acne, scabies, ringworm, psoriasis and tinea versicolor.

The product has been continuously official since the first U.S.P. (1820).

Official recognition is based on its employment in the preparation of *White Lotion* wherein it reacts with zinc sulfate to form a precipitate of zinc sulfide(s).

20

NON-OFFICIAL POTASSIUM COMPOUNDS

Potassium Carbonate, N.F. XI, $K_2CO_3 \cdot 1\frac{1}{2}H_2O$ is a white granular powder. It is odorless and is readily soluble in water to the extent of 1 Gm. in less than 1 ml. of water. When fully hydrated, the salt does not have the hygroscopic character associated with the anhydrous form. Aqueous solutions are quite alkaline (pH 11.6) due to hydrolysis of the carbonate ion. The anhydrous form is variously known as *potash, pearl ash, salt of tartar* and *salt of wormwood*. The name potash alludes to the fact that it was originally prepared only from wood ashes through a process of lixiviation, filtration, evaporation and calcination in iron pots to the anhydrous form. Since then other methods of preparation have been utilized as, for example, the method wherein a cold slurry of concentrated potassium chloride and tri-hydrated magnesium carbonate is treated with CO_2 under pressure (1). The double salt that separates from the more soluble magnesium chloride is mixed with water and heated to boiling to convert the bicarbonate to the carbonate which is much more soluble than the magnesium carbonate that is liberated (2). Filtration and concentration to crystallization yields the product.

(1) $3MgCO_3 \cdot 3H_2O + 2KCl + CO_2 \rightarrow 2MgCO_3 \cdot KHCO_3 \cdot 4H_2O \downarrow + MgCl_2$

(2) $2MgCO_3 \cdot KHCO_3 \cdot 4H_2O \rightarrow 2MgCO_3 \downarrow + K_2CO_3 + 9H_2O + CO_2 \uparrow$

Although this salt has been used in the past as a systemic antacid, its excessive alkalinity has caused it to fall into disfavor. In recent years its official recognition depended on its use as a pharmaceutical necessity in the preparation of such preparations as Ferrous Carbonate Pills, N.F. XI. Since all of the products for which it was used have been deleted from the official compendia, it too has lost its official standing.

Potassium Chlorate, N.F. X, $KClO_3$, occurs as colorless, lustrous, monoclinic prisms or plates, or as a white granular powder. It is odorless and has a characteristic cooling taste. It is stable in air.

One Gm. of the salt is soluble in 16.5 ml. of water at 25° C. or in about 1.8 ml. of boiling water. It is almost insoluble in alcohol, but is slightly soluble in hydroalcoholic solutions. It dissolves readily in glycerin.

When the salt is heated to about 360° C. it melts, and decomposes into oxygen and potassium chloride (1).

(1) $2KClO_3 \xrightarrow{\Delta} 2KCl + 3O_2 \uparrow$

The most important property of the salt is its strong oxidizing action and, therefore, it reacts readily with reducing agents (2,3).

(2) $KClO_3 + 6FeSO_4 + 3H_2SO_4 \rightarrow KCl + 3Fe_2(SO_4)_3 + 3H_2O$

(3) $KClO_3 + 3HNO_2 \rightarrow 3HNO_3 + KCl$

Its oxidizing action should be kept in mind by the pharmacist and its sale to minors who are experimenting with explosives should be restricted. Many serious accidents have ensued from such unrestricted sale and pharmacists have been held liable. Indeed, the N.F. X carried the following warning:

Great caution should be observed in handling this salt, as dangerous explosions are liable to occur when it is heated or subjected to concussion, or to trituration with organic substances, such as cork, tannic acid, dust, sucrose, etc., or with charcoal, sulfur, sulfides, hypophosphites, reduced iron, or other easily oxidizable substances.

Nearly all potassium chlorate made today is made by the electrolysis of warm, alkaline solutions of potassium chloride, a process first developed in Switzerland in 1891. An essential feature of the process is that the products of electrolysis (KOH and Cl_2) are permitted to react together by means of a porous diaphragm separating the anode and cathode compartments (4,5). The potassium

(4) $3Cl_2 + 6KOH \rightarrow 3KCl + 3KClO + 3H_2O$

(5) $3KClO \rightarrow 2KCl + KClO_3$

or

(4) and (5) $3Cl_2 + 6KOH \rightarrow 5KCl + KClO_3 + 3H_2O$

chlorate crystallizes out of the solution as it supersaturates. This salt is more easily prepared than is sodium chlorate by this process because the greater solubility of the latter makes it difficult to separate from sodium chloride.

Because of the oxidizing power of potassium chlorate it was introduced into medicine as an oxidizing antiseptic. This action, however, is not validated by experimental findings since it is found to be no more antiseptic than inert salts. It has, however, found use as a component of gargles and mouth washes. Its value in these circumstances depends principally on the cooling, mildly saline taste and, indeed, the use of potassium chlorate tablets which are allowed to slowly dissolve in the mouth in conditions of stomatitis and sore throat depends largely on this taste-freshening effect.

The toxic properties of potassium chlorate should be recognized. The toxic dose has been given as approximately 5 Gm. although death and/or survival have occurred with smaller and larger amounts. The salt is not decomposed to any degree in the body and is excreted slowly by the kidney. Lysis of red blood corpuscles occurs and the protein debris liberated by this destruction irritates the kidney and produces a marked interstitial nephritis due to blocking of the vessels. Some conversion of hemoglobin to methemoglobin also occurs. In general, patients should be warned to use the salt only for short term therapy and to avoid internal ingestion of large quantities of gargles or mouth washes containing it.

Potassium Hypophosphite, N.F. X, KPH_2O_2, occurs as white, opaque, hexagonal plates, but on account of it being extremely deliquescent, it is usually found in crystalline masses, or as a white, granular powder. The salt is odorless and has a pungent, saline taste. It has a specific gravity of 2.338.

One Gm. of the salt is soluble in about 0.6 ml. of water and in about 9 ml. of alcohol, at 25° C.; it is somewhat more soluble in boiling water or boiling alcohol.

When potassium hypophosphite is heated, phosphine $(PH)_3$ is evolved and the pyrophosphate is left as a residue (1).

$$(1) \quad 4KPH_2O_2 \xrightarrow{\Delta} K_4P_2O_7 + 2PH_3 \uparrow + H_2O \uparrow$$

When potassium hypophosphite is heated or triturated with any oxidizing agent (*e.g.*, potassium chlorate, nitrate, or permanganate) it explodes violently. The chemical properties are principally due to the hypophosphite ion.

Caution should be observed in compounding Potassium Hypophosphite with other substances, as an explosion may occur if it is triturated or heated with nitrates, chlorates, or other oxidizing agents.

The salt may be made by boiling phosphorus with a solution of potassium hydroxide (2) or it may be made by the double decomposition reaction employing calcium hypophosphite and potassium carbonate (3).

$$(2) \quad 6KOH + 8P + 6H_2O \rightarrow 6KPH_2O_2 + 2PH_3 \uparrow \text{ (inflammable)}$$

$$(3) \quad Ca(PH_2O_2)_2 + K_2CO_3 \rightarrow 2KPH_2O_2 + CaCO_3 \downarrow$$

The salt has been used as a nerve tonic although this use is illogical and, because of this, it has lost official recognition together with other hypophosphites. When administered, they are excreted almost quantitatively in the urine. The usual dose is 0.5 Gm.

Potassium Nitrate, N.F. XI, KNO_3, occurs in the form of a white crystalline powder or in long, colorless, transparent six-sided rhombohedrons or prisms. It is odorless, has a saline taste, and produces a cooling sensation in the mouth. It is slightly hygroscopic in moist air. It has a density of 2.11 (10.6° C.) and melts without decomposition at about 337° C.

One Gm. is soluble in 3 ml. of water, and in about 620 ml. of alcohol at 25° C. One Gm. is soluble in 0.5 ml. of boiling water. It is soluble in glycerin.

Large quantities of potassium nitrate are made from the comparatively cheap sodium nitrate which occurs naturally in enormous deposits in Chile and Peru. Sodium nitrate and potassium chloride are heated with a small quantity of water when the following reaction takes place (1).

$$(1) \quad NaNO_3 + KCl \rightleftharpoons KNO_3 + NaCl$$

The following observations may be made regarding the solubility of the respective products of the reaction: Except for mutual solubility, about the same quantity of sodium chloride dissolves in a definite volume of water at 0° C. as it does in a like volume of water at 100° C. (35.7 Gm. NaCl in 100 Gm. of water at 0° C., 39.8 Gm. of NaCl in 100 Gm. of water at 100° C.), whereas potassium nitrate is very much less soluble in cold water than it is in hot water (13.3 Gm. of KNO_3 in 100 Gm. of water at 0° C., 247 Gm. of KNO_3 in 100 Gm. of water at 100° C.). Therefore, when the concentrated solution is strained through filter cloth, most of the sodium chloride remains behind, whereas nearly all of the potassium nitrate remains in solution in the hot liquor. When this is allowed to cool, most of the potassium nitrate, on account of its lesser solubility in cold water, crystallizes out, whereas the sodium chloride remains in solution.

Potassium nitrate is often employed internally when the diuretic action of potassium ion is desired. The nitrate ion is said to increase the rapidity of absorption of the potassium ion. In fact, of all the potassium salts, the nitrate possesses the most potent diuretic action. The nitrate ion produces an irritation of mucous membrane and hence large doses are prohibitive. Usually enteric coated tablets are used. In medicinal doses potassium nitrate is a diuretic and diaphoretic, although the harmless organic potassium salts are to be preferred. Excess nitrate in the system tends to promote the formation of nitrite in the intestinal tract. In some cases, ill effects are noted and even death may result due to methemoglobinemia. It has the same dangers as other potassium salts when there is faulty kidney elimination.

Stramonium leaves are sometimes burned to volatilize the alkaloidal components to alleviate the paroxysms of asthma although this treatment is much less popular than it was years ago. Potassium nitrate is often added to the leaves as an oxidizing agent to facilitate burning. Sodium nitrate is not used because it is less stable and absorbs moisture. Potassium nitrate is used in fusions where oxidation is required (in place of sodium nitrate) because the potassium nitrite does not crystallize during the subsequent isolation procedures. Usual dose—1 Gm.

A caution for the pharmacist in connection with the sale of this salt to minors is in order. The oldtime use of potassium nitrate in gunpowder does not escape the attention of junior experimenters and, as a result, serious injuries have resulted from uncontrolled experimentation. The pharmacist is well advised to restrict sale only to adults.

Potassium Thiocyanate, N.F. X, KSCN, occurs as colorless, transparent, prismatic crystals that are hygroscopic. It is odorless and has a cooling, saline taste. It is affected by light.

One Gm. of the salt is soluble in about 0.5 ml. of water and in about 12 ml. of alcohol at 25° C.   It is soluble in about 0.2 ml. of boiling water and about 8 ml. of boiling alcohol.

The chemical properties and preparation of this salt are essentially the same as those for sodium thiocyanate (*q.v.*).

Potassium thiocyanate has been used as a hypotensive in a dose of 0.3 Gm. although it has fallen into disuse and has lost its official status.

15

Rubidium and Cesium

RUBIDIUM

Symbol, Rb.   Valence, 1.   Atomic Weight, 85.47;

Atomic Number, 37

History.—Rubidium was discovered by Bunsen and Kirchhoff in 1861. Employing the spectroscope which he and Kirchhoff had but recently invented, they examined the residue from Durkheim mineral water and found two new, bright lines in the blue portion of the spectrum. They, therefore, named the elements rubidium (red) and cesium (blue) in allusion to their spectra.

Occurrence.—Rubidium is widely distributed, but only in small quantities. It occurs, usually along with potassium, in many mineral waters, notably those of Durkheim in Baden. This metal is found in combination in lepidolite, phosphorite, petalite and carnallite. It is found in the ashes of some plants, such as tea, coffee and tobacco.

Properties.—Rubidium is a silver-white metal that has a faint yellowish tinge. Its density is 1.525, its melting-point 39° C., and its boiling-point 696° C. It should be kept under benzene, petroleum, or other non-oxygen containing liquids. It closely resembles potassium. It inflames spontaneously upon exposure to air and acts energetically when placed in water, decomposing the latter and burning with a violet flame.

Rubidium forms four oxides, having the following compositions: Rb_2O, Rb_2O_2, Rb_2O_3, Rb_2O_4. The formulas of rubidium compounds are analogous to those of corresponding potassium compounds.

Preparation.—The discoverers of this element recommended the residues remaining after the preparation of lithium from its minerals, as a source of rubidium. Rubidium chloroplatinate is less soluble than the corresponding potassium salt; therefore, a mixture of their platinum precipitates is repeatedly boiled with small quantities of water, which dissolves the more soluble potassium chloroplatinate. The less soluble rubidium compound is reduced by hydrogen and a chloride is obtained. The hydroxide or carbonate of rubidium may be prepared from the chloride in the usual way, and these, when heated with magnesium powder in a current of hydrogen, yield metallic rubidium.

Uses.—Rubidium and its compounds are very seldom used in medicine. If it is used, the action is that of the anion produced by the dissociation of the rubidium salt.

CESIUM

Symbol, Cs.   Valence, 1.   Atomic Weight, 132.905;
Atomic Number, 55

History.—Cesium, like rubidium, was discovered by Bunsen and Kirchhoff in 1860. It was the first element discovered by the use of the spectroscope.

Occurrence.—Cesium is usually associated with rubidium but in smaller amounts. The largest quantity of the metal occurs in the rare mineral *pollucite* (syn. pollux), a cesium-aluminum silicate, found on the Island of Elba and at Hebron, Maine. This mineral is an association of pegmatite minerals and contains 31.4 per cent of cesium oxide. It is found also in the waters of many mineral springs.

Properties.—Cesium is a silver-white, soft metal, having a density of 1.873 and a melting-point of 28.5° C. It boils at 705° C. Its properties closely resemble those of potassium and rubidium.

Preparation.—Cesium metal is obtained by a process similar to that used for the preparation of rubidium (*q.v.*).

Uses.—Cesium and its compounds are of no commercial importance. They are never used in medicine.

16

Ammonium Compounds

Attention has been called to the fact (p. 66) that when ammonia gas is passed into water, a solution containing dissolved ammonia, undissociated ammonium hydroxide, ammonium ions, and hydroxide ions is produced. The positive ammonium cation behaves in all respects like an alkali metal ion. It unites with anions to form salts which have a very great physical and chemical resemblance to the corresponding potassium salts with which they are ordinarily isomorphous. When a solution of an ammonium salt is electrolyzed, the ammonium cation, upon its discharge, ordinarily gives ammonia and hydrogen, and thus far, all efforts to isolate the "ammonium metal" have failed. If, however, a mercury cathode is used and an ammonium salt decomposed by electrolysis, the mercury swells to a spongy mass of ammonium amalgam and then gives off the decomposition products of ammonium radical, *viz.*, ammonia and hydrogen. Likewise, if sodium amalgam is added to a strong solution of an ammonium salt (NH_4Cl), an amalgam having a metallic luster is produced. This physical property of the amalgam points strongly toward the metallic character of the ammonium radical.

$$Na \text{ (in solution in Hg)} + NH_4^+ + Cl^- \rightarrow NH_4 \text{ (in solution in Hg)} + Na^+ + Cl^-$$

By virtue of the formation of such an amalgam, and because only metals are miscible with mercury, it may be assumed that, if "ammonium" is ever isolated, it will have the physical and chemical properties of a metal.

Chemical Properties of the Ammonium Ion.—Although ammonia has already been discussed (see p. 66), there are a few general reactions of ammonium compounds which are worthwhile mentioning.

The addition of strong bases, *e.g.*, NaOH, KOH, etc., to aqueous solutions of ammonium salts causes the evolution of ammonia when the solution is heated. The reaction is represented as taking place between ammonium ions (NH_4^+) and the introduced hydroxide ions (OH^-) as follows (1):

$$(1) \quad NH_4^+ + OH^- \rightarrow NH_3 \uparrow + H_2O$$

The above reaction illustrates very nicely the Lowry-Brönsted concept of acids and bases, inasmuch as the ammonium ion is essentially an acid which is capable of ionizing into ammonia and a proton (2), and the hydroxide ion is a strong base capable of combining with the proton (1).

$$(2) \quad NH_4^+ \rightleftharpoons NH_3 + H^+$$

The reaction of ammonium salts with strong bases is made use of in testing for ammonium compounds and also in the preparation of small amounts of ammonia gas for laboratory use, as for example from ammonium chloride (3).

$$(3) \quad NH_4Cl + NaOH \rightarrow NH_3 \uparrow + H_2O + NaCl$$

Ammonium salts will form a white, crystalline precipitate of ammonium bitartrate with tartaric acid (4). If this reaction mixture is buffered with a little sodium acetate to remove the protons (as relatively non-ionized acetic acid) the precipitate forms more readily.

$$(4) \quad H_2C_4H_4O_6 + NH_4Cl \rightleftharpoons NH_4HC_4H_4O_6 \downarrow + HCl$$

Ammonium salts in general are rather unstable and may decompose under conditions varying from room temperature to strong heating. Many of the ammonium salts are volatilized without decomposition on heating, but if any one of them is heated in a closed tube it will decompose. Among the salts which are not volatilized by heating are the borate, phosphate, chromate and vanadate. Practically all of the ammonium salts (*q.v.*) will liberate ammonia on decomposition with the exception of ammonium nitrate (5) and nitrite (6).

$$(5) \quad NH_4NO_3 \xrightarrow{\Delta} N_2O \uparrow + 2H_2O$$
$$(6) \quad NH_4NO_2 \xrightarrow{\Delta} N_2 \uparrow + 2H_2O$$

The ammonium ion is precipitated as magnesium ammonium phosphate ($MgNH_4PO_4.6H_2O$), ammonium phosphomolybdate ($(NH_4)_3PO_4.12MoO_3$) (See phosphoric acid), and magnesium ammonium arsenate ($MgNH_4AsO_4$) (see magnesium ion).

Official Test for Identity of Ammonium Ion.—The test for ammonium salts is carried out by adding an excess of sodium hydroxide T.S. to the salt (1). A positive test is obtained if ammonia is evolved. The ammonia may be recognized by its odor or by the fact that it turns moistened red litmus paper blue. If the solution is warmed, the decomposition is accelerated because ammonia is less soluble in hot solutions than in cold.

Pharmacology of the Ammonium Ion.—The pharmacology of the ammonium ion falls into certain more or less well-defined categories, namely (1) acid-base equilibrium of the body, (2) diuretic effect, (3) expectorant effect and (4) anti-caries effect.

1. Ammonium ion plays a rather important rôle in the mainte-nance of the acid-base equilibrium of the body, particularly in combating acidosis.

It had been known that ammonia was rapidly converted to urea in the body, but it was only after the realization that the kidney was capable of reconverting urea to ammonia that the full impor-tance of ammonia in the body economy was understood. By its ability to excrete ammonia (essentially ammonium ion) the kidney saves base (*e.g.*, sodium) for the body by substituting the ammo-nium cation for the base cation in the compounds being excreted. The effect of conserving base to prevent acidosis is well known and is an important body defense mechanism.

2. The diuretic effect of certain ammonium salts (*e.g.*, the chloride and nitrate) is well known and has been extensively studied. The effect is produced by conversion of the ammonium cation (a so-called "labile" cation) to urea (7) with consequent formation of a proton (H^+) and a chloride ion (Cl^-), *i.e.*, the equivalent of hydro-chloric acid. The hydrogen ion reacts with the body buffers, mainly bicarbonate (HCO_3^-) (8), to form CO_2 and the net effect is, therefore, a displacement of the bicarbonate ion by a chloride ion.

(7) $2NH_4Cl + CO_2 \longrightarrow CO(NH_2)_2 + 2H^+ + 2Cl^- + H_2O$

(8) $H^+ + HCO_3^- \leftrightharpoons H_2CO_3 \rightleftarrows H_2O + CO_2 \uparrow$

The fact that bicarbonate (usually considered as $NaHCO_3$) is lost indicates that the alkali reserve of the body has been reduced below normal, *i.e.*, an acidosis has been induced. It is well to note, however, that this does not imply any significant change in blood pH. The actual diuresis is brought about by the increased chloride load presented to the tubule causing a state of affairs where all of it cannot be reabsorbed and some thus escapes with an equivalent amount of cation (mostly Na^+) and an iso-osmotic equivalent of water.

Termination of the diuretic action is believed to rest upon the acidosis produced which calls into play a renal defense of the acid-base pattern in which the kidney converts urea to ammonia and also produces H^+ in exchange for Na^+. Thus, the net effect becomes one of excreting increasing amounts of NH_4^+ and Cl^- (*i.e.*, NH_4Cl) until the amount of NH_4Cl excreted becomes equivalent to the amount ingested for the diuretic action. Obviously, diuretic action ceases.

3. The expectorant action of the ammonium salts is probably due to local irritation which in turn is due to a salt action, but this is merely a postulation. However, the ammonium salts have been used extensively in the treatment of coughs associated with a thick viscid sputum. The action of the ammonium salt is to thin out and perhaps increase the quantity of the mucus. Ammonium chloride and ammonium carbonate particularly have been used in cough preparations.

4. The ammonium ion has been found effective in combating acidity of the oral cavity and thus helps prevent dental caries. Since most ammonium salts in solution are acidic and thus contain few ammonium ions, the dibasic ammonium phosphate $((NH_4)_2HPO_4)$ is the salt used in dentrifices (9).

$$(9)\ (NH_4)_2HPO_4 \xrightarrow{H_2O} 2NH_4^+ + HPO_4^=$$

Urea (carbamide), also, is usually present. It slowly yields more ammonium ions by enzymatic action.

OFFICIAL AMMONIUM COMPOUNDS

AMMONIUM BROMIDE

Ammonium Bromide, N.F. XII

Formula, NH_4Br.   Molecular Weight, 97.95

Physical Properties.—Ammonium Bromide occurs as colorless, prismatic, cubical crystals, or as a white, crystalline or granular powder. It is odorless and has a pungent, saline taste. It is slightly hygroscopic and, when exposed to the air, it undergoes slight decomposition and acquires a yellowish color. It has a density of about 2.548.

One Gm. of Ammonium Bromide dissolves in about 1.3 ml. of water and in about 12 ml. of alcohol, at 25° C. One Gm. is soluble in about 0.9 ml. of boiling water and in about 1.2 ml. of boiling alcohol. It is soluble in ether.

Freshly prepared aqueous solutions are nearly neutral but increase in acidity on standing.

When the salt is heated, it volatilizes completely without decomposition.

Chemical Properties.—This salt has all of the activity mentioned under Chemical Properties of Ammonium Ion, and also gives the reactions of the bromide ion (see p. 213).

The assay of ammonium bromide is carried out by dissolving a weighed sample in water and treating the solution with an excess of 0.1N silver nitrate solution to which a small amount of ferric ammonium sulfate has been added as an indicator. The excess silver nitrate is then determined by residual titration with standard ammonium thiocyanate solution.

Official Tests for Identity.—1. The salt gives the test for *Ammonium (q.v.).*

2. The salt gives the tests for *Bromide (q.v.).*

Commercial Manufacture.—This salt is prepared by mixing boiling solutions of ammonium sulfate and potassium bromide (1). When the liquid is cooled, most of the potassium sulfate settles out. After the solution has been concentrated to about one-half its volume, it is again allowed to cool and alcohol added to facilitate the precipitation of the remaining potassium sulfate. Then the clear liquid is concentrated to crystallization or evaporated to dryness with constant stirring to form the granular salt.

$$(1) \quad (NH_4)_2SO_4 + 2KBr \rightarrow K_2SO_4 \downarrow + 2NH_4Br$$

Although ammonium bromide may also be made by neutralizing hydrobromic acid with ammonium hydroxide, it is customary to utilize the reaction between the cheaper bromine and ammonia (2) at low temperatures.

$$(2) \quad 3Br_2 + 8NH_4OH \rightarrow 6NH_4Br + N_2 \uparrow + 8H_2O$$

or

$$3Br_2 + 8NH_3 \rightarrow 6NH_4Br + N_2 \uparrow$$

When the reaction is completed the solution is evaporated to dryness to obtain the crystalline ammonium bromide. (Note how this differs from the iodine reaction.)

Uses.—*Ammonium Bromide*, N.F. XII, dried at 105° C. for 2 hours, contains not less than 99 per cent and not more than 101 per cent of NH_4Br. Ammonium bromide is used for the centrally depressant activity of the bromide ion (see p. 214). In doses large enough to produce the physiological effect of the bromide ion, the salt is irritating to mucous membranes. Therefore, it is best administered in small doses in combination with other bromides, *e.g.*, sodium and potassium bromides. Although the preparations containing mixed bromides are quite popular as sedatives, there is much question as to whether there is any advantage in administering the mixture as contrasted to a single salt, *e.g.*, sodium bromide. A technical grade of the salt is used in photography, lithographing and in engraving. Usual dose—1 Gm.

Official preparations containing ammonium bromide for its central depressant sedative action are *Three Bromides Elixir* and *Tablets*.

AMMONIUM CARBONATE

Ammonium Carbonate, N.F. XII

Formula, $(NH_4HCO_3)_n.(NH_4CO_2NH_2)_n$

Molecular Weight of NH_4HCO_3, 79.06

Molecular Weight of $NH_4CO_2NH_2$, 78.07

Physical Properties.—Ammonium Carbonate occurs in the form of a white powder or as white, hard, translucent masses or "cubes," having a strong odor of ammonia, without empyreuma, and with a sharp, ammoniacal taste. It contains between 30 and 34 per cent of NH_3. When exposed to the air, it loses both carbon dioxide and ammonia and is converted into porous, opaque, easily broken lumps or a white powder, the latter consisting chiefly of ammonium bicarbonate (NH_4HCO_3).

One Gm. of the salt is very slowly soluble in about 4 ml. of water at 25° C. It is decomposed by hot water into carbon dioxide and ammonia and upon prolonged boiling it is completely decomposed into the aforementioned volatile products. Alcohol, even as dilute as 70 per cent, does not completely dissolve it but leaves a residue of ammonium bicarbonate.

Chemical Properties.—Although this salt actually contains little, if any, normal ammonium carbonate, $(NH_4)_2CO_3$, it is readily converted into the normal carbonate by dissolving it in dilute ammonia water (1).

$$(1)\ NH_4HCO_3.NH_4CO_2NH_2 + NH_3 + H_2O \rightarrow 2(NH_4)_2CO_3$$

The decomposition of the salt from its original hard, translucent state to that of a white powder is caused entirely by loss of ammonia and carbon dioxide from the ammonium carbonate and leaves the white powder, ammonium bicarbonate (2).

$$(2)\ NH_4HCO_3.NH_4CO_2NH_2 \rightarrow CO_2 \uparrow + 2NH_3 \uparrow + NH_4HCO_3$$

Only the hard translucent pieces composed of approximately equivalent parts of ammonium bicarbonate and ammonium carbamate are to be used for prescription compounding.

The salt is decomposed, either dry or in solution by the addition of acids (3). This constitutes one of its principal incompatibilities, although occasionally the combination of acidic ingredients with the salt is intentional.

$$(3)\ 2NH_4HCO_3.NH_4CO_2NH_2 + 3H_2SO_4 \rightarrow 3(NH_4)_2SO_4 + 2H_2O + 4CO_2 \uparrow$$

Because of hydrolysis, the aqueous solutions of the salt are alkaline in reaction. Aqueous solutions possess all the properties of carbonate and ammonium hydroxide. (See ammonium ion and ammonia.)

The assay of Ammonium Carbonate is carried out by carefully weighing a sample, dissolving it in water and then treating this with an excess of a standard sulfuric acid solution (3). The excess acid is then determined by residual titration with 1N sodium hydroxide using methyl orange as an indicator.

Official Tests for Identity.—1. When heated, the salt is volatilized without charring and the vapor is strongly alkaline to moistened litmus paper.

2. A 1 in 20 aqueous solution of the salt effervesces with acids (3).

Commercial Manufacture.—1. Large quantities of ammonium carbonate are made by heating ammonium sulfate with an excess of calcium carbonate (chalk) in iron retorts, condensing the vapors of the salt in leaden chambers (4) and recovering the liberated ammonia by passing it into sulfuric acid. The product thus obtained is purified of empyreuma by sublimation either with or without a small quantity of charcoal. The reaction taking place may be represented in a general way by the following equation:

(4) $2(NH_4)_2SO_4 + 2CaCO_3 \rightarrow NH_4HCO_3.NH_4CO_2NH_2 \uparrow + NH_3 \uparrow + H_2O + 2CaSO_4$

Occasionally, ammonium chloride (5) is used in place of ammonium sulfate but it is more expensive. Sometimes, barium carbonate is used in place of chalk for the reason that a valuable by-product may be obtained.

(5) $4NH_4Cl + 2CaCO_3 \rightarrow NH_4HCO_3.NH_4CO_2NH_2 \uparrow + 2CaCl_2 + NH_3 \uparrow + H_2O$

2. Crude commercial ammonium carbonate has been made by introducing ammonia (liberated from ammoniacal gas liquors by lime), carbon dioxide and steam into lead-lined chambers.

Uses.—*Ammonium Carbonate*, N.F. XII, "consists of ammonium bicarbonate (NH_4HCO_3) and ammonium carbamate (NH_2COONH_4) in varying proportions, and yields not less than 30 per cent and not more than 34 per cent of NH_3." The salt is also known by the common names: *Ammonium Sesquicarbonate, Sal Volatile, Preston Salt* and *Hartshorn*. It has been used internally as an expectorant and carminative in a dose of about 0.3 Gm. When combined with Strong Ammonia Solution it has been used as "smelling salts." Excessive internal use may cause gastritis and excessive inhalation will irritate the nasal mucosa.

Ammonium carbonate is officially recognized because it is employed in the preparation of the official *Aromatic Ammonia Spirit*. This preparation is used as a reflex stimulant by inhalation of the vapor as required for syncope (fainting). Translucent (undecomposed) pieces of ammonium carbonate are dissolved in a diluted ammonia solution by gentle agitation and then the solution is allowed to stand for 12 hours to effect the conversion of the ammonium carbonate into normal ammonium carbonate (6 and 7)

(6) $NH_4HCO_3 + NH_3 \rightarrow (NH_4)_2CO_3$
(7) $NH_4CO_2NH_2 + H_2O \rightarrow (NH_4)_2CO_3$

and to allow the system to come to equilibrium. The aqueous solution of normal ammonium carbonate is gradually added to an alcoholic solution of the oils of lemon, lavender and nutmeg and sufficient distilled water added to make the required volume. After standing for 24 hours with occasional agitation the product is filtered in a covered funnel.

Moore and Abraham[1] have pointed out that previous explanations of difficulties attendant on the use of decomposed ammonium carbonate (essentially ammonium bicarbonate) are erroneous. There is actually enough ammonia allowed in the official formulation to convert ammonium bicarbonate to normal carbonate even though the official salt has completely decomposed to ammonium bicarbonate. However, the preparation will be deficient in total ammonia unless an allowance is made by adding an extra amount of ammonia solution to compensate for the deficiency. In this way, these workers actually have made an unofficial preparation from ammonium bicarbonate that meets the analytical standards of the official spirit. They also have pointed out that the fine precipitate that forms in the preparation of the spirit from decomposed ammonium carbonate is composed of volatile oils, rather than ammonium bicarbonate, thrown out of the alcoholic solution by the aqueous solution. They also noted that, if the ammonium carbonate solution was not allowed to stand for the prescribed 12 hours, a crystalline precipitate of normal ammonium carbonate was thrown out on addition to the alcoholic solution. The authors offer an interesting postulation concerning this precipitation. To quote, "The precipitation may be due to changes in dipolar solute-solvent bonding. In aqueous solution, ammonia reacts rapidly with ammonium bicarbonate to form normal ammonium carbonate. The ionization of the salt is rapid and the ions produced will then hydrolyze to produce carbonic acid and ammonium hydroxide.

If Pauling's concept of ammonium hydroxide[2] is accepted, a four-component equilibrium is found in its solutions; ammonia, ammonia solvated through the hydrogen bond, ammonium ion, and hydroxide ion.

When the alcoholic solution of the volatile oils is added to the aqueous solution, water and alcohol associate intimately and rapidly through dipole-dipole bonding.[3] It is possible, therefore, that some ammonia-water dipole bonds (*i.e.*, hydrogen bonds) are broken to permit the formation of water-alcohol dipole bonds. The above-mentioned four-component equilibrium is disturbed. The concentration of dissolved, but unbonded ammonia must increase.

The basicity of the ammonia liberated thusly is apparently more rapidly neutralized through coordinate covalence by the more highly acidic carbonic acid (from hydrolysis) than by the much less acidic water. Because of stoichiometric relationships, the normal carbonate is formed in preference to the primary carbonate. The normal carbonate then precipitates until such time as it can be ionized by the weak dielectric effect of the approximately 65 per cent alcoholic solution. (Approximate dielectric constant is equal to 45.)

[1] Moore, W. E., and Abraham, D., J. Am. Pharm. Assoc. (Sci. Ed.), **45**, 257 (1956).

[2] Pauling, L. C., *College Chemistry*, W. H. Freeman and Co., San Francisco, 1952, p. 381.

[3] Lyman, R. A., *Pharmaceutical Compounding and Dispensing*, J. B. Lippincott Co., Philadelphia, 1949, pp. 159, 209.

Experimental evidence supports this postulate since the quantity of precipitate that formed rapidly redissolved and it was impossible to isolate more than 40 per cent of the theoretical yield of normal ammonium carbonate at 0°.

If this is the explanation of why the precipitate occurs upon immediate mixing, it may be inferred that no precipitate occurs after aqueous ammonia and ammonium bicarbonate have been in contact for twelve hours because solute-solvent interaction equilibria have been established. In the process of cooling, mixing and precipitation within five minutes, equilibria between the ammonium ion created by reaction, ammonia-water dipole bonds, and free ammonia must not yet be established."

Aromatic ammonia spirit is nearly colorless when freshly prepared. On standing, it gradually acquires a yellow color, which is thought to be caused by the action of liberated ammonia upon either the essential oils or the aldehydes present in the alcohol. The color does not impair the medicinal value of the spirit. The spirit is stable for 24 months in glass-stoppered bottles or 12 months in cork-stoppered bottles when protected from light.[1]

AMMONIUM CHLORIDE

Ammonium Chloride, U.S.P. XVII

Formula, NH_4Cl. Molecular Weight, 53.49

Physical Properties.—Ammonium Chloride occurs in the form of a white, fine or coarse, crystalline powder. Technical grades occur as concave-convex cakes of tough, fibrous crystals. The salt is odorless, has a cooling, salty taste and a density of about 1.536. It is slightly hygroscopic.

Ammonium Chloride is very soluble in water; 1 Gm. dissolving in 2.6 ml. of water, at 25° C. and in 1.4 ml. of boiling water. One Gm. of the salt is soluble in about 100 ml. of alcohol and in about 8 ml. of glycerin, at 25° C.

Chemical Properties.—Ammonium chloride is volatilized when heated, but is not decomposed in the process. It is said that the salt decomposes reversibly when heated (1), but the components reunite when cooled again. It is impossible to obtain ammonia from ammonium chloride by ordinary heating.

(1) $NH_4Cl \rightleftarrows NH_3 + HCl$

Freshly prepared solutions of ammonium chloride are neutral in reaction, but, due to hydrolysis (2), the solutions quickly become slightly acid in reaction on standing. A molar solution will develop a pH of about 4.6.

[1] J. Am. Pharm. Assoc. Sci. Ed., **34**, 216 (1945).

21

$$(2) \ NH_4^+ + Cl^- + 2H_2O \ \rightleftarrows NH_4OH + H_3O^+ + Cl^-$$
$$\text{(slightly}$$
$$\text{dissociated)}$$

All other reactions of ammonium chloride are typical of ammonium (q.v.) or chloride ion (q. v.), respectively.

The assay procedure for Ammonium Chloride determines the chloride ion content and is identical to the procedure used for sodium chloride (see p. 223).

Official Tests for Identity.—1. A 1 in 10 solution responds to the test for *Ammonium* (q.v.).

2. The solution also responds to the tests for *Chloride* (q.v.).

Commercial Manufacture.—Sal ammoniac (crude ammonium chloride) was first prepared by the Egyptians by subliming the ashes resulting from the slow burning of camels' dung. It also has been made by the direct union of equal volumes of ammonia and hydrogen chloride in the presence of a small amount of moisture.

Ammonium chloride is prepared today by a process analogous to that used for making ammonium sulfate. Ammoniacal gas liquors are treated with lime and the liberated ammonia passed into hydrochloric acid. The salt is purified by crystallization and sublimation. Crystalline and granular ammonium chlorides are prepared by adding a hot, concentrated solution of the salt to powdered ammonium chloride. The crystalline magma that results is drained, pressed, and dried in molds. A pure product is readily obtained by interaction of ammonia from the Haber process with hydrochloric acid.

Uses.—*Ammonium Chloride*, U.S.P. XVII, contains not less than 99.5 per cent of NH_4Cl, calculated on the dried basis. Because of the characteristic action of the ammonium ion in thinning the secretions, particularly the saliva and mucus, this salt is a valuable expectorant. It probably increases the amount of mucus and at the same time makes it less viscous and tenacious.

It also exhibits a diuretic action (see p. 303) and in large doses produces an acid urine since it is a systemic acidifier. Effective acidification of the urine requires 6 to 8 Gm daily. It is used also to intensify the action of mercurial diuretics. Ammonium chloride is effective in treating alkalosis when introduced intravenously. For intravenous use the U.S.P. recognizes *Ammonium Chloride Injection* which is obtainable in various concentrations and which is used in a 500 ml. dose of a 2 per cent solution by infusion over a 3-hour period (range, I.V., 100 to 500 ml. of a 2 per cent solution).

The usual oral dose of Ammonium Chloride is 1 Gm. four times a day with a range of from 0.3 to 2 Gm. For convenience in oral administration *Ammonium Chloride Tablets* are available in 300 and 500 mg. sizes. Enteric coated tablets are also available and are said to minimize gastric irritation. When enteric coated tablets are used for urinary acidification it is well to monitor the urine using pH paper since these tablets may pass through unabsorbed.

Ammonium Iodide, N.F. X, NH₄I, occurs as small, colorless, cubical crystals, or as a white, granular powder. It is odorless, has a sharp, saline taste, and a density of 2.56. The salt absorbs moisture very readily. Upon exposure to air and light, it loses ammonia and soon becomes colored yellow or yellowish-brown, due to liberated iodine. If the salt is mixed with a small amount of ammonium hypophosphite, the liberated iodine is readily converted back to iodide. In fact, the N.F. X permitted 1 per cent ammonium hypophosphite in the salt for this purpose.

One Gm. of ammonium iodide is soluble in about 0.6 ml. of water, in about 3.7 ml. of alcohol, and in about 1.5 ml. of glycerin at 25° C. It dissolves in about one-half its weight of boiling water.

In absence of air, the salt may be sublimed unchanged. However, when it is strongly heated in air, it volatilizes with slight decomposition.

An aqueous solution of ammonium iodide is neutral or slightly acid to litmus. In common with many soluble iodides, solutions of ammonium iodide are slowly colored brown due to oxidation upon exposure to air.

Ammonium iodide has been used in all conditions for which iodides are indicated. It is particularly useful as an expectorant. The presence of the ammonium ion lessens the tendency to depress the circulation, but increases the irritating effect upon the mucous membrane. Usual dose—0.3 Gm. (approximately 5 grains).

THE COINAGE METALS

COPPER, SILVER AND GOLD

Introduction.—The three members of this family are designated as the "coinage metals" because, from early times, they have been employed for ornamental and for coinage purposes. These elements form Division B of Group I in the Periodic Table, but their properties differ in many respects from those of the alkali metals which comprise Division A of this same group. It is quite evident that Mendeléeff was cognizant of these facts because he gave them an alternate place in Group VIII. This latter classification associated them with nickel, palladium and platinum to which they are closely related. The differences between the alkali metals and the coinage metals are tabulated below:

Alkali Metals	*Copper, Silver, Gold*
A. Do not occur free in Nature.	*A.* Occur free in Nature and are easily recovered from their compounds by reduction.
B. Very active chemically; displacing all other elements from their compounds. The chemical activity increases as the atomic weight increases.	*B.* Are low in the electromotive series and hence are not very active chemically; they are displaced by most other metals. The chemical activity decreases as the atomic weight increases.
C. Oxides and hydroxides are strongly basic.	*C.* Oxides and hydroxides are feebly basic (excepting Ag_2O which is an active basic oxide).
D. Alkali halides are soluble in water, and are not hydrolyzed.	*D.* Silver, Copper^I and Gold^I halides are nearly insoluble in water. With the exception of the silver halides they are readily hydrolyzed and form numerous basic salts.
E. Univalent; forming but one series of compounds.	*E.* Copper^I and Copper^{II} each form a series of compounds; Silver,^{I} one series; and Gold^I and Gold^{III}, one series each.
F. They form simple cations, never occur in complex anions and do not form complex cations with ammonia.	*F.* All of them form complex anions, *e.g.*, $Cu(CN)_2^-$, $Ag(CN)_2^-$, $Au(CN)_2^-$, and complex cations with ammonia, *e. g.*, $Ag(NH_3)_2^+$, $Cu(NH_3)_4^{++}$ $Au(NH_3)_2^+$.
G. All are rapidly oxidized in air.	*G.* Copper is only slowly oxidized in air, but rapidly when finely divided and heated in oxygen.

PROPERTIES OF THE COINAGE METALS

Properties	Copper	Silver	Gold
Atomic Number . . .	29	47	79
Atomic Weight . . .	63.54	107.870	196.967
Isotopes	63, 65	107, 109	197
Electrons	2–8–18–1	2–8–18–18–1	2–8–18–32–18–1
Density	8.94	10.5	19.32
Melting point . . .	1083°	960.5°	1063°
Boiling point . . .	2595°	2000°	2600°
Common oxidation states	0, +1, +2	0, +1	0, +1, +3
Radius (cov.) Å . . .	1.17	1.34	1.34
Radius (ionic) Å .	0.69 (+2) 0.95 (+1)	1.13	1.2 (probable)
Ionization potential, first, volts	7.724	7.574	9.223
Oxidation potential, volts, $M \rightarrow M^+$ . . .	−0.522	−0.7995	ca. −1.68

All of these elements occupy positions in their respective periods representing the end of a transition sequence. Consultation of the accompanying table of physical properties indicates that each has a kernel with an outer shell of 18 electrons together with a single valence electron in the outermost shell. With respect to the single valence electron they resemble the alkali metals but the resemblance can hardly be construed as going any further. The differences have been well illustrated in the comparative tabulation already given.

The table of physical properties indicates that the monovalent cations of group IB are smaller in size than those of the alkali metals and that they have a higher ionization potential. Because of their size and because of the somewhat imperfect screening (as compared to inert gas configuration kernels) of nuclear charge by the 18 electron shell (see p. 12), these elements have a tendency toward covalent bond formation with increasing atomic number. This is certainly much stronger and in a reverse direction in the group than the corresponding tendency in the alkali metals although the ions (e.g., Na and K) are approximately in the same size range. In the polyvalent states, the increased ionic charge results in greater covalency in the compounds, notably in the case of trivalent gold where the covalency has been increased by coordination to 4 (e.g., $HAuCl_4$). In fact, there is good reason to believe that polyvalent gold does not exist as such at all but is always present as a complex with a coordination number of 4. It is curious to note that, judging from the crystal structures of the monovalent halides of copper and silver, the copper compounds are all covalent in nature whereas the silver compounds (with the exception of the iodide) are all ionic. It has been shown, however, that in the gas state the halides of silver are all covalent, a not too surprising circumstance if one considers that in the gaseous state the ion pair is freed from other ion attractions and can lead to greater deformation of the anion. The potentiality of this happening had already been indicated by the covalent nature of solid AgI inasmuch as iodide is one of the most deformable ions.

Two different valence states exist, at least for copper and gold and very probably for silver, and give rise to compounds which can almost be looked upon as having originated from two different elements. Although the kernels have a complete shell of 18 electrons, this shell can contribute one or more of these electrons to form bonds in addition to using the normal valence electron. When the element is in the monovalent state, *i.e.*, when the cation is the normally expected one, the ion is colorless and diamagnetic. However, in the polyvalent form where the 18-electron outer shell has become deficient in electrons the ions correspond in structure to the transition elements and, accordingly, are colored and paramagnetic. The transition elements, with partially filled d-shells, are usually colored and ions that possess this incomplete shell are no exception.

The hydration energies of these cations are high because of their small ionic size. However, although the hydration energies of the IB cations are high, their ionization potentials and heats of sublimation are also high, which accounts for the low oxidation potentials and the fact that these elements are not easily oxidized and, in fact, are frequently found in the elemental state in Nature.

There is a definite tendency toward disproportionation of the monovalent ions, particularly of copper and gold, to the free element and the higher oxidation state. Thus, we can write the following reactions:

$$2Cu^+ \rightleftarrows Cu^{++} + Cu; \ 2Ag^+ \rightleftarrows Ag^{++} + Ag; \ 3Au^+ \rightleftarrows Au^{+++} + 2Au.$$

The point of equilibrium in the above is far to the right in the case of copper and gold, but to the left for silver. Thus, salts of monovalent copper and gold are unstable in a medium that permits ionization, whereas salts of monovalent silver are stable. It is because of these instabilities that the commonly occurring valence states are 2 for Cu, 1 for Ag and 3 for Au.

17

Copper and Copper Compounds

COPPER

Symbol, Cu.   Valences, 1, 2.   Atomic Weight, 63.54;
Atomic Number, 29

History and Occurrence.—Copper was probably the first metal used by man in fashioning various domestic implements and weapons. Because the metal occurs as such in Nature, the mining and methods of refining it were very simple. The Romans obtained copper from the island of Cyprus and called it *cuprum*, from which the name, *copper*, is derived.

Both free and combined copper occur in Nature. Large deposits of free copper are found in the state of Michigan and in the so-called Lake Superior region. The most important minerals containing combined copper are *chalcopyrite* [$CuFeS_2$] and *chalcocite* [Cu_2S]. These minerals are found in Montana, Utah, Arizona, and in southwest England, Spain and Germany. *Malachite*, a basic copper carbonate [$CuCO_3.Cu(OH)_2$], is found in Siberia, Arizona, the Urals and elsewhere. *Cuprite*, a red copper ore [Cu_2O], occurs abundantly and is one of the most important copper ores. The feathers of certain birds contain pigments in which copper is found.

Physical Properties.—Copper is a malleable and ductile metal having a red color by reflected light and a greenish color by transmitted light. Electrolytic copper has a density of 8.94. It melts at 1083° C. and boils at 2595° C. Copper, crystallized in octahedrons, is found in Nature. For reagent purposes U.S.P. XVII, (p. 971) permits copper in the form of wire, foil, turnings, filings, granules or gauze.

Copper is an excellent conductor of heat (surpassed only by silver and gold) and electricity (surpassed by silver), although the presence of small amounts of impurities, especially arsenic, adversely affects the conductivity.

Chemical Properties.—The chemical properties of copper and its salts may be conveniently discussed under the headings: (1) copper, (2) cuprous salts and (3) cupric salts.

1. Copper is permanent in dry air, but on exposure to moist air it slowly becomes covered with a green basic sulfate, $CuSO_4.3Cu$-

(OH)$_2$ or (CuOH)$_2$SO$_4$ (in inland areas) or CuCl$_2$.3Cu(OH)$_2$ (or CuOHCl) (by the sea). This green color was formerly (erroneously) thought to be a basic copper carbonate.

Copper reacts quite readily with oxygen to form cupric oxide (CuO), although when a sheet of copper is heated in air it forms a thin coating of the black oxide which serves to retard further oxidation. Sulfur and the halogens react more readily with copper than does oxygen. The metal does not react with water nor does it liberate hydrogen from acids since it is below hydrogen in the electromotive series. The only acids which will react with the metal are those which have oxidizing properties, *e.g.*, nitric acid, hot concentrated sulfuric acid, etc. However, metallic copper is dissolved when in contact with an acidified solution of a cupric salt regardless of the acid used. The mechanism whereby this takes place is that the cupric ion (easily reducible) will obtain an electron from the metallic copper atom and in so doing is itself reduced to the cuprous form as well as oxidizing the copper atom to the cuprous form (1).

(1) $Cu + Cu^{++} \rightarrow 2Cu^+$

Then in the presence of atmospheric oxygen and hydronium ions (contributed by the acid) the cuprous ions are oxidized to the cupric form (2).

(2) $4Cu^+ + 4H_3O^+ + O_2 \rightarrow 4Cu^{++} + 6H_2O$

It has been stated that when copper is heated in air it forms a copper oxide known as cupric oxide. This is not the only oxide of copper, because at least one other common oxide, cuprous oxide (Cu$_2$O) exists.

The two copper oxides represent the two forms of oxidation in which copper compounds may exist, namely, (1) red cuprous (Cu$^+$) and (2) black cupric (Cu^{++}).

2. Although numerous compounds are known in which the copper apparently has a single valence, all of these compounds are water-insoluble and it is questionable whether it is possible to have the cuprous ion in solution in significant concentrations. The *cuprous salts*, *e.g.*, cuprous chloride, will dissolve in concentrated hydrohalide acids but their state of existence in such a solution is probably not represented by the simple formula, CuX, but by a more complex formula of the general type, H$_4$(Cu$_2$X$_6$), in which X may be Cl, Br, or I. It is interesting to note that the hydrochloric acid solution of cuprous chloride has an application in gas analysis because of its capacity to absorb carbon monoxide. The reaction is undoubtedly more complex than the following equation indicates (3) but for all practical purposes it may suffice to show what happens. Ammoniacal copper formate is also used to remove carbon monoxide from gases.

(3) $CO + CuCl + H_2O \rightleftarrows CuCl.CO.H_2O$

Cuprous chloride forms a soluble complex in ammonium hydroxide $(Cu(NH_3)Cl)$. The assay of oxygen depends upon this complex (see oxygen and also cuprous chloride).

All of the cuprous compounds are white when freshly prepared with the exception of the sulfide (Cu_2S) which is black and the cuprous oxide which is red. Cuprous compounds are insoluble in water.

3. Most of the cupric salts are blue in color, some are greenish-blue, and a few have miscellaneous colors. When the water of crystallization is removed from the salts they usually become white or yellowish in color. The water-soluble cupric salts are the nitrate, chloride, bromide, fluoride, sulfate and acetate (citrate sl. sol.). Most of the water-insoluble salts are soluble in acidified solutions.

These include the tannate, proteinate, arsenate, arsenite, hydroxide, carbonate and phosphate. Usually the precipitation of copper salts can be prevented by using sequestering agents such as citrates (Benedict's Solution), tartrates (Fehling's Solution), glycerin (Haine's Reagent), or sugar.

The blue color of aqueous solutions of cupric salts may be attributed to the presence of the blue cupric ion (Cu^{++}). Solutions of some cupric salts exhibit a green or brown color but these colors may be ascribed to the presence of undissociated molecules since the solutions will turn blue on dilution.

The cupric ion actually exists in solution in a hydrated form, *i.e.*, it has 4 moles of water, $Cu(H_2O)_4^{++}$. This method of representing the ion is not common. The cupric ion has a tendency to hydrolyze (4) and therefore solutions of the salts are usually slightly acidic.

(4) $Cu(H_2O)_4^{++} + H_2O \rightleftarrows Cu(H_2O)_3OH^+ + H_3O^+$

or

$Cu^{++} + 2H_2O \rightleftarrows CuOH^+ + H_3O^+$

It is interesting to note that in this case we have a cation which is subject to hydrolysis. Usually anions are the ones affected.

Cupric salts are readily reduced to cuprous compounds in many cases, although the anion of the cuprous compound is not necessarily the anion associated with the cupric compound. Falling into this type of reaction we have that of cupric salts reacting with iodides (reducing agent) to form cuprous iodide (cupric iodide is quite unstable) and iodine (5) (see assay for Cupric Sulfate N.F. XII) and with cyanides to form cuprous cyanide (6).

(5) $Cu^{++} + 2I^- \rightarrow CuI_2$
$2CuI_2 \rightarrow 2CuI \downarrow + I_2 \downarrow$

(6) $Cu^{++} + 2CN^- \rightarrow Cu(CN)_2$
$2Cu(CN)_2 \rightarrow 2CuCN \downarrow + (CN)_2 \uparrow$

An excess of cyanide will redissolve the cuprous cyanide to form the soluble cuprocyanide ion (7).

(7) $CuCN + CN^- \rightarrow Cu(CN)_2^-$

Reducing agents such as aldehydes (formaldehyde and glucose) and hypophosphites in alkaline solution reduce cupric ions to red cuprous oxide (8).

(8) $2Cu(OH)_2 + HCHO + NaOH \rightarrow Cu_2O \downarrow + HCOONa +$
$3H_2O$ (red)

In acid solution the hypophosphite ion reduces the cupric ion to cuprous hydride (8a).

(8a) $4CuSO_4 + 3HPH_2O_2 + 6H_2O \xrightarrow{H_2SO_4} 4CuH + 3H_3PO_4 +$
$4H_2SO_4$

Reduction with phosphorus is complete to metallic copper (9).

(9) $6CuSO_4 + 2P + 8H_2O \rightarrow Cu(H_2PO_4)_2 + 5Cu \downarrow +$
$6H_2SO_4$

Addition of alkali hydroxides, e.g., NaOH or KOH, to solutions of cupric salts results in the precipitation of a light-blue cupric hydroxide (10) which on boiling is converted to brownish-black cupric oxide (11).

(10) $Cu^{++} + 2OH^- \rightarrow Cu(OH)_2 \downarrow$

(11) $Cu(OH)_2 \rightarrow CuO + H_2O$

When ammonia water is added to a solution of a cupric salt, a bluish precipitate of cupric hydroxide is formed. However, upon addition of an excess of ammonia water the precipitate redissolves and forms a deep-blue colored solution. The deep-blue color is occasioned by the formation of the cupric-ammonium complex ion which is water-soluble and is colored deep blue (12). The soluble complex formed is often called a copper amine (see chemical properties of ammonia).

(12) $Cu^{++} + 4NH_3 \rightarrow Cu(NH_3)_4^{++}$

The cupric hydroxide precipitate dissolves because the cupric-ammonium complex removes cupric ions from the solution, thus disturbing the equilibrium between the slightly ionized cupric hydroxide and its constituent ions (13), and the cupric hydroxide keeps dissolving in an effort to supply the demand for cupric ions.

Ammoniated copper was at one time official in the U.S.P. and recommended in the external treatment of ulcers.

(13) $Cu(OH)_2 \rightleftarrows Cu^{++} + 2OH^-$

The addition of potassium ferrocyanide to neutral or acidic solutions of cupric salts results in the precipitation of reddish-brown cupric ferrocyanide (14). This precipitate is not soluble in dilute acids but it is quite soluble in excess ammonia water giving the characteristic blue color of the cupric-ammonium complex.

$$(14)\ 2Cu^{++} + Fe(CN)_6^{==} \rightarrow Cu_2Fe(CN)_6 \downarrow$$
$$\text{(reddish-brown)}$$

The antidotal treatment of acute cupric salt poisoning depends on this reaction (14).

Potassium thiocyanate when added to cupric salts causes the precipitation of insoluble, black cupric thiocyanate (15). This precipitate will gradually turn white upon standing because of formation of white cuprous thiocyanate (CuSCN). In the quantitative determination of sugar in urine the Benedict's Solution used contains potassium ferrocyanide which reacts with the cuprous oxide (Cu_2O) formed. There is a soluble compound formed that is perhaps cuprous ferrocyanide. However, in the assay the cuprous ion is immediately precipitated as white cuprous thiocyanate (CuSCN)

$$(15)\ Cu^{++} + 2SCN^- \rightarrow Cu(SCN)_2 \downarrow$$
$$\text{(black)}$$

The position of copper in the electromotive series is responsible for its ability to "plate-out" on metallic iron. This is done by placing the iron in a solution of the cupric salt. Since iron is higher in the electromotive series than is copper, the copper is displaced from solution by the iron which becomes ionized (16).

$$(16)\ Fe + Cu^{++} \rightarrow Fe^{++} + Cu \downarrow$$

Cupric ions form a black cupric sulfide with hydrogen sulfide or any other source of sulfide ions (17).

$$(17)\ Cu^{++} + H_2S \rightarrow CuS \downarrow + 2H^+$$
$$\text{(black)}$$

Official Tests for Copper Ion.—1. When a bright untarnished surface of metallic iron is introduced into an acidified (HCl) solution of a cupric salt, a red film of copper is deposited on the iron (16).

2. An excess of ammonia T.S. will first produce a bluish colored precipitate of cupric hydroxide (10) which dissolves on addition of more ammonia water to form a deep-blue colored solution (12).

3. Solutions of cupric salts will yield a reddish-brown precipitate of cupric ferrocyanide when treated with potassium ferrocyanide T.S. (14). The precipitate is insoluble in diluted acids.

Commercial Manufacture.—Most of the metallic copper is obtained from ores containing under 6 per cent copper and it is not infrequent that the ores run less than 1 per cent copper. These ores are mostly sulfide and oxide ores, although a small amount of metallic copper is secured, especially in the Michigan district.

These ores are first crushed to a size to liberate the mineral, which is ordinarily finer than 60 mesh. The flotation process of concentration is used in most cases. The finely crushed ore is mixed with water and a small amount (usually under 1 per cent) of various kinds of oils and soaps. Considerable quantities of other chemical compounds, *e.g.*, lime and acids, are sometimes added to certain ores to meet particular requirements. This mixture is agitated by compressed air or otherwise. This causes small air bubbles to adhere to the mineral particles, and brings them to the surface as a froth or foam which is continuously removed. The process is very efficient and, when properly controlled by adding other chemicals and flotation agents between the various flotation cells, several different froths can be made, each of which will contain a different mineral concentrate. Thus, in complex ores, it is often possible by selective flotation to separate three or four different minerals.

The sulfide concentrate is roasted for the removal of sulfur to the desired point, so that the mixture of ores which is later added to the furnace will contain the proper amount of sulfur (18 and 19). All of the ore, especially oxide ore, is not always roasted, but is often added directly to the furnace.

(18) $2Cu_2S + 3O_2 \rightarrow 2Cu_2O + 2SO_2 \uparrow$

(19) $2Cu_2O + Cu_2S \rightarrow 6Cu + SO_2 \uparrow$

The copper obtained from the furnace is usually covered with black blisters, formed by the escape of sulfur dioxide during solidification, and is known as *"blister copper."* It is from 96 to 98 per cent metal but contains some cuprous oxide in solution. It is very brittle. The complete "de-oxidation" of the metal is accomplished by melting the *"blister copper"* and stirring the melted mass with an oak or birch pole. This phase of the refining process is known as "poling." The copper is cast into large plates and then is ready to be purified by electrolysis.

The presence in copper of very small quantities of such impurities as cuprous oxide and sulfide, arsenic, antimony, lead, zinc, gold, silver, etc., materially affects its physical constants and, because its many uses require it to be in a high state of purity, it is usually refined electrolytically.

Pharmacological Action of the Copper Ion.—Copper is essential to the human metabolic processes, but as yet no deficiency syndrome in man has been reported. This is probably a consequence of its normal presence in more than adequate amounts in foodstuffs. Foods particularly rich in copper are liver, mushrooms, nuts, chocolate and shellfish. On the other hand, copper deficiency may be induced in various animals (swine, rats, rabbits, dogs, etc.) and it is quite certain that copper and iron metabolism are interrelated and that copper has importance in hemopoiesis. The normal metabolism of copper is shown by Cartwright and Wintrobe in Figure 6.

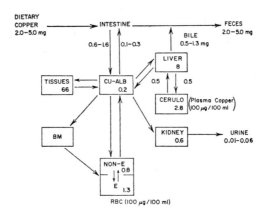

FIG. 6. Schematic representation of some metabolic pathways of copper. The numbers in the boxes refer to milligrams of copper in the pool. The numbers next to the arrows refer to milligrams of copper transversing the pathway each day. CU-ALB, direct-reacting fraction; CERULO, ceruloplasmin; NON-E, nonerythrocuprein; E, erythrocuprein; BM, bone marrow; RBC, red blood cell. (From Cartwright, G. E., and M. M. Wintrobe: Am. J. Clin. Nutr., 14, 224 (1964).

A rare disease known as hepatolenticular degeneration (Wilson's disease) results from a familial inability to regulate copper balance with the consequence that toxic amounts of copper are deposited in various tissues (eye, liver, brain, and kidney). The disease has customarily been treated with chelating agents such as Dimercaprol and the edetates. More recently, penicillamine[1] (Cuprimine) has been shown to be much more effective in promoting urinary excretion of the excess copper in the chelated form (20). Penicillamine is particularly effective because of the adjacent amino and sulfhydryl groups coupled with the fact that it is highly resistant to metabolic inactivation by amino acid oxidase since it lacks a hydrogen on the beta-carbon atom. It is often coupled with oral administration of 25 mg. of Sulfurated Potash with meals to precipitate the dietary copper as sulfide and thus to remove it in the feces.

Internally, as therapeutic agents, copper salts have two effects depending on the dosage used: (1) potential aid to iron assimilation and (2) emesis.

(1) The use of copper as a "catalyst" to promote the better assimilation of iron is based on the work of Hart, Steenbock *et al.*[2] in 1928 in which they noted that the uptake of iron in copper deficient animals could be improved only by addition of dietary copper but not by added iron. This finding was extended to humans and a number of pharmaceutical products (Cofron, Ciagen, Heptron, etc.)

[1] Walshe, J. M.; Lancet, **1**, 188 (1960); Scheinberg, I. H. and I. Sternlieb; Am. J. Med., **29**, 316 (1960).

[2] Hart, Steenbock *et al* : J. Biol. Chem., **77** 797 (1928).

$$(20) \quad CH_3-\underset{\underset{CH_3}{|}}{\overset{\overset{SH}{|}}{C}}-\overset{\overset{NH_2}{|}}{CH}-COOH + Cu^{++} \longrightarrow CH_3-\underset{\underset{CH_3}{|}}{\overset{\overset{Cu^+}{\diagup \diagdown}}{\underset{S}{}\quad \underset{NH_2}{}}}{C}---\overset{\overset{NH_2}{|}}{CH}-COOH \longrightarrow$$

$$HOOC-\underset{\underset{H_2N}{|}}{CH}---\underset{\underset{S}{|}}{\overset{\overset{CH_3}{|}}{C}}-CH_3$$

$$\underset{\diagup \quad \nwarrow}{Cu}$$

$$\underset{S \qquad NH_2}{}$$

$$CH_3-\underset{\underset{CH_3}{|}}{\overset{\overset{S}{|}}{C}}---\overset{\overset{NH_2}{|}}{CH}-COOH$$

were licensed and marketed under the existing patent. The optimum ratio of elemental copper to iron for maximum effectiveness was said to be 1:25. There is some question today whether humans ever need supplementary copper for maximum iron utilization.

(2) Because of their irritant action, copper salts are prompt acting emetics. The nausea accompanying the emesis is of short duration. Ordinarily, in small doses (0.3 Gm. copper sulfate per 30 ml.), it causes emesis safely although if the emetic response is not obtained the salt should be removed by gastric lavage to forestall toxicity. Large doses may be toxic and can cause corrosion of the gastric mucosa as well as characteristic lesions of the kidneys, spleen and other organs. After absorption, copper is found principally as copper nucleinate in the liver, blood and bile.

Externally, because of its reversible protein precipitant action, it acts as an effective astringent when applied to mucous membranes and abraded surfaces. It is an effective fungicide in minute amounts (1:1,000,000) and has proven of value in water treatment to remove algae as well as in fungous infections afflicting humans. A copper compound in tetralin (Cuprex) is used in pediculosis of the head, body or clothing. In spite of its efficacy as a fungicide, copper ion is not an effective bactericide, being only a mild antiseptic in most cases. Its action is principally bacteriostatic, even in somewhat high dilutions. Metallic copper, itself, has an *oligodynamic action,* i.e., bacteriostasis will occur in copper vessels provided the solution is not too heavily contaminated.

OFFICIAL COPPER COMPOUND

CUPRIC SULFATE

Cupric Sulfate, N.F. XII

Formula, $CuSO_4.5H_2O$; Molecular Weight, 249.68

Physical Properties.—Cupric Sulfate occurs in the form of deep blue, triclinic crystals of the pentahydrate, or as blue crystalline granules or powder. It effloresces slowly in dry air and the crystals become covered with a white coating of the anhydrous salt. The salt is odorless, and has a nauseous, metallic taste.

One Gm. of Cupric Sulfate dissolves in 3 ml. of water, in about 500 ml. of alcohol, and very slowly in 3 ml. of glycerin, at 25° C. One Gm. is soluble in 0.5 ml. of boiling water.

Chemical Properties.—The salt ($CuSO_4.5H_2O$) is stable to heat up to 60° C. but upon heating to 100° C. it loses two moles of water ($CuSO_4.3H_2O$). At 140° C. another mole of water is lost ($CuSO_4-H_2O$) and at 200° C. the white anhydrous salt is obtained ($CuSO_4$). At higher temperatures it is decomposed into sulfur dioxide, oxygen, and black cupric oxide (1).

$$(1)\ 2CuSO_4 \xrightarrow{\Delta} 2CuO + 2SO_2\uparrow + O_2\uparrow$$

Copper sulfate, of course, conforms to the chemical properties of its constituent ions, namely the cupric ion and the sulfate ion.

Solutions of the salt are acid to litmus paper and blue-green in color. This salt is used extensively in the determination of reducing sugars. It is used in the form of (1) Fehling's Solution and (2) Benedict's Solution.

1. Cuprous oxide is precipitated from alkaline solutions of cupric salts when they are boiled with reducing agents, *e.g.*, dextrose and other monosaccharides. Fehling's Solution is used for detecting sugars in the urine. Herman von Fehling developed this solution in 1850. *Solution 1*, the copper sulfate solution, and *Solution 2*, the alkaline tartrate solution, are prepared separately and mixed in equal volumes at the time of making the test. Solution 1 is made by dissolving 34.64 Gm. of crystalline copper sulfate in sufficient distilled water to make 500 ml. at standard temperature. Solution 2 is made by dissolving 173 Gm. of crystallized Potassium Sodium Tartrate and 50 Gm. of sodium hydroxide in sufficient distilled water to make 500 ml. at standard temperature. When a portion of Solution 1 is mixed with an equal volume of Solution 2, the copper sulfate and sodium hydroxide probably react to form cupric hydroxide which immediately is converted by the Potassium Sodium Tartrate into a soluble blue-colored compound.[1] It is generally conceded today

---

[1] J. Indian Chem. Soc., **27**, 443 (1950).

that the solution probably contains a sequestered form of the cupric ion. A soluble cupric-tartrate ion exists that prevents the cupric ion *per se* from reacting with the hydroxide ions present but does not prevent the cupric ions from being reduced (see sequestering agents).

(2) Cu^{++} [from $Cu(OH)_2$] $+ NaKC_4H_4O_6 \rightarrow$

$$
\begin{array}{c}
\text{H} \\
|\\
\text{O—C—COONa} \\
\text{Cu}\diagup \qquad\quad |\qquad\qquad + \text{2H}_2\text{O} \\
\diagdown \\
\text{O—C—COOK} \\
|\\
\text{H} \\
\text{(soluble)}
\end{array}
$$

The copper ion in the solution is readily converted to cuprous oxide (Cu_2O) when heated with a few drops of a solution containing reducing sugars, *e.g.*, diabetic urine. In testing urine it is found that traces of sugar in the urine (0.1 per cent) will only cause a bluish-green coloration of the solution without a precipitate and that with increasing amounts of sugar the color changes gradually to a red accompanied by a precipitate (10 per cent and over).

2. Benedict's solution is used both as a qualitative reagent and as a quantitative solution. The *qualitative* solution contains 17.3 Gm. of crystalline copper sulfate, 173 Gm. of sodium citrate, 117 Gm. of monohydrated sodium carbonate and enough distilled water to bring the volume to 1000 ml. The cupric ion is combined with the citrate ion to form cupric citrate which is insoluble except in alkali citrates. It is used for much the same purpose as Fehling's Solution, namely, to detect sugar in urine, and the color changes are very similar. It has an advantage over Fehling's Solution in that the solution is stable as it is, whereas Fehling's Solution must be mixed at the time of use.

Benedict's Solution is less alkaline than Fehling's Solution and utilizes a citrate which is a better sequestering agent. In Benedict's test the reagent must be boiled before a reduction by sugar will take place.

The qualitative reagent should not be confused with the *quantitative* solution which contains 18.0000 Gm. of crystalline copper sulfate (reagent grade), 117 Gm. $Na_2CO_3 . H_2O$, 200 Gm. sodium citrate, 125 Gm. potassium thiocyanate, 5 ml. of a 5 per cent potassium ferrocyanide solution and enough distilled water to bring the volume to 1000 ml. The quantitative solution is less commonly used than the qualitative but it is useful for determining the sugar content of urine more accurately than is possible with the qualitative solution. (For chemistry see chemical properties of cupric ion.)

Official Tests for Identity.—1. A solution (1 in 10) of Cupric Sulfate responds to the tests for *Copper* (*q.v.*).

2. A solution also responds to the tests for *Sulfate* (*q.v.*).

22

Commercial Manufacture.—Cupric sulfate is made by roasting copper-bearing sulfide ores in the presence of air, or by heating copper in a furnace with sulfur. The mixture of copper sulfate and copper oxide, obtained by either process, is lixiviated or percolated with dilute sulfuric acid and the resulting solution filtered, concentrated and allowed to crystallize. It is also made by permitting dilute sulfuric acid to trickle over granulated copper in the presence of air (3).

(3) $2Cu + 2H_2SO_4 + O_2 \rightarrow 2CuSO_4 + 2H_2O$

Cupric sulfate may be made by the action of very hot, concentrated sulfuric acid upon copper (4, 5, and 6).

(4) $Cu + H_2SO_4 \xrightarrow{\Delta} CuO + SO_2 \uparrow + H_2O$

(5) $CuO + H_2SO_4 \xrightarrow{\Delta} CuSO_4 + H_2O$

(6) $CuSO_4 + 5H_2O \rightarrow CuSO_4.5H_2O$

Uses.—*Cupric Sulfate* (Copper Sulfate), N.F. XII, contains not less than 98.5 per cent and not more than 104.5 per cent of $CuSO_4\cdot 5H_2O$. This purity rubric indicates that the official salt is a mixture of the various hydrates of cupric sulfate. It is also commonly known as "blue vitriol" or "blue stone" and was official in the U.S.P. from I through XIV. Copper sulfate stimulates the vomiting reflex before there is time for any local irritant action. It is not absorbed (except by corroded stomachs) and hence does not produce any systemic effects. The nausea is very short and the after-depression is small. Copper sulfate is used to empty the stomach of indigestible food and poisons by inducing vomiting with oral doses of about 0.3 Gm. in 30 ml. warm water. If the expected emetic action is not obtained the stomach must be washed by gastric lavage. In treating phosphorus poisoning the cupric ion oxidizes the phosphorus thereby inactivating the unabsorbed particles by forming a coating of metallic copper over them (7).

(7) $2P + 6CuSO_4 + 8H_2O \rightarrow Cu(H_2PO_4)_2 + 5Cu \downarrow +$
     $6H_2SO_4$

Copper sulfate is used externally for its fungicidal action in 1 to 5 per cent solutions. Although it is not a reliable bactericide it has been used in 0.1 to 1 per cent concentrations for this purpose. As an astringent and irritant it is used in 0.75 per cent concentration. In collyria and for urethral injection it has been used in 0.5 to 1 per cent solutions.

The widest use of copper sulfate is as an algacide and fungicide. Bordeaux Mixture, used as a fungicide, is a combination with lime. Copper sulfate has been used to purify water for drinking and in swimming pools, usually in conjunction with chlorine. In small, but yet effective, concentration it is harmless to humans and fish. Frequently small quantities are used with iron and/or vitamins for the hematinic property.

18

Silver and Silver Compounds

SILVER

Symbol, Ag.   Valence, 1.   Atomic Weight, 107.870;
Atomic Number, 47

History and Occurrence.—Silver has been known from the earliest
times. It is of great importance as a "noble" metal because of its
use in making articles of value, *e.g.*, coins, ornaments and jewelry.
The name *silver* is derived from the Anglo-Saxon word *seolfor*.
The Latin *Argentum*, from which the symbol Ag is taken, is allied
with the Greek ἀργυρος, silver, which in turn is derived from ἀργός,
shining. The alchemists named it Luna and characterized it by
the crescent moon. The name Luna has survived in *Lunar caustic*
(silver nitrate).

Silver occurs widely distributed in Nature, the principal supplies
coming from Mexico, United States, and Australia. Native silver
is found in metalliferous veins, where it has been formed presumably by the reduction of silver sulfides or other silver-bearing
minerals. Silver is also found as an amalgam and as alloys with
gold, platinum, copper, and other metals. It occurs combined
with tellurium in the minerals *hessite* [Ag_2Te], *petzite* [$(AgAu)_2Te$],
and *sylvanite* [$AuAgTe_4$]. As the sulfide [Ag_2S], silver is found in
the minerals *argentite* and *acanthite*. In the form of the double sulfides of antimony or arsenic, silver occurs in the minerals, *pyrargyrite*
[$3Ag_2S.Sb_2S_3$], *proustite* [$3Ag_2S.As_2S_3$], *polybasite* [$9Ag_2S.Sb_2S_3$] and
pearcite [$9Ag_2S.As_2S_3$]. Silver is found combined with the respective
halogens in the minerals *cerargyrite* or *horn-silver* [$AgCl$], *bromyrite*
[$AgBr$], and *iodyrite* [AgI].

Physical Properties.—Pure silver is a white metal having a metallic
luster. With the exception of gold it is the most malleable and
ductile of all the metals. Its density is about 10.5 and its hardness
is greater than gold but less than copper. It melts at 960.5° C.
and boils at about 2000° C. Molten silver occludes about 22
volumes of oxygen which is not permanently retained. On cooling
it is given off with great violence. This phenomenon is called the
"spitting" or "sprouting" of silver and causes the silver to form in
irregular masses. Silver is the best conductor of electricity.

(327)

Chemical Properties.—The chemical properties of silver may be conveniently discussed under the headings: (1) metallic silver, and (2) silver ion.

1. Under ordinary conditions *silver metal* is not oxidized by oxygen, but like mercury, it is oxidized by ozone. On heating, silver combines with free halogens and with sulfur. Black silver sulfide is formed when silver comes in contact with substances containing sulfur, *e.g.*, coal gas, eggs, rubber, perspiration, hydrogen sulfide, sulfur dioxide, etc. The presence of oxygen is necessary for the reaction with hydrogen sulfide (1)

$$(1) \quad 2\,Ag + H_2S + \tfrac{1}{2}\,O_2 \rightarrow Ag_2S + H_2O$$

Because the metal stands below hydrogen in the electromotive series it does not displace hydrogen from acids, but it is attacked by the oxidizing acids (see also copper), *e.g.*, nitric acid (2) and hot sulfuric acid (3). To make solutions of silver for testing purposes, nitric acid is the proper solvent to use.

$$(2) \quad 3Ag + 4HNO_3 \text{ (cold, dilute)} \rightarrow 3AgNO_3 + NO \uparrow + 2H_2O$$

$$(3) \quad 2Ag + 2H_2SO_4 \rightarrow Ag_2SO_4 + SO_2 \uparrow + 2H_2O$$

2. Silver forms only one series of salts, the monovalent *silver ion* (Ag^+) being the form in which it exists. Most of the silver salts are insoluble, but there are a few soluble ones, namely, the nitrate, sulfate (1%), chlorate, nitrite, fluoride, lactate and acetate (1%). Exposure of silver salts to sunlight either in the solid state or in solution results in a darkening of the material because of reduction to free silver. Silver is one of the so-called heavy metals and forms a precipitate with sulfide, tannin, proteins, alkaloids, etc.

When hydrochloric acid or a solution of a soluble chloride is added to a neutral or acid solution of a silver compound, a white, curdy precipitate of silver chloride is produced (4). The precipitate is insoluble in dilute acids, but soluble in ammonium hydroxide (5) forming a cation and in potassium cyanide (6) or sodium thiosulfate solutions forming anions (7).[1]

$$(4) \quad Ag^+ + Cl^- \rightleftarrows AgCl \downarrow$$

$$(5) \quad AgCl + 2NH_3 \rightleftarrows Ag(NH_3)_2{}^+ + Cl^-$$

$$(6) \quad AgCl + 2CN^- \rightleftarrows [Ag(CN)_2]^- + Cl^-$$

$$(7) \quad 2AgCl + 3S_2O_3{}^= \rightarrow [Ag_2(S_2O_3)_2]^= + 2Cl^-$$

The solubility of silver chloride in ammonium hydroxide is due to the formation of the complex silver ammonia cation (5). This is due to the fact that silver chloride ionizes to a greater extent than does

---

[1] Composition of complex depends on the concentration of the thiosulfate ion.

the silver ammonia complex cation (in an excess of ammonium hydroxide) and, therefore, silver ions are "used up" in the formation of the complex cation causing the AgCl to go into solution. In a normal solution of ammonia in which silver chloride has been dissolved it is found that there are 10,000,000 complex ions to every simple silver ion (Ag+).

On the other hand, it is found that while silver ion is precipitated by bromides and iodides to give insoluble silver bromide and silver iodide, these precipitates are nearly insoluble in an excess of ammonium hydroxide, the iodide being less soluble than the bromide. The reason for this is that the bromide and iodide do not ionize to furnish silver ions to as great an extent as does the silver ammonia complex cation and, therefore, they do not go into solution as easily by the mechanism outlined for silver chloride. However, potassium cyanide (6) dissolves all of the silver halides and the mechanism is exactly the same as that for ammonium hydroxide except that the silver cyanide anion is formed (6) instead of the silver ammonia cation.

Soluble silver salts react with alkali hydroxides to form silver hydroxide (8) which immediately decomposes to brown silver oxide (9). In this case, the precipitate (AgOH or Ag_2O) is insoluble in excess alkali hydroxide because no complex ion is formed, but it is soluble in nitric acid or ammonium hydroxide.

(8) $Ag^+ + OH^- \rightarrow AgOH \downarrow$

(9) $2AgOH \rightarrow Ag_2O + H_2O$

Careful addition of ammonium hydroxide to a solution of a silver salt results in exactly the same kind of precipitate as with the alkali hydroxides (8, 9), but excess ammonia, of course, dissolves the precipitate for reasons previously mentioned (5).

If ammonium hydroxide is added to a solution of a silver salt, e.g., silver nitrate, most of the silver ions in the solution are converted to the silver-ammonia complex. This leaves relatively few silver ions in the solution. If to this solution is then added a reducing agent such as formaldehyde, glucose, hypophosphites, eugenol, etc., the free silver ions are reduced to the metallic state (10) and form a "silver mirror" on the walls of the container. As the silver ions are being converted to metallic silver the equilibrium between the silver-ammonia complex and silver ions (11) is disturbed and more silver ions are gradually liberated until all of the silver from the complex ion is deposited as the metal (see Ammoniacal Silver Nitrate). This is the basis for its use in dentistry to protect dentin.

(10) $HCHO + 2Ag(NH_3)_2OH \rightarrow HCOONH_4 + 2Ag \downarrow + 3NH_3 \uparrow + H_2O$ (mirror)

(11) $Ag(NH_3)_2^+ \rightleftarrows Ag^+ + 2NH_3$

In commercial solutions used for electroplating it is common practice to use a bath containing the silver-cyanide complex (6) since this has even fewer silver ions in equilibrium with it than the silver-ammonia complex. The object to be plated acts as a cathode and silver metal is the anode in these plating baths. The fact that there is such a low concentration of silver ions in the solution is the principal reason why silver is plated out in such fine crystals on the surface of the object to be plated.

Addition of sodium carbonate to solutions of silver salts causes precipitation of white silver carbonate (12) which can be decomposed by boiling to give silver oxide (13).

(12) $2Ag^+ + CO_3^= \rightarrow Ag_2CO_3 \downarrow$

(13) $Ag_2CO_3 \overset{\triangle}{\rightarrow} Ag_2O + CO_2 \uparrow$

Numerous other salts of silver are precipitated on the addition of suitable reagents, e.g., phosphates (see Phosphoric Acid) and borate (Sodium Borate).

Addition of silver nitrate solution, for example, to a protein solution causes the formation of a heavy precipitate of a complex protein-silver compound. Although this reaction is not well defined it is the basis of much of the medicinal efficiency of silver salts.

Official Tests for Silver Ion.—1. Solutions of silver salts will give a white, curdy precipitate of silver chloride when treated with hydrochloric acid (4). The precipitate is soluble in excess ammonia T.S. (5) but is insoluble in nitric acid.

2. An ammoniacal solution of a silver salt when treated with a small quantity of formaldehyde and warmed, causes the formation of a silver mirror on the walls of the test-tube (10).

Commercial Manufacture of Silver.—A number of processes have been devised for obtaining silver from its ores. They vary according to the chemical composition of the ores to be worked.

Amalgamation Process.—As previously indicated, silver readily forms an amalgam. Some silver ores containing free silver or silver chloride may be finely powdered and then extracted with mercury. The amalgam is washed free of powdered rock and the mercury recovered by distillation in an iron retort. The remaining retort silver is then cast into bars and shipped to a refinery.

Certain complex silver minerals (pyrargyrite, proustite, etc.) are very difficult to amalgamate and hence must be made amenable to such a process. This is accomplished by either the flotation process (see Copper) or by converting the metal in the ore to silver chloride and sulfate by roasting with about 10 per cent of sodium chloride. The volatile arsenic and antimony chlorides are expelled during the roasting of the ore. When the mixture of silver chloride, silver sulfate, rock, etc., is treated with mercury, the chloride and sulfate are reduced to metallic silver (14) which combines at once with the mercury to form an amalgam.

(14) $2AgCl + 2Hg \rightarrow 2Ag + 2HgCl$

Lixiviation or Leaching Process.—When simple silver sulfide ores are roasted, the sulfide is converted into soluble silver sulfate which is dissolved from the mass with water. Scrap copper now is added to the solution in order to precipitate the silver (15).

(15) $Ag_2SO_4 + Cu \overset{\triangle}{\rightarrow} 2Ag \downarrow + CuSO_4$

Cyanide Process.—In this process silver ores are treated with sodium cyanide to solubilize the compounds of silver as the silver cyanide complex (see Chemical Properties). The silver is obtained from the silver cyanide complex by displacing it with zinc, or by precipitating it as the sulfide by the addition of sodium sulfide.

Silver is also obtained from the sludge formed in the electrolytic refining of copper.

Pharmacology of the Silver Ion.—Silver ion, in common with other heavy metals is a protein precipitant and, because it makes no distinction between bacterial and human protein it has a high germicidal efficiency. The action of silver ion on tissue may be said to be antiseptic, astringent, irritant or corrosive, depending upon the concentration of free silver ion on the tissue.

As a rule, the irritant and corrosive effects are desired only when it is wished to destroy tissue or stimulate slow healing wounds. For this purpose, the more highly ionized silver salts, *e.g.*, silver nitrate or picrate, are used exclusively. Because of the precipitation of the silver ion by proteins and chlorides in the tissues this irritant and corrosive effect is easily localized.

Although accompanied by some protein precipitation and silver chloride formation, dilute solutions of silver salts such as silver nitrate may be used for astringent and antiseptic effects and, indeed, are required for the astringent action. However, the antiseptic effect may be obtained with less highly ionized substances, namely, the silver halides and silver proteinates. The mechanism of action of these substances is exactly the same as that of the so-called "late action" of silver nitrate. When silver nitrate is applied to the tissues it, of course, gives the immediate irritant and corrosive effect (also highly germicidal). After that effect has passed, however, the precipitated proteins and chlorides begin to redissolve and ionize off small amounts of silver ion. This small amount of silver ion exerts a definite antiseptic action. Therefore, rather than applying silver nitrate to obtain the antiseptic action it is more desirable to apply the silver proteinate or halide as such. This avoids the formation of a coagulation membrane which may hinder the action and likewise may eliminate the pain accompanying silver nitrate application.

In view of the above statements a distinction may be made between two principal types of silver salts which are used therapeutically:

1. Highly ionized silver salts, *i.e.*, silver nitrate, silver picrate, etc.

2. Slightly ionized silver salts, *i.e.*, silver halides (chloride and iodide), silver proteinates (*mild* and *strong*, depending on amount of ionized silver and not on total per cent of Ag), etc. These are usually referred to as the "colloidal silver preparations."

The internal use of silver salts results in no systemic action because of the readiness with which the silver is precipitated, and for this reason silver salts are not used for internal medication. The toxic dose of silver nitrate is about 10 Gm. although survival has been noted with larger doses.

Whenever silver preparations are used for long periods of time they are apt to cause a discoloration of the skin (darkening) called "argyria" which is probably due to deposition of free silver in the skin. This condition is irremediable, although it is said that injection of a solution of 6 per cent sodium thiosulfate (see eq. 7) and 1 per cent potassium ferricyanide subcutaneously will remove the color. However, this treatment requires innumerable small injections into the area involved and if the area is extensive the difficulties can be appreciated.

OFFICIAL COMPOUNDS OF SILVER

SILVER NITRATE

Silver Nitrate, U.S.P. XVII

Formula, $AgNO_3$; Molecular Weight, 169.87

Physical Properties.—Silver Nitrate occurs as colorless or white, odorless, rhombic crystals, commonly tabular, having a bitter, caustic, metallic taste. It has a density of about 4.35. When pure, the salt is not affected by light. However, in the presence of organic matter (skin, cloth, etc.) and light it soon becomes gray or grayish-black due to liberated silver, hence its use in marking-inks.

One Gm. of Silver Nitrate dissolves in 0.4 ml. of water and in 30 ml. of alcohol, at 25° C. One Gm. of the salt is soluble in slightly more than 0.1 ml. of boiling water and in 6.5 ml. of boiling alcohol. It is slightly soluble in ether.

At 212° C. the salt melts to a slightly yellow liquid which, on cooling, congeals to a white crystalline mass. At higher temperatures it slowly decomposes, evolving oxides of nitrogen.

Chemical Properties.—Silver nitrate embodies the chemical reactions of the silver ion (*q.v.*) and the nitrate ion (*q.v.*).

Aqueous solutions are neutral to litmus paper.

Official Tests for Identity.—1. A 1 in 50 solution responds to all tests for *Silver* (*q.v.*).

2. When a 1 in 10 solution of Silver Nitrate is mixed with a drop of diphenylamine T.S. and then carefully superimposed on concentrated sulfuric acid, a blue color appears at the interface of the two layers. This test is the "Lunge test" and is a sensitive test for the nitrate ion, but is also a sensitive test for a number of other oxidizing agents, e.g., nitrous acid, ferric chloride, etc.

Commercial Manufacture.—About 3 parts of metallic silver are mixed in a large porcelain dish with 10 parts of 25 per cent nitric acid. If necessary, the mixture is gently warmed to hasten the reaction (1). When the silver is dissolved, the solution is filtered through glass-wool and evaporated to dryness on a sand-bath. The temperature is then raised to fusion and any cupric nitrate present as an impurity is converted into insoluble oxide (2). The fused mass is then dissolved in double its weight of water, filtered, and set aside in a dark, dust-proof room to crystallize.

(1) $3Ag + 4HNO_3 \rightarrow 3AgNO_3 + 2H_2O + NO \uparrow$

(2) $2Cu(NO_3)_2 \xrightarrow{\Delta} 2CuO + 4NO_2 \uparrow + O_2 \uparrow$

Uses.—*Silver Nitrate* (Argenti Nitras), U.S.P. XVII, when powdered and dried in the dark over silica gel for 4 hours, contains not less than 99.8 per cent of $AgNO_3$. Depending on the concentration of its solution, silver nitrate may be used for effects that vary from a caustic effect to that of an antiseptic. It is routinely used in the form of a 1 per cent solution as an instillation in the eyes of newborn babies. This procedure was adopted years ago to combat the high incidence of gonorrheal infection of the eyes of babies born to infected mothers. It is still a legal requirement in many states. For this use the dose is 1 drop in each eye and it is used to guard against *ophthalmia neonatorum* (see Silver Nitrate Ophthalmic Solution).[1] The use of silver nitrate on tender mucous membranes even in dilute solution is not as popular as it was at one time. This is due largely to the advent of the colloidal silver preparations and various other less irritant medications. However, the use of the "silver nitrate pencil" (Toughened Silver Nitrate) has been retained to some degree for removing warts and other skin excrescences and as an application to the so-called "canker sores" in the mouth.

A dramatic new development in the use of silver nitrate as an antiseptic was observed by Dr. C. A. Moyer[2] at Washington University School of Medicine when they utilized 0.5 per cent silver nitrate to treat severe third-degree burn cases with an 80 per cent recovery rate. Since then the treatment has become standard in many hospitals and even better recovery rates have been noted in many cases. In this case it is undoubtedly a combination of the

[1] For adjusting pH of silver nitrate solutions see: W. F. Charnicki and M. L. Kober, J. Am. Pharm. Assoc. (Sci. Ed.), **44**, 25 (1955).
[2] Moyer, C. A.: Some Effects of 0.5 Per Cent Silver Nitrate and High Humidity Upon the Illness Associated with Large Burns. Natl. Med. Assoc. J., **57**, 95–99 (1965).

highly ionized silver nitrate initially and the slightly ionized silver proteinate and silver chloride (formed by interaction with tissue) later which combats the infective organisms, *i.e.*, chiefly *Pseudomonas aeruginosa.*

The removal of silver nitrate stains from the skin and clothing sometimes is a problem for the pharmacist. According to a U.S.D.A. Bulletin,[1] fresh stains may be removed from the skin by painting the places with tincture of iodine and then removing this with sodium thiosulfate solution. Stains from the clothing may sometimes be removed by the judicious use of potassium cyanide, the operator constantly keeping in mind the poisonous character of the cyanide.

Toughened Silver Nitrate U.S.P. XVII (Moulded Silver Nitrate, Fused Silver Nitrate, Silver Nitrate Pencils, Lunar Caustic), contains not less than 94.5 per cent of $AgNO_3$, the remainder consisting of silver chloride (AgCl). This preparation is a white, hard, crystalline, odorless solid usually in the form of pencils or cones. It becomes gray or grayish-black on exposure to light due to formation of free silver. Lunar caustic is usually made by adding to silver nitrate about 4 per cent of its weight of hydrochloric acid, melting the mixture at as low a temperature as possible and casting in silver molds. The presence of about 5 per cent of silver chloride toughens the silver nitrate and thus lessens the friability of the pencils. Some of the common commercial "caustic pencils" may contain approximately 40 per cent silver nitrate and 60 per cent potassium nitrate. One such applicator contains 75 per cent $AgNO_3$ and is marketed as Arzol. As indicated under Silver Nitrate, it is used for local application.

Ammoniacal Silver Nitrate Solution N.F. XII (Ammoniacal Silver Nitrate, Howe) is an aqueous solution of silver diammino nitrate, containing in each 100 Gm. the equivalent of not less than 28.5 Gm. and not more than 30.5 Gm. of silver (Ag), and not less than 9 Gm. and not more than 9.7 Gm. of ammonia (NH_3).

The silver nitrate (704 Gm.) is powdered in a glass mortar and dissolved in 245 ml. of purified water, warming if necessary. The solution is cooled to room temperature and about 680 ml. of Strong Ammonia Solution added from a burette until all but the last trace of black precipitate is dissolved (3, 4, and 5).

(3) $AgNO_3 + NH_4OH \rightarrow AgOH \downarrow + NH_4NO_3$

(4) $AgOH + 2NH_4OH \rightarrow Ag(NH_3)_2OH + 2H_2O$

(5) $AgNO_3 + 2NH_3 \rightarrow Ag(NH_3)_2NO_3$

This last trace of precipitate is filtered from the solution. This dental preparation should be preserved in small glass-stoppered containers, or in ampuls, and protected from light. For oral use— mix Ammoniacal Silver Nitrate Solution with a reducing agent, such

[1] U. S. D. A. Bulletin No. 1474.

as 10 per cent formaldehyde or eugenol, so as to deposit the metallic silver in the infected area in a state of fine subdivision. It is used in dentistry to protect dentin (see Chem. Properties reaction 10).

Silver Nitrate Ophthalmic Solution U.S.P. XVII is a buffered aqueous solution of silver nitrate at a pH of between 4.5 and 6 and is available in wax-composition capsules containing about 5 drops of solution. It may be buffered with sodium acetate and the concentration is usually not less than 0.95 and not more than 1.05 per cent of silver nitrate.

Saline solution may be used to wash out the eyes after instillation of silver nitrate solution but some physicians feel that the silver chloride formed is irritating.

MILD SILVER PROTEIN

Mild Silver Protein, N.F. XII

Formula, Indefinite

Physical Properties.—Mild Silver Protein occurs as dark brown or almost black, odorless shining scales or granules. It has a tendency to be hygroscopic. It is freely soluble in water, but almost insoluble in alcohol, chloroform and ether. The material and its solutions are prone to decompose upon exposure to light and consequently should be well protected.

Chemical Properties.—Mild Silver Protein is a preparation which forms a colloidal solution when dissolved in water. It contains very little free silver ion. Some believe that even in the case of the mild silver protein, silver chloride is formed upon contact with chlorides (*e.g.*, perspiration, tears, etc.) but is held in colloidal suspension by the very nature of the preparation.

Official Tests for Identity.—1. A small amount of the preparation is ignited to remove all organic material and the residue is dissolved in nitric acid (1, 2).

(1) $Ag\ Prot \xrightarrow[\Delta]{(o)} Ag + Ag_2O + CO_2 \uparrow$

(2) $Ag + Ag_2O + 4HNO_3 \rightarrow 3AgNO_3 + NO_2 \uparrow + 2H_2O$

The diluted nitric acid solution yields a precipitate of silver chloride when treated with a few drops of hydrochloric acid. The silver chloride precipitate is soluble in ammonia T.S.

2. Addition of ferric chloride T.S. to a 1 in 100 solution of Mild Silver Protein discharges the dark color and gradually produces a precipitate.

Ferric ions are oxidizing agents and convert any free silver or silver oxide to silver ions which are then precipitated as silver chloride. The ferric and ferrous ions also react with the protein present to form an insoluble precipitate.

3. Addition of a few drops of mercury bichloride to 10 ml. of a 1 in 100 solution of Mild Silver Protein causes the formation of a white precipitate together with a nearly colorless supernatant liquid.

Mercuric ions are oxidizing agents, also, resulting in the precipitation of silver chloride. The reduced product (mercurous chloride) and the mercuric-protein complex likewise precipitate, resulting in a clear supernatant liquid. Mercuric ions are more efficient protein precipitants than are ferric ions.

4. It gives no turbidity in a 1 to 100 solution on addition of a 1 to 100 solution of sodium chloride.

Without an oxidizing agent there are not sufficient silver ions to form silver chloride.

Commercial Manufacture.—The procedure for preparing Mild Silver Protein is not a standardized one. In general, commercial preparations of this kind are manufactured by a process which involves the reduction and subsequent "solution" of silver or silver oxide, or some silver-protein precipitate, in an excess of denatured protein (made by destroying the complement by electrolysis or by heating to 56° C.) and drying *in vacuo*. The difference in methods of manufacture is well illustrated by the fact that not only do preparations of the different manufacturers have a different ionizable silver content (the criterion for antiseptic efficiency) but even different lots made by the same manufacturer vary in the silver content.

Uses.—*Mild Silver Protein* (Mild Protargin), N.F. XII, is silver rendered colloidal by the presence of, or combination with, protein. It contains not less than 19 per cent and not more than 23 per cent of Ag. The N.F. cautions, *"Solutions of Mild Silver Protein should be freshly prepared or contain a suitable stabilizer, and should be dispensed in amber colored bottles."* This preparation is practically non-irritant and may be applied to tender mucous membranes with impunity, although continued application may result in "argyria." It is used as a local antibacterial in aqueous solution in concentrations from 5 to 25 per cent as a mild antiseptic in the eye, ear, nose and throat. It is interesting to note that while this preparation actually contains more silver than the Strong Silver Protein it yields less ionized silver and for this reason is termed "mild."

Since ionization tends to increase with dilution, the irritant property of the solutions decreases as the concentration increases. In other words, a 10 per cent solution is less irritating than a 5 per cent solution. Due to the "late action" of silver protein compounds, the silver ion concentration increases as the solutions age. Irritation increases on application and a precipitate develops in the container. A stabilizer used is disodium calcium ethylenediamine tetra-acetate in an amount equal to 10 mg. per ml. It is a chelating agent that helps to maintain a more uniform concentration of silver ions and aids in preventing the breakdown of the protein compounds. This is used in the stabilized solution of Argyrol. (See caution.) Some of the commercial preparations are *Silvol, Solargentum, Argyn, Argyrol,* and *Lunargen.*

Non-Official Silver Compounds

Colloidal Silver Chloride (Argenti Chloridum Colloidale, Lunosol), N.F. IX, is silver chloride rendered colloidal by the presence of sucrose or other suitable colloid stabilizing agent. It contains not less than 9 per cent and not more than 11 per cent of AgCl. It occurs as a white, slightly hygroscopic, granular powder with a sweetish, metallic taste. It is readily dispersed in water, forming an opalescent suspension of variable color depending on the light. It is affected by light and accordingly should be protected in light-resistant containers.

The prototype of this preparation, Lunosol, was marketed as liquid preparation rather than as the solid material. It was used for prophylaxis against and treatment of infections of the accessible mucous membranes, such as the genito-urinary tract and the eye, ear, nose and throat (see N.N.R., 1950). It was employed in concentrations of from 3 to 100 per cent as determined by the indications.

Colloidal Silver Iodide (Argenti Iodidum Colloidale, Neosilvol), N.F. X, is silver iodide rendered colloidally stable by the presence of gelatin. It contains not less than 18 per cent and not more than 22 per cent of AgI. It consists of pale yellow granules which are readily dispersed into an aqueous medium to form a colorless, milky, or opalescent suspension. Aqueous solutions are best prepared by adding the total amount of Colloidal Silver Iodide to the requisite amount of water in a bottle and shaking vigorously for one minute. Solutions of this product should be freshly prepared and should be dispensed in amber-colored bottles because it is prone to decomposition when stored for long periods of time. It was used as are other colloidal silver preparations, *viz.,* in concentrations ranging from 4 per cent for irrigating sinuses to 50 per cent in the female genital tract.

Silver Picrate (Picragol, Picrotol, Silver Trinitrophenolate), N.N.R., 1957 has the formula, $C_6H_2(OAg)(NO_2)_3.H_2O$ and occurs as yellow crystals which are sensitive to sunlight. They are soluble to the extent of about 2 Gm. in 100 ml. of water, sparingly soluble in alcohol, slightly soluble in acetone and glycerin and practically insoluble in chloroform and ether.

Inasmuch as this salt is a highly ionized silver salt, the silver ion is readily precipitated from aqueous solutions by means of chlorides as well as other precipitants.

The salt was used in the treatment of vaginitis resulting from *Trichomonas vaginalis* and *Monilia albicans* infections. It may be used either as suppositories or in the form of a powder insufflation with a concentration of from 1 to 2 per cent of the active ingredient in the dosage form. Caution should be exercised when this salt is used for long periods of time to prevent argyria because of the silver content and nephritis because of the picric acid content.

Strong Silver Protein (Argentum Proteinicum Forte, Strong Protargin, Protargol), N.F. X, contains not less than 7.5 per cent and not more than 8.5 per cent of Ag. It occurs as a pale yellowish-orange to brownish-black, odorless powder. It is usually somewhat hygroscopic and is affected by light. The product is freely but slowly soluble in water and is best put into solution by dusting the powder on the surface of the water and allowing it to dissolve slowly. It is prepared, at least in the case of Protargol (a commercial product), by precipitating a "peptone" (albumose) solution with silver nitrate or with moist silver oxide; dissolving the silver peptonate in an excess of albumose; and drying in vacuo. (N.N.R., 1949).

Strong Silver Protein has a higher degree of free silver ions than does Mild Silver Protein, N.F., but at the same time contains less total silver. It is a more potent germicide than the latter and was used in concentrations of about 0.25 to 0.5 per cent for irrigation of the bladder and urethra.

19

Gold and Gold Compounds

GOLD

Symbol, Au. Valences, 1, 3. Atomic Weight, 196.967,
Atomic Number, 79

History and Occurrence.—Since the earliest times, gold has been recognized as the "king of all metals." Because of its color, scarcity, and permanency in contact with the atmosphere, it has been valued from the earliest ages for making jewelry, coins, etc. The symbol, Au, is derived from its Latin name, *Aurum*. Ornaments of great variety and elaborate workmanship have been discovered in ruins belonging to the earliest known civilizations, *viz.*, Minoan, Egyptian, Assyrian, Etruscan, etc. In ancient literature, it was the universal symbol of highest purity and value. No doubt because of its yellow color, the alchemists associated gold with the sun.

Gold is found widely but sparingly distributed in Nature. It occurs principally as the metal *per se*, or alloyed with other metals, such as lead, copper and silver. The free metal occurs mixed with alluvial sand. Gold alloys are found disseminated in veins of quartz. Associated with tellurium, small quantities occur with the sulfide ores of copper, iron and lead. The principal minerals containing the double telluride of gold and silver are *sylvanite* [Au Ag-Te$_4$], *petzite* [(Au Ag)$_2$Te] and *calaverite* [Au Te$_2$]. The Transvaal of South Africa and the United States (California, South Dakota, and Colorado) lead in gold production. Other great gold producing centers are Alaska, British Columbia, Australia, Canada, India, China, Russia and Mexico.

Physical Properties.—Gold has a yellow color, which is lowered by small quantities of silver, but heightened by copper. Gold that has been beaten into a thin leaf transmits a greenish light. It is the most malleable and ductile metal known. When pure, it is almost as soft as lead. It has a density of about 19.32, melts at 1063° C., and boils at about 2600° C. Native gold has been found crystallized in the cubic system, the octahedron being the most common form.

Chemical Properties.—Gold is one of the most inactive and permanent of the metals. Air, oxygen, water, or hydrogen sulfide do not

affect it at any temperature.   Selenic acid reacts with gold to form
auric selenate [$Au_2(SeO_4)_3$], and is the only single acid that dissolves
it.   It unites directly with chlorine and bromine, but not with
sulfur.   It dissolves easily in acid solutions containing free chlorine,
bromine or iodine (slowly).   Thus, a mixture of nitric and hydrochloric acids (aqua regia), containing free chlorine, nitrosyl chloride
and water, dissolves gold with formation of chlorauric acid (1).

(1) $2Au + 2HNO_3 + 8HCl \rightarrow 4H_2O + 2NO \uparrow + 2HAuCl_4$

Although aqua regia is the best reagent for dissolving gold, the
metal can also be dissolved by bromine or chlorine water (2) to
form the corresponding gold trihalide.

(2) $2Au + 3X_2 \rightarrow 2AuX_3$ (X = Cl or Br)

Gold forms two series of salts, the aurous (Au^+) and auric (Au^{+++}),
all members of which are quite unstable in that they revert to gold
upon sufficient heating.   Auric chloride ($AuCl_3$), for example, is
easily converted to aurous chloride ($AuCl$) by gentle heating (3)
and upon stronger heating the aurous chloride is converted to
metallic gold (4).

(3) $AuCl_3 \xrightarrow[180°]{\Delta} AuCl + Cl_2 \uparrow$
(yellowish-white)

(4) $2AuCl \xrightarrow{\Delta} 2Au + Cl_2 \uparrow$

The reactions of the *auric* series are the most important and will be
discussed briefly.

Upon the addition of alkali hydroxides, *e.g.*, sodium hydroxide,
there develops a brown precipitate which is soluble in an excess of
the reagent.   The brown precipitate is auric hydroxide (5), and is
easily converted to the aurate (6) with excess alkali.   In fact, it is
sometimes difficult, especially in dilute gold solutions, to obtain the
brown precipitate because of the rapid formation of the aurate.

(5) $Au^{+++} + 3OH^- \rightarrow Au(OH)_3 \downarrow$
(brown)

(6) $Au(OH)_3 + NaOH \rightarrow 2H_2O + NaAuO_2$

The characteristic of an element which causes it to form soluble
salts with both acids and bases is called an amphoteric property.
Other elements that are amphoteric include aluminum, tin, zinc and
lead (see sodium hydroxide).

When ammonium hydroxide is added, a brown precipitate first
forms but redissolves by formation of gold ammonia complex (7) (8).

(7) $AuCl_3 + 3NH_4OH \rightarrow Au(OH)_3 \downarrow + 3NH_4Cl$

(8) $Au(OH)_3 + 6NH_4OH \rightarrow Au(NH_3)_6^{+++} + 3OH^- + 6H_2O$

It is important to note that auric compounds are strong oxidizing agents and many of their reactions can be attributed to this property. For example, ferrous salts are readily oxidized to the ferric form with deposition of metallic gold (9).

(9) $HAuCl_4 + 3Fe^{++} + H_2O \rightarrow 3Fe^{+++} + H_3O^+ + 4Cl^- + Au \downarrow$

Addition of potassium iodide to gold solutions results in the formation of metallic gold together with iodine (10).

(10) $2Au^{+++} + 6I^- \rightarrow 2Au \downarrow + 3I_2$

The reaction of gold with stannous chloride is important. In a highly acidic solution stannous chloride precipitates metallic gold (11), but in a weakly acid or dilute neutral solution the stannous chloride slowly throws down a purple precipitate which is known as the *purple of Cassius*. The reaction is widely used to identify gold. The precipitate is said to consist of colloidal gold and tin hydroxide.

(11) $2Au^{+++} + 3Sn^{++} \rightarrow 3Sn^{++++} + 2Au \downarrow$

In photographic work, gold is used to produce a reddish-brown tone to a picture (12).

(12) $NaAuCl_4 + 3Ag \rightarrow NaCl + 3AgCl + Au \downarrow$

Auric salts are quickly reduced to the "ous" form and then to the metallic state by the weakest of reducing agents such as the organic constituents of tinctures, syrups, etc. Gold salts must, in most cases, be dispensed separately.

Official Tests for Gold Ion.—1. With sodium hydroxide T.S., solutions of auric salts give a brown precipitate (5), which is soluble in an excess of the reagent (6).

2. When treated with stannous chloride T.S., solutions of gold salts slowly form a purple precipitate (purple of Cassius).

Commercial Manufacture.—1. Gold is obtained from its alluvial or "placer" deposits by a method that is based on the disintegration of the earthy matter by the action of a stream of water, which washes away the lighter rock (specific gravity about 2.5) and leaves the heavier gold (specific gravity 19.32) in the bottom of a pan, cradle or sluice.

2. The method of mining auriferous quartz rock is about the same as that used for similar deposits of other metals. First, the ore is pulverized in stamping or ball mills and then separated by means of the flotation process or by washing the pulverized material over copper plates amalgamated with mercury. The latter unites with a little over half of the gold to form an amalgam which is

23

then scraped off the plates and separated into gold and mercury by distillation. The "tailings" that run off the separator are treated with a dilute solution of sodium cyanide and the mixture exposed to the air to permit of the formation of soluble sodium aurocyanide (13). Gold is obtained from the solution by electrolysis or by displacement with metallic zinc (14).

(13) $4Au + 8CN^- + O_2 + 2H_2O \rightarrow 4[Au(CN)_2]^- + 4OH^-$

(14) $2[Au(CN)_2]^- + Zn \rightarrow [Zn(CN)_4]^= + 2Au \downarrow$

Pyrites, containing gold, is usually roasted and then treated with chlorine water (see p. 340), which converts the gold into auric chloride. This is leached out with water and the metal precipitated with ferrous sulfate (see p. 341).

Pharmacological Action of Gold.—A discussion of the pharmacology and therapeutic applications of gold may advantageously be prefaced by a brief historical introduction.

The early use of gold in medicine was of an empirical nature, based largely on legend and folklore. The discovery by Koch in 1890, that gold cyanide was effective *in vitro* against the tubercle bacillus may be said to mark the beginning of modern gold therapy. This discovery led investigators to use various gold salts (less toxic, however, than gold cyanide) in the treatment of many diseases believed to be tuberculous in origin. In all useful gold compounds used today the gold is attached to the rest of the molecule through sulfur. For the most part they are non-ionized and are used in suspension in vegetable oils. Its use in the treatment of tuberculosis has been investigated extensively, but the results have been far from satisfying. At present gold is not used in the treatment of this condition. However, from these investigations have stemmed the two principal uses of gold salts today: (1) for non-disseminated lupus erythematosus, and (2) for rheumatoid arthritis.

1. The N.N.D. statement from 1946 to 1964 pointed out that the Council recognized the use of gold salts by injection for the systemic treatment of nondisseminated lupus erythematosus. Gold should never be used in the treatment of disseminated lupus erythematosus. A review of the literature in regard to the use of gold and sodium thiosulfate in the treatment of lupus erythematosus reveals, in general, quite satisfactory clinical results, and it is considered a distinct advance in the therapy of this condition. Although there have been many recurrences in cases originally thought cured, nevertheless the beneficial and often curative action of the drug in a fair percentage of the cases seems to warrant giving it a definite place in the treatment of the disease.

2. The use of gold salts in the treatment of rheumatoid arthritis has been the result of an early belief that this disease was an atypical form of tuberculosis. Although this belief has been dispelled, the sometimes beneficial results of gold therapy in this (the crippling)

type of arthritis has led to its retention. Forestier had much to do with the popularization of this form of therapy, and with an increasing appreciation of the toxic possibilities of gold salts the drug is being utilized with less side-effects than previously. The literature on the use of BAL (2,3-dimercaptopropanol) and more recently corticotropin (almost a specific) in treating the toxic manifestations of gold salts, namely, the gold dermatitides, has been very encouraging and should lead to a more extensive use of gold.[1,2] However, it is probably advisable to restrict its use to experienced chrysotherapists, and it is well to remember that gold salts probably are not the best answer to the treatment of rheumatoid arthritis.

The soluble gold salts are administered intravenously and most of the drug is excreted in the urine although some is excreted in the feces. Inasmuch as most of the gold is excreted in the urine, it is common to find renal damage as one of the symptoms of gold toxicity. However, the most common difficulty is associated with the skin, the so-called "gold dermatitides."

There are several products of colloidal gold available for intravenous, intramuscular or oral use. These forms are less toxic and find application in treating arthritis, lupus erythematosus, and carcinoma. Colloidal gold may also enhance the effects of x-ray and radium therapy.

Gold bromide was at one time suggested as a cough depressant in whooping cough.

OFFICIAL COMPOUNDS OF GOLD

GOLD SODIUM THIOSULFATE

Gold Sodium Thiosulfate, N.F. XII

Formula, $Na_3Au(S_2O_3)_2 . 2H_2O$.   Molecular Weight, 526.22

Physical Properties.—Gold Sodium Thiosulfate occurs in white, glistening, needle-like or prismatic crystals. It darkens slowly on exposure to air.

One Gm. of Gold Sodium Thiosulfate dissolves in 2 ml. of water; it is insoluble in alcohol and most other organic solvents.

Chemical Properties.—Aqueous solutions of the salt are neutral or alkaline to litmus paper. The compound, a double salt composed of 3 molecules of sodium thiosulfate ($Na_2S_2O_3$) and 1 molecule of aurous thiosulfate ($Au_2S_2O_3$), gives the characteristic reactions of the thiosulfate ion, *e.g.*, decolorization of iodine, precipitation of sulfur with hot hydrochloric acid, sulfide formation with base and warming, etc. (see also Sodium Thiosulfate). It also gives reactions for aurous gold rather than auric.

[1] New Drugs, American Medical Assoc. 1966, p. 489.
[2] Drugs for Rheumatoid Disorders, British Med. J., Feb. 1964, p. 545.

Official Tests for Identity.—Dissolve the salt (50 mg.) in 1 ml. of water in a test tube. Add 1 ml. of diluted hydrochloric acid and heat the mixture on a water-bath causing the evolution of sulfur dioxide (SO_2), chlorine, and the formation of a brown precipitate composed of gold sulfide and sulfur (1 to 4).

(1) $Na_3Au(S_2O_3)_2 + 4\,HCl \rightarrow 2H_2S_2O_3 + 3NaCl + AuCl$

(2) $2AuCl + H_2S_2O_3 \rightarrow Au_2S \downarrow + H_2O + SO_2 \uparrow + Cl_2$

(3) $H_2S_2O_3 \rightarrow H_2O + SO_2 \uparrow + S \downarrow$

Complete reaction:

(4) $2Na_3Au(S_2O_3)_2 + 8HCl \rightarrow Au_2S \downarrow + 6NaCl + 3S \downarrow + 4SO_2 \uparrow + Cl_2 \uparrow + 4H_2O$

Wash the precipitated mixture of gold sulfide and sulfur thoroughly with hot water by decantation and then transfer to a porcelain crucible. Then treat it with 3 ml. of hydrochloric acid and 1 ml. of nitric acid to dissolve the gold sulfide (5) and sulfur (6) and evaporate almost to dryness on a water-bath.

(5) $Au_2S + 8HCl + 4HNO_3 \rightarrow HAuCl_4 + H_2SO_4 + 4H_2O + 4NO \uparrow$

(6) $S + 2HNO_3 \rightarrow H_2SO_4 + 2NO \uparrow$

Treat the residue with 10 ml. of water and filter to remove any sulfur particles and dilute 2 ml. of the filtrate with 5 ml. of water. To this add 2 ml. of sodium hydroxide T.S., 1 ml. of hydrogen peroxide T.S. and heat the mixture on a water-bath (7 to 11).

(7) $HAuCl_4 \xrightarrow[75°]{\triangle} AuCl_3 + HCl \uparrow$

(8) $AuCl_3 + 3NaOH \rightarrow Au(OH)_3 \downarrow + 3NaCl$
(brown)

(9) $Au(OH)_3 + NaOH \rightarrow NaAuO_2 + 2H_2O$
(excess)

(10) $NaAuO_2 \rightarrow Na^+ + AuO_2^-$

(11) $AuO_2^- + 2H_2O_2 \rightarrow Au \downarrow + 2H_2O + 2O_2 \uparrow$
(colloidal
purple-red)

Another portion of the filtrate when tested with a few drops of stannous chloride T.S. gives the characteristic purple color (purple of Cassius) (12).

(12) $2HAuCl_4 + 3SnCl_2 \rightarrow 2Au \downarrow + 2HCl + 3SnCl_4$
(colloidal)

Commercial Manufacture.—Gold Sodium Thiosulfate is a complex and is probably formed according to the following reaction (13).[1] Although auric chloride is usually used as a starting material, at least one firm uses gold and sodium chloride instead of gold chloride. The gold sodium thiosulfate which forms in the reaction mixture is precipitated and freed of the other products by the addition of alcohol. No matter what method of preparation is utilized, the gold is reduced from the auric to the aurous state by the thiosulfate.

(13) $8Na_2S_2O_3 + 2AuCl_3 \rightarrow (3Na_2S_2O_3 + Au_2S_2O_3) + 2Na_2S_4O_6 + 6NaCl$

Uses.—*Gold Sodium Thiosulfate*, N.F. XII, contains not less than 97.9 per cent and not more than 100.6 per cent of $Na_3Au(S_2O_3)_2.2H_2O$. It is used intravenously for the treatment of nondisseminated lupus erythematosus and rheumatoid arthritis. Usual dose—5 to 25 mg. intramuscularly.

Sterile Gold Sodium Thiosulfate is the sterile salt in dry form packaged in individual containers of 10 mg. (1/6 gr.), 25 mg. (3/8 gr.), 50 mg. (3/4 gr.), 75 mg. ($1\frac{1}{4}$ gr.), and 100 mg. ($1\frac{1}{2}$ gr.). Solutions must be freshly prepared with Water for Injection U.S.P. Ampules of the solutions are not practical since thiosulfates are unstable in solution.

NON-OFFICIAL GOLD COMPOUNDS

Aurothioglycanilide, N.N.D. (Lauron, α-Auromercaptoacetanilide), C_8H_8AuNOS, occurs as a grayish-yellow powder that is practically insoluble in water, ether, chloroform, benzene, acids and bases. It is prepared by the method of Lewenstein[2] by the action of aurous bromide on thioglycolic acid anilide (1).

(1) $C_6H_5NHCO—CH_2—SH + AuBr \rightarrow C_6H_5NHCO— CH_2—SAu + HBr$

This product is used in the treatment of rheumatoid arthritis in a manner similar to the other insoluble non-ionized gold salts. It is administered as a suspension in sesame oil containing 250 or 750 mg. in 5 ml. and is used intramuscularly. The initial dose should not exceed 25 mg. weekly with a maximum single dose of 150 mg. and the dose is then increased by 25 mg. increments until the desired effects are obtained over a period of 22 weeks.

Aurothioglucose, N.F. XI occurs as a yellow powder that is odorless or nearly so and stable in air. Aqueous solutions can be made readily because it is freely soluble in water. It is practically insoluble in acetone, alcohol, chloroform and in ether. It is also insoluble in

---

[1] Private communication from G. D. Searle & Co., Chicago, Ill., May 13 (1947).
[2] U. S. pat. 2, 451, 841 (1948).

vegetable oils. It contains not more than 5 per cent sodium acetate as a stabilizer. Aurothioglucose is used, as are other non-ionizing gold products, for the treatment of rheumatoid arthritis and non-disseminating lupus erythematosus and is subject to the contra-indications and toxic possibilities cited earlier. It is administered intramuscularly in the form of a suspension in vegetable oil in a usual dose of 50 mg.

Gold Sodium Thiomalate, N.F. XI consists of a white to yellowish-white, odorless, fine powder which is affected by light. It is very soluble in water but insoluble in alcohol, ether and most other organic solvents. Aqueous solutions of the salt are slightly acidic with a 10 per cent solution having a pH of 5.8 to 6.5.

It is classified as an antirheumatic and was administered intravenously for the treatment of rheumatoid arthritis. The dosage is variable and is to be determined by the physician according to the patient's needs. A commercial preparation that was used is named Myochrysine.

GROUP II ELEMENTS

Introduction.—Beryllium and magnesium represent the typical elements of the short periods in Group II of the Periodic Table. The two subgroups consist of IIA:—calcium, strontium, barium and radium, commonly known as the "alkaline earth" metals; and IIB:—zinc, cadmium and mercury. In this introduction we will consider briefly the general aspects of beryllium, magnesium and the elements of subgroup IIA followed by a similar consideration of the IIB subgroup, although the difference in the two subgroups is not as marked as it is in Group I of the Periodic Table.

Consultation of the accompanying table of properties will illustrate the fact that the typical elements of Group II and the elements of the IIA subgroup are all bivalent. They all possess the kernel of the preceding inert gas and strongly resist the removal of any more than the two valence electrons. The ionization potentials in the table are for the removal of the first electron and it may be noted that as the atomic radius increases the ease of removal of the electron increases. The ionization potential gives an indication as to how well the kernel electrons are screening the central nuclear charge from exerting its attractive effect on the valence electrons. Actually, the ions formed are divalent and two electrons must be removed to form the ion. The second electron requires approximately twice as much energy to be removed as does the first. This suggests the possibility of a monovalent ion, but the possibility is dispelled when the heat of hydration is taken into account. The heat of hydration of a divalent ion is so much greater than that of a monovalent ion that the energy released on hydration is sufficient to take care of the energy requirements for removal of the second electron.

The oxidation potential, measuring the tendency of the metal to go to the hydrated form in aqueous solution, increases with a decrease in ionization potential. There is no peculiarity in trends due to unusual hydration effects as was noted with lithium among the alkali metals. The reduction of the cation to the free metal is, of course, more difficult with the higher oxidation potentials.

Although the compounds of these metals are largely ionic in their salts and oxides there is, nevertheless, a definite trend toward a covalent type of linkage as the ion size becomes smaller. This, naturally, is a result of greater deformation of the electron cloud on the anion by the greater density of positive charge on the smaller sized cations. This trend is not peculiar to the alkaline earth metals but is a general property in other families of elements as well.

The chemical activities of these metals increases as the atomic radius increases indicating a greater availability of the electrons for bond formation. This activity, however, is not as great as that of the alkali metals. This is evident in their activity in reducing water because beryllium and magnesium do not reduce water although the other alkaline earth metals do so with the liberation of hydrogen and formation of an alkaline solution. All of the metals, with the exception of beryllium, are attacked by atmospheric oxygen but in the case of magnesium the oxide coating protects it from further attack. The tendency to form and stability of the peroxides of these metals increases markedly with rise in atomic number. The stability of the carbonates with respect to their dissociation into the oxide and carbon dioxide varies in a similar way.

It is well to point out that the greatest differences in these elements occur in passing from beryllium to magnesium and the next greatest difference is in passing from magnesium to calcium. From then on the alkaline earth group behaves in a very regular fashion. Beryllium has many similarities to aluminum and magnesium to zinc which illustrates the general principle that the first element in a group has a diagonal relationship with the second element of the next group and that the second element of a group has a close relationship with its own B subgroup. In fact, magnesium also has some similarities to lithium which again illustrates the diagonal relationship. These relationships are due in some cases to similarities in ion sizes (Li^+ and Mg^{++}) and in others to similarities in the charge-per-unit-size values (especially if the ion sizes vary considerably). Where these criteria are important considerations, then the properties of the two ions will also be markedly similar.

The salts of these metals are not as soluble as are those of the alkali metals. Although there is a tendency toward covalency among the smaller cations, the chemistry of Group IIA metals is that of an ionic species, namely the divalent cations. Many of the salts in this group are hydrated, with the smaller cations having a high hydration affinity because of the greater density of positive charge. There is no simple distinction between the solubilities of salts derived from weak and strong acids as exists with the alkali metals. In general, the relative solubilities of any one anion combined with the cations of the alkaline earth metals will run $Ca > Sr > Ba > Ra$. It is only with the hydroxides that there is a reverse order of solubility to the above (e.g., $Ca < Ba$). In general, one can say that the most soluble salts of these metals are derived from monovalent anions and that the least soluble ones are derived from the divalent or polyvalent anions. This probably reflects the increased interionic forces holding the polyvalent ions together against the dipole-ion attractions of the solvent molecules. However, water of hydration within the crystal may alter this picture somewhat (e.g., $MgSO_4 \cdot 7H_2O$).

PROPERTIES OF ALKALINE EARTH METALS AND TYPICAL ELEMENTS OF GROUP II.

Properties	Beryllium	Magnesium	Calcium	Strontium	Barium	Radium
Atomic Number	4	12	20	38	56	88
Atomic Weight	9.0122	24.312	40.08	87.62	137.34	226.05
Isotopes	9	24, 25, 26	40, 42, 43, 44, 46, 48	84, 86, 87, 88	130, 132, 134–8	223, 224, 226, 228
Electrons	2–2	2–8–2	2–8–8–2	2–8–18–8–2	2–8–18–18–8–2	2–8–18–32–18–8–2
Density	1.84	1.74	1.54	2.6	3.5	ca. 6
M.P.	1284–1300°	651°	850°	757°	850°	700°
B.P.	1500°	1100°	1440°	1366°	1140°	<1737°
Oxidation States	0, +2	0, +2	0, +2	0, +2	0, +2	0, +2
Radius (cov.), Å	0.89	1.36	1.74	1.91	1.98	—
Radius (ionic), Å	0.30	0.65	0.94	1.10	1.29	1.52
Ionization Potential, first, volts	9.28	7.61	6.09	5.67	5.19	—
Oxidation Potential, M→M++, volts	+1.70	+2.34	+2.87	+2.89	+2.90	—
Hydration Energy, Kg.Cal./Gm. mole	—	490	410	376	346	—
Flame Color	—	—	Brick-red	Crimson	Yellow-green	Carmine-red

SUBGROUP IIB

These metals have a kernel consisting, not of the configuration of the previous inert gas, but rather with an additional ten electrons (total of 18) to give a "pseudo-inert-gas" structure. They utilize both of the electrons in the outer shell for bonding purposes but do not use any others. All of these metals form the normal divalent ions but mercury, in addition, has the unique property of having a monovalent ion. They are smaller in size than the IIA subgroup and, therefore, are less active. Consider, for example, their inertness to the action of water and oxygen as compared to the A group. These elements tend to form covalent compounds much more than the A subgroup elements, probably due to the more incomplete screening of the nuclear charge by the pseudo-inert-gas kernel. Although magnesium and zinc are approximately the same size the tendency toward covalency is greater with zinc. Similarly, cadmium and mercury tend toward covalent compounds to a greater extent than calcium and cadmium shows a greater tendency than zinc although the latter has a smaller radius. Divalent mercury has an even greater tendency toward covalent bond formation than its congeners in the subgroup. Although there are some compounds where it is definitely in an ionic state the covalent type of compound predominates.

The B group elements show much more individual character than do the A group elements (alkaline earths). This is a general characteristic of B groups in comparison to A groups and was also evident in the IB subgroup (Cu, Ag, Au).

Basicity increases in the group with increase in ionic radius, with mercuric oxide the most basic and zinc oxide even exhibiting the property of dissolving in alkali. This property of dissolving in base always decreases in subgroups with increasing atomic number. This is a normally expected property, but the tendency toward oxidation of the metals is in the opposite direction which is a reversal of the trend in other groups of elements (see alkali metals). Consultation of the oxidation potentials confirms this fact although the ionization potentials would indicate an opposite trend. This reverse trend is no doubt due to the hydration energies and heats of sublimation entering into the net oxidation potential and illustrates the fact that the oxidation potential is composed of at least three energy considerations that may alter the ease of oxidation. The oxides of these metals become less stable to heat as the atomic number increases. The chlorides are hydrolyzed with decreasing ease in the order $Zn > Cd > Hg$.

The elements cadmium and zinc form complex ions with considerable ease although cadmium has a stronger tendency toward coordination than zinc, the increase with increasing atomic number being a common characteristic of B group elements in contrast to A group elements where the opposite trend is normal. The common complexes are the ammine, cyano-, and halo- and the coordination number of zinc and cadmium is 6 in the divalent state. Mercury, on the other hand, shows a peculiarity in not entering into complex formation with any readiness.

The solubilities of these metals are quite similar to those of the IIA subgroup and particularly those of magnesium. The halides of zinc, where covalent linkage is somewhat evident, are soluble in both water and organic solvents. Cadmium salts, in general, are less soluble than the corresponding zinc salts indicating a greater degree of covalency. Indeed, the cadmium and zinc salts which are predominantly covalent do not exhibit this disparity in solubilities and are approximately equal.

PROPERTIES OF SUBGROUP IIB

Properties	Zinc	Cadmium	Mercury
Atomic Number	30	48	80
Atomic Weight	65.37	112.40	200.59
Isotopes	64, 66, 67, 68, 70	106, 108, 110–114, 116	196, 198–202, 204
Electrons	2-8-18-2	2-8-18-18-2	2-8-18-32-18-2
Density	7.14	8.65	13.5939
M.P.	419.4°	321°	−39°
B.P.	907°	767°	356.9°
Oxidation States	0, +2	0, +2	0, +1, +2
Radius (cov.), Å	1.25	1.41	1.44
Radius (ionic), Å	0.70	0.92	1.05
Ionization Potential, first, volts	6.92	8.99	10.42
Oxidation Potential, $M \rightarrow M^{++}$, volts	+0.762	+0.4020	−0.854

20

Beryllium and Magnesium

Symbol, Be. Valence, 2. Atomic Weight, 9.0122; Atomic Number, 4

History and Occurrence.—Beryllium was discovered in 1797 by L. B. Vauquelin. It was isolated by Wöhler and Bussy in 1828 and obtained in pure form by Humpidge in 1885. It was named after the mineral *beryl*, from which it was obtained. The element is also called *glucinum* in allusion to the sweet taste of its salts. Although a somewhat rare metal, small quantities of it are found in quite a number of minerals. The widely distributed mineral known as *beryl*, a metasilicate of beryllium and aluminum [$Be_3Al_2(SiO_3)_6$], is the principal source of this element. Beryls, containing a little chromium silicate, are known as *emeralds*. The mineral, *beryllonite*, is a double phosphate of beryllium and sodium ($BeNaPO_4$) and is found in Maine. It also occurs in *chrysoberyl* [$Be(AlO_2)_2$], *phenakite* (Be_2SiO_4), and in some other silicates.

Physical and Chemical Properties.—Beryllium is a hard, white, ductile and malleable metal. It is often obtained as hexagonal crystals. It has a density of 1.84, and a melting point of 1284–1300° C. At ordinary temperatures the metal is quite permanent in air or oxygen. When heated, it becomes coated with oxide (BeO). It is soluble in dilute acids and, when heated with caustic alkalies, it forms beryllates with the evolution of hydrogen (1); a behavior similar to that of aluminum.

$$(1) \quad Be + 2KOH \rightarrow K_2BeO_2 + H_2 \uparrow$$

Beryllium combines readily with fluorine, chlorine and bromine.

Commercial Manufacture.—Beryl is crushed and fused with potassium carbonate. The soluble beryllium carbonate is separated from insoluble forms of iron and aluminum. This is converted to the oxide and then dissolved in hydrochloric acid. The metallic beryllium is obtained by electrolysis of the fused chloride. The metal may also be prepared by heating the chloride with sodium in an atmosphere of hydrogen.

Compounds.—Beryllium salts are usually obtained by dissolving either the oxide (BeO) or the hydroxide [$Be(OH)_2$] in the desired acids. These salts are hydrolyzed so readily that it is difficult to obtain a normal salt. Beryllium nitrate [$Be(NO_3)_2$] may be prepared by dissolving beryllium hydroxide in nitric acid and crystallizing from the latter (not water). Beryllium sulfate ($BeSO_4.7H_2O$) is isomorphous with magnesium sulfate ($MgSO_4.7H_2O$) and may be obtained by dissolving the oxide in sulfuric acid and crystallizing from acid solution. Like the hydroxides of aluminum and zinc, beryllium hydroxide (also oxide) is soluble in an excess of caustic alkalies and forms beryllates. Upon boiling or diluting their solutions, the hydroxide is reprecipitated.

Pharmacological Action of Beryllium Ion.[1]—The action of beryllium sulfate was investigated by Seaman[2] in 1912. He observed that when this salt was administered orally to dogs, there resulted nutritional disturbances with loss of nitrogen, sulfur and phosphorus. In large doses, the salt was toxic. When injected intravenously, this compound was especially toxic, disturbing the respiration, circulation and temperature.

Interest has developed in recent years because of poisoning resulting from cuts obtained by glass of broken fluorescent light tubes. Beryllium oxide is often a component of the inside coating material. Manufacturers of the light tubes, however, have taken steps to eliminate the use of beryllium oxide.

The metal is now regarded as one of the most toxic in common use. Indications are that beryllium[3] inhibits the carbohydrate metabolic cycle by preventing the breakdown of the phosphorus compounds. Also the metal appears to replace calcium and magnesium. No specific antidotes for either acute or chronic beryllium poisoning are known.

Uses.—Beryllium is never employed in medicine. Beryllium affects copper very much as carbon does iron. Because of the resonance possessed by beryllium-copper alloys, they are used to make wires for pianos and other musical instruments, artificial precious stones, and special electrical and scientific instruments. Beryllium compounds have been used in the fluorescent lighting industry.

MAGNESIUM

Symbol, Mg.   Valence, 2.   Atomic Weight, 24.312;
Atomic Number, 12

History and Occurrence.—In 1695, N. Grew, a London physician, obtained magnesium sulfate by evaporating the water of a mineral spring at Epsom. This salt soon became celebrated for its medicinal properties and was called *Epsom Salt*. Magnesium oxide was not distinguished from calcium oxide until 1755, when J. Black showed

---

[1] For an informative article on beryllium and berylliosis see: Schubert, J., Scientific American, **199**, 27 (1958) (August).

[2] Biochem. Bull., **2**, 184 (1912).

[3] Science, **110**, 420 (1949); Chem. and Eng. News, **27**, 2905 (1949).

them to be entirely different. The impure metal was first isolated by Davy in 1808. It is said that the element was named after Magnesia, a town in Asia Minor. A. B. Bussy succeeded in preparing a quantity of fairly pure metal by treating the molten chloride with potassium. In 1852, Bunsen obtained magnesium metal by the electrolysis of the chloride and in 1857, H. Sainte Claire Deville devised a process for making it on a commercial scale.

Magnesium is closely associated with calcium and occurs widely and abundantly distributed. As the free metal, it never occurs in Nature, and its compounds are not as plentiful as those of calcium. It is found chiefly in the forms of the silicate, carbonate and chloride. The principal silicates are *talc* [$Mg_3H_2(SiO_3)_4$], *asbestos* [$CaMg_3(SiO_3)_4$] and *meerschaum* [$Mg_2Si_3O_8.2H_2O$]. As the carbonate, it occurs in the mineral *magnesite* [$MgCO_3$] and in large quantities as *dolomite* [$CaCO_3.MgCO_3$] and *dolomitic limestone*. The Stassfurt deposits of *carnallite* [$KCl.MgCl_2.6H_2O$] have been referred to before (see potassium chloride). Native magnesium sulfate [$MgSO_4.H_2O$] is known as *kieserite*. Magnesium is the metallic element present in chlorophyll and magnesium salts are associated with calcium compounds in plants. Magnesium phosphate occurs in bones and is one of the inorganic physiological constituents of urine.

Physical Properties.—Magnesium is a silver-white metal having a density of 1.74. The malleable and ductile properties of the metal permit it to be drawn into wire and then rolled into ribbons, in which form it comes into the trade. Magnesium alloys, *e.g.*, *magnalium* (aluminum containing about 2 per cent of magnesium) are light in weight, have a high tensile strength and take a brilliant polish. Magnesium melts at about 651° C. and boils at about 1100° C.

Chemical Properties.—*Magnesium* is permanent in dry air, but tarnishes in moist air. When heated in air, oxygen or even in carbon dioxide, it burns with a blinding white light that is rich in actinic rays of the violet and ultra-violet regions; hence its use in photography (1). "Flash-light" powders are mixtures of powdered magnesium and potassium chlorate or barium peroxide. This mixture is also used in pyrotechnics, tracer bullets, fire-bombs, night flares, etc.

$$(1) \quad 4Mg + air \xrightarrow{\Delta} MgO + Mg_3N_2$$

The metal will also burn in steam, carbon dioxide, sulfur vapors, sulfur dioxide, nitric oxide and nitrogen dioxide.

When burning magnesium is introduced into a current of steam, it decomposes the latter into hydrogen with the formation of magnesium hydroxide (2).

$$(2) \quad Mg + 2H_2O \rightarrow Mg(OH)_2 + H_2 \uparrow$$

At high temperatures the metal acts as a reducing agent, reducing many metallic oxides to the metals, silica to silicon, and boron trioxide to boron. When heated in an atmosphere of nitrogen, it forms the nitride (Mg_3N_2) (see Nitrogen). Magnesium occurs after calcium and before aluminum in the electromotive series of the metals (q.v.) and hence replaces many metals from solutions of their salts. The metal is readily soluble in most acids with the evolution of hydrogen and the formation of salts. It is insoluble in alkalies. It never enters into complex ions. The usual insoluble salts are carbonate, phosphate and arsenate.

The chemical reactions of interest that involve the *magnesium ion* are based upon solubility since the divalent ion is neither reduced nor oxidized. Magnesium ion is precipitated by caustic alkalies (3).

(3) $Mg^{++} + 2OH^- \rightarrow Mg(OH)_2 \downarrow$

Ammonium hydroxide incompletely precipitates magnesium hydroxide from solutions of magnesium salts. In the presence of an ammonium salt, ammonium hydroxide does not precipitate magnesium ion, because the concentration of the hydroxide ion produced by the ammonium hydroxide is depressed by the excess of ammonium ions from the salt.

(4) $NH_4OH \rightleftarrows NH_4^+ + OH^-$

(5) $NH_4Cl \rightleftarrows NH_4^+ + Cl^-$

Before magnesium ions can be precipitated as magnesium hydroxide there must be available an adequate concentration of hydroxide ions. Ammonium salts (ammonium chloride) will prevent this condition by ionizing to supply a large amount of ammonium ion (5). This, added to the concentration of ammonium ion from ammonium hydroxide (4) by the law of mass action, forces reaction (4) to the left and decreases the hydroxide ion concentration by maintaining it as undissociated ammonium hydroxide. Furthermore, when the concentration of magnesium ion is multiplied by the square of the concentration of the hydroxide ion, there is obtained a product that is *less* than the ion-product constant (solubility product) of magnesium hydroxide and hence no precipitate will be formed. (See Magnesia Mixture T.S., U.S.P.)

When a solution of a magnesium salt is mixed with a solution of sodium phosphate containing an equal volume of a solution of ammonium chloride and a little ammonia water, a white crystalline precipitate of magnesium ammonium phosphate is produced (6), (7), (8).

(6) $Na_2HPO_4 \rightarrow 2Na^+ + HPO_4^=$

(7) $HPO_4^= + NH_3 \rightarrow NH_4^+ + PO_4^\equiv$

(8) $Mg^{++} + NH_4^+ + PO_4^\equiv + 6H_2O \rightarrow MgNH_4PO_4 \cdot 6H_2O \downarrow$

The presence of ammonium chloride prevents the precipitation of magnesium hydroxide (4) and (5) and the ammonium hydroxide lessens the hydrolysis (9) and decreases the solubility of the salt.

$$(9) \quad MgNH_4PO_4 + H_2O \rightleftarrows Mg^{++} + HPO_4^= + NH_4OH$$

By ignition, magnesium ammonium phosphate is converted into the pyrophosphate (10).

$$(10) \quad 2MgNH_4PO_4 \xrightarrow{\Delta} Mg_2P_2O_7 + 2NH_3\uparrow + H_2O\uparrow$$

Official Tests for Identity of Magnesium Ion.—Magnesium ion in the presence of ammonium chloride will not be precipitated by ammonium carbonate T.S. The ammonium chloride prevents the ionization of ammonium carbonate by a similar mechanism given for ammonium hydroxide (4) and (5). The addition of sodium phosphate T.S. to the above solution yields a white, crystalline precipitate (6), (7), and (8) which is insoluble in ammonia T.S.

Commercial Manufacture.—Magnesium metal is obtained by the electrolysis of fused magnesium chloride. The source of magnesium chloride is from (1) underground brines and (2) sea water.

1. Underground brines contain among other salts about 3 per cent of magnesium chloride. This is obtained by evaporation and fractional crystallization as the double salt, $2MgCl_2 \cdot CaCl_2 \cdot 12H_2O$. The double salt is then treated to yield $MgCl_2 \cdot 6H_2O$. Anhydrous magnesium chloride suitable for electrolysis is obtained by heating.

2. Sea water has become an important source of magnesium since 1940. It contains about 0.5 per cent $MgCl_2$. The magnesium is precipitated as the hydroxide by alkali. Hydrochloric acid is then added to form magnesium chloride which is removed by crystallization and made anhydrous by heating.

The electrolysis is carried out in quite a normal manner at the fusion point of magnesium chloride (about 750° C.). The chlorine is removed at the anode and molten magnesium rises to the top and is skimmed off.

Pharmacological Action of Magnesium Ion.[1,2]—The magnesium ion is essential to life in the human body. It is present to the extent of about 20 Gm. in the body with bone containing 11 Gm., muscle about 6 Gm., and the remainder widely distributed in tissues and fluids. A daily intake of 7 to 10 mg./Kg. has been suggested as being sufficient to maintain magnesium balance with the typical occidental diets as well as to restore any pre-existing deficits of magnesium. The actual daily requirement is probably closer to 5 mg./Kg. It is obtained mainly from leafy green vegetables, milk and meat. Its most important function appears to be as an activator

[1] Engbaelk, L., Pharmacol. Rev., **4**, 396 (1952).

[2] See also "Clinical Abstracts from the Medical Literature," Vol. 5, No. 1, pub. by E. R. Squibb and Sons, New York, N. Y., pub. July 1965, for an excellent review of the recent literature on magnesium entitled "The Value and Importance of Magnesium to Man in the Prevention of Disease," pp. 1–29.

of many enzyme systems such as splitters of peptides and phosphate compounds. It is also apparently indispensable for the smooth functioning of the neuromuscular system. In spite of its demonstrated importance there has been no clear cut reported dietary deficiency in humans although it can be demonstrated in rats and dogs where the deficiency causes increased nerve excitability and fatal convulsions. (See, however, use in alcoholics.)

Meltzer in 1909 pointed out that magnesium salts when injected intramuscularly or intravenously have a powerful general anesthetic action which resembles that produced by chloroform. This depressant action is on the cellular portion of the neuron and the neuromuscular junction. An excess of magnesium decreases the amount of transmitter substance, acetylcholine, liberated at the end plate. The blocking effect of Mg ions at the neuromuscular junction is in certain respects similar to that of curare which depresses the sensitivity of the muscle to intra-arterially injected acetylcholine and to acetylcholine applied directly to the single end plate. Calcium ions relieve the block produced by Mg ions and restore output of acetylcholine from nerve endings. For this reason soluble magnesium salts (usually sulfate) are used as central nervous system depressants in obstetrics, convulsant states, and symptoms of tetanus.

Magnesium ion is not readily absorbed from the gastro-intestinal tract as its absorption is retarded by alkaline media and increased by acid media. Most of the absorption takes place in the acid media of the duodenum. Due to the slow absorption of magnesium ions a saline laxative action occurs upon the ingestion of any magnesium compound (see Sodium Phosphate).

Hirschfelder and Haury reported, in 1932, that a large amount (40 to 44 per cent) of a single orally administered purgative dose of magnesium sulfate was excreted in the urine without significantly increasing the normal serum levels[1] of this ion. They also found that in the presence of kidney deficiency the Mg ion serum level could be raised to dangerous levels (approximately two-thirds of coma level) with a single purgative dose. Pritchard,[2] on the other hand, could not confirm this finding and agreed with the findings of McCance and Widdowson[3] as well as Suter and Klingman[4] who found no elevating effect on serum levels by oral dosage and only about 2 per cent excreted in the urine. Indeed, Suter and Klingman have utilized intravenous magnesium sulfate injection with good results in raising Mg serum levels in chronic alcoholics (serum levels 1.25 to 1.5 mEq./L.) and thereby relieving tremor, delirium, hallucinosis and convulsions. In any case, however, intravenous (or intramuscular) injection of magnesium sulfate for this purpose

[1] Normal serum values are given variously as 1.4 to 2.5 mEq./L., 1.5 to 1.8 mEq./L., 1.5 to 3 mEq./L., etc.
[2] Pritchard, J. A., Surg., Gynec. and Obst., 100, 131 (1955).
[3] McCance, R. A., and Widdowson, E. M., Biochem. J., 33, 523 (1939).
[4] Suter, C., and Klingman, W. O., Neurology, 5, 691 (1955).

24

should be carried out on patients with good kidney function. The toxic possibilities in the presence of deficient kidney function should probably also be kept in mind for oral use of magnesium salts.

Soluble magnesium salts are used externally because they exert an anti-inflammatory action when applied as a hypertonic solution (sitz bath). When applied to minor suppurating surface infections they often promote healing and granulation of the tissue.

OFFICIAL MAGNESIUM COMPOUNDS

MAGNESIUM CARBONATE

Magnesium Carbonate, N.F. XII

Approximate Formula, $(MgCO_3)_4.Mg(OH)_2.5H_2O$
Molecular Weight, 485.69

Physical Properties.—Magnesium Carbonate is a white, bulky, odorless powder having a slightly "earthy" taste. It often occurs in light, white, friable masses or cakes. It is stable in air.

The salt is nearly insoluble in water, to which it imparts a slightly alkaline reaction which is due, no doubt, to a slight dissociation of $Mg(OH)_2$. It is insoluble in alcohol but dissolves with effervescence in dilute acids.

Chemical Properties.—Magnesium carbonate is insoluble in most solvents and thus is quite inert chemically. Dilute acids dissolve it with effervescence (1). An acid solution gives the tests for the magnesium ion (*q.v.*). By heating in solution with sodium bicarbonate the normal magesium carbonate forms.

Analytical determination of Magnesium Carbonate depends upon dissolving in an excess of 1 N sulfuric acid and back titrating with 1 N sodium hydroxide using methyl orange as an indicator.

Official Tests for Identity.—1. When Magnesium Carbonate is treated with dilute hydrochloric acid, it dissolves with the evolution of carbon dioxide (1).

$(1)\ (MgCO_3)_4.Mg(OH)_2.5H_2O + 10HCl \rightarrow 5MgCl_2 + 4CO_2 \uparrow + 11H_2O$

2. The solution obtained in (1) responds to the tests for *Magnesium* (*q.v.*).

Commercial Manufacture.—When solutions of sodium carbonate and magnesium sulfate are mixed, a precipitate of basic magnesium carbonate is formed. The composition of this basic salt varies according to the concentrations and temperatures of the solutions of the reacting substances and also according to the temperatures at which the precipitate is dried. Thus, when cold dilute solutions of sodium carbonate and magnesium sulfate are mixed, no carbon dioxide is evolved, a very bulky, white precipitate of basic carbonate is thrown down and an appreciable amount of magnesium bicarbonate [$Mg(HCO_3)_2$, soluble] remains in solution (2), (3), and (4).

(2) $Na_2CO_3 + 2H_2O \rightleftarrows 2NaOH + H_2CO_3$

(3) $MgSO_4 + OH^- \rightleftarrows MgOH^+ + SO_4^=$

(4) $2MgOH^+ + CO_3^= \rightleftarrows Mg_2(OH)_2CO_3 \downarrow$
(white)

In dilute solution there is a competition between the hydroxide ions and carbonate ions for the magnesium ion. A basic magnesium carbonate is formed when both (OH) and (CO₃) are attached to magnesium. Generally speaking these conditions produce a *light magnesium carbonate* recognized by the B.P. and available in the U.S.

As the pH of the reaction is reduced to about 8.3 by the removal of hydroxide ions, the carbonic acid present (H_2CO_3) ionizes to supply bicarbonate ions (HCO_3^-). The bicarbonate of magnesium is soluble in water. This can be precipitated as basic carbonate by boiling (5 and 6).

(5) $Mg(HCO_3)_2 \rightleftarrows Mg^{++} + 2HCO_3^-$

(6) $2HCO_3^- \xrightarrow{\triangle} CO_3^= + H_2O + CO_2 \uparrow$

The ($CO_3^=$) carbonate ions now create the same conditions that existed for equations (2), (3) and (4).

When hot, concentrated solutions of the reacting substances are mixed, carbon dioxide is given off and a salt containing a greater proportion of magnesium hydroxide is obtained. By this method a *heavy magnesium carbonate* is produced which is recognized by the B.P. and which may be purchased in the United States.

Consistent with the ease of manufacture, bulkiness of product, N.F. requirements, etc., a process has been devised whereby an aqueous solution of magnesium sulfate (125 Gm. per liter) is mixed with an aqueous solution of sodium carbonate (150 Gm. per liter), the temperature of the solutions not exceeding 55° C. The resulting precipitate is washed to remove sodium sulfate and dried without heat. This product meets the N.F. *purity rubric.* The following equation approximately represents the metathesis (7).

(7) $5MgSO_4 \cdot 7H_2O + 5Na_2CO_3 \cdot 10H_2O \rightarrow (MgCO_3)_4 \cdot Mg(OH)_2 \cdot 5H_2O \downarrow + 5Na_2SO_4 + CO_2 \uparrow + 79H_2O$

Uses.—*Magnesium Carbonate,* N.F. XII, is a basic hydrated magnesium carbonate or a normal hydrated magnesium carbonate. It contains the equivalent of not less than 40 per cent and not more than 43.5 per cent of MgO.

Official magnesium carbonate is used as an antacid. It is contra-indicated only when the stomach must not be burdened with carbon dioxide. In the alimentary tract, this basic salt is converted into soluble magnesium bicarbonate and, therefore, acts as a laxative when given in adequate dosage (8 Gm.). Soluble salts of magnesium act as saline cathartics and act by the absorption of water. This aqueous solution, together with the salts, is retained in the intestines, increases the quantity and fluidity of the intestinal contents and mechanically stimulates peristalsis. In preparations that are alkaline, magnesium carbonate may be used as a clarifying or filtering agent. Examples of this are its uses in *Tolu Balsam Syrup*, and *Aromatic Eriodictyon Syrup*. It is also used as an abrasive in some tooth powders, as a cosmetic, and as an ingredient in silver polishes. *Magnesium Citrate Solution* is an alkaline solution (pH 8.2) containing the equivalent of 1.55 to 1.9 Gm. of MgO in each 100 ml. Reaction (8) accounts for the formation of magnesium citrate and (9) the liberation of carbon dioxide by the use of sodium or potassium bicarbonate. It appears that the magnesium ion is sequestered by citrate ions to maintain solution. Usual dose—Antacid, 600 mg.—Laxative, 8 Gm.

$$(8) \ 5C_3H_4(OH)(COOH)_3 + (MgCO_3)_4 \cdot Mg(OH)_2 \cdot 5H_2O \rightarrow 5C_3H_4(OH)(COOH)(COO)_2Mg + 4CO_2 \uparrow + 11H_2O$$

$$(9) \ C_3H_4(OH)(COOH)_3 + 3KHCO_3 \rightarrow C_3H_4(OH)(COOK)_3 + 3CO_2 \uparrow + 3H_2O$$

MAGNESIUM HYDROXIDE

Magnesium Hydroxide, N.F. XII

Formula, $Mg(OH)_2$. Molecular Weight, 58.33

Physical Properties.—Magnesium Hydroxide occurs as a bulky white powder. It is practically insoluble in water (1 in 80,000) and in alcohol but soluble in dilute acids.

Chemical Properties.—Although virtually insoluble in water, it will impart a slight alkalinity to water when mixed with it. Sodium hydroxide or potassium hydroxide reduce the solubility of magnesium hydroxide, whereas the addition of ammonia or ammonium chloride increases it. Magnesium hydroxide in aqueous solution ionizes into magnesium ions and hydroxide ions (1).

$$(1) \ Mg(OH)_2 \rightleftarrows Mg^{++} + 2OH^-$$

The addition of ammonium chloride provides a supply of ammonium ions (2).

$$(2) \ NH_4Cl \rightleftarrows NH_4^+ + Cl^-$$

The ammonium ions combine with the hydroxide ions (equation 1) to form practically non-ionized ammonium hydroxide. This causes the reaction represented in (1) to proceed to the right and results in more magnesium hydroxide going into solution. This process goes on until the solubility product of magnesium hydroxide is reached. (See Magnesia Mixture T.S., U.S.P.)

Like many hydroxides, that of magnesium will readily absorb carbon dioxide,particularly when in aqueous mixtures. A novel use of magnesium hydroxide is its incorporation into cheese before canning as a carbon dioxide absorbent.

Magnesium Hydroxide is assayed by dissolving in diluted hydrochloric acid, making alkaline with ammonium chloride T.S. and ammonia T.S. and precipitating as 8-magnesium quinolate [$Mg(OC_9H_6NO)_2$]. The precipitate is dried and weighed.

Official Tests for Identity.—A solution of Magnesium Hydroxide (1 in 20) in diluted hydrochloric acid responds to the tests for *Magnesium* (*q.v.*).

Commercial Manufacture.—Most of the magnesium hydroxide is prepared by the hydration of light magnesium oxide (3). The oxide is boiled with 20 to 30 times its weight of water for about 20 minutes.

$$(3)\ MgO + H_2O \rightarrow Mg(OH)_2$$

The hydroxide is collected and washed on a filter and dried at a temperature not over 100° C.

It is also prepared by mixing a solution of magnesium sulfate and sodium hydroxide (4).

$$(4)\ MgSO_4 + 2NaOH \rightarrow Mg(OH)_2 \downarrow + Na_2SO_4$$

This method has the disadvantage of having a long and tedious washing process to remove the sodium sulfate.

Uses.—*Magnesium Hydroxide*, N.F. XII, dried at 105° for 2 hours, contains not less than 95 per cent of $Mg(OH)_2$. Due to its basic character it is an efficient antacid and the magnesium chloride formed in the stomach exerts a "salt action" in the intestinal tract (see sodium phosphate), causing a mild laxative action. Usual dose—300 mg.

Milk of Magnesia (Magnesia Magma) U.S.P. XVII is a suspension of magnesium hydroxide containing not less than 7 per cent and not more than 8.5 per cent of $Mg(OH)_2$. For purposes of minimizing the alkalinity of Milk of Magnesia, 0.1 per cent of citric acid may be added. Normally, magnesium hydroxide ionizes into magnesium ion and hydroxide ions (5). The citric acid upon addition immediately reacts to form magnesium citrate which ionizes to supply magnesium and citrate ions (6). This increase in the concentration of magnesium ions according to the law of mass action forces the reaction expressed by equation (5) to the left. Such an action decreases hydroxide ion concentration giving the product a milder and less chalky taste.

(5) $Mg(OH)_2 \rightleftarrows Mg^{++} + 2OH^-$

(6) $Mg_3(C_6H_5O_7)_2 \rightleftarrows 3Mg^{++} + 2C_6H_5O_7^{\equiv}$

The alkalinity contributed by the glass container is likewise counteracted.

Most Milk of Magnesia is prepared by the hydration of magnesium oxide (3). It previously was prepared by the old method of double-decomposition by slowly adding a solution of sodium hydroxide to a boiling solution of magnesium sulfate (4).

A blue-colored glass bottle enhances the white character and is usually used to dispense milk of magnesia. The white magma in a clear glass container has a pasty, nonpleasing appearance. Studies on the effect of light on storage indicate that protection from light is unnecessary. It should be stored at temperatures not exceeding 35°C., and should not be permitted to freeze. Besides breaking the bottle, freezing changes the density and character of the hydroxide so that a greater settling out occurs and the precipitate is coarser and more granular. The altered magma is not unfit for use but is not as pleasant to the taste. Usual dose—Antacid, 5 ml. four times a day; Laxative, 15 ml.

It is also available as *Milk of Magnesia Tablets*, N.F. XII.

MAGNESIUM OXIDE

Magnesium Oxide, U.S.P. XVII

NOTE:—*Magnesium Oxide* is official in two different varieties commonly known as "light" magnesium oxide and "heavy" magnesium oxide.

Formula, MgO.   Molecular Weight, 40.31

Physical Properties.—Magnesium Oxide (light) usually occurs as a very bulky, white powder but it may be molded into cubes. The heavy magnesium oxide occurs as a relatively dense, white powder. Both are odorless, insoluble in water and alcohol but soluble in dilute acids. The two oxides differ from one another in density; the bulk of a definite weight of light magnesium oxide being about three and a half times that of the same weight of heavy magnesium oxide.

Chemical Properties.—Upon exposure to air, they absorb carbon dioxide and moisture. Light magnesium oxide hydrates to $Mg(OH)_2$ more easily than the heavy oxide and will dissolve readily in water containing carbon dioxide (1), (2).

(1) $CO_2 + 2H_2O \rightleftarrows H_2CO_3 + H_2O \rightleftarrows HCO_3^- + H_3O^+$

(2) $MgO + 2HCO_3^- + 2H_3O^+ \rightarrow Mg(HCO_3)_2 + 3H_2O$

When the light oxide is finely ground and mixed with a solution of magnesium chloride the mass sets to a hard, strong and durable cement. The composition is thought to be $3MgO.MgCl_2.10H_2O$, although some $Mg(OH)_2$ could also be present. A mixture of this type is known as magnesia cement, oxychloride cement, Sorel's cement, or zylolith.

Magnesium oxide fuses at about 2800° C. and at such high temperatures is reduced by carbon, forming magnesium carbide.

This oxide is a good acid neutralizer and, for this reason, is found in numerous antacid formulations.

In the assay the oxide is dissolved in an excess of 1 N sulfuric acid and the residual acid titrated with 1 N sodium hydroxide using methyl orange T.S. as an indicator.

Official Tests for Identity.—When the oxides are converted into magnesium chloride by treatment with hydrochloric acid, the resulting solution responds to all tests for *Magnesium* (*q.v.*).

Commercial Manufacture.—*Light Magnesium Oxide.*—This form of magnesium oxide is made by firmly pressing official magnesium carbonate into a crucible and heating to *dull redness* (3) until a small test-sample no longer effervesces with hydrochloric acid.

$$(3)\ (MgCO_3)_4.Mg(OH)_2.5H_2O \triangleq 5MgO + 4CO_2 \uparrow + 6H_2O \uparrow$$

Heavy Magnesium Oxide.—A heavy oxide may be obtained by heating to *white heat* official magnesium carbonate that has been firmly packed in a crucible. Magnesium oxide of greatest compactness is obtained by heating to redness the washed and dried magnesium carbonate (heavy) that is obtained by mixing boiling aqueous solutions of magnesium sulfate and sodium carbonate (4) (see preparation of magnesium carbonate).

$$(4)\ MgSO_4 + Na_2CO_3 \xrightarrow{100°C.} MgCO_3 \downarrow + Na_2SO_4$$

Uses.—*Magnesium Oxide*, U.S.P. XVII, contains after ignition, not less than 96 per cent of MgO. When Magnesium Oxide is labeled, the label should indicate whether it is of the "light" or "heavy" variety. It is used principally as an antacid and to a lesser extent as a laxative. Its water absorptive property is utilized in compounding and in preserving powdered drug extracts.

In *Aromatic Cascara Sagrada Fluidextract*, U.S.P. XVII it is allowed to react for forty-eight hours with the bitter principles of the cascara bark. This mitigates the bitterness of the finished preparation. The antacid properties were formerly officially recognized and used in the tablet and powder forms of *Sodium Bicarbonate and Magnesium Oxide*, N.F. XI. A mixture of magnesium oxide, tannic acid and charcoal is well known as "Universal Antidote." Usual dose—Antacid, 250 mg. four or more times a day; Laxative, 4 Gm.

TRIBASIC MAGNESIUM PHOSPHATE

Tribasic Magnesium Phosphate, N.F. XII

Formula, $Mg_3(PO_4)_2.5H_2O$.   Molecular Weight, 352.96

Physical Properties.—Tribasic Magnesium Phosphate is a white, odorless, and tasteless powder. It is almost insoluble in water but is readily soluble in diluted mineral acids.

Chemical Properties.—Tribasic magnesium phosphate is readily precipitated by treating solutions of magnesium salts with trisodium phosphate (1). Ordinary sodium phosphate, Na_2HPO_4, slowly precipitates magnesium hydrogen phosphate, $MgHPO_4.7H_2O$.

$$(1)\ 2Na_3PO_4 + 3MgSO_4 \rightarrow Mg_3(PO_4)_2 \downarrow\ + 3Na_2SO_4$$

The phosphate ion may be removed by dissolving tribasic magnesium phosphate in diluted acetic acid and adding a solution of ferric chloride T.S. (2, 3).

$$(2)\ Mg_3(PO_4)_2 + 6CH_3COOH \rightarrow 3Mg(CH_3COO)_2 + 2H_3PO_4$$

$$(3)\ H_3PO_4 + FeCl_3 \rightarrow FePO_4 \downarrow\ + 3HCl$$
$$\text{(white)}$$

The solution thus obtained by filtering out the white ferric phosphate will respond to all the tests for the magnesium ion.

The assay is similar to that of aluminum phosphate and tribasic calcium phosphate (*q.v.*). Tribasic Magnesium Phosphate is dissolved in diluted nitric acid, and the phosphate is precipitated as ammonium phosphomolybdate. This precipitate is dissolved in excess 1 N sodium hydroxide and back titrated with 1 N sulfuric acid using phenolphthalein as an indicator.

Official Tests for Identity.—1. Ammonium molybdate T.S. added to a solution of Tribasic Magnesium Phosphate in diluted nitric acid produces a precipitate of yellow ammonium phosphomolybdate which is soluble in ammonia T.S. (See Phosphoric Acid.)

2. Dissolve 0.1 Gm. of Tribasic Magnesium Phosphate in 0.7 ml. of diluted acetic acid and 20 ml. of distilled water (2). Add 1 ml. of ferric chloride T.S. (3), let stand five minutes and filter. Five ml. of the filtrate responds to the test for *Magnesium* (*q.v.*).

Commercial Manufacture.—When a solution of trisodium orthophosphate is added to a solution of magnesium sulfate, tribasic magnesium phosphate is precipitated (1). The precipitate is washed with water until free from sodium sulfate and dried.

Uses.—*Tribasic Magnesium Phosphate*, N.F. XII, when ignited to constant weight, contains not less than 98 per cent and not more than 101.5 per cent of $Mg_3(PO_4)_2$. This insoluble compound is used extensively as an antacid. When so used, an amount sufficient only to neutralize excess acid in the stomach is rendered soluble and, therefore, it does not produce systemic alkalization as do magnesium hydroxide, sodium bicarbonate, etc. The antacid action is accounted for by the fact that magnesium phosphate, although insoluble in water, nevertheless does ionize slightly to give Mg^{++} and $PO_4^{\equiv}$. The phosphate ions hydrolyze readily to $HPO_4^{=}$ ions in the presence of H_3O^+ ions in the stomach. This withdraws $PO_4^{\equiv}$ ions so that more $Mg_3(PO_4)_2$ dissolves. This dissolution of magnesium phosphate and neutralization of acid by phosphate ion hydrolysis continues as long as there are H_3O^+ ions available. In the presence of a large excess of H_3O^+ ions the $HPO_4^{=}$ ions go successively to $H_2PO_4^-$ ions and H_3PO_4. A mild laxative action has been attributed to Tribasic Magnesium Phosphate. Usual dose—1 Gm.

MAGNESIUM STEARATE

Magnesium Stearate, U.S.P. XVII

Formula (approx.), $[CH_3(CH_2)_{16}COO]_2Mg$. Molecular Weight, 591.27

Physical Properties.—Magnesium Stearate occurs as a fine, white, bulky powder, having a faint characteristic odor. It is unctuous, adheres readily to the skin, and is free from grittiness. It is insoluble in water, alcohol and ether.

Chemical Properties.—This salt is virtually inert insofar as the usual chemical incompatibilities are concerned because of its water insolubility. However, it will decompose with either hydrochloric acid (1) or with sulfuric acid (2) to liberate the free fatty acids in each case. The salt is not a pure stearate since the product of commerce invariably contains palmitate, *i.e.*, $[CH_3(CH_2)_{14}COO]_2Mg$.

(1) $[CH_3(CH_2)_{16}COO]_2Mg + 2HCl \rightarrow MgCl_2 + 2CH_3(CH_2)_{16}COOH$

(2) $[CH_3(CH_2)_{16}COO]_2Mg + H_2SO_4 \rightarrow MgSO_4 + 2CH_3(CH_2)_{16}COOH$

The assay of this salt is carried out by boiling an accurately weighed sample with 50 ml. of 0.1N sulfuric acid for 10 minutes to liberate the free fatty acids (2). Following separation of the fatty acids from the aqueous layer containing the residual amount of sulfuric acid it is then possible to determine the excess acid by titration with 0.1N sodium hydroxide solution using methyl orange T.S. indicator.

Official Tests for Identity.—Two tests are provided, one being for the magnesium ion and the other for the fatty acid component of the salt.

A. Heat 1 Gm. of Magnesium Stearate with a mixture of 25 ml. of water and 5 ml. of hydrochloric acid. Free fatty acids are liberated (1) and float on the surface of the liquid as an oily layer. The aqueous layer responds to all tests for *Magnesium* (*q.v.*).

B. Mix 25 Gm. of Magnesium Stearate with 200 ml. of hot water, then add 60 ml. of diluted sulfuric acid, and heat the mixture with frequent stirring (2), until the separated fatty acid layer is clear. This fatty acid layer is washed with boiling water to free it completely of sulfate and the layer is then transferred to a beaker which is heated on a steam bath until all water has separated and the fatty acid layer is clear. The acids are allowed to cool, the water layer poured off, the acids again melted and filtered into a dry beaker wherein they are dried at 105° C. for 20 minutes. The fatty acids obtained in this way congeal at a temperature not below 54° C. (see N.F. XII, p. 451, for determination of "Solidification Temperature of Fatty Acids").

Commercial Manufacture.—Although there are various methods by which magnesium stearate has been made, a suitable product can be prepared by interacting a soluble magnesium salt with sodium stearate and the product washed free of by-product salt (3). Alternatively, stearic acid may be heated with magnesium oxide (4) or magnesium carbonate.

$$(3)\ 2CH_3(CH_2)_{16}COONa + MgSO_4 \rightarrow [CH_3(CH_2)_{16}COO]_2Mg \downarrow + Na_2SO_4$$

$$(4)\ 2CH_3(CH_2)_{16}COOH + MgO \rightarrow [CH_3(CH_2)_{16}COO]_2Mg + H_2O$$

Uses.—*Magnesium Stearate*, U.S.P. XVII, "is a compound of magnesium with variable proportions of stearic acid and palmitic acid. It contains the equivalent of not less than 6.8 per cent and not more than 8.0 per cent of MgO." This salt is recognized only as a pharmaceutic aid (see also Calcium Stearate) for its use as a tablet lubricant. Its relatively non-toxic nature and unctuous character make it quite suitable as a lubricant useful in the tabletting procedure.

Magnesium Stearate has also been used as a baby dusting powder (see also Zinc Stearate) because of its ability to cling to the skin.

MAGNESIUM SULFATE

Magnesium Sulfate, U.S.P. XVII

Formula, $MgSO_4 \cdot 7H_2O$.　　Molecular Weight, 246.48

Physical Properties.—This form of Magnesium Sulfate occurs in small, colorless, prismatic needles or rhombic prisms that are odorless and have a bitter, cooling, saline taste.

One Gm. of Magnesium Sulfate dissolves in 1 ml. of water and slowly in about 1 ml. of glycerin, at 25° C. One Gm. dissolves in 0.2 ml. of boiling water. It is sparingly soluble in alcohol at 25° C.

The salt is efflorescent. When gently heated, it readily loses some of its water of hydration and is converted into the monohydrate (a white powder) which quickly becomes anhydrous at 200° C.

Magnesium Sulfate crystallizes from cold water in the form of rhombic prisms or in needles of the heptahydrate ($MgSO_4.7H_2O$). It is known as *Epsom salt*. With many other sulfates, Magnesium Sulfate forms double salts that are isomorphous with one another and also with analogous salts of zinc. They have a general formula $M_2SO_4.MgSO_4.6H_2O$, where M represents potassium, sodium, ammonium, etc.

Chemical Properties.—An aqueous solution of magnesium sulfate is neutral to litmus paper. Aqueous solutions of the salt respond to the chemical reactions of the magnesium ion (*q.v.*) and the sulfate ion (see sulfuric acid).

In the analysis of the salt the magnesium is precipitated as magnesium ammonium phosphate ($MgNH_4PO_4.6H_2O$) and then by ignition converted to magnesium pyrophosphate ($Mg_2P_2O_7$) and weighed.

Official Tests for Identity.—Aqueous solutions of the salt respond to all tests for *Magnesium* (*q.v.*) and for *Sulfate* (*q.v.*).

Commercial Manufacture.—1. Magnesium sulfate is made by treating native magnesium carbonate (*magnesite*) with sulfuric acid (1). The evolved carbon dioxide is usually used for "carbonating" waters. The residue is dissolved in hot water and the excess of sulfuric acid neutralized with magnesite. The clear supernatant liquid is drawn off, concentrated and allowed to crystallize.

$$(1) \quad MgCO_3 + H_2SO_4 \rightarrow MgSO_4 + CO_2 \uparrow + H_2O$$

2. Large quantities of magnesium sulfate are obtained from *kieserite* ($MgSO_4.H_2O$), a native form of the salt. This mineral is only sparingly soluble in cold water and therefore must be heated to change it to the soluble anhydrous salt. When the solution is concentrated and allowed to cool, crystals of the heptahydrate ($MgSO_4.7H_2O$) separate out. The product may be purified by recrystallization from water.

Uses.—*Magnesium Sulfate* (Epsom Salt), U.S.P. XVII, rendered anhydrous by ignition, contains not less than 99 per cent of $MgSO_4$. It loses not less than 40 per cent and not more than 52 per cent of water when ignited.

This salt is very widely used as a saline cathartic (see also Sodium Phosphate). Its action depends on the osmotic withdrawal of water from the tissues by a hypertonic solution. It has also been used orally as an antidote for barium, barbiturate and other types of poisoning. Intravenous and intramuscular injection of *Magnesium Sulfate Injection* is used mostly for the depressant property of magnesium. Examples are seasickness, hypertension, tetanus spasm, and convulsions. It has also been used in paroxysmal auricular and ventricular tachycardia by the intravenous route. Usual dose—15 Gm. as a cathartic and 1 Gm. in the injection form as an anticonvulsant. Solutions for intramuscular use are usually 25 to 50 per cent and those for intravenous use are 10 per cent in concentration.

MAGNESIUM TRISILICATE

Magnesium Trisilicate, U.S.P. XVII

Formula, $2MgO.3SiO_2.xH_2O$ or $(MgSiO_3)_2.SiO_2.xH_2O$

Molecular Weight, 260.88 (anhyd.)

Physical Properties.—Magnesium Trisilicate is a fine, white, odorless, tasteless powder, free from grittiness. It is almost insoluble in water and in alcohol. Water of hydration and crystallization are present to the extent of 34 per cent.

Chemical Properties.—Magnesium trisilicate when treated with an acid such as diluted hydrochloric acid decomposes to form magnesium chloride and gelatinous trisilicic acid (1).

Equation (1) expresses the compound as a salt of trisilicic acid which is not necessarily true. Due to methods of manufacture the official product is most likely a mixture of magnesium metasilicate $(MgSiO_3)$ and colloidal silicon dioxide (SiO_2) with varying amounts of water.

$$(1) \quad Mg_2Si_3O_8 + 4HCl \rightarrow 2MgCl_2 + H_4Si_3O_8 \downarrow (\text{or } 3SiO_2 + 2H_2O)$$

or,

$$(MgSiO_3)_2.SiO_2.nH_2O + 4HCl \rightarrow 2MgCl_2 + 2H_2SiO_3 + SiO_2 + nH_2O$$
(colloidal)

In the stomach a similar reaction takes place with hydrochloric acid and a gelatinous mass is formed with the gastric contents.

Magnesium trisilicate is assayed by removing the magnesium as magnesium sulfate with sulfuric acid. The residue is weighed, treated with hydrofluoric acid, and weighed again. (2). The loss in weight represents the quantity of SiO_2 present.

$$(2) \quad SiO_2 + 4HF \xrightarrow{\triangle} SiF_4 \uparrow + 2H_2O \uparrow$$

Official Tests for Identity.—1. Mix about 0.5 Gm. of Magnesium Trisilicate with 10 ml. of diluted hydrochloric acid, filter, and neutralize the filtrate to litmus paper with ammonia T.S.; the neutralized filtrate responds to the tests for *Magnesium* (*q.v.*).

2. Prepare a bead by fusing a few crystals of sodium ammonium phosphate on a platinum loop in the flame of a Bunsen burner. Place the hot, transparent bead in contact with magnesium trisilicate, and again fuse. Silica floats about in the bead, producing, upon cooling, an opaque bead with a web-like structure.

Commercial Manufacture.—In 1936 a study of magnesium silicates revealed that a trisilicate possesses adsorbent and antacid properties. The best ratio found was 2MgO to 3SiO$_2$ or corresponding to the formula Mg$_2$Si$_3$O$_8$.nH$_2$O. To prepare a magnesium trisilicate that will meet the official specification, care must be taken to use a sodium silicate having a ratio of Na$_2$O:SiO$_2$=1:1.5. Most of the available sodium silicate has a ratio from 1:1.7 to 1:3.9. In order to obtain an official product, sodium hydroxide is added to sodium silicate until upon analysis a compound of Na$_2$O:1.5SiO$_2$ (ratio 2:3) results. A sodium silicate of this composition added in equimolar quantities to magnesium sulfate produces official magnesium trisilicate.[1]

In general, magnesium trisilicate is prepared by slowly running a solution of magnesium sulfate into a solution of sodium silicate (3). The precipitate is washed, dried, and powdered.

$$(3)\ 2MgSO_4 + 2(Na_2O:1.5SiO_2) + nH_2O \rightarrow (MgSiO_3)_2.SiO_2.\ nH_2O \downarrow + 2Na_2SO_4$$

It may also be prepared by adding hydrochloric acid to the sodium silicate solution and then adding cream of magnesia or precipitated magnesium hydroxide. Instant granulation takes place throughout the whole mass. No silica will be precipitated immediately upon the addition of hydrochloric acid to the sodium silicate solution provided the solutions are well diluted. The granular material is washed, dried, and powdered.[2]

Uses.—*Magnesium Trisilicate*, U.S.P. XVII, is a compound of magnesium oxide and silicon dioxide with varying proportions of water. It contains not less than 20 per cent of magnesium oxide (MgO) and not less than 45 per cent of silicon dioxide (SiO$_2$). This magnesium salt of trisilicic acid is used to relieve gastric hyperacidity and pain in gastric and duodenal ulcer. Its action is chemical but it does not interfere with peptic digestion nor does it normally induce systemic alkalization. In normal amounts it is nontoxic but administration over several days has a tendency to produce an alkaline urine. In large doses it sometimes induces diarrhea because of the magnesium chloride formed with the hydrochloric acid in the stomach. For this reason it is often present in aluminum hydroxide and phosphate preparations to overcome the constipating tendency of aluminum as well as to provide an antacid action.

[1] Roseman, R. *et al.*, J. Am. Pharm. Asso. Sci. Ed., **29**, 271 (1940).
[2] Glass, Norman: Quart. J. Pharm. and Pharmacol., **9**, 445 (1936).

The silicon dioxide and silicic acids which are formed and hydrated in the stomach pass into the intestine and there function as adsorbents. This adsorbent property makes magnesium trisilicate more than just a good antacid. In the stomach a gelatinous mass is formed that is protective to ulcers and prolongs the antacid properties for several hours. One Gm. of magnesium trisilicate can neutralize about 155 ml. of 0.1 N hydrochloric acid. Because it is insoluble in neutral and basic solutions, the antacid action stops in the stomach when all the hydrochloric acid is neutralized and thus prevents the development of an alkaline condition. *Magnesium Trisilicate Tablets* are official.

Magnesium trisilicate powder is an emulsifying agent for mineral, vegetable and animal oils when used in the proper proportions. An oil-in-water emulsion is produced which is probably brought about by mechanical action.[1] Usual dose—1 Gm. four times a day with a usual range of 1 to 4 Gm. allowable per dose.

TALC

Talc, U.S.P. XVII

Physical Properties.—Talc is a very fine white or grayish-white, crystalline powder. It is unctuous, adhering readily to the skin, and is free from grittiness. Because the mineral is extremely soft and has a smooth greasy feeling to the touch, it is known as *soapstone*. It is the softest mineral known, having the lowest degree of hardness. The specific gravity of unground talc is 2.6 to 2.8.

Talc occurs in three physical forms known as foliated, fibrous, and steatite. Foliated talc is best since it occurs in plates and is most desirable in cosmetics and pharmaceuticals. Fibrous talc occurs as matted shreds and is useless for pharmacy. Steatite talc is widely used and when pulverized yields granular particles.

Talc is odorless, tasteless, and insoluble in water or in dilute solutions of acids or alkaline hydroxides. Processing talc is a laborious task of air-sifting and finally bolting it through a fine sieve. Cosmetic and pharmaceutical talc differ only in particle size.

Talc is not an efficient absorbent, being less so than kaolin, bentonite, magnesium carbonate, kieselguhr, etc. Its adsorbent ability is also low, thus making it desirable to filter pharmaceuticals with no danger of removing ingredients such as alkaloids, dyes, etc.

Chemical Properties.—Chemically, talc is a hydrated magnesium silicate having the formula $3MgO.4SiO_2.H_2O$ or may be looked upon as a salt of dimetasilicic acid, $Mg_3H_2(Si_2O_6)_2$. It should contain about 31 per cent MgO and 63.5 per cent SiO_2 if this formula is to be correct. Analysis usually shows a wide variation in composition with MgO being between 28.1 and 31.2 per cent, silica from 57 to 61.7 per cent, and water from 3 to 7 per cent.

[1] J. Am. Pharm. Assn., Pr. Ed., **7**, 123 (1946).

Impurities most frequent in talc are:

Al$_2$O$_3$	.	.	.	0.78% to 2.55%
CaO	.	.	.	0.54% to 8.58%
Fe$_2$O$_3$	.	.	.	0.26% to 0.99%

Talc is formed by the breaking down of tremolite (1), instatite (2), and other magnesium minerals. The reactions may be represented as follows (1) and (2):

(1) $CaMg_3Si_4O_{12} + H_2O + CO_2 \rightarrow Mg_3H_2(Si_2O_6)_2 + CaCO_3$

(2) $Mg_4Si_4O_{12} + H_2O + CO_2 \rightarrow Mg_3H_2(Si_2O_6)_2 + MgCO_3$

Talc is an inert magnesium polysilicate showing little activity to acids or bases and thus is useful as a filtering aid and diluent. It loses water at red heat (850°–960°) yielding instatite or tremolite. Upon fusion with sodium and potassium carbonate, the magnesium is converted into the carbonate (3) and then treated with dilute hydrochloric acid to bring it into solution.

Official Tests for Identity.—Mix 500 mg. of Talc with 200 mg. of anhydrous sodium carbonate and 2 Gm. of anhydrous potassium carbonate, and heat the mixture in a platinum crucible until fusion is complete (3).

(3) $Mg_3H_2(Si_2O_6)_2 + Na_2CO_3 + 2K_2CO_3 \xrightarrow{\Delta} 3MgCO_3 + Na_2SiO_3 + 2K_2SiO_3 + H_2SiO_3$

Cool, and transfer the fused mixture to a dish or beaker with the aid of about 50 ml. of hot water. Add hydrochloric acid to the liquid until it ceases to cause effervescence, then add 10 ml. more of the acid (4, 5, 6),

(4) $MgCO_3 + 2HCl \rightarrow MgCl_2 + H_2O + CO_2\uparrow$

(5) $Na_2SiO_3 + 2HCl \rightarrow 2NaCl + (SiO_2 + H_2O)$
(Soluble)

(6) $K_2SiO_3 + 2HCl \rightarrow 2KCl + (SiO_2 + H_2O)$
(Soluble)

and evaporate the mixture to dryness on a water-bath. The silicic acid formed by the reactions expressed in equations (5) and (6), H$_2$SiO$_3$ (SiO$_2$ + H$_2$O), when heated to 100° C. loses all but 13 per cent of its water and the silica becomes insoluble. Cool, add 20 ml. of water, boil, and filter the mixture. An insoluble residue of silica remains. The filtrate contains soluble magnesium chloride and responds to the tests for *Magnesium* (*q.v.*).

Commercial Manufacture.—Purified talc is made by boiling very finely powdered talc with water containing about 2 per cent of hydrochloric acid, allowing the insoluble matter to subside, decanting the supernatant liquid and repeating the process with a weaker hydrochloric acid. The talc that has been freed of iron and other soluble impurities is thoroughly washed with water and dried at 110° C.

Uses.—*Talc* (Talcum, Purified Talc), U.S.P. XVII, is a native, hydrous magnesium silicate, sometimes containing a small proportion of aluminum silicate.

The unctuous nature of Talc and its ready adherence to skin make it useful as a dusting powder for various dermatoses. It may be used alone or together with starch or boric acid as well as other medicaments. Its use as a dusting powder for surgeon's gloves has lost its one-time status because of the possibility of sterile abscess formation around unabsorbed particles. Absorbable dusting powders (see U.S.P.) are gradually displacing it. However, it finds extensive use in toilet preparations that are to be dusted on the skin surface.

Because of its insolubility, it is employed as a filtering and distributing medium. For such use it should not be finer than the powder which passes through a No. 80 sieve but is retained by a No. 100 sieve. A powder finer than No. 100 is not retained by the average filter paper and causes murky filtrates. As a filtering agent, it is used in the preparation of numerous pharmaceutical solutions, *e.g.*, the aromatic waters, Magnesium Citrate Solution, Aromatic Elixir, Antiseptic Solution, Orange Syrup, etc.

21

Calcium and Calcium Compounds

CALCIUM

Symbol, Ca. Valence, 2. Atomic Weight, 40.08;
Atomic Number, 20

History.—A description of the process of calcining limestone (lime burning) is found in the writings of Dioscorides and Pliny. The ancients used lime in mortar for building purposes. In 1808, Davy obtained the first calcium metal by electrolysis.

Occurrence.—Calcium is never found free in Nature. In combination it is widely distributed and occurs most abundantly in the form of the carbonate. This is found in a comparatively pure condition as *chalk, marble, limestone, calcite, aragonite,* and *marl.* Many other minerals, notably *dolomite,* contain the carbonate as one of the constituents. Calcium also occurs in large quantities as *fluorspar* or *fluorite* [CaF_2], *gypsum* or *selenite* [$CaSO_4.2H_2O$], *anhydrite* [$CaSO_4$], *phosphate rock* [$Ca_3(PO_4)_2$], and as a constituent of nearly all silicates. Both plants and animals contain calcium in some combined form. In animals it is the primary element in bones.

Physical Properties.—Calcium is a silvery-white, crystalline (cubic) metal, which gradually becomes gray by oxidation. It is harder than lead and may be cut, drawn, and rolled. It has a density of 1.54, melts at 850° C., and boils at 1440° C.

Chemical Properties.—The chemical properties of calcium will be considered under the headings: (1) metallic calcium, and (2) the calcium ion.

1. *Calcium* readily decomposes water at ordinary temperatures with the rapid evolution of hydrogen. The heat developed by this reaction is insufficient to inflame the latter (difference from alkali metals). Oxygen, hydrogen, nitrogen, sulfur, phosphorus, and the halogens do not readily attack the metal in the cold. However, when it is heated they combine vigorously with it. Calcium burns in air with a brilliant white flame to form calcium oxide (CaO) and calcium nitride (Ca_3N_2). The latter is acted upon by water and forms ammonia and the hydroxide of the metal (1).

(1) $Ca_3N_2 + 6H_2O \rightarrow 3Ca(OH)_2 + 2NH_3 \uparrow$

(373)

25

Calcium forms an amalgam with mercury.

2. The chief chemical reactions involving the *calcium ion* are those of precipitation. The calcium ion forms insoluble compounds with carbonate, hydroxide, sulfate, oxalate and phosphate. A typical example is that of the carbonate ion which readily precipitates calcium as the insoluble carbonate (2).

$$(2) \ Ca^{++} + CO_3^= \rightarrow CaCO_3 \downarrow$$

This reaction is involved in the testing of solutions for calcium, *e. g.*, by passing CO_2 into a solution of calcium hydroxide. It is interesting to note that even though insoluble calcium carbonate does form, it is possible to solubilize it by passing into the cold solution more CO_2 (3) to form soluble calcium bicarbonate. (See temporary hard water.)

$$(3) \ CaCO_3 + CO_2 + H_2O \rightleftarrows Ca(HCO_3)_2$$

Ammonium salts (not carbonate) also increase the solubility (4 or 5).

$$(4) \ CaCO_3 + H_2O \rightleftarrows Ca(OH)_2 + H_2CO_3$$
$$Ca(OH)_2 \rightleftarrows Ca^{++} + 2OH^-$$
$$+$$
$$2NH_4Cl \rightleftarrows 2Cl^- + 2NH_4^+$$
$$\updownarrow$$
$$2NH_4OH \rightleftarrows 2NH_3 \uparrow + 2H_2O$$

$$(5) \ CaCO_3 + 2NH_4Cl \rightarrow CaCl_2 + 2NH_3 \uparrow + H_2O + CO_2 \uparrow$$

Soluble oxalate salts also precipitate calcium as insoluble calcium oxalate (6).

$$(6) \ C_2O_4^= + Ca^{++} \rightarrow CaC_2O_4 \downarrow$$

When neutral solutions of calcium salts are treated with soluble phosphates such as sodium phosphate, a white, flocculent precipitate of insoluble secondary calcium phosphate forms (7). (See Dibasic Calcium Phosphate.) If, however, the solution is made ammoniacal, the precipitate which forms is tertiary calcium phosphate (8), (9). (See Tribasic Calcium Phosphate.)

$$(7) \ Ca^{++} + Na_2HPO_4 \rightarrow CaHPO_4 \downarrow + 2Na^+$$
$$(8) \ HPO_4^= + OH^- \rightarrow H_2O + PO_4^\equiv$$
$$(9) \ 3Ca^{++} + 2PO_4^\equiv \rightarrow Ca_3(PO_4)_2 \downarrow$$

Calcium ion is also precipitated by sulfate ions as more or less insoluble calcium sulfate (10), but it requires a fairly high concentration of sulfate ion because calcium sulfate is appreciably soluble (1 in 500).

$$(10) \ Ca^{++} + SO_4^= \rightleftarrows CaSO_4 \downarrow$$

Calcium ions are precipitated in basic media as the hydroxide and also form insoluble soaps. Sequestering agents are used to remove these ions by inactivating them. These agents also increase the solubility of some calcium salts. Glycerin, for example, will dissolve both calcium hydroxide and calcium oxide. (See sequestering agents.)

Volatile compounds of calcium impart a reddish-yellow color to a non-luminous flame, and non-volatile calcium salts will do the same when moistened with hydrochloric acid.

Many of the calcium salts exhibit a peculiar solubility in that they are more soluble in cold solutions than they are in hot solutions.

Official Tests for Identity.—1. In neutral or alkaline solutions calcium salts produce a white precipitate when treated with ammonium oxalate T.S. (6). The precipitate is insoluble in acetic acid but is soluble in hydrochloric acid.

2. Calcium salts when moistened with hydrochloric acid will impart a transient yellowish-red color to a non-luminous flame.

Commercial Manufacture.—Calcium is made by the electrolysis of the molten chloride. The process is carried out in a crucible made of iron and lined with blocks of graphite securely fastened together. This acts as the anode. A rod of iron serves as the cathode. The crucible is filled with anhydrous calcium chloride, which is melted by temporarily connecting the anode and cathode with a thin rod of carbon. As soon as fusion has begun, the carbon rod is removed. The resistance of the fused material is sufficient to maintain the temperature. The calcium is liberated at the end of the cathode and collects upon the surface of the melt. When the cathode is drawn slowly from the bath, the calcium, which adheres to it, is obtained in the form of an irregular rod. At no time during the run is the calcium rod separated from the molten metal cathode on the surface of the bath, as this would cut off the current and the reaction would cease.

The metal is sometimes used instead of Na or K as a reducing agent in organic synthesis and for dehydrating oils, etc.

Pharmacological Action of the Calcium Ion.[1]—Calcium is extremely important in the maintenance of certain normal body functions. It is important in the following capacities:

1. As an indispensable cation relating to the functional integrity of the voluntary and autonomic nervous systems.

2. As a factor in proper cardiac function.

3. As a factor in blood coagulation.

4. As the structural basis of the skeleton and like tissue.

Ordinarily, sufficient calcium is ingested in the normal diet (0.45 Gm. daily requirement) to supply the body needs. The

[1] Treatise on calcium see "Calcium Metabolism" by J. T. Irving, New York, Wiley, 1957.

ingested calcium is absorbed in the upper portion of the intestinal tract and is excreted in the urine and feces. An acid condition in the intestine favors absorption of calcium salts because of better solubility in the acid medium. An alkaline reaction retards absorption by favoring precipitation of insoluble calcium salts. Likewise, a high fatty acid content in the bowel slows down absorption by forming insoluble calcium soaps.

The calcium of the body exists principally in the form of the bony skeleton as calcium carbonate and phosphate. The calcifying mechanism has been elucidated recently by Sobel and his coworkers.[1] The mechanism is as follows: "A space between two thin collagen fibrils is arranged so that it captures calcium and phosphate ions from body fluids. The captured ions fit into a mold where they are converted to the exact shape of a nucleus of a calcium phosphate crystal. Once the nucleus is formed it begins to grow into a crystal at the given site. The mold-forming substance is collagen activated by a complicated mucopolysaccharide which requires energy released by ATP or UTP or both and probably a system that highly concentrates calcium and phosphate ions in the surrounding fluid.

Another factor in the complete system for producing nuclei, says Dr. Sobel, is probably an enzyme system or systems such as the glycolic or citric acid cycles. The shape of the nuclei-forming mold is so specific that strontium ions, which have properties closely related to calcium, but are slightly larger, cannot replace the calcium." The rest of the calcium is found in the extracellular fluid (see pharmacology of sodium ion), in the form of soluble simple salts, combinations with serum protein (as undissociated calcium), and soluble calcium forms. There is a balance in the body between the various forms of calcium, but the ionic form of calcium is the only one which is physiologically active.

Reduction in the amount of ionized calcium in the blood causes a hypocalcemic tetany characterized by an increased irritability of all types of nerve and muscle. On the other hand, serum calcium in excess has the opposite effect and from the pharmacological point of view may be considered as a nerve sedative.

Calcium has a cardiac action similar to digitalis, and it is believed that high calcium concentrations increase the toxicity of digitalis. The cardiac effects of calcium are related to the delicate balance between calcium and potassium ion, either one when in excess causing cessation of heart beat. Excess potassium causes a diastolic arrest, whereas excess calcium causes systolic arrest.

Oral administration of calcium salts during calcium therapy is not necessarily contraindicated because it is difficult to achieve a significant rise in blood calcium by this route. It is well, however, to exercise some care in this connection if large doses of vitamin D or parathyroid extract are being administered simultaneously.

[1] Chem. and Eng. News, Sept. 28, 1959, p. 42.

It is believed by some that calcium decreases the permeability of the capillaries and thereby prevents edemas, etc. This belief has not been well received and consequently calcium is little used for this purpose.

The role of calcium in blood clotting is well known and does not require further elaboration. However, it is well to point out that calcium deficiency rarely, if ever, is the cause of prolonged blood clotting time. Increasing calcium intake never shortens the clotting time.

Nutritional deficiencies of calcium lead to faulty growth. The need for calcium therapy in these conditions may result from insufficient intake, insufficient vitamin D, etc. Vitamin D is essential for the maximum absorption of dietary calcium and this fact is reflected in the many calcium preparations on the market to which vitamin D has been added. Insufficient calcium in the diet tied together with too little calcium in the skeleton results in rickets in children and osteomalacia in adults.

A more or less new use of calcium salts is in the control or relief of various allergic manifestations, *i.e.*, eczema, pruritus and urticaria. On the theory that these allergies are exhibitions of vagotonia (irritability of the vagus nerve) and because calcium and magnesium are nerve sedatives, it would logically follow that intensive calcium therapy would relieve such conditions. This has proven correct and therefore calcium is much used intravenously in combination with bromine (as calcium bromide or organic calcium bromide combinations) to decrease skin sensitivity in the aforementioned diseases.

"The application of bromides to dermatology[1] can be understood readily when one realizes the embryologic relationship between the skin and the nervous system, both being derived from the ectoderm, and the numerous symptoms of cutaneous diseases which are associated with nervous irritation such as itching, nerve reflex hyperirritability, anxiety with itching, nervous insomnia with itching and certain types of allergic disturbances with a known psychiatric basis."

A recent use of calcium salts (calcium gluconate) in ointment form has been in the treatment of atopic eczema. A 10 per cent ointment adjusted to pH 5.5 was used. Calcium ions are said to be important in tissue defense and in metabolism.

Calcium salts are also used as acid-forming diuretics, the mechanism of action in the case of calcium chloride being analogous to that of ammonium chloride. However, the calcium ion is removed from the chloride as insoluble calcium phosphate, whereas ammonium ion is disposed of as urea. (See pharmacology of ammonium ion.)

Some of the insoluble calcium salts, *e.g.*, calcium carbonate and tribasic calcium phosphate, are used as gastric antacids. It is claimed that salts of this type are less apt to cause a systemic alkalosis than are soluble antacids such as sodium bicarbonate.

[1] Parker, W.: J. Mo. St. Med. Assoc., 812–814 (Nov. 1950).

OFFICIAL CALCIUM COMPOUNDS

CALCIUM CARBONATE

Precipitated Calcium Carbonate, U.S.P. XVII

Formula, $CaCO_3$.   Molecular Weight, 100.09

Occurrence.—Calcium carbonate is the most abundant and widely distributed calcium salt.   It occurs as chalk, limestone, marble, aragonite and calcite, and is one of the chief constituents of shells (eggs and mollusks), corals and pearls. (See Calcium.)   In chalk it is amorphous, in limestone it is in a massive, indistinctly crystalline form, in marble it is crystalline, whereas in calcite and aragonite it occurs as distinct crystals.   The dimorphic character of calcium carbonate is illustrated by the last two forms.   When carbon dioxide is passed into cold lime water, or when a cold aqueous solution of a calcium salt is treated with a solution of a carbonate, a flocculent, amorphous precipitate is produced, which soon becomes crystalline (calcite).   Calcite is more abundant than aragonite in Nature and occurs as hexagonal crystals having a density of 2.711.   On the other hand, if hot solutions of the reacting substances are mixed, a crystalline precipitate is formed immediately (aragonite). Aragonite occurs in Nature as rhombic prisms having a density of 2.93.

Physical Properties.—Precipitated Calcium Carbonate is a fine, white microcrystalline powder.   It is odorless and tasteless.   It is stable in air.

The salt is nearly insoluble in water (0.065 Gm. per liter at 20° C.).   The water solubility is increased by the presence of CO_2 (see chemical properties) and also by ammonium salts (except ammonium carbonate) (2).   The water solubility is decreased in the presence of alkali hydroxides.   It is insoluble in alcohol, but is soluble in most acids with effervescence.

Chemical Properties.—One of the principal chemical properties of calcium carbonate, of course, is its ability to neutralize acids. This is a common property of all other carbonates.   A typical example is the reaction with hydrochloric acid (1).

(1) $CaCO_3 + 2HCl \rightarrow CaCl_2 + CO_2 \uparrow + H_2O$

The solubility of calcium carbonate in ammonium salts is accounted for in the following equation (2).   The reaction does not go to completion unless the mixture is boiled with a large excess of the ammonium salt.   It is interesting to observe that all ammonium salts (except carbonate and bicarbonate) are acid in solution and will effervesce with a carbonate.

(2) $CaCO_3 + 2NH_4^+ \rightarrow Ca^{++} + 2NH_3 \uparrow + H_2O + CO_2 \uparrow$

The assay of this salt is carried out by dissolving an accurately weighed sample in diluted hydrochloric acid, making an appropriate dilution, alkalinizing with sodium hydroxide and then titrating to a distinctly blue end-point with standard disodium ethylenediaminetetraacetate solution using hydroxy naphthol blue as an indicator.

Official Tests for Identity.—The addition of acetic acid to calcium carbonate produces an effervescence (3), and the resulting solution, after boiling to expel carbon dioxide and neutralizing the excess acid, responds to all tests for *Calcium* (*q.v.*).

$$(3) \quad CaCO_3 + 2CH_3COOH \rightarrow (CH_3COO)_2Ca + CO_2 \uparrow + H_2O$$

Commercial Manufacture.—Calcium carbonate is prepared commercially by the interaction of sodium carbonate and calcium chloride (4). It is prepared in various grades for widely different uses.

$$(4) \quad Na_2CO_3 + CaCl_2 \rightarrow CaCO_3 \downarrow + 2NaCl$$

Uses.—*Precipitated Calcium Carbonate* (Precipitated Chalk), U.S.P. XVII, when dried at 200° for 4 hours, contains calcium equivalent to not less than 98 per cent of $CaCO_3$. This preparation is used *externally* as a dentifrice, *N.F. Dentifrice* N.F. XI, because it has a mild abrasive quality due to its microcrystalline structure. It is used *internally* as an antacid because of its acid neutralizing powers. For use as an antacid *Calcium Carbonate Tablets* are available as well as a powder and tablet combination of *Sodium Bicarbonate and Calcium Carbonate*. Although its water insolubility suggests that calcium in this form is not appreciably absorbed, it has been found that occasional patients treated with calcium carbonate[1,2,3] show a significant alkalosis and hypercalcemia. Ivanovich *et al.*[4] have shown that all persons who were able to secrete acid gastric juice readily absorbed calcium from $CaCO_3$ and, indeed, there was little difference between the absorption of calcium from calcium carbonate and from calcium gluconate.

Usual dose—1 Gm. four or more times daily with a dosage range of 1 to 2 Gm.

Calcium carbonate in other grades than the pharmaceutical grade is used for a variety of purposes.

Prepared Chalk (Creta Praeparata, Drop Chalk), last recognized in N.F. XI, is a *native* form of calcium carbonate that has been freed from most of its impurities by elutriation. It contains, when dried to constant weight at 180° for four hours, not less than 97 per cent of $CaCO_3$.

[1] Cope, C. L., Clin. Sci., 2, 287 (1936).
[2] Punsar, S. and Somer, T., Acta. Med. Scand., 173, 435 (1963).
[3] McMillan, D. E. and Freeman, R. B., Medicine (Balt.), 44, 485 (1965).
[4] Ivanovich, P., Fellows, H. and Rich, C., Ann. Int. Med., 66, 917 (1967).

It is a white to grayish-white, microcrystalline powder. It is often prepared in cones, sometimes called "conical drops." It is odorless, tasteless, and stable in the air. Prepared chalk responds to all the tests for identity given under calcium carbonate (*q.v.*).

Prepared chalk is made by the process of elutriation. This consists in suspending the powdered native chalk in cold water, allowing the heavier materials to subside and straining the milky aqueous suspension of the finer particles through suitable cloths. The pasty mass is transferred from the strainer to a funnel, from which it is dropped upon porous tiles. The more or less coarse material that settles out is known as "whiting."

Prepared chalk is to be preferred to precipitated calcium carbonate *for internal* administration because it is more impalpable and because it possesses marked adhesive properties. It is an excellent antacid and, on account of its mild, non-irritating protective action, is employed in the treatment of various forms of diarrhea. Usual dose—1 Gm.

CALCIUM CHLORIDE

Calcium Chloride, U.S.P. XVII

Formula, $CaCl_2.2H_2O$. Molecular Weight, 147.03

Occurrence.—Calcium chloride occurs as *tachhydrite* ($CaCl_2.2MgCl_2.12H_2O$) at Stassfurt. It is found in some other minerals, in sea water and in many mineral waters. In the fourteenth century, Isaac Hollendus prepared it by heating a mixture of lime and sal ammoniac (ammonium chloride).

Physical Properties.—Calcium Chloride occurs as white, hard fragments or granules. It is odorless and has a sharp, bitter, saline taste. It is very deliquescent. Water solutions of the salt are acid in reaction.

One Gm. of Calcium Chloride dissolves in 1.2 ml. of water and in about 10 ml. of alcohol, at 25° C. One Gm. also dissolves in 0.7 ml. of boiling water and in about 2 ml. of boiling alcohol. It is insoluble in ether, chloroform, and in fixed and volatile oils. Because of its great solubility in water, the salt forms an excellent freezing mixture with ice. When 1 part of the salt is mixed with two-thirds of its weight of crushed ice it gives a temperature of −45° C.

Chemical Properties.—Calcium chloride forms several hydrates, *viz.*, the monohydrate, $CaCl_2.H_2O$, the dihydrate, $CaCl_2.2H_2O$, the tetrahydrate, $CaCl_2.4H_2O$, and the hexahydrate, $CaCl_2.6H_2O$. When aqueous solutions of the salt are evaporated, there are obtained large, hexagonal prisms of the hexahydrate, which melt at 29.92° C. and have a specific gravity of 1.6817 at $\frac{20°}{4}$ C. Upon the application of heat, all of the hydrates lose part of their water of hydration and are converted into a porous mass which is used for drying gases and liquids. It should be noted that during the heating, some calcium oxide is formed by the reaction of some of the calcium chloride with water (1) (2).

(1) $CaCl_2 + 2HOH \rightleftarrows Ca(OH)_2 + 2HCl$

(2) $Ca(OH)_2 \xrightarrow{\Delta} CaO + H_2O$

Although anhydrous calcium chloride is widely used for drying organic liquids, gases, etc., it is unsuited as a drying agent for alcohols because it forms crystalline compounds known as *alcoholates* with them: $CaCl_2.4C_2H_5OH$; $CaCl_2.4CH_3OH$. It is likewise unsuited for drying ammonia gas, since it unites directly with it, forming a compound, $CaCl_2.4NH_3$. The chemical properties of calcium chloride are exhibited by the reactions of the calcium ion and of the chloride ion.

The assay is conducted essentially according to the procedure for Precipitated Calcium Carbonate (*q.v.*).

Official Tests for Identity.—1. A 1 in 10 aqueous solution of Calcium Chloride responds to the tests for *Calcium* (*q.v.*).

2. The aqueous solution also responds to the tests for *Chloride* (*q.v.*).

Commercial Manufacture.—Calcium chloride is a by-product of many industrial processes of which perhaps the Solvay soda process is the most important. (See sodium carbonate.) In this process ammonium chloride is a by-product at the time sodium bicarbonate is formed. The sodium bicarbonate is in suspension in the solution containing the ammonium chloride and is then filtered out. The recovery of the ammonia from the ammonium chloride is accomplished by treating this solution with milk of lime, $Ca(OH)_2$ (3), leaving calcium chloride as a by-product. The liberated ammonia, of course, is easily obtained from the solution by heating, and the remaining solution needs only to be concentrated to obtain the solid calcium chloride.

(3) $2NH_4Cl + Ca(OH)_2 \rightarrow CaCl_2 + 2NH_3 \uparrow + 2H_2O$

Uses.—*Calcium Chloride*, U.S.P. XVII, contains an amount of $CaCl_2$ equivalent to not less than 99 per cent and not more than 107 per cent of $CaCl_2 \cdot 2H_2O$. From the definition it may be observed that the official salt is a mixture of the hydrates. This salt is one of the important calcium salts used in therapy. When calcium chloride is administered, the calcium is disposed of by the body as insoluble calcium phosphate $[Ca_3(PO_4)_2]$ and is excreted by way of the bowel. The chloride portion of the molecule acts in a manner similar to hydrochloric acid, *i.e.*, to decrease the alkali reserve of the body. It is for this reason that calcium chloride is often administered to produce an acid urine or a definite acidosis (as in the treatment of calcium tetany). Although calcium chloride may be used for its calcium content, and sometimes is, it has never been shown that it is superior to any other calcium salt. In fact, calcium chloride is inferior for oral administration because of its unpleasant taste and highly irritating nature. If it is to be administered orally, however, it should be combined with a demulcent vehicle, such as milk, to minimize the irritation. Likewise, it is not the best preparation for parenteral administration since it cannot be used intramuscularly or subcutaneously due to its irritating and corrosive characteristics. Therefore, its use is confined to intravenous injection as the official preparation *Calcium Chloride Injection.* Solutions utilizing this salt are *Ringer's Injection* and *Lactated Ringer's Injection.* The usual intravenous dose of calcium chloride as an electrolyte replenisher is 1.5 to 3.75 Gm. injected very slowly. Because of the disadvantages associated with the use of calcium chloride, efforts have been made to modify the calcium chloride molecule in such a way as to minimize the unpleasant side-effects. As a result, a compound chemically called calcium chloride urea, $CaCl_2.4(NH_2)_2CO$, and commercially named Afenil was made. It is administered intravenously, not orally, and is said to be much better tolerated and less irritating than calcium chloride. Calcium salts such as the lactate, gluconate and levulinate are in more general use.

CALCIUM GLUCONATE

Calcium Gluconate, U.S.P. XVII

Formula, $C_{12}H_{22}CaO_{14}$;$[CH_2OH(CHOH)_4.COO]_2Ca$.

Molecular Weight, 430.38

Physical Properties.—Calcium Gluconate occurs as a white, crystalline or granular powder without odor or taste. It is stable in air.

One Gm. of Calcium Gluconate dissolves slowly in about 30 ml. of water at 25° C., and in about 5 ml. of boiling water. It is insoluble in alcohol and in other organic solvents.

Chemical Properties.—Solutions of calcium gluconate respond to all reactions of the calcium ion. Addition of hydrochloric acid or other acids to solutions of calcium gluconate causes the formation of gluconic acid in solution (1). The gluconic acid is said to be converted quite easily to d-gluconolactone (2).

(1) Calcium Gluconate + 2HCl→

$$CH_2OH-CH-\overset{\overset{\displaystyle OH}{|}}{CH}-CH-CH-COOH + CaCl_2$$

$$\underset{OH}{|}\ \underset{OH}{|}\qquad\underset{OH}{|}$$

(Gluconic Acid)

(2) Gluconic acid $\xrightarrow{-H_2O}$ CH$_2$OH—CH—CH—CH—CH—C=O

with OH above the third CH, and OH below the first CH and below the fourth CH, and O bridging below.

Calcium Gluconate is assayed essentially by the same procedure used for Precipitated Calcium Carbonate (*q.v.*).

Official Tests for Identity.—1. A 1 in 50 solution of Calcium Gluconate responds to the tests for *Calcium* (*q.v.*).

2. To 5 ml. of a warmed 1 in 10 aqueous solution of Calcium Gluconate is added about 0.7 ml. of glacial acetic acid (3) and 1 ml. of freshly distilled phenylhydrazine. The mixture is heated on a water-bath for thirty minutes and allowed to cool. When the solution is cool and, particularly when the inside of the tube is scratched with a glass rod, crystals of gluconic-acid-phenylhydrazide form (4).

(3) $[CH_2OH(CHOH)_4.COO]_2Ca.H_2O + 2CH_3COOH \rightarrow 2CH_2OH.$- $(CHOH)_4.COOH + Ca(CH_3COO)_2 + H_2O$

(4) $CH_2OH(CHOH)_4.COOH + C_6H_5NH.NH_2 \rightarrow CH_2OH$- $(CHOH)_4CO.NH.NH.C_6H_5 \downarrow + H_2O$

Commercial Manufacture.—Calcium gluconate may be prepared either by the oxidation of glucose to gluconic acid in the presence of calcium carbonate or by first preparing gluconic acid and then adding calcium carbonate to form the salt. In the former method the oxidation of glucose is effected either by bromine or by electrolytic oxidation in the presence of sodium bromide. In the latter procedure, the gluconic acid is usually obtained by the action of various molds or bacteria of the *Acetobacter* group upon glucose.

Uses.—*Calcium Gluconate*, U.S.P. XVII, dried at 105° for 16 hours, contains not less than 98 per cent and not more than 102 per cent of $C_{12}H_{22}CaO_{14}$. It is used as a source of calcium ion both for oral, intravenous and intramuscular use, and is much superior to calcium chloride in that it has a better taste and is much less irritating. It is classified as an electrolyte replenisher (calcium). *Calcium Gluconate Tablets* are used extensively in supplementing the diet of convalescents and expectant mothers. Usual dose—Oral, 1 Gm. three or more times a day; Intramuscular or intravenous, 1 Gm. daily. The usual daily oral dosage range is 3 to 15 Gm.

Calcium Gluconate Injection is a sterile solution of Calcium Gluconate in Water for Injection. It is permissible to add calcium D-saccharate, or other calcium salts as stabilizers provided, however, that the amount of such added calcium salts, calculated as calcium (Ca), does not exceed 5 per cent of the calcium (Ca) present as calcium gluconate. Calcium D-saccharate functions as a sequestering agent to increase the solubility and prevent precipitation of the calcium salt. For the purpose of insuring greater stability, it is also permitted to adjust the pH with sodium hydroxide to not above 8.2.

The injection has been used in the treatment of black widow spider bite but is of no value for the scorpion sting.

CALCIUM HYDROXIDE

Calcium Hydroxide, U.S.P. XVII

Formula, Ca(OH)$_2$.   Molecular Weight, 74.09

Physical Properties.—Calcium Hydroxide occurs as a soft, white, crystalline powder, possessing an alkaline, slightly bitter taste. One Gm. of it dissolves in 630 ml. of water at 25° C., and in 1300 ml. of boiling water. It is soluble in glycerin and in syrup, but is insoluble in alcohol.

Chemical Properties.—When mixed with three or four times its own weight of water, it forms a smooth magma called "Milk of Lime." This is different from "Lime Water" which is a clear, saturated aqueous solution of calcium hydroxide.

Calcium hydroxide solutions are basic in reaction (pH 12.3) and are capable of neutralizing acids, *e.g.*, hydrochloric acid, with the formation of the corresponding calcium salt (1). This is the basis for its assay. As a special type of neutralizing action one may consider the ability of calcium hydroxide to absorb carbon dioxide with the formation of calcium carbonate (2, 3).

(1) $Ca(OH)_2 + 2HCl \rightarrow CaCl_2 + 2H_2O$

(2) $H_2O + CO_2 \rightleftarrows H_2CO_3$

(3) $Ca(OH)_2 + H_2CO_3 \rightarrow CaCO_3 \downarrow + 2H_2O$

This property of calcium hydroxide is exerted either in the solid form (requiring a little moisture) (see Soda Lime) or in the form of a solution. For this reason lime water is often cloudy and develops a precipitate of CaCO$_3$.

When strongly heated, calcium hydroxide loses water and is converted into calcium oxide (4).

(4) $Ca(OH)_2 \overset{\Delta}{\rightarrow} CaO + H_2O$

Official Tests for Identity.—1. When mixed with water to form "Milk of Lime" and allowed to stand, it settles to give a clear supernatant liquid. This liquid is distinctly alkaline to litmus (pH 12.3).

2. When calcium hydroxide is dissolved with acetic acid the resulting solution gives all the tests for *Calcium* (*q.v.*).

Commercial Manufacture.—Calcium hydroxide, commonly known as "hydrated lime," is made by the careful addition of a limited amount of water to lime (CaO). This process is known as "slaking" and is characterized by the avid absorption of water by the oxide to form calcium hydroxide (5) accompanied by the evolution of much heat, swelling of the CaO lumps and a final disintegration into a fine, white powder. Of course, the quality of the finished product depends upon the purity of the original limestone used to make the CaO. Several grades of calcium hydroxide are produced commercially.

(5) $CaO + H_2O \rightarrow Ca(OH)_2$

Uses.—*Calcium Hydroxide* (Slaked Lime), U.S.P. XVII, contains not less than 95 per cent of $Ca(OH)_2$. The medicinal and pharmaceutical applications of calcium hydroxide depend upon both the alkalinity (and consequent soap forming property) and the calcium-ion content of the compound. Internally, a solution of it is used as an antacid. The solution may be added to babies' formulae for the purpose of preventing curdling of the milk in the presence of acid gastric contents, thus promoting the digestibility of the milk. Occasionally, the solution is used as a source of calcium during pregnancy, etc., but there are more efficient and more pleasant ways of ingesting the required amount of calcium.

Inasmuch as calcium hydroxide has potentially a fairly high concentration of hydroxide ions, it is used in many pharmaceutical preparations to react with the free fatty acids of an oil, *e.g.*, oleic acid to form a calcium soap; in many cases to permit of better mixing of other ingredients in the oily preparations because of the resulting soap's emulsifying property. In addition, calcium hydroxide is mildly astringent and protective. (See application in *Calamine Lotion.*)

Calcium Hydroxide Solution has a variable temperature-dependent $Ca(OH)_2$ concentration, being about 0.17 Gm. per 100 ml. at 15° C., and less at a higher temperature. It may be prepared by adding 3 Gm. of Calcium Hydroxide to 1000 ml. of cool Purified Water. The mixture is agitated vigorously and repeatedly for one hour, and then the excess Calcium Hydroxide is allowed to settle. When the solution is dispensed, it is decanted from the settled residue and filtered if necessary. This residue is primarily insoluble calcium carbonate. A practice too often resorted to in pharmacy is to continue adding water to a lime water container as long as a residue remains. Calcium Hydroxide U.S.P. is available in 5 and 10 Gm. airtight vials and may be used to freshly prepare each solution. Because of the tendency for lime water to react with carbon dioxide in the air to form insoluble calcium carbonate, it is desirable to protect it in storage. The undissolved residue in the bottle is not suitable for preparing additional quantities of Calcium Hydroxide Solution. Externally, it is used as an astringent and is applied topically as needed. Internally, it has been used in a usual dose of 15 ml.

The carbon dioxide absorbing properties are utilized in *Soda Lime*.

CALCIUM LACTATE

Calcium Lactate, N.F. XII

Formula, $C_6H_{10}CaO_6.5H_2O$; $(CH_3CH(OH).COO)_2Ca.5H_2O$

Molecular Weight, 308.30

Physical Properties.—Calcium Lactate occurs as a nearly odorless and tasteless white powder. It effloresces slightly and when heated at 120° C., it loses its 5 molecules of water and becomes anhydrous.

One Gm. of Calcium Lactate dissolves in 20 ml. of water at 25° C. It is very soluble in hot water. Aqueous solutions are acid in reaction and slowly cause effervescence with a carbonate. It is nearly insoluble in alcohol.

Chemical Properties.—The chemical properties of Calcium Lactate are those of the calcium ion (*q.v.*) and the lactate ion. (See Sodium Lactate.) The assay follows the principles of Precipitated Calcium Carbonate (*q.v.*).

Official Tests for Identity.— A solution of Calcium Lactate (1 in 20) responds to the tests for *Calcium* (*q.v.*) and *Lactate* (*q.v.*).

Commercial Manufacture.—Calcium Lactate may be made by neutralizing a hot solution of lactic acid with calcium carbonate, filtering, and allowing the salt to crystallize from the filtrate.

Large quantities of the salt are obtained by mixing a solution of a monosaccharide ($C_6H_{12}O_6$) with milk and chalk and inducing lactic acid fermentation by the addition of putrid cheese, which is rich in lactic acid bacilli (1) (2). The mixture is digested for several weeks at a temperature of about 30° C. The calcium lactate thus obtained is purified by recrystallization. It is worthy of note that the lactic acid bacillus is very sensitive to free acid, hence the necessity of immediately neutralizing any lactic acid produced. The fermentation period should be comparatively short (two weeks or so), and thus eliminate the danger of the calcium lactate being converted into calcium butyrate through the agency of butyric acid ferments.

(1) $C_6H_{12}O_6 \rightarrow 2CH_3CH(OH)COOH$

(2) $2CH_3CH(OH)COOH + CaCO_3 \rightarrow (CH_3CH(OH)COO)_2$-
$Ca + CO_2\uparrow + H_2O$

Uses.—*Calcium Lactate*, N.F. XII, contains not less than 98 per cent and not more than 101 per cent of $C_6H_{10}CaO_6$, calculated on the dried basis. It is used orally and parenterally for the action of the calcium ion. It is much less irritating than calcium chloride, although it is said to be more irritating than calcium gluconate. It is commonly used as *Calcium Lactate Tablets*. Usual dose—5 Gm. three times a day.

CALCIUM OXIDE

Lime, N.F. XII

Formula, CaO.   Molecular Weight, 56.08

Physical Properties.—This compound occurs as hard, white or grayish-white masses or granules, or a white powder.   It is odorless but has a burning caustic taste.

One Gm. of Lime is soluble in about 840 ml. of water at 25° C., and in about 1740 ml. of boiling water.   It is soluble in syrup and glycerin, but is insoluble in alcohol.   Solubility in syrup and glycerin is explained by the principle of sequestration (see discussion on sequestering agents).

Chemical Properties.—Calcium oxide slowly absorbs moisture and carbon dioxide from the air, to form "air-slaked" lime.   It unites vigorously with water (1) as previously described (see Calcium Hydroxide), to form calcium hydroxide (slaked lime).

(1) $CaO + H_2O \rightarrow Ca(OH)_2$

When dissolved in water, its actions are those of calcium hydroxide and when dissolved in acids (2) it responds to the reactions for calcium ion.

(2) $CaO + 2HCl \rightarrow CaCl_2 + H_2O$

The assay principle is the one outlined for Precipitated Calcium Carbonate (*q.v.*).

Official Tests for Identity.—1. When Lime is moistened with water heat is generated and a white powder is obtained.   If this powder is mixed with 3 or 4 times its own weight of water it forms a smooth magma known as "Milk of Lime" which is alkaline to litmus.

2. When 1 Gm. is slaked with water, and the slaked material dissolved in acetic acid, the solution responds to the tests for *Calcium* (*q.v.*).

Commercial Manufacture.—Calcium oxide is made by calcining a comparatively pure native calcium carbonate, *e.g.*, marble, chalk, or limestone, in a suitable kiln.   One of the newer forms of lime kilns consists of a vertical cylinder of steel or masonry lined with fire brick, and heated by fire boxes located near the base of the kiln. The kiln is arranged so that the entire charge of limestone is exposed to the heated products of combustion of a fuel, without actually coming in contact with them.   The carbon dioxide (see vapor density of CO_2, 1.5; air = 1) is removed from the kiln by a current of air entering at the bottom.   Large quantities of lime are being made in rotary furnaces or kilns.

Native calcium carbonates contain naturally occurring impurities, *e.g.*, magnesia, oxides of iron, silica, and clay. When clay is present in excessive amounts, a quicklime is obtained that slakes only feebly or not at all. Such a product is called "over-burnt lime" and is not fit for use.

Uses.—*Lime* (Calx, Calcium Oxide, Quicklime), N.F. XII, when freshly ignited to constant weight with a blast lamp, contains not less than 95 per cent of CaO. Lime, as such, is not used internally. Calcium oxide is used in making various insecticides (*e.g.*, Bordeaux Mixture) and is a constituent of many fertilizers. Most specifications for the above preparations, however, call for hydrated lime (calcium hydroxide).

Sulfurated Lime Solution (Vleminckx's Solution) requires 165 Gm. of Lime and 250 Gm. of Sublimed Sulfur together with enough water to give 1000 ml. of preparation. The reaction probably is represented by this equation (3):

$$(3)\ 3Ca(OH)_2 + 12S \rightarrow 2CaS_5 + CaS_2O_3 + 3H_2O$$

When sulfur reacts with a base, there is formed primarily a sulfide and a thiosulfate. Due to presence of sulfide ions, some sulfur is also in solution.

This clear, brownish-red liquid is useful as a scabicide and in treating acne and many other skin diseases, its action being that of sulfides and sulfur. A similar commercial preparation is Vlem-Dome.

DIBASIC CALCIUM PHOSPHATE

Dibasic Calcium Phosphate, U.S.P. XVII

Formula, CaHPO₄.   Molecular Weight (anhydrous) 136.06

Physical Properties.—This salt occurs as a white, odorless, and tasteless powder which is stable in air.

It is almost insoluble in water but is soluble in diluted hydrochloric and nitric acids. It is insoluble in alcohol.

Chemical Properties.—Because this salt is almost insoluble in water its chemical reactions are few and relatively unimportant. Solutions of the salt in acids respond to the reactions of calcium ion and phosphate ion.

It is interesting to note that the nomenclature of this compound, *i.e.*, *dicalcium phosphate* as it is commonly known, is somewhat confusing in that one would normally look for two calciums instead of the one which actually is present. In this case, the prefix *di* refers to the number of hydrogens which have been replaced rather than to the number of calcium atoms present.

The assay of Dibasic Calcium Phosphate involves dissolving a carefully weighed and previously ignited sample in dilute hydrochloric acid and then precipitating the calcium ion as calcium oxalate with the aid of ammonium oxalate T.S. in a slightly alkaline solution. The calcium oxalate precipitate, after thorough washing, is decomposed with sulfuric acid and the liberated oxalic acid determined by titration with standard potassium permanganate solution (see eq. 7, p. 287).

Official Tests for Identity.—1. Dibasic Calcium Phosphate, when dissolved in diluted hydrochloric acid, gives a solution which will react with ammonium oxalate T.S. to give a white precipitate of calcium oxalate. (See chemical properties for calcium ion.)

2. The salt, when dissolved with the aid of a slight excess of nitric acid, gives the usual test for phosphate with an excess of ammonium molybdate T.S. (*q.v.*).

Commercial Manufacture.—Dibasic Calcium Phosphate is usually prepared as a white, flocculent precipitate by the interaction of secondary sodium phosphate and calcium chloride in a neutral solution (1). It is necessary that the solution be neutral because an ammoniacal solution of the same reactants will precipitate tribasic calcium phosphate.

$$(1) \quad Na_2HPO_4 + CaCl_2 \rightarrow CaHPO_4 \downarrow + 2NaCl$$

Uses.—*Dibasic Calcium Phosphate*, U.S.P. XVII (Dicalcium Phosphate), is anhydrous or contains two molecules of water of hydration. It contains not less than 98 per cent of $CaHPO_4$, calculated on the anhydrous basis. Because it provides an optimum ratio of calcium to phosphorus, namely 1 to 1, this is the calcium salt most frequently recommended for oral consumption as an electrolyte replenisher. It is stated by some workers that the greater the difference between the intake levels of the two minerals (calcium and phosphorus) the less satisfactory is the absorption. Because of the fact that this salt supplies both calcium and phosphorus, it is said to be especially valuable for bone growth in children, pregnant women and lactating mothers. It is supplied either with or without vitamin D, which favors better utilization of the salt. Usual dose—1 Gm. three times a day with a range of 1 to 5 Gm.

TRIBASIC CALCIUM PHOSPHATE

Tribasic Calcium Phosphate, N.F. XII

Formula, approximately $10 CaO.3P_2O_5.H_2O$ or $[Ca_3(PO_4)_2]_3.Ca(OH_2)$.

Molecular Weight, 1004.67

Physical Properties.—Tribasic Calcium Phosphate is a bulky, white, amorphous or microcrystalline powder. It is odorless and tasteless. Its density is 3.14. The salt is stable in air. At 1670° C. the salt fuses without decomposition.

26

Tribasic Calcium Phosphate is almost insoluble in water and is decomposed slightly by boiling water. It is insoluble in alcohol. The salt readily dissolves in diluted nitric or hydrochloric acids. Except when freshly precipitated, it is almost insoluble in acetic acid.

Chemical Properties.—Although the chemical formula is not represented accurately by $Ca_3(PO_4)_2$ it can be considered by this formula with respect to its chemical reactions without significantly deviating from the chemical reactions actually observed. This compound is even more insoluble than Dibasic Calcium Phosphate, and consequently has few chemical reactions. It is interesting to note, however, that the salt is an antacid and is used as such in therapy. The antacid action is dependent upon the phenomenon of hydrolysis of the phosphate ion. Calcium phosphate is classed as an insoluble salt but all salts in contact with a solvent ionize to a slight extent (1). The phosphate ion is a fairly strong base and will combine with hydrogen ions to form the slightly ionized ion, HPO_4^- (secondary phosphate ion) (2).

(1) $Ca_3(PO_4)_2 \rightleftarrows 3Ca^{++} + 2PO_4^{\equiv}$

(2) $PO_4^{\equiv} + HCl \rightleftarrows HPO_4^= + Cl^-$

Another viewpoint is that the phosphate ion ($PO_4^{\equiv}$) reacts with water present (3).

(3) $PO_4^{\equiv} + HOH \rightleftarrows HPO_4^= + OH^-$

The hydroxide ion, of course, will react with acidic hydrogens which are introduced (from hydrochloric acid, for example) to form undissociated water. This disturbs the equilibrium and causes more of the calcium phosphate to ionize to furnish more phosphate, etc.

The assay is by dissolving the salt in dilute nitric acid and precipitating the phosphate with ammonium phosphomolybdate T.S. This precipitate is dissolved in an excess of sodium hydroxide followed by back titration with 1 N sulfuric acid using phenolphthalein as an indicator (see chemical properties of phosphoric acid).

Official Tests for Identity.—1. When the salt is dissolved in nitric acid, the solution will give a precipitate of ammonium phosphomolybdate (yellow) when treated with ammonium molybdate T.S.

2. When 100 mg. of the salt is dissolved in 5 ml. of diluted hydrochloric acid and 5 ml. of water and 1 ml. of ammonia T.S. added dropwise with shaking, the solution will give a white precipitate of calcium oxalate when 5 ml. of ammonium oxalate is added (see p. 374).

3. The salt gives a characteristic flame test for calcium.

Commercial Manufacture.—Tribasic Calcium Phosphate is usually prepared by the mutual decomposition of calcium chloride and secondary sodium phosphate in the presence of ammonia water, which reacts with the slightly ionized anion HPO_4^- to form water, ammonium ion, and phosphate ion (4, 5, 6). A small amount of calcium hydroxide also forms (7).

(4) $Na_2HPO_4 \rightarrow 2Na^+ + HPO_4^-$

(5) $HPO_4^= + NH_4OH \rightarrow PO_4^\equiv + NH_4^+ + H_2O$

(6) $3Ca^{++} + 2PO_4^\equiv \rightarrow Ca_3(PO_4)_2 \downarrow$

(7) $CaCl_2 + 2NH_4OH \rightarrow Ca(OH)_2 + 2NH_4Cl$

Complete reaction:

(8) $10CaCl_2 + 6Na_2HPO_4 + 8NH_4OH \rightarrow [Ca_3(PO_4)_2]_3.Ca(OH)_2 + 12NaCl + 8NH_4Cl + 6H_2O$

The white precipitate is washed with hot water until free from chlorides and dried at 100° C.

Uses.— *Tribasic Calcium Phosphate* (Precipitated Calcium Phosphate), N.F. XII, after ignition at 800° for 30 min., contains an amount of phosphate (PO_4) corresponding to not less than 90 per cent of $Ca_3(PO_4)_2$. Although this salt may be used as a source of calcium (especially when both calcium and phosphorus are desired) it is less effective than the dibasic form. However, it is a valuable gastric antacid. Usual dose—1 Gm.

CALCIUM STEARATE

Calcium Stearate, N.F. XII

Formula (approx.), $[CH_3(CH_2)_{16}COO]_2Ca$ Molecular Weight, 607.00

Physical Properties.—Calcium Stearate occurs as a fine, white to yellow-white, bulky powder having a slight, characteristic odor. It is unctuous and is free from grittiness. It is insoluble in water, alcohol and ether.

Chemical Properties.—Because of the water-insolubility of this salt it may be considered chemically inert for all practical purposes. It will, however, decompose with either hydrochloric acid (1) or sulfuric acid (2).

(1) $[CH_3(CH_2)_{16}COO]_2Ca+2HCl \rightarrow CaCl_2+2CH_3(CH_2)_{16}COOH$

(2) $[CH_3(CH_2)_{16}COO]_2Ca+H_2SO_4 \rightarrow CaSO_4+2CH_3(CH_2)_{16}COOH$

to liberate the free fatty acids. Although the salt is here represented as a stearate it contains an appreciable quantity of palmitate, $[CH_3(CH_2)_{14}COO]_2Ca$, and the liberation of the free fatty acid portion results in a mixture of both acids.

The assay of this compound is carried out by boiling an accurately weighed sample with 1N hydrochloric acid (1) in order to liberate the free fatty acids and to obtain all the calcium in the aqueous layer. After complete washing of the fatty acid layer with water to obtain all the calcium, the aqueous filtrate is neutralized with sodium hydroxide solution (1 in 5) and then titrated with standard disodium ethylenediaminetetraacetate. The titration is carried out by first adding about 30 ml. of the titrant to complex most of the calcium, alkalinizing the solution with sodium hydroxide T.S. and then finishing the titration with the titrant to a blue end point with hydroxy naphthol blue. It is necessary to have an alkaline medium for the final titration in order to obtain an accurate endpoint.

Official Tests for Identity.—Two tests are provided, one for the calcium portion and the other for the fatty acid portion of the salt.

A. Heat 1 Gm. of Calcium Stearate with a mixture of 25 ml. of water and 5 ml. of hydrochloric acid. Free fatty acids are liberated (1) and float on the surface of the liquid as an oily layer. The aqueous layer responds to all tests for *Calcium* (*q.v.*).

B. Mix 25 Gm. of Calcium Stearate with 200 ml. of hot water, then add 60 ml. of diluted sulfuric acid, and heat the mixture with frequent stirring (2) until the separated fatty acid layer is clear. This fatty acid layer is then washed with boiling water to free it completely of sulfate following which it is transferred to a beaker and heated on a steam bath until water has separated and the fatty acids are clear. The acids are allowed to cool, the water layer is poured off, the acids again melted and filtered into a dry beaker where they are dried at 105° C. for 20 minutes. The fatty acids so obtained congeal at a temperature not below 54° C. (see N.F. XII, p. 451, for determination of "Solidification Temperature of Fatty Acids").

Commercial Manufacture.—Although there are various methods by which calcium stearate can be made, a suitable product can be prepared by interacting a soluble calcium salt with sodium stearate (3) and the product washed free of by-product salt with hot water. Alternatively, stearic acid may be heated with calcium oxide (4) or calcium carbonate (5).

(3) $CaCl_2 + 2CH_3(CH_2)_{16}COONa \rightarrow [CH_3(CH_2)_{16}COO]_2Ca + 2NaCl$

(4) $CaO + 2CH_3(CH_2)_{16}COOH \rightarrow [CH_3(CH_2)_{16}COO]_2Ca + H_2O$

(5) $CaCO_3 + 2CH_3(CH_2)_{16}COOH \rightarrow [CH_3(CH_2)_{16}COO]_2Ca + H_2O + CO_2 \uparrow$

Uses.—*Calcium Stearate*, N.F. XII, "is a compound of calcium with variable proportions of stearic and palmitic acids. It contains the equivalent of not less than 9.0 per cent and not more than 10.5 per cent CaO." The sole purpose for official recognition of this salt is in keeping with the need to set up standards for chemicals that are taken internally, not as medications *per se* but as pharmaceutical adjuncts. In this capacity, Calcium Stearate is found in many tabletted preparations by virtue of its use as a lubricant in the tabletting process. Its virtually non-toxic nature and unctuous properties make it ideal for this purpose.

CALCIUM SULFATE

Calcium Sulfate, N.F. XII

Formula, $CaSO_4.2H_2O$ Molecular Weight, 172.17

Physical Properties.—Calcium Sulfate occurs as a fine, white to slightly yellow-white odorless powder. The salt is only slightly soluble in water, its solubility increasing with rising temperature to a maximum at 40° C. and then decreasing. One gram is soluble in about 500 ml. of water at 18° C. but requires about 650 ml. of boiling water to effect solution. It is insoluble in alcohol, ether and chloroform.

Chemical Properties.—Calcium Sulfate is easily soluble in diluted hydrochloric acid to provide a solution (1) which gives the usual precipitation reactions of the calcium and sulfate ions which are not affected by acidic medium.

(1) $CaSO_4.2H_2O + 2HCl \rightarrow CaCl_2 + H_2SO_4 + 2H_2O$

One of the most costly reactions from an economic standpoint is the one with ordinary soaps (see p. 40) since it is one of the most common hardening agents in permanently hard water. Its removal by various means is the basis for the large water-softening industry. In general, however, because of its very low water-solubility it does not figure largely in the usual chemical type incompatibilities.

The assay of this salt is carried out by dissolving a weighed sample in diluted hydrochloric acid to which is added almost enough standard disodium ethylenediaminetetraacetate to completely chelate the calcium (see p. 44). Since a quantitative result cannot be obtained in an acid medium, a modest quantity of sodium hydroxide T.S. is added to alkalinize the solution and the titration is then continued with the standard disodium ethylenediaminetetraacetate until the hydroxy naphthol blue indicator changes from a rose-pink to a deep blue color.

Official Tests for Identity.—About 200 mg. of Calcium Sulfate is dissolved in a mixture of 4 ml. of diluted hydrochloric acid and 16 ml. of water. Ten ml. of this solution is treated with 5 ml. of ammonium oxalate T.S. to give a white precipitate of calcium oxalate (2) which is a positive test for *Calcium*. The remaining 10 ml. is treated with barium chloride T.S. to give a white precipitate of barium sulfate (3) indicating a positive test for *Sulfate*.

(2) $CaCl_2 + (NH_4)_2C_2O_4 \rightarrow CaC_2O_4 \downarrow + 2NH_4Cl$

(3) $H_2SO_4 + BaCl_2 \rightarrow BaSO_4 \downarrow + 2HCl$

Commercial Manufacture.—Calcium Sulfate occurs naturally as *gypsum* but the food and medicinal grade is better prepared by adding a soluble sulfate to a solution of a calcium salt (4). The white precipitate of the dihydrate is washed thoroughly with hot water and dried.

(4) $CaCl_2 + Na_2SO_4 + 2H_2O \rightarrow CaSO_4.2H_2O \downarrow + 2NaCl$

Uses.—*Calcium Sulfate*, N.F. XII, has no medicinal application although it is used as a nutritional supplement supplying calcium. Its reason for inclusion in the N.F. is a recognition of the need to provide standards for a chemical which is finding extensive use as a tablet diluent, *i.e.*, as a pharmaceutical aid. It has little toxicity and is sufficiently inert chemically to prevent undesirable reactions with other medications when incorporated into tablets as a diluent.

Plaster of Paris (Calcii Sulfas Exsiccatus, U.S.P. VIII; Exsiccated Calcium Sulfate; Dried Calcium Sulfate) is a white or grayish-white powder, odorless and tasteless. It is prepared from gypsum by heating the powdered material at about 125 to 150° C. until three-fourths of the water of crystallization has been driven off (5). A material prepared in this way, when mixed with a little water,

(5) $2CaSO_4.2H_2O \rightarrow (CaSO_4)_2.H_2O + 3H_2O \uparrow$

forms a smooth paste which rapidly "sets" or hardens to a stone-like mass. The reaction which ensues is not well understood but is most likely a rehydration (6) and it is thought that during the rehydration

(6) $(CaSO_4)_2.H_2O + 3H_2O \rightarrow 2CaSO_4.2H_2O$

process the saturated solution of calcium sulfate loses enough water to cause crystallization of a portion of it in long thin microscopic needles which mesh through the mass of material imparting the observed rigidity. If the gypsum is heated above 200° C., it loses this property of setting into a hard mass and is known as *"dead-burnt."* Similarly, if the dried material is exposed to moist air for any length of time, it slowly rehydrates and will not exhibit the setting-up characteristic. A number of substances may be added to slow down the setting-up process; among these are dextrin, acacia, glue, alcohol, etc. The setting-up process is accelerated by addition of gypsum, sodium chloride, alum and potassium sulfate.

Plaster of Paris is used mostly for preparing bandages that will set up into a rigid form when wet with tepid water and wound onto a limb. About 1.5 to 2 parts of water are used per part of the powder in making a cream into which a bandage may be dipped and then applied. A 5 per cent solution of dextrin is occasionally used in place of the water in order to slow down the setting time. Alternatively, the bandage material may be impregnated with generous amounts of Plaster of Paris, rolled up, and stored until required, at which time it is simply wetted and wrapped around the limb to be immobilized. Usually a 15- to 20-minute period suffices for the setting process and it is noteworthy that the plaster expands slightly on setting so that it fills all minute spaces. It is also employed extensively in dentistry for making plaster cast impressions.

NON-OFFICIAL CALCIUM COMPOUNDS

Bleaching Powder (Chlorinated Lime, Chloride of Lime), $CaOCl$-$(Cl).H_2O$.—Bleaching powder is a white or grayish-white, granular powder, having a distinct odor of chlorine. It is partially soluble in water and in alcohol. *It is not deliquescent.* When it is exposed to the air it slowly decomposes (1).

(1) $2CaOCl(Cl) + CO_2 + H_2O \rightarrow CaCl_2 + CaCO_3 + 2HOCl$

Bleaching powder is a product resulting from the action of chlorine upon calcium hydroxide and is best represented by the formula, $CaOCl(Cl).H_2O$. The idea that this substance is an equimolecular mixture of calcium chloride and calcium hypochlorite is erroneous because bleaching powder does not possess the properties of the admixed salts and, furthermore, although it does become moist upon exposure to air, it does not deliquesce.

The method used today for manufacturing bleaching powder is the same as that employed by Tennant and Knox at Glasgow in 1799. Thoroughly slaked lime is spread upon shelves in a box-like container and subjected to the action of chlorine (gas), which is introduced at the top of the chamber and "flows" down over and through the contents of the shelves. The temperature of the absorption vessel is maintained below 25° C., thus minimizing the formation of calcium chlorate. When the absorption of chlorine is complete, powdered lime is blown into the chamber to take up any excess chlorine.

This preparation was recognized in the U.S.P. X as Calx Chlorinata (Chlorinated Lime). Its official recognition is as a reagent in the N.F. XII, p. 530. It is used today principally for its disinfecting properties and as a bleaching agent.

Calcium Bromide, N.F. XI, $CaBr_2 \cdot xH_2O$, is a white, granular salt. It is odorless and has a bitter taste. It is very deliquescent.

One Gm. of the salt dissolves in about 0.7 ml. of water and in about 1.3 ml. of alcohol, at 25° C. One Gm. is soluble in about 0.4 ml. of boiling water. It is insoluble in chloroform and in ether.

When heated at red heat, the salt fuses and gives off vapors of bromine. Anhydrous calcium bromide ($CaBr_2$) melts at 765° C.; the trihydrate ($CaBr_2.3H_2O$) at 80.5° C., and the hexahydrate ($CaBr_2.6H_2O$) at 38.2° C.

Calcium bromide is usually prepared by adding precipitated calcium carbonate to dilute hydrobromic acid until effervescence ceases (1). The neutral solution is filtered to remove excess of calcium carbonate and then evaporated to dryness.

(1) $2HBr + CaCO_3 \rightarrow CaBr_2 + CO_2 \uparrow + H_2O$

Calcium bromide is used for the same purposes as any other bromide salt, namely, for the sedative action of the bromide ion by virtue of its central depressant action. It may be used to take advantage of the synergistic action of calcium and bromide, since both are nerve sedatives. However, calcium bromide is unsatisfactory because of its unpalatability, irritant action, etc. If administered parenterally, it should only be given intravenously and then in dilute solutions. Another disadvantage claimed for calcium bromide is that the ratio of bromine to calcium is too high, it being 4 to 1. In an effort to overcome these difficulties workers have turned to organic combinations with calcium bromide. The usual oral dose of this salt is 1 Gm.

Calcium Glycerophosphate, N.F. X, is the normal calcium salt of glycerophosphoric acid and, when dried at 130° C. for 5 hours, it contains not less than 98 per cent of $C_3H_7CaPO_6$. It is a fine, white, odorless and almost tasteless powder. It is slightly hygroscopic.

One Gm. of the salt dissolves in about 50 ml. of water at 25° C. Its solubility in water increases as the temperature decreases. The presence of citric acid increases its solubility in water. It is insoluble in alcohol. This salt is useful chiefly as a source of the calcium ion although the presence of combined phosphorus lends itself to the simultaneous administration of both elements. The use of glycerophosphoric acid salts was originally based on their similarity to lecithins. The lecithins are the esters of fatty acids and glycerophosphoric acid combined with a nitrogenous base (chiefly choline). They occur in animal cells generally combined with proteins. When administered orally they are broken up into glycerophosphates in the intestines. In 1894 Berlow, Pasqualis and Robin suggested that the direct administration of glycerophosphates (calcium and sodium) might produce the same results as obtained by using lecithin. Despite the facts that glycerophosphoric acid is so similar to a part of the lecithin structure, and that the phosphorus of the lecithin of foods is changed into glycerophosphoric acid before being assimilated, Willstaetler claims that synthetic glycerophosphoric acid is not the same as that formed by the decomposition of lecithin. It is generally conceded that the real usefulness and value of glycerophosphates is still very much in doubt and it is for this reason that it has been dropped from official recognition. The usual dose is 0.3 Gm.

Calcium and Calcium Compounds 397

Calcium Hypophosphite, N.F. X, when dried at 105° for an hour contains not less than 98 per cent of $Ca(PH_2O_2)_2$. It occurs as a white, crystalline powder and as colorless, transparent, monoclinic prisms and as thin flexible scales having a pearly luster. It is odorless and has a bitter, nauseous taste. It is stable in air. The salt is slowly soluble in about 6.5 parts of water at 25° C. It is slightly more soluble in boiling water. The salt is insoluble in alcohol.

The only therapeutic value possessed by this salt lies in the calcium ion and, on this basis, it may be used as a source of calcium. The hypophosphite portion of the salt is of little value in treating "nerve disorders and wasting diseases" for which it has been proposed and for this reason it has been deleted from official recognition in current compendia. The usual dose is 0.5 Gm.

Calcium Levulinate, N.F. X, is a hydrated calcium salt of levulinic acid and contains not less than 97.5 per cent and not more than 100.5 per cent of $C_{10}H_{14}CaO_6$ calculated on a dry basis. It occurs as a white, crystalline or amorphous powder, having a faint odor suggesting burnt sugar and a bitter salty taste. It is freely soluble in water (more than calcium gluconate), and slightly soluble in alcohol. It is insoluble in ether and chloroform.

It is an organic salt of calcium possessing less irritating action than calcium chloride. Another advantage of this salt is its high solubility permitting the preparation of more highly concentrated solutions. It is used as a source of calcium by intravenous or subcutaneous injection in a usual dose of 1 Gm.

22

Strontium and Strontium Compounds

STRONTIUM

Symbol, Sr.   Valence, 2.   Atomic Weight, 87.62;
Atomic Number, 38

Occurrence.—Strontium belongs to the alkaline earth family. It is found as the sulfate ($SrSO_4$) in the mineral, *celestite,* and as carbonate ($SrCO_3$) in the mineral, *strontianite.* The latter occurs in large quantities in Salzburg, Germany, in Scotland, England, and in Pennsylvania and New York states. In these same countries, *celestite* is found in even greater quantities. In 1807, Davy isolated the element by the electrolysis of the hydroxide and named it *strontium,* from a village (Strontian) in Argyleshire, Scotland, near which the mineral strontianite is found.

Physical Properties.—Strontium is a "brass-yellow" metal, having a density of about 2.6. It melts at 757° C. and boils at a temperature of 1366°. It should be kept under naphtha. The metal is malleable and ductile and burns in air with an intense illumination. Strontium salts impart a red color to a flame. Strontium and its compounds closely resemble calcium in both physical and chemical properties (*q.v.*). The solubilities of strontium salts are between those of barium and calcium.

Chemical Properties.—The chemical properties of strontium are almost identical with those of calcium (*q.v.*). However, it is of interest to note that strontium sulfate is much less soluble than is calcium sulfate. This is easily shown by the fact that addition of a solution of soluble strontium salt to a saturated solution of calcium sulfate will produce a precipitate of strontium sulfate (1).

(1) $CaSO_4 + SrBr_2 \rightarrow SrSO_4 \downarrow + CaBr_2$

Strontium salts such as the hydroxide, carbonate, nitrate, and the salts of various organic acids yield strontium oxide (SrO) when strongly heated. Calcium salts are more readily converted to the oxide by heating than are the strontium salts.

The volatile strontium salts impart a carmine-red color to a nonluminous flame when heated, this being the basis for their use in fireworks, Yule log salts, etc.

Official Tests for Identity.—1. Calcium sulfate T.S. will produce a white precipitate of strontium sulfate with solutions of strontium salts (1).

2. When moistened with hydrochloric acid, all strontium salts will impart a crimson color to a non-luminous flame.

Commercial Manufacture.—The metal may be made by the electrolysis of the chloride or by heating a saturated solution of strontium chloride with sodium amalgam and then distilling off the mercury. A mixture of magnesium oxide and metallic strontium is obtained when strontium oxide is heated with magnesium metal (2).

$$(2)\ SrO + Mg \xrightarrow{\Delta} Sr + MgO$$

Pharmacological Action of Strontium Ion.—This cation produces effects that closely resemble the characteristic physiological actions of calcium ion. The principal difference with regard to skeletal deposition and functional activities of organ systems, tissues and chemical processes between strontium and calcium is that when the former replaces Ca completely the rates of most of these processes are slowed. A small amount of calcium, inadequate in itself, will restore the rates to normal, however. The early researches of Lehnerdt (1909, 1910) sought to show that strontium ion had a special value in stimulating unusually abundant production of osteoid (bonelike, bony) tissue. His observed effects were, however, later shown to be due to development of rickets because of the low phosphorus content of his diets and not to any specific osteoid-stimulating property. Lehnerdt's studies, nevertheless, stimulated the utilization of strontium as an adjuvant for calcium in the remineralization of depleted skeletal systems. Some of the observations of Shorr and Carter[1] are pertinent, *viz.*: "Sr, in amounts sufficient to achieve significant retention of this element, has been well tolerated over several years of administration and without toxic effects. The retention of Sr is augmented by agents such as Vitamin D, estrogens and androgens in a similar manner to Ca. When given in equal amounts, Sr is found to have certain distinct advantages over Ca for the remineralization of the skeleton. There is greater retention of Sr; and when the ceiling for Ca retention has been reached, the addition of Sr results in a retention of the latter. Hence, the deposition of Ca plus Sr is greater than the total Ca storage which can be achieved with Ca alone, regardless of Ca intake and auxillary therapy. This combination should hasten the rate of remineralization of the skeleton as compared with Ca alone, an inference that is supported by the objective and subjective improvement observed under the combined regime. Maximal retention of Sr and Ca is achieved with the assistance of three auxillary agents—Vitamin D, estrogens and androgens. Finally, the useful-

---

[1] Shorr, E. and Carter, A. C., Bull. of the Hosp. for Joint Dis., **13**, 59, 1952.

ness of Sr as a means of measuring mineral salt turnover in bone is suggested." The findings of these authors have been confirmed by McCaslin and Janes[1] who used strontium lactate in the same dosage (6.4 Gm. daily in divided doses) as Shorr and Carter. The mechanism for improvement in osteoporotic (bone demineralized) conditions by the use of strontium has recently been elucidated in conjunction with the mechanism of bone-formation (see p. 376). The fact that strontium ions are larger than calcium ions and cannot replace calcium in the formation of crystal nuclei necessary for bone formation probably explains the reason why the skeleton develops a rachitic condition when strontium replaces calcium completely in the diet. Although strontium cannot form nuclei for bone forming crystals it can, nevertheless, be incorporated into bone because it will attach itself to the surface of the calcium phosphate microcrystal. This permits it to build up bone structure with calcium phosphate as the seed on which to build. It also means that it may be possible to remove the deposited strontium by means of chelating agents and, indeed, such experiments have been carried out and are now in progress because of their importance for possible future radiation victims.

Aside from the possible values of strontium in bone remineralization it should be mentioned that at one time there was a hypothesis prevalent that strontium ions had a special virtue in that they released their accompanying anions more slowly than other salts and would, therefore, be useful for providing a more gradual and milder action. This notion was dispelled by the work of Krahulik and Pilcher (1918) who showed that the rate of absorption of iodide ion from strontium iodide was the same as that from potassium iodide. Where pharmacologically active anions are concerned, one can expect the same type of action from the corresponding strontium salt as from alkali metal or calcium salts.

Uses.—Strontium has been used in the form of strontium lactate for its adjuvant action with calcium to promote remineralization of depleted skeletons. Strontium metal, itself, has no medicinal value. The strontium salts that have been official, *e.g.*, bromide and salicylate, are no longer recognized although they may serve some useful purpose as an alternative to officially recognized salts.

NON-OFFICIAL STRONTIUM COMPOUNDS

Strontium Bromide, N.F. X, contains not less than 98 per cent of $SrBr_2.6H_2O$ and occurs in colorless, transparent, hexagonal crystals. It is odorless, and has a bitter, saline taste. It is deliquescent in moist air, but effloresces in very dry air. One Gm. of the salt dissolves in about 0.35 ml. of water at 25° C. It is soluble in alcohol but not in ether.

[1] McCaslin, F. E. and Janes, J. M., Proc. Staff Meet., Mayo Clinic, **14**, 329, 1959.

It is used solely for the sedative effect of the bromide ion, but possesses no advantages over other bromides. It is thought by some to be less irritating to the stomach, however, and is preferred by them for this reason. Ampuls of strontium bromide are available (10 per cent for intravenous use in treating asthma). Its usual dose is 1 Gm.

Strontium Lactate (Strontolac).—This salt is used as the trihydrate $[Sr(C_3H_5O_3)_2.3H_2O]$ which occurs as a white, odorless, granular powder. It is soluble in 3 parts of water and 0.5 part of boiling water but is only slightly soluble in alcohol. Aqueous solutions are practically neutral.

This salt has been used for the treatment of osteoporosis (see Pharmacological Action of the Strontium Ion) in a dose of 6.4 Gm. daily in divided doses.

23

Barium and Barium Compounds

BARIUM

Symbol, Ba. Valence, 2. Atomic Weight, 137.34;
Atomic Number, 56

History and Occurrence.—In 1808 Davy isolated metallic barium by electrolyzing the chloride in the presence of mercury and subsequently decomposing the amalgam.

In combination, barium is widely and abundantly distributed in Nature. As the sulfate ($BaSO_4$) it occurs in the mineral *barite* or *heavy spar* and as the carbonate ($BaCO_3$) in the mineral *witherite*. In smaller quantities it also occurs in manganese ores, *e.g.*, *psilomelane*, $(MnBa)O.MnO_2$, and in combination as the silicate. It is found in sea water, in mineral waters, in marine plants, and in the ashes of some woods, notably those of beech.

Physical Properties.—Barium is a silver-white or slightly yellowish-white metal having a density of 3.5. It melts at 850° C., boils at 1140° C., and is not volatile under ordinary conditions.

Chemical Properties.—Upon exposure to air it oxidizes rapidly and hence must be kept under petroleum or other oxygen-free liquids. When placed on water, it acts energetically, liberating hydrogen and forming a solution of the hydroxide which is an active base. The physical and chemical properties of barium compounds closely resemble those of calcium and strontium.

It is interesting to note that just as strontium sulfate is more insoluble than calcium sulfate, barium sulfate is less soluble than either calcium or strontium sulfates. The solubility even in acids is so low that large quantities of barium sulfate can be ingested without untoward reactions; this in spite of the known toxicity of the barium ion. The solubilities of barium salts parallel those of calcium.

Official Tests for Identity.—1. Solutions of barium salts will yield a precipitate of barium sulfate when treated with diluted sulfuric acid (1).

$$(1) \quad Ba^{++} + SO_4^{=} \rightarrow BaSO_4 \downarrow$$

This precipitate is insoluble in hydrochloric or nitric acids.

(402)

2. Barium salts impart a characteristic yellowish-green color to a non-luminous flame. This flame appears blue when viewed through a green glass.

Commercial Manufacture.—Metallic barium is made (1) by the electrolysis of the molten chloride or (2) by the electrolysis of an aqueous solution of barium chloride using a mercury cathode. In the latter method, the barium forms an amalgam with the mercury and the mercury is then removed from the barium by heating in an atmosphere of hydrogen gas.

Pharmacological Action of Barium Ion.—Barium ion differs from calcium and strontium ions by being very toxic. Its effects closely resemble those of the digitalis group. Attempts have been made to substitute barium chloride for digitalis, but from a therapeutic standpoint it has been proven decidedly inferior on account of its marked coronary vasoconstriction. However, it has been found useful in treating special forms of heart disease.

Barium ion produces a local irritation. It also stimulates smooth muscle and is commonly used by the pharmacologist in studying antispasmodics. A laxative action is produced by increasing peristalsis of the intestines. On account of their toxicity, soluble barium compounds or those that may be made soluble by the weak acids of the digestive fluids are not used in therapeutics.

Uses of Barium.—Metallic barium is of some use commercially in the manufacture of radio tubes and automobile ignition systems, but is of little pharmaceutical importance.

OFFICIAL BARIUM COMPOUND

BARIUM SULFATE

Barium Sulfate, U.S.P. XVII

Formula, $BaSO_4$.   Molecular Weight, 233.40

Physical Properties.—Barium Sulfate is a fine, white, odorless, tasteless, bulky powder, free from grittiness.

The salt is insoluble in water, organic solvents, and in dilute acids and alkalies. It is soluble in concentrated sulfuric acid (1).

(1) $BaSO_4 + H_2SO_4 \rightarrow Ba(HSO_4)_2$

Chemical Properties.—Barium Sulfate is so insoluble that it enters into very few chemical reactions. It can be solubilized by concentrated sulfuric acid (1) or by fusing it with alkali carbonates. An equal mixture of sodium and potassium carbonates is often used to convert the barium sulfate to the carbonate form (2). Once the barium has been converted to the carbonate form it is easily solubilized by the use of acids other than sulfuric, *e.g.*, acetic acid (3).

$$(2)\ 2BaSO_4 + Na_2CO_3 + K_2CO_3 \rightarrow 2KNaSO_4 + 2BaCO_3 \downarrow$$

$$(3)\ BaCO_3 + 2CH_3COOH \rightarrow (CH_3COO)_2Ba + H_2O + CO_2 \uparrow$$

Official Tests for Identity.—1. Five-tenths Gm. of barium sulfate is mixed with 2 Gm. each of anhydrous sodium carbonate and potassium carbonate and the mixture fused (2) in a crucible. The fused mixture is then lixiviated with distilled water and filtered. The filtrate gives a test for *Sulfate* (*q.v.*).

2. The residue from the filtration is barium carbonate and when it is dissolved in acetic acid, the solution gives the usual tests for *Barium* (*q.v.*).

Commercial Manufacture.—1. Barium sulfate, for roentgen-ray (x-ray) purposes, is made by precipitating the barium ions from a cold, dilute solution of a soluble barium salt with dilute sulfuric acid (4). The salt is filtered off, thoroughly washed, dried, and screened.

$$(4)\ BaCl_2 + H_2SO_4 \rightarrow BaSO_4 \downarrow + 2HCl$$

2. Barium sulfate for industrial uses, *e.g.*, making paint, filler for glazed cards, etc., is made by treating a soluble barium salt with sulfuric acid (5). It is also a by-product of several industries, *e.g.*, the manufacture of H_2O_2 from $BaO_2 \cdot 8H_2O$ and H_2SO_4. The industrial grade of barium sulfate should never be administered internally.

$$(5)\ BaS + H_2SO_4 \rightarrow BaSO_4 \downarrow + H_2S \uparrow$$

Uses.—*Barium Sulfate*, U.S.P. XVII, should be free from soluble barium compounds. On account of the danger of confusing the poisonous sulfide and sulfite with the insoluble sulfate, the U. S. P. cautions: *When Barium Sulfate is prescribed, the title always should be written out in full to avoid confusion with the poisonous barium sulfide of barium sulfite.* It has been observed that the absorption coefficients of elements for roentgen-rays (x-rays) are directly proportional to the number of electrons in the respective atoms. Therefore, it may be correctly assumed that the atomic weight of an element is a criterion of its worth in absorbing roentgen-rays. Because of the relatively high atomic weight of barium and because of the insolubility of barium sulfate in dilute acids and alkalies (thereby eliminating barium ion action), this compound is of great value in roentgen-ray diagnosis and is used as a radiopaque medium in the alimentary tract. It has a distinct advantage over bismuth compounds because it does not delay the gastric movements and, furthermore it is less expensive. Three hundred grams is the usual oral dose in a suitable suspension. Many of the commercial preparations are agreeably flavored. It may be used in a 400 Gm. usual dose in suitable suspension for rectal instillation for examination of the lower bowel.

Pharmaceutical products are Baropaque Suspension and Skray-bart. The compound is also used in Ray-X-Sponges as a means of locating "lost" sponges.

An aqueous suspension is employed in the lungs to form a thin coating over the inner lung area and thus accentuate abnormalities for x-ray examination.

Commercial barium sulfate ("Blanc Fixe," "permanent white") is used for making lithopone paints, paper fillers, sizes, modifying colors of pigments, etc. The commercial grade should never be used for roentgen-ray work as it usually contains poisonous soluble barium salts.

24

Zinc and Zinc Compounds

ZINC

Symbol, Zn. Valence, 2. Atomic Weight, 65.37;
Atomic Number, 30

History.—In the writings of Aristotle, references are found to an "earth" which when fused with copper, gave a bright, light colored metal that was called the "metal of the Masynœci" (brass). Pliny also wrote about a mineral that he called *cadmia* (zinc ores). When this mineral was heated with copper, the latter was converted into *aurichalcum* (brass). He called especial attention to the fact that the deposit (zinc oxide) formed in brass furnaces could be used in place of this mineral. In 1677, Kunckel advanced the theory that "cadmia" was a "metallic calx" that dyed copper yellow by "giving its metal up to it." The word *zinc* was first used by Paracelsus in the sixteenth century. He regarded the substance as a "semi-metal" and the word was indiscriminately used both for the metal and its ores. In 1720, Henckel prepared metallic zinc in a fair state of purity. In England, the art of zinc smelting came into being about 1730.

Occurrence.—Zinc does not occur free in Nature. In combination, it is widely distributed. The most important zinc ores are *sphalerite* or *zinc blende* [ZnS], the anhydrous silicate, *willemite* [Zn_2SiO_4], *calamine* [$Zn_2SiO_4.H_2O$], and *smithsonite* [$ZnCO_3$]. The term *Calamine* is used for the official product and also for impure, naturally-occurring zinc carbonate. Other zinc-bearing minerals are *wurtzite* [ZnS], *zincite* [ZnO], *goslarite* [$ZnSO_4.7H_2O$], *Franklinite* [(Fe, Zn, Mn)O.(Fe, Mn)$_2O_3$] and *hydrozincite* [$ZnCO_3.2Zn(OH)_2$]. Belgium, Silesia, Saxony, Poland, Spain, and England are the most noteworthy of the zinc producing European countries. In the United States, Missouri (Joplin region) produces about 50 per cent of all the zinc. Other important zinc producing states are New Jersey, Montana, Kansas, Oklahoma, Wisconsin, Idaho, and Colorado.

Physical Properties.—Zinc is a bluish-white, moderately hard metal that crystallizes in hexagonal prisms and pyramids. When cold, zinc is brittle. From 100° to 150° C., it becomes both malleable and ductile, but when heated at 210° to 300° C., it again becomes brittle and may be powdered in a mortar. Zinc that has been rolled into sheets remains flexible when cooled. The metal

(406)

fuses at 419.4° C., and boils at 907° C. Its density is 7.14. The vapor density shows that it is monatomic.

Chemical Properties.—Zinc is bivalent in all of its compounds. The metal is not attacked to any appreciable extent by the oxygen in the air, because it soon becomes covered with a thin coating of a non-porous protective basic carbonate. (See basic salt discussion.) Zinc vapor burns with a bluish-white flame, the oxide of the metal being formed. Metallic zinc dissolves in acids (1) and alkali hydroxides (2) (*not* ammonium hydroxide since only zinc ion forms a complex with ammonia) with the evolution of hydrogen. Zinc is readily attacked by dilute nitric acid to form zinc nitrate and ammonium nitrate (3). (See nitric acid.) Nitric acid (concentrated) gives zinc nitrate and nitrous oxide (4). The element enters into complex ions.

(1) $Zn + 2H_3O^+ \rightarrow Zn^{++} + H_2 \uparrow + 2H_2O$

(2) $Zn + 2OH^- \rightarrow ZnO_2^= + H_2 \uparrow$

(3) $4Zn + 10HNO_3 \rightarrow 4Zn^{++} + 8NO_3^- + NH_4NO_3 + 3H_2O$

(4) $4Zn + 10HNO_3 \rightarrow 4Zn^{++} + 8NO_3^- + N_2O \uparrow + 5H_2O$

The *zinc ion* enters into several characteristic reactions as follows:

Ammonium sulfide [$(NH_4)_2S$] precipitates *white* zinc sulfide from neutral, alkaline or faintly acid solutions of a zinc salt (5). Also other basic sulfides such as Sulfurated Potash will precipitate the white sulfide. The precipitate is insoluble in acetic acid but is dissolved by diluted hydrochloric acid.

(5) $Zn^{++} + S^= \rightarrow ZnS \downarrow$

On the other hand, zinc ion is incompletely precipitated by passing hydrogen sulfide into a solution of zinc sulfate (6).

(6) $Zn^{++} + H_2S + 2H_2O \rightleftarrows ZnS \downarrow + 2H_3O^+$

The hydronium ion from the hydrosulfuric acid formed in the reaction reduces the concentration of the sulfide ion ($S^=$) more and more as the reaction proceeds, and tends to reverse the reaction. Therefore, when the product of the zinc- and sulfide-ion concentrations no longer exceeds the ion-product constant (solubility product) for zinc sulfide, precipitation ceases. In the presence of sufficient alkali acetate to take care of the hydronium ions, precipitation is complete.

Fixed alkalies precipitate zinc ion as white flocculent zinc hydroxide (7), which exhibits amphoteric properties by dissolving both in acids (8) to form salts and in alkalies (9) to form zincates. It is soluble in ammonium hydroxide or ammonium carbonate because of the formation of soluble tetrammino-zinc hydroxide [$Zn(NH_3)_4$-$(OH)_2$]. (See ammonia.)

(7) $Zn^{++} + 2OH^- \rightarrow Zn(OH)_2$

(8) $Zn(OH)_2 + 2H_3O^+ \rightarrow Zn^{++} + 4H_2O$

(9) $Zn(OH)_2 + 2OH^- \rightarrow ZnO_2^= + 2H_2O$

Note that gold and zinc ions are the only well known ones that are soluble in both ammonium hydroxide and fixed alkali.

With a solution of a zinc salt, soluble carbonates and phosphates produce white precipitates of basic zinc carbonate or phosphate, respectively (10 and 11). Borate solutions produce insoluble zinc salts also.

(10) $2Zn^{++} + 2Na_2CO_3 + 2H_2O \rightarrow Zn_2(OH)_2CO_3 \downarrow + 4Na^+$ $+ CO_2 \uparrow + H_2O$

(11) $3Zn^{++} + 4HPO_4^= \rightarrow 2H_2PO_4^- + Zn_3(PO_4)_2 \downarrow$

Alkali ferrocyanides precipitate white zinc ferrocyanides (12) which are converted into the less soluble zinc-potassium ferrocyanides by an excess of the potassium ferrocyanide (13). Alkali ferricyanides precipitate brownish-yellow zinc ferricyanide (14).

(12) $[Fe(CN)_6]^{\equiv} + 2Zn^{++} \rightarrow Zn_2[Fe(CN)_6] \downarrow$

(13) $3Zn_2[Fe(CN)_6] + K_4Fe(CN)_6 \rightarrow 2K_2Zn_3[Fe(CN)_6]_2$

(14) $2[Fe(CN)_6]^{\equiv} + 3Zn^{++} \rightarrow Zn_3[Fe(CN)_6]_2 \downarrow$

When a zinc salt is heated in a Bunsen flame with any cobalt salt, cobalt zincate is formed (Rinmann's green). Potassium cobalticyanide is a good salt to use in this test. If test paper is to be used, it may be prepared with a solution containing 1 Gm. $K_3Co(CN)_6$, and 0.25 Gm. $KClO_3$ in 25 ml. of H_2O.

When metallic zinc is placed in a solution of a tin salt that has been acidified with hydrochloric acid, the tin is precipitated in metallic form. (See chemical properties of tin.)

Official Tests for Identity of Zinc Ion.—Zinc salts in a solution containing sodium acetate yield a white precipitate (ZnS) with hydrogen sulfide (6). Zinc sulfide is soluble in diluted hydrochloric acid but insoluble in acetic acid. Ammonium sulfide T.S. will precipitate zinc sulfide from solutions of zinc salts (5). Potassium ferrocyanide T.S. produces a white precipitate (zinc ferrocyanide) with zinc ion (12). It is insoluble in diluted hydrochloric acid.

Commercial Manufacture.—It is usually necessary to concentrate zinc ores before they can be smelted profitably. This is accomplished by means of the flotation and gravity processes. (See copper.) The concentrated oxide and carbonate ores are usually mixed with about one-half their weight of coal and heated in large furnaces. The molten zinc that collects in the lower part of the receivers is withdrawn into large iron ladles and cast in suitable molds into slabs, called *spelter*.

Sulfide ores cannot be reduced directly by heating with coal. Therefore, they are pulverized and roasted in suitable furnaces (15).

(15) $2ZnS + 3O_2 \overset{\triangle}{\rightarrow} 2ZnO + 2SO_2 \uparrow$

Crude zinc (spelter) contains various impurities, *e.g.*, lead, iron, cadmium, antimony, arsenic, silver, copper, and sulfur. Zinc obtained from mixed ores is always impure and large quantities are purified by electrolysis. A very high grade zinc (99.9+ per cent) that needs no purification is now obtained by reducing high grade ores.

Pharmacological Action of Zinc Ion. — "The body of the normal man contains about 2 Gm. of zinc. All tissues and organs of the body have been found to contain this metal, but highest concentrations are present in testes, hair and nails, bone, and pigmented tissues of the eye. It is found as an essential part of an enzyme structure in the red blood cells, gastric mucosa, and renal cortex. Zinc is associated with a number of enzyme systems, is involved in the acceleration of carbon dioxide exchange and is thought to be involved in acid secretion by the stomach, and may be involved in regulation of acid-base balance by the kidney. A true zinc deficiency has not been shown to exist in man, but the vital part played by it in the body systems will be noted."[1]

Until recently zinc salts have not been used internally in therapeutics except for the pronounced emetic action. When zinc salts are ingested there is strong local astringent action due to the precipitation of the protoplasm of the mucosa and they rarely produce any systemic effect. Excess zinc salts in the diet of animals affect reproduction and produce anemia. The parenteral administration of a soluble zinc salt produces serious symptoms such as vomiting, diarrhea, and hemorrhagic enteritis.

By far the most interesting development in recent years in internal zinc therapy has been its use in wound healing.[2] The origins of this usage came from a finding in 1955 by Major W. J. Pories (USAF), then a sophomore medical student at the University of Rochester, that zinc impurities in an amino acid analogue stimulated healing of wounds in rats rather than retarding healing as expected. Controlled clinical studies, particularly on airmen with surgical wounds, have confirmed the fact that healing takes place three to four times faster than normal. In these studies up to 220 mg. of zinc sulfate (50 mg. of metallic zinc) were given three times a day with meals to avoid possible emetic side effects. Apparently, the 150 mg. equivalent of metallic zinc was well tolerated by all of the patients. Healing was calculated both by time and wound volume and no great difference in healing was noted during the first 15 to 20 postoperative days. Following this, however, there was a significant difference. In one study the zinc-medicated patients took a mean of 45 days to heal against a mean of 63 days for unmedicated patients and another study showed a mean of 45 days vs. 71.3 days combined

[1] See Modern Pharmacy, No. 3, 1958, p. 4 (published by Parke, Davis and Co.).
[2] See J. Am. Med. Assoc., **196**, 33 (1966).

410   Zinc and Zinc Compounds

with a remarkably rapid healing rate as measured by volume of granulization per day.

Another interesting experimental finding connected with internal zinc administration was noted in 1965 and appears to link atherosclerosis with zinc deficiency.[1] Initial studies in this connection showed that subjects with atherosclerosis had extremely low stores of zinc as determined by analysis of their hair. Hair analysis showed that virtually all patients with diagnosed atherosclerosis had only about 30 per cent of the normal 200 ppm zinc. Preliminary clinical tests have shown encouraging responses to a dosage level of 220 mg. zinc sulfate three times daily given over several months in that essentially chair-ridden patients made notable improvements in exercise tolerance.

Zinc ion is employed in therapeutics primarily for its local actions. It exhibits astringent, corrosive and mild antiseptic properties depending upon the ion concentration. These effects are due to the precipitation of protein by the zinc ion.

Uses.—Sheet zinc is used for making roofing, gutters, etc. It is largely used for *galvanizing* iron. Sheets of iron are thoroughly cleaned with sulfuric acid or by a sand blast and immersed in a bath of molten zinc. When cold, the thin coating of zinc protects the iron from atmospheric corrosion. Other methods have been devised for applying this protective coating, *e.g.*, electroplating; covering the metal with zinc dust and baking at 800° C. (sherardizing); spraying molten zinc upon iron (Shoop process), etc. Zinc is used in batteries and in many alloys, brass (containing 60 to 82 per cent copper and 18 to 40 per cent zinc) being the most important. Zinc metal is employed in the metallurgical processes for obtaining gold and silver (*q.v.*). Zinc dust is a fine gray powder composed of at least 90 per cent of Zn, the remainder being oxide, sulfide, etc. It is used extensively as a reducing agent in technological chemistry. Granulated zinc is made by pouring a thin stream of the molten metal into water. Mossy zinc is another form prepared in a similar manner. With acids, it is used for generating hydrogen.

OFFICIAL ZINC COMPOUNDS

ZINC CHLORIDE

Zinc Chloride, U.S.P. XVII

Formula, $ZnCl_2$. Molecular Weight, 136.29

Physical Properties.—Zinc Chloride occurs as a white, or nearly white, odorless, crystalline powder, or in porcelain-like masses, or

---

[1] See "Geriatric Focus," pub. by Knol Pharmaceutical Co., Vol. 5, No. 13, Sept. 15, 1966, p. 1.

fused sticks or pencils. It is very deliquescent, has a density of about 2.907, and melts at about 290° C.

One Gm. of Zinc Chloride dissolves in 0.5 ml. of water and in about 1.5 ml. of alcohol, at 25° C. These solutions are usually slightly turbid due to the presence of a small amount of the oxychloride. The turbidity disappears upon the addition of a small quantity of hydrochloric acid. It is soluble in glycerin (2 parts) and also in ether.

At about 290° C., zinc chloride fuses to a clear liquid. When heated to about 730° C., a part of the salt is volatilized as dense white fumes whereas the remainder is decomposed and leaves a residue of zinc oxide.

Chemical Properties.—An aqueous solution of zinc chloride is acid to litmus paper. Zinc salts, in general, hydrolyze in water and thus release hydrogen ions (1). Solutions of the salt should be filtered through asbestos or glass wool because they dissolve paper and cotton.

$$(1)\ ZnCl_2 + H_2O \rightarrow Zn(OH)Cl + HCl$$

Auto-complex halides are salts in which the same metal appears in both cation and anion. The metals that have a tendency to form auto-complexes are copper, zinc, and cadmium (see also mercuric chloride). Chlorides of these elements are usually encountered but the same characteristic is true for the bromides and iodides.

Instead of these halides ionizing in solution in the conventional manner, an anion forms containing the metal and only half of the expected element occurs as a cation (2).

$$(2)\ 2ZnCl_2 \rightleftarrows Zn(ZnCl_4) \rightleftarrows Zn^{++} + (ZnCl_4)^=$$

In dilute solutions the auto-complex is less stable and the $(ZnCl_4)^=$ ionizes to some extent into Zn^{++} and Cl^-.

When a strong solution of zinc chloride is mixed with zinc oxide it results in the formation of the oxychloride and sets up into a hard mass. This is the basis for some dental cements.

The chemical properties of zinc chloride are expressed in the reactions of the zinc ion and of the chloride ion (see hydrochloric acid).

Zinc chloride is determined by first precipitating the zinc ion as zinc carbonate and then converting to zinc oxide by ignition. The dried oxide is then weighed.

Official Tests for Identity.—1. A solution responds to the tests for *Zinc* (*q.v.*).

2. A solution responds to the tests for *Chloride* (*q.v.*).

Commercial Manufacture.—Zinc chloride may be produced by several methods.

1. Zinc is heated and dry hydrogen chloride gas is passed through it (3).

$$(3)\ Zn + 2HCl \xrightarrow{\Delta} ZnCl_2 + H_2 \uparrow$$

2. Zinc chloride may be made by distilling a mixture of zinc and mercuric chloride (4). The mercury distills off and zinc chloride remains as a residue.

(4) $HgCl_2 + Zn \xrightarrow{\Delta} Hg \uparrow + ZnCl_2$

3. Hydrochloric acid will act upon zinc, zinc oxide or the carbonate to form the chloride (5).

(5) $ZnO + 2HCl \rightarrow ZnCl_2 + H_2O$

The technical grade of zinc chloride is usually made by treating zinc with an *excess* of hydrochloric acid and evaporating to dryness. The residue is fused and poured into iron drums in which it solidifies.

The official salt may be made by dissolving the technical grade of zinc chloride in water acidulated with hydrochloric acid and evaporating the solution to crystallization. Official Zinc Chloride is also prepared by a process similar to the one given in the U.S. Pharmacopœia IX for the manufacture of the official Solution of Zinc Chloride, *viz.*, 240 Gm. of granulated zinc are digested with a mixture of 840 Gm. of hydrochloric acid and 250 ml. of distilled water until the reaction ceases (6). The liquid is decanted from the excess of zinc, mixed with 12 Gm. of nitric acid to oxidize the ferrous to ferric iron (7), and heated on a sand-bath at 115° C. to expel the excess of nitric acid and until a small portion of the liquid solidifies on cooling. The cooled, solidified mass is dissolved in about 1000 ml. of distilled water, 12 Gm. of precipitated zinc carbonate added and the mixture shaken occasionally during twenty-four hours (8). The supernatant liquid is decanted, rendered distinctly acid with hydrochloric acid to prevent hydrolysis to basic chloride (9), and concentrated until a portion solidifies upon cooling. The liquid is then poured into suitable pencil-shaped molds and, when the salt has solidified but is still warm, it is packed in glass bottles.

(6) $Zn + 2HCl \rightarrow ZnCl_2 + H_2 \uparrow$

(7) $6FeCl_2 + 2HNO_3 + 6HCl \rightarrow 6FeCl_3 + 2NO \uparrow + 4H_2O$

(8) $10FeCl_3 + 3([ZnCO_3]_2 \cdot [Zn(OH)_2]_3) + 6H_2O \rightarrow 15ZnCl_2 + 10Fe(OH)_3 \downarrow + 6CO_2 \uparrow$

(9) *a.* $ZnCl_2 + H_2O \rightarrow Zn(OH)Cl + HCl$
   b. $2Zn(OH)Cl \rightarrow Zn_2OCl_2 + H_2O$

Uses.—*Zinc Chloride*, U.S.P. XVII, contains not less than 97 per cent of $ZnCl_2$. It is used medicinally in 1 or 2 per cent concentrations (skin) and 0.2 to 0.5 per cent (mucous membranes) as an astringent and antiseptic in much the same manner as zinc sulfate. Zinc chloride is used when a more powerful escharotic action is needed

Zinc and Zinc Compounds

such as in the treatment of malignant growths and gangrenous sores. The salt is also used in mouth washes to impart antiseptic and astringent properties to them. Its official recognition, however, is based on its action as a desensitizer of dentin for which use it is applied topically to the teeth as required.

ZINC OXIDE

Zinc Oxide, U.S.P. XVII

Formula, ZnO. Molecular Weight, 81.37

Physical Properties.—Zinc Oxide is a very fine, odorless, white or yellowish-white, amorphous powder free from gritty particles. It has a density of about 5.47. When the oxide is heated to 400° or 500° C. a yellow color develops that disappears on cooling.

Zinc Oxide is insoluble in water and in alcohol but is soluble in dilute acids, ammonia water and ammonium carbonate T.S.

Chemical Properties.—Upon exposure to air it gradually absorbs carbon dioxide and is converted into a basic carbonate [$Zn_2(OH)_2CO_3$] It readily dissolves in dilute acids (1), in ammonia water (2) and in ammonium carbonate test solution (3).

(1) $ZnO + 2HCl \rightarrow ZnCl_2 + H_2O$

(2) $ZnO + 4NH_4OH \rightarrow Zn(NH_3)_4(OH)_2 + 3H_2O$

(3) $ZnO + 2(NH_4)_2CO_3 \rightarrow Zn(NH_3)_4(OH)_2 + 2CO_2\uparrow + H_2O$

Acid solutions exhibit the reactions of the zinc ion.

The assay of zinc oxide depends upon dissolving the oxide in an excess of 1 N sulfuric acid and back titrating with 1 N sodium hydroxide using methyl orange T.S. as an indicator.

Official Tests for Identity.—1. When Zinc Oxide is strongly heated, it acquires a yellow color which disappears on cooling.

2. A solution of Zinc Oxide in dilute hydrochloric acid responds to all tests for *Zinc* (*q.v.*).

Commercial Manufacture.— *Technical Grade.*—Metallic zinc is strongly heated in earthenware retorts and the vapors, upon coming in contact with air, ignite to form the oxide which settles out in large chambers. This technical grade is known as *"zinc white."*

Medicinal Grade.—Precipitated zinc carbonate is heated to low redness (4) until a sample taken from the center of the material does not effervesce when treated with an acid. It is claimed that a whiter, softer product is obtained when the calcination is conducted over a long period of time at a low temperature (250° to 300° C.). (See also magnesium oxide.) Excessive heating results in a yellowish-white zinc oxide that is not free from gritty particles. Some manufacturers sieve their product before packaging.

(4) $[ZnCO_3]_2.[Zn(OH)_2]_3 \xrightarrow{\Delta} 5ZnO + 2CO_2\uparrow + 3H_2O\uparrow$

Uses.—*Zinc Oxide*, U.S.P. XVII, when freshly ignited, contains not less than 99 per cent of ZnO. It has no specific activity to account for its popularity in dermatologic usage other than its mild astringency and weak antiseptic action. It is officially designated as an astringent and protectant. In the form of *Zinc Oxide Ointment* or dusting powder, it is employed in the treatment of eczema, impetigo, ringworm, varicose ulcers, pruritus and psoriasis. It is also used extensively in the manufacture of adhesive tape.

Zinc Oxide is an ingredient in *Coal Tar Ointment*, *Calamine*, *Calamine Lotion*, *Phenolated Calamine Lotion*, *Compound Resorcinol Ointment*, *Zinc-Eugenol Cement*, *Zinc Oxide Paste*, *Zinc Oxide Paste with Salicylic Acid* and *Zinc Gelatin*.

ZINC PEROXIDE

Medicinal Zinc Peroxide, U.S.P. XVII

Formula, ZnO_2

Physical Properties.—Medicinal Zinc Peroxide is a white, or faintly-yellow, fine, odorless powder. It is almost insoluble in water and in organic solvents. Dilute acids dissolve it with decomposition (1). The dry powder may be heated to 140° C. without decomposition but it is unstable at higher temperatures.

Chemical Properties.—When mixed with water for 5 minutes, the pH of the supernatant liquid will range from 7.0 to 8.5. Diluted mineral acids react to form hydrogen peroxide and a soluble zinc salt (1).

$$(1) \quad ZnO_2 + 2HCl \rightarrow ZnCl_2 + H_2O_2$$

Although it appears to be insoluble in water there is a slow decomposition with the liberation of hydrogen peroxide (3).

After boiling to remove the hydrogen peroxide, an acid solution will give the reactions of the zinc ion.

A fresh acid solution of the peroxide is a good oxidizing agent and will give those reactions characteristic of hydrogen peroxide. (See Hydrogen Peroxide.)

Zinc peroxide is assayed by determining the amount of oxygen released in a water mixture held at 37.5° for specified periods of time.

Official Tests for Identity.—1. A solution of Medicinal Zinc Peroxide in a slight excess of diluted hydrochloric acid, and boiled to remove the hydrogen peroxide formed (1), responds to the tests for *Zinc* (*q.v.*).

2. A small quantity of the peroxide is shaken with a few ml. of water and 1 drop of diluted sulfuric acid. When a few ml. of ether and a few drops of potassium dichromate T.S. are added, the water

layer becomes blue. On shaking the mixture the blue color passes into the ether. This blue ether solution contains a higher oxygen compound of chromium. (See Hydrogen Peroxide.) On standing over dilute acid, the solution in ether slowly loses its color and the dilute acid becomes green, due to the formation of a chromic salt.

Commercial Manufacture.—Medicinal Zinc Peroxide is a special grade both in purity and particle size. It was developed by the research laboratories of DuPont in collaboration with Dr. Frank L. Meleney from 1934 to 1938. It is prepared from very pure zinc oxide and hydrogen peroxide (2).

(2) $ZnO + H_2O_2 \rightarrow ZnO_2 + H_2O$

Uses.—*Medicinal Zinc Peroxide*, U.S.P. XVII, consists of a mixture of zinc peroxide, zinc carbonate and zinc hydroxide. Each Gm. of Medicinal Zinc Peroxide, previously heated at 135° to 140° for 4 hours, evolves not less than 2.16 ml. of oxygen in 20 hours and not less than 0.24 ml. of oxygen in the following 4 hours.

The product on the market usually contains about 55 per cent ZnO_2 and yields 9 per cent by weight of actual oxygen. The material is supplied as a dry powder and should be sterilized before using. It can be kept for about a month following sterilization, but deteriorates by that time because the heat used in sterilization also activates the evolution of oxygen.

The compound is of value in controlling surgical infections resulting from micro-aërophilic and anaërobic bacteria. In general, one can state that the more strict an organism is in its oxygen requirements, the more susceptible it is to the action of zinc peroxide. Many types of wounds are suspected of harboring anaërobic bacteria. Gunshot wounds, human bites, most puncture and deep surgical wounds are among them. It possesses deodorizing properties and is often used as a dusting powder.

Zinc peroxide is used by mixing it with water to form a 40 per cent heavy creamy suspension which is distributed over the surface of the wound, wrapped with gauze and then coated with petrolatum or zinc ointment to make the dressing air-tight.

Formulas for making ointments and suspensions have been published.[1]

No doubt the activity of zinc peroxide is due to the release of oxygen by the following mechanism (3).

(3) $ZnO_2 + H_2O \rightarrow ZnO + H_2O_2$
$$2H_2O_2 \xrightarrow{\text{cat.}} 2H_2O + O_2 \uparrow$$

A vanishing cream containing zinc peroxide (10 to 45 per cent) is useful in treating ringworm and dermatophytosis. The powder applied directly is effective against Vincent's stomatitis.

[1] J. Am. Pharm. Assn., Pr. Ed., **3,** 7 (1942).

ZINC STEARATE

Zinc Stearate, U.S.P. XVII

Physical Properties.—Zinc Stearate is a fine, white, bulky powder, free from grittiness, having a faint, characteristic odor. It is unctuous to the touch and readily adheres to the skin.

It is insoluble in water, in alcohol, and in ether.

Chemical Properties.—The salt fuses when heated to about 120° C. It decomposes at higher temperatures into inflammable vapors having the odor of burning fat, and zinc oxide containing some free carbon. When the compound is placed on moist litmus paper no change of color is observed.

When Zinc Stearate is heated with dilute sulfuric acid, stearic acid is liberated and floats as an oily layer on the surface of the liquid (1).

(1) $(C_{17}H_{35}COO)_2Zn + H_2SO_4 \rightarrow 2C_{17}H_{35}COOH + ZnSO_4$ (in solution)

The aqueous solution obtained in (1) should respond to all tests for zinc ion.

The stearic acid may be separated and tested.

To assay zinc stearate it is treated with excess 0.1 N sulfuric acid which forms insoluble stearic acid and soluble zinc sulfate. The excess 0.1 N sulfuric acid is back titrated with 0.1 N sodium hydroxide using methyl orange T.S. as an indicator.

Official Tests for Identity.—1. Zinc stearate is converted with dilute sulfuric acid to stearic acid and a solution of zinc sulfate (1). This acid solution responds to all the tests for *Zinc* (*q.v.*).

2. Stearic acid may be isolated by treatment with water, sulfuric acid and heat. The solidification temperature of the fatty acid is not below 54° C. (See also Calcium Stearate, p. 391.)

Commercial Manufacture.—Zinc Stearate is usually made by decomposing a boiling solution of sodium stearate (animal or curd soap) with a hot solution of either zinc acetate or sulfate (2). The precipitate is washed with hot water, dried, powdered, and sieved. A much superior product may be obtained by decomposing a sodium stearate that has been prepared by adding Stearic Acid U.S.P. to a hot solution of sodium carbonate (3).

(2) $2C_{17}H_{35}COONa + ZnSO_4 \rightarrow (C_{17}H_{35}COO)_2Zn \downarrow + Na_2SO_4$

(3) $Na_2CO_3.H_2O + 2C_{17}H_{35}COOH \rightarrow 2C_{17}H_{35}COONa + CO_2 \uparrow + 2H_2O$

Uses.—*Zinc Stearate,* U.S.P. XVII, is a compound of zinc with stearic acid and consists chiefly of variable proportions of zinc stearate and zinc palmitate equivalent to not less than 12.5 per cent and not more than 14.0 per cent of ZnO.

Zinc stearate is mildly antiseptic and astringent and in the form of powder or ointment is often used to treat various types of skin diseases. It has been used as a dusting powder as a replacement for talcum but is prone to cause pulmonary inflammation. Its routine use as a dusting powder for small infants should be strongly discouraged. In *Compound Iodochlorhydroxyquin Powder* it is used as a diluent.

Although this salt has some therapeutic value as cited above, its official recognition derives from its extensive use as a lubricant in tablet manufacture.

ZINC SULFATE

Zinc Sulfate, U.S.P. XVII

Formula, $ZnSO_4.7H_2O$.   Molecular Weight, 287.54

Physical Properties.—Zinc Sulfate occurs in the form of colorless transparent, rhombic prisms or needles, or as a granular, crystalline powder, odorless, and having an astringent, metallic taste. It effloresces in dry air. It has a density of 1.967.

One Gm. of Zinc Sulfate dissolves in 0.6 ml. of water and in about 2.5 ml. of glycerin, at 25° C. It is insoluble in alcohol.

The salt melts at about 50° C. When strongly ignited, it decomposes, losing both water and sulfuric acid.

Chemical Properties.—Zinc sulfate (like cupric sulfate) combines with potassium and ammonium sulfates to form double salts, *e.g.*, $ZnSO_4.K_2SO_4.6H_2O$. These compounds exist as such only in the solid state. When they are dissolved in water, they separate into the respective components, which in turn dissociate into their respective ions. The salt produces a solution that is acid to litmus paper due to hydrolysis. (See zinc chloride.)

It exhibits all the reactions of the zinc ion and the sulfate ion.

Zinc Sulfate is assayed by the same method that is used for zinc chloride.

Official Tests for Identity.—Its aqueous solutions respond to all tests for *Zinc* (*q.v.*) and for *Sulfate* (*q.v.*)

Commercial Manufacture.—1. Commercial zinc sulfate is made by roasting zinc sulfide ore (blende) in the presence of air under very specific conditions of temperature and amount of air used. The zinc sulfate formed by the oxidation of the sulfide is dissolved in hot water and the solution concentrated to crystallization.

2. The U. S. Pharmacopœia grade of zinc sulfate is usually made by digesting an excess of granulated zinc in diluted sulfuric acid. The resulting solution is filtered and treated with chlorine water, which oxidizes any ferrous sulfate to ferric sulfate. The ferric ion is precipitated as hydroxide by agitating the solution with either zinc oxide or precipitated zinc carbonate. The mixture is filtered,

the filtrate concentrated, and the salt allowed to crystallize. The product should be free from heavy metals (arsenic, copper, lead, iron, etc.), alkali metals, alkaline earth metals, and free acid.

Uses.—*Zinc Sulfate,* U.S.P. XVII, contains not less than 55.6 per cent and not more than 61 per cent of $ZnSO_4$, corresponding to not less than 99.0 per cent and not more than 108.7 per cent of the hydrated salt ($ZnSO_4.7H_2O$). Of the zinc salts the sulfate is most desirable for pharmaceutical use because of its stability and solubility.

Zinc sulfate may be used internally as an emetic. It acts so quickly upon the vomiting reflex that emesis is produced before there is time for any other local irritant effect. It is an excellent and certain emetic to use for emptying the stomach of undigested foods and non-corrosive poisons.

The emetic dose is about 2 Gm. as a 1 per cent solution.

It is also used in a dose of 220 mg. three times a day with meals for stimulation of wound healing (see p. 409).

Externally it is used in powders and solutions. The officially recognized use is as an ophthalmic astringent in 0.25 per cent aqueous solution. A common application is in 0.1 to 1 per cent solution as collyria. In solution an acidic reaction is produced (pH 5) and buffering for eye use is desirable. Gifford's Buffers or the barbiturate buffers may be used at pH 6 to 6.4. To maintain zinc ion in a basic medium, the use of sodium citrate[1] is recommended to sequester the ion. It is possible to prepare solutions having a pH of 8.

White Lotion, a popular zinc sulfide preparation, is formed when a filtered solution of Sulfurated Potash (40 Gm. in 450 ml. H_2O) is added slowly and with constant stirring to a filtered solution of Zinc Sulfate (40 Gm. in 450 ml. H_2O) (1) and water added to 1000 ml.

$$(1) \quad K_2S + ZnSO_4 \rightarrow ZnS \downarrow + K_2SO_4$$

The order of mixing is necessary to prevent the formation of basic zinc salts or some zinc hydroxide. Sulfurated Potash solution contains hydroxide ions that are neutralized by the acid solution of Zinc Sulfate thus permitting a more complete formation of white zinc sulfide. Also, by reversing the order of mixing a precipitate of larger particles will be obtained.

A yellow color in the supernatant liquid may be caused by the reaction of acidic zinc sulfate solution on the polysulfide or on thiosulfate.

In the alkaline solution, the precipitation of the zinc as sulfide is practically complete, potassium sulfate and excess Sulfurated Potash remaining in solution. The precipitate tends to become lumpy upon standing so this preparation should be freshly prepared and shaken thoroughly before using.

It is used in skin diseases for the sulfide effect. The zinc ion provides an astringent action.

[1] Husa, W. J. and Dale, J. K.:   J. Am. Pharm. Assoc., **34**, 163 (1945); **37**, 79 (1948)

25

Cadmium and Cadmium Compounds

CADMIUM

Symbol, Cd.   Valence, 2.   Atomic Weight, 112.40;
Atomic Number, 48

History and Occurrence.—This metallic element was discovered in 1817 by F. Stromeyer. He showed that the yellow color of a particular sample of iron-free zinc oxide was due to the presence of the oxide of a new metal. He named the element *cadmia fornacum* ("furnace zinc") because he found the substance also in the zinc dust or first runnings obtained in the distillation of zinc. At about the same time, Hermann, a manufacturing chemist of Schönebeck, showed that a specimen of zinc oxide that was thought to contain arsenic, really contained the oxide of a new element.

Cadmium does not occur as such in Nature. In combination as the carbonate or sulfide, it occurs in small amounts (about 0.5 per cent) in the corresponding zinc ores (zinc blende, calamine, etc.). The rare mineral *greenockite*, found in Scotland, Bohemia, Pennsylvania and Missouri, consists largely of cadmium sulfide.

Physical Properties.—Cadmium is a white metal, having a slight bluish tinge, usually occurring as bars, sheets, wire or as a gray, granular powder. It is quite stable in dry air, but in moist air it becomes covered with a film of the oxide. It readily takes a high polish, but will quickly tarnish. It is a little harder than tin, but is softer than zinc. The metal is ductile and malleable. It has a density of 8.65, melts at about 321° C., and boils at 767° C., forming a deep yellow vapor. It is insoluble in water. The vapor density shows it to be monatomic.

Chemical Properties.—*Cadmium* is always bivalent and enters into complex ions, *e.g.*, $Cd(NH_3)_4^{++}$. Its oxide and hydroxide are basic, and its salts are not hydrolyzed. Like the halides of zinc and copper (see mercuric chloride), these salts of cadmium are only slightly ionized in concentrated solution. This is due to the fact that they form autocomplexes (see zinc) and also because their crystal structure shows them not to be true ionic compounds. It immediately precedes iron in the electromotive series and hence displaces hydrogen from dilute acids. Cadmium unites with a number of the heavy metals to form alloys. The melting-point of an alloy is usually lowered by cadmium and hence it finds a useful application in the so-called *fusible alloys*. The amalgams which it forms with mercury are sometimes employed as fillings in dentistry.

Some of the characteristic reactions of the *cadmium ion* are as follows: Hydrogen sulfide precipitates a bright yellow cadmium sulfide from neutral or alkaline solutions of cadmium salts (1). Cadmium sulfide is insoluble in alkali hydroxides, in alkali sulfides, *e.g.*, Na_2S (distinction from arsenic) and in cold diluted acids. It is soluble in cold, moderately diluted nitric acid, in hot diluted hydrochloric acid, or in hot, moderately diluted sulfuric acid. The formation of a yellow sulfide in alkaline solution is a distinctive test for cadmium ion as arsenic and tin sulfides are relatively soluble under alkaline conditions.

$$(1) \quad Cd^{++} + S^{=} \rightarrow CdS \downarrow$$

In moderately strong acid solutions (2 to 9 per cent H_2SO_4 or 0.5 to 1.8 per cent HCl) a yellow precipitate changing quickly to orange is thrown down. The precipitate is not pure CdS but contains more or less $Cd_2(SO_4)S$ or Cd_2Cl_2S.

This is due to the fact that cadmium salts in solution form auto-complexes that are precipitated by sulfide (2).

$$(2) \quad 2CdCl_2 \rightleftarrows Cd^{++} + (CdCl_4)^{=}$$
$$Cd^{++} + (CdCl_4)^{=} + S^{=} \rightarrow Cd_2Cl_2S \downarrow + 2Cl$$

Also there are assumed to exist two forms of cadmium sulfide, alpha and beta. The alpha or yellow form is obtained usually from slightly alkaline or neutral solutions whereas the beta or red form is a polymer of the alpha form produced in acid solutions.

Alkali hydroxides precipitate a white cadmium hydroxide $[Cd(OH)_2]$ from solutions of cadmium salts (3). It is insoluble in excess of reagent.

$$(3) \quad Cd^{++} + 2OH^{-} \rightarrow Cd(OH)_2 \downarrow$$

Ammonium hydroxide forms the same precipitate $[Cd(OH)_2]$ as in (3). The cadmium hydroxide dissolves in an excess of the precipitant (difference from lead) (4).

$$(4) \quad Cd(OH)_2 + 4NH_3 \rightarrow [Cd(NH_3)_4]^{++} + 2OH^{-}$$

Tests for Identity of Cadmium Ion.—Cadmium salts in neutral, alkaline or slightly acid solutions produce a yellow precipitate (1 and 2) with hydrogen sulfide. This sulfide is insoluble in alkali hydroxides or sulfides and in cold diluted acids. It is soluble in moderately concentrated cold nitric or hot sulfuric acids and in hot diluted hydrochloric acid.

Commercial Manufacture.—Cadmium is usually obtained from the first flue-dust caught in the sheet iron adapters of zinc retorts.

On account of the relatively low boiling-point of cadmium (767° C.) as compared to zinc (907° C.), cadmium distils over first. This "zinc dust" is mixed with coal and distilled at the lowest possible temperature, thus obtaining a distillate that is rich in cadmium and cadmium oxide. The crude product is dissolved in sulfuric acid and the cadmium precipitated with hydrogen sulfide (zinc is not precipitated by H_2S in acid solution). The cadmium sulfide is then dissolved in concentrated hydrochloric acid, precipitated as the carbonate ($CdCO_3$-white, insoluble in excess) with ammonium carbonate (Cu and As remaining in solution) and the product calcined. The cadmium oxide is mixed with charcoal and distilled and the metallic distillate is collected in suitable receivers. The metal is purified by dissolving it in hydrochloric acid and digesting the solution with metallic zinc, which displaces cadmium from solutions of its salts.

Pharmacological Action of Cadmium Ion.—Cadmium ion closely resembles zinc ion in its action, but is more toxic. The chloride is a powerful emetic. Systemically it is said to behave like mercury and after absorption, produces death by arresting respiration. Symptoms of poisoning are nausea, vomiting, abdominal cramps, and diarrhea, producing weakness and prostration. Cadmium poisoning can result from intake of the metal if food containers are cadmium plated. It probably reacts with the hydrochloric acid of the stomach forming soluble cadmium chloride. In fatal cases it is found chiefly in the liver and kidney.

Cadmium sulfate has been suggested in collyria since the ion is strongly antiseptic and fungicidal. Concentrations for use are similar to those of zinc sulfate (0.1 to 1.0 per cent).

Cadmium chloride and aerosol OT (each 1 per cent) in 30 per cent alcohol is used topically for ringworm.

Intramuscular injections of cadmium sulfide (1 per cent in oil) were found to be better than gold therapy in treating tuberculosis. No untoward reactions or cumulative effects were observed.

More recently, cadmium sulfide has been employed in the form of a shampoo preparation (Capsebon) for the treatment of seborrheic dermatitis of the scalp (seborrhea capitis). It is of the order of effectiveness of Selenium Sulfide (q.v.) and, while it is not a cure, it does afford a measure of relief from excessive oiliness, scaling, etc. It has the advantage over Selenium Sulfide that it is non-irritating to the conjunctiva. It is administered topically in the form of a 1 per cent suspension in shampoo form. It may be used daily if needed or, more usually, a weekly application is sufficient.

Uses of Cadmium.—Cadmium is used to electroplate those metals in which no high polish or luster is desired. It apparently forms an alloy with the surface metal, does not peel or flake off, and hence is superior to the other metals for rust-proofing screws and nails. It is a constituent of easily fusible alloys, e.g., Wood's Metal, Rose's Metal, etc.

28

26

Mercury and Mercury Compounds

MERCURY

Symbol, Hg.   Valence, 1, 2.   Atomic Weight, 200.59;
Atomic Number, 80

History.—Apparently this element was unknown to the ancient Jews and no mention was made of it by the early Greek writers. Theophrastus (about 300 B.C.) described it as *liquid silver* or *quick-silver*, and stated that it could be obtained from *cinnabar* (HgS) by treatment with copper and vinegar. In the first century, Dioscorides obtained it from the same mineral by sublimation with charcoal. Pliny named the liquid metal *hydrargyrum* from the Græco-Latin ὕδωρ, water, and ἄργυρος, silver. The metal has always been associated with the planet Mercury, from which it takes its present name. Geber held that the predominant element in this liquid substance entered into the composition of all metals, and in fact was the cause of metallicity. His theory was accepted quite generally and led to many attempts to convert the baser metals into silver and gold.

Occurrence.—Mercury occurs in Nature chiefly as the red crystalline sulfide called *cinnabar*. It is found also in small globules disseminated through rocks, and as an amalgam of silver and gold. The principal deposits of cinnabar are found in Spain (Almaden), Illyria (Idria), United States (California, Nevada and Texas), Japan, China and Mexico. Mexico has been producing a sizeable quantity.

Physical Properties.—At ordinary temperatures, mercury is a bright, shining, silvery-white metal, liquid at ordinary temperatures, and easily divisible into spherical globules. At −39° C., it forms a white malleable and ductile solid, which exhibits cubical crystals. It boils at 356.9° C. It has a density of 13.5939 and has a noticeable vapor tension at ordinary temperatures (0.0002 mm. at 0° C. to 0.0013 mm. at 20° C.). Mercury expands rapidly and uniformly when heated and because of its wide range of fluidity, it is used in making thermometers. Mercury vapor is colorless and its density indicates that the molecules are monatomic.

Superheated mercury vapor is a conductor of electricity and, when acting as such, radiates light that is rich in ultraviolet rays. The mercury lamp, used in the sterilization of water, public toilets, etc. consists of a quartz tube about 50 or 60 cm. long in which there is a very high vacuum. The two poles are united by a thin thread of mercury. When the current is turned on, the mercury is rapidly heated and the vapors readily conduct the current and become incandescent by doing so. As soon as a sufficient amount of the mercury has been vaporized to carry the current, the tube should be inclined in order to collect all of the mercury at one end.

Mercury amalgamates with most of the familiar metals such as Na, K, Li, Ca, etc., excepting iron and platinum.

Chemical Properties.—The consideration of the chemistry of mercury is best taken up under the following headings: (1) metallic mercury, (2) mercurous compounds, and (3) mercuric compounds.

1. At ordinary temperatures, *mercury* is permanent in air, ammonia, carbon dioxide, nitrous oxide and in some other gases. When heated near its boiling-point in air, the metal slowly combines with oxygen to form red mercuric oxide (HgO), which decomposes at higher temperatures into the free metal and oxygen (1). Sulfur and the halogens combine directly with it. This may be demonstrated by triturating mercury and iodine together to form mercuric iodide (2).

(1) $2HgO \overset{\triangle}{\rightleftharpoons} 2Hg + O_2 \uparrow$

(2) $Hg + I_2 \rightarrow HgI_2$

The position of mercury in the electromotive series makes it insoluble in many of the common acids. However, it is soluble in the oxidizing acids, such as hot concentrated sulfuric acid (3) and cold nitric acid (4). In the latter case, the NO which is evolved is readily oxidized by atmospheric oxygen to nitrogen dioxide (brown). If to the mercuric nitrate which is obtained in reaction (4) is added an excess of metallic mercury, the mercurous salt is formed (5).

(3) $Hg + 2H_2SO_4 \overset{\triangle}{\rightleftharpoons} HgSO_4 + SO_2 \uparrow + 2H_2O$

(4) $3Hg + 8HNO_3 \rightarrow 3Hg(NO_3)_2 + 2NO \uparrow + 4H_2O$

(5) $Hg(NO_3)_2 + Hg \rightarrow Hg_2(NO_3)_2$

It is interesting to note that, although mercury is below hydrogen in the electromotive series, it is acted upon by one of the hydrohalide acids, namely, hydriodic acid. Hydriodic acid dissolves mercury readily with the evolution of hydrogen (6), although hydrochloric and hydrobromic acids are without appreciable effect.

(6) $Hg + 4HI \rightarrow H_2HgI_4 + H_2 \uparrow$

424 Mercury and Mercury Compounds

The reason for its solution in hydriodic acid follows from the fact that even metals below hydrogen in the electromotive series and in sufficiently dilute solution can be oxidized by hydronium ion (hydrogen ion). This fact, together with the knowledge that the $HgI_4^=$ ionizes only slightly into Hg^{++} and I^- (ionization constant of $HgI_4^= = 5 \times 10^{-31}$), shows why the hydronium ion can act in this case as an oxidizing agent and in that manner dissolve mercury.

The complex anions, $HgCl_4^=$ and $HgBr_4^=$, ionize so completely that a similar reaction does not take place. (See potassium mercuric iodide.)

Mercury resembles copper by forming two series of compounds, viz., *mercurous* (bivalent Hg_2^{++})[1] and *mercuric* (bivalent Hg^{++}). Also, the mercurous halides, like the cuprous halides, are nearly insoluble in water and are decomposed by light. Both mercurous and mercuric hydroxides lose water spontaneously and are changed into the corresponding oxides (Hg_2O and HgO). These oxides are very feebly basic and hence their salts are easily hydrolyzed to basic salts. Mercury enters into a few complex ions, e.g., $Hg(CN)_4^=$, $HgI_4^=$, etc.

2. *Mercurous salts*, in general, are prone to split off an atom of mercury to form the more stable mercuric series. This is primarily an auto-oxidation-reduction reaction. Mercurous mercury may be considered to be of the following structure: Hg—
|
Hg—

Many reactions of mercurous compounds indicate that a break occurs producing metallic mercury and the mercuric ion. Examples are reactions (8, 10, 12, 14, and 29).

Soluble mercurous salts, e.g., the nitrate (7) tend to hydrolyze in aqueous solution to form basic salts. A slight excess of nitric acid will stabilize the solution and prevent reaction (7).

(7) $Hg_2(NO_3)_2 + H_2O \rightleftarrows Hg_2(OH)NO_3 \downarrow + HNO_3$

Hydrogen sulfide or soluble sulfides precipitate black mercuric sulfide and mercury (gray) from solutions of mercurous salts (8). Mercurous sulfide (Hg_2S) does not exist at ordinary temperatures.

(8) $Hg_2^{++} + H_2S + 2H_2O \rightarrow HgS \downarrow + 2H_3O^+ + Hg \downarrow$

Most reducing agents such as hypophosphites and stannous chloride (26) will reduce mercurous salts to free mercury. (See Hypophosphorous Acid.)

---

[1] The bivalent mercurous ion, Hg_2^{++}, is used here since it has been shown more or less conclusively that mercurous mercury exists in this form both in solutions and in compounds. The older method of writing mercurous ion (still retained by the N.F. XII) is Hg^+.

Soluble iodides precipitate mercurous ion as the yellow mercurous iodide (9) which is insoluble in water and in alcohol. The precipitate may become green upon standing. The precipitate is partly soluble in an excess of precipitant (10).

(9) $Hg_2^{++} + 2I^- \rightarrow Hg_2I_2 \downarrow$

(10) $Hg_2I_2 + 2I^- \rightarrow (HgI_4)^{=} + Hg \downarrow$

Fixed alkali hydroxides and those of calcium or barium, precipitate mercurous ion as black-brown mercurous oxide (11) which is insoluble in alkali but is readily solubilized by acids. It is very unstable toward heat and light (12).

(11) $Hg_2(NO_3)_2 + 2OH^- \rightarrow Hg_2(OH)_2 \downarrow + 2NO_3^-$
$Hg_2(OH)_2 \rightarrow H_2O + Hg_2O \downarrow$

(12) $Hg_2O \overset{\Delta}{\rightarrow} HgO + Hg$

From solutions of mercurous salts, ammonium hydroxide precipitates gray *mixtures* of mercury and mercuric amido compounds

Ammine formation or simultaneous ammonolysis and hydrolysis occurs by the action of ammonia on the better dissociated mercurous salts of oxyacids. (13)

(13) $Hg_2(NO_3)_2 + 4NH_3 \rightarrow Hg_2(NH_3)_4(NO_3)_2$

However, the binucleate basic salts are usually obtained, and these are half hydrolyzed and half ammonolyzed (14, 14a).

(14) $2Hg_2(NO_3)_2 + 4NH_4OH \rightarrow 2Hg \downarrow + 3H_2O +$
$NH_2-Hg-O-Hg-NO_3 \downarrow + 3NH_4NO_3$
(black)

or:

(14a) $Hg_2(NO_3)_2 + 2NH_4OH \rightarrow HgNH_2NO_3 \downarrow + Hg \downarrow +$
$NH_4NO_3 + 2H_2O$

Hydrochloric acid and soluble chlorides precipitate white mercurous chloride from solutions of mercurous salts (15). The precipitate is insoluble in water but slowly soluble in hot concentrated hydrochloric acid. It is blackened by ammonia T.S. (*i.e.*, 29)

(15) $Hg_2(NO_3)_2 + 2Cl^- \rightarrow 2Hg_2Cl_2 \downarrow + 2NO_3^-$

When a piece of bright copper is immersed in a solution of a mercurous salt (also mercuric) that is free from excess of nitric acid, it becomes coated with a dark film of metallic mercury (16), which may be given a bright and silvery polish by rubbing. The deposit is readily volatilized by heat. Copper, like all of the elements above mercury in the electromotive series, has a greater tendency toward the ionic state than mercury and hence will displace the latter from solutions of its salts.

(16) $Cu + Hg_2^{++} \rightarrow Cu^{++} + 2Hg \downarrow$

Mercurous carbonate readily hydrolyzes in solution giving off carbon dioxide and precipitating Hg_2O (17). In the presence of heat and light, free mercury and mercuric oxide form (12). (See carbonate test with sodium carbonate.)

(17) $Hg_2(NO_3)_2 + Na_2CO_3 \rightarrow Hg_2CO_3 + 2NaNO_3$
$Hg_2CO_3 \rightarrow Hg_2O \downarrow + CO_2 \uparrow$

3. *Mercuric salts* are similar to mercurous in that they are also readily hydrolyzed to form insoluble basic salts. This is especially true of the sulfate (18) and nitrate (19). Mercuric chloride will also form a brown mercuric basic chloride but usually requires slight alkalinity. (See reactions 6 to 12 under Sodium Bicarbonate.) The presence of an excess of acid prevents the formation of these basic salts.

(18) $3HgSO_4 + 2H_2O \rightarrow HgSO_4 . 2HgO \downarrow + 2H_2SO_4$

(19) $Hg(NO_3)_2 + H_2O \rightarrow Hg(OH)NO_3 \downarrow + HNO_3$

Hydrogen sulfide or soluble sulfides precipitate black mercuric sulfide from solutions of mercuric salts (20). The precipitate is first white ($HgCl_2 . 2HgS$, a complex of the original mercuric salt with mercuric sulfide) then yellow (complex having greater proportions of HgS), then brown, and finally black (21).

(20) $3HgCl_2 + 2H_2S \rightarrow HgCl_2 . 2HgS + 4HCl$

(21) $HgCl_2 . 2HgS + H_2S \rightarrow 3HgS \downarrow + 2HCl$
(black)

Soluble iodides precipitate mercuric ion as scarlet, microcrystalline mercuric iodide (22). The precipitate is yellow at first but quickly changes to a scarlet color. It is very insoluble in water, but readily dissolves in ether, in alcohol, and in an excess of potassium iodide (23). With the latter, it forms the complex compound potassium mercuri-iodide (K_2HgI_4) which dissociates into potassium ion and the complex anion, $HgI_4^=$. A solution of this salt is known as Valser's Reagent.

(22) $Hg^{++} + 2I^- \rightarrow HgI_2 \downarrow$

(23) $HgI_2 + 2KI \rightarrow K_2HgI_4$

Fixed alkali hydroxides or those of calcium or barium precipitate yellow mercuric oxide from solutions of mercuric salts (24). The hydroxide that is first formed, spontaneously decomposes into the oxide and water.

(24) $Hg^{++} + 2OH^- \rightarrow Hg(OH)_2 \downarrow$
$Hg(OH)_2 \rightarrow HgO \downarrow + H_2O$
(yellow)

Due to the alkalinity of the carbonate, rapid hydrolysis takes place producing the insoluble oxide. Advantage is taken of this reaction to distinguish between carbonates and bicarbonates. For a discussion and equations see Sodium Bicarbonate.

Ammonium hydroxide precipitates white mercuric amido chloride (Ammoniated Mercury) from a solution of mercuric chloride (25) (compare with silver ammino chloride).

(25) $HgCl_2 + 2NH_3 \rightarrow Hg \begin{smallmatrix} \diagup NH_2 \\ \diagdown Cl \end{smallmatrix} \downarrow + NH_4\,Cl$

Stannous chloride precipitates white, insoluble mercurous chloride (26) from solutions of mercuric salts. By heating the precipitate in an excess of the precipitant, it turns gray, due to the reduction of the mercurous chloride to metallic mercury (27).

(26) $2HgCl_2 + Sn^{++} \rightarrow Hg_2Cl_2 \downarrow + Sn^{++++} + 2Cl^-$

(27) $Hg_2Cl_2 + Sn^{++} \rightarrow 2Hg \downarrow + Sn^{++++} + 2Cl^-$

Mercuric salts, like mercurous salts, deposit mercury on the surface of copper foil (28), iron wire, or zinc. (See assay of Ammoniated Mercury.)

(28) $Cu + Hg^{++} \rightarrow Cu^{++} + Hg \downarrow$

Official Tests for Identity.—1. Solutions of mercurous or mercuric salts which are free from an excess of nitric acid will deposit mercury upon a bright copper foil (16, 28), the deposit becoming bright and silvery upon rubbing.

2. Solutions of mercury compounds yield a black precipitate (8, 21) with hydrogen sulfide which is insoluble in ammonium sulfide T.S., or in boiling diluted nitric acid.

Mercuric Salts.—(a) Mercuric salts yield a yellow precipitate of yellow mercuric oxide when treated with sodium hydroxide T.S. (24).

(b) In neutral solutions, mercuric salts yield a scarlet precipitate of mercuric iodide with potassium iodide T.S. (22). This precipitate is soluble in an excess of the reagent (23).

Mercurous Salts.—(a) Sodium hydroxide T.S. decomposes mercurous compounds forming a black color due to mercurous oxide (11).

(b) Hydrochloric acid added to solutions of mercurous salts produces a white precipitate (15) which is blackened by ammonia T.S. (29).

(29) $Hg_2Cl_2 + 2NH_4OH \rightarrow HgNH_2Cl \downarrow + Hg \downarrow + NH_4Cl$
     $+ 2H_2O$

(c) Potassium iodide T.S. produces a yellow precipitate of mercurous iodide (9) which may turn green on standing.

Commercial Manufacture.—Mercury is readily obtained by roasting its principal ore (cinnabar, HgS) in huge shaft furnaces (capacity about 50 tons of ore) at a temperature of about 650° C. with access of air. Any mercuric oxide formed during the roasting is instantly decomposed into mercury and oxygen at the temperature of the process. The vapors are condensed in a series of stone towers in which the ascending gases are cooled by a descending spray of water and the mercury is collected under water. Formerly, lime and iron were used to destroy the combination between the mercury and sulfur (30).

(30) $4HgS + 4CaO \rightarrow 4Hg + 3CaS + CaSO_4$

Another procedure known as "retorting" of high grade ore or concentrates is less well known but is gaining in popularity. It requires preliminary treatment of the ore by flotation procedures in order to effect concentration. It depends on the fact that HgS will dissociate into mercury and sulfur vapors at about 620° and lime is used as above (30) to prevent recombination of sulfur with mercury.

The mercury thus obtained is often separated from its impurities by mechanically stirring it in an iron bowl having a perforated bottom. The soot, containing some ash and traces of kerosene, is thrown out at the top of the bowl and the mercury runs through the holes in the bottom. The metallic impurities, e.g., tin, lead, copper, zinc, silver, etc., may be eliminated by allowing the finely divided metal to drop through a column of nitric acid and mercury nitrate. The mercury is then dried, pressed through chamois and distilled in vacuum from a glass retort.

Pharmacological Action of Mercury.—The therapeutic values of mercury and its compounds may well be prefaced by a brief consideration of their inherently toxic nature. Mercury poisoning is usually the result of ingestion of bichloride of mercury although mercurial salts given by inunction may also cause serious intoxication. Poisoning may be caused by any of the inorganic or organic mercury compounds, however. The early symptoms of poisoning are a burning metallic taste, thirst and soreness in the throat. This is followed by salivation, sore gums, bloody diarrhea, severe gastric pain and usually vomiting. The fact that the kidney has a unique ability to concentrate mercury ion in an effort to detoxify or excrete it accounts for the fact that death usually results from its reaction on the kidneys. Emergency treatment consists of administering protein material such as egg white or milk to inactivate the mercury ions by coagulation, followed by extensive gastric lavage to remove all of the poisonous material possible. Dimercaprol has been the agent of choice intramuscularly for inactivating mercury ions via mercaptide formation but should be administered within 4 hours for maximal effect. A usually overlooked source of mercury poisoning is based on the vapor pressure of the metal even at room temperature (see p. 422), the vapors being capable of causing serious toxic symptoms.[1]

Mercury and its salts have enjoyed several uses in therapeutics. Practically all of the therapeutic applications may be looked upon as modifications of the principal action of the mercuric ion, *i.e.*, a protoplasmic poison. It is probably of more advantage to discuss them from this standpoint than from the action of specific chemical types such as metallic, mercuric and mercurous mercury. The most important therapeutic uses of mercury and its salts are (1) diuretic, (2) antiseptic, (3) antisyphilitic, (4) cathartic, (5) parasiticidal and fungicidal.

1. *Diuretic Action*.[2]—The diuretic action of mercury salts, inorganic and organic, is due to a direct renal effect by mercuric ion. It is believed that mercurial diuretics, by reaction with sulfhydryl groups to form mercaptides, inactivate specific enzymes of the renal tubules to prevent sodium ion transport in the proximal tubule and thus inhibit the reabsorption of sodium to bring about a sodium and water diuresis. To obtain a diuretic effect the organic mercurials are used almost exclusively, *e.g.*, Salyrgan, Mercurin, Mercupurin, etc. They are much less highly ionized than the inorganic mercurials and for this reason are less apt to cause undesirable toxic reactions. Furthermore, it is probable that they insure selective distribution to the tubule since comparable doses of inorganic (*e.g.*, $HgCl_2$) salts could be dissipated by reaction with sulfhydryl groups throughout the body. The chief use of mercurial diuretics is to rid the body of excess fluid in the case of cardiac edema. It should be emphasized that the mercury compounds are used simply as potent diuretics in these conditions and have no curative action whatsoever except that incidental to the diuretic action. It is interesting to note the synergistic action of acid-forming diuretic salts with mercurials. If salts which produce an acidosis are administered for two days prior to the use of the mercurial, it has been found that the sum total of the diuresis is usually greater than that which might be expected on an additive basis. Likewise, it has been found that salts which produce an alkalosis, *e.g.*, sodium bicarbonate, inhibit the action of the mercurial diuretics.

[1] "How Poisonous is Mercury" by J. B. Lawrence, Chem. and Eng. News, **29**, 3529 (1951).

[2] For a more extended discussion of mercury compounds as diuretics see: New and Nonofficial Drugs 1960, Philadelphia, Lippincott, 1960, p. 664; and Drill's *Pharmacology in Medicine*, ed. by J. R. DiPalma, 3rd edition, New York, McGraw-Hill Book Co., 1965, pp. 662-668.

2. *Antiseptic Action.*—Mercury salts, both mercurous and mercuric, possess a pronounced antiseptic activity. The antiseptic action is often said to be due to the mercuric ion which is a protein precipitant, although it is difficult to explain on this basis the antiseptic activity of organic compounds. Fildes, in 1920, presented evidence to show that mercurials exerted their antiseptic action by combining with sulfhydryl (-SH) groups of bacterial cells (30) and thus interfered with cellular metabolism. This could explain the action of organic mercurials as antiseptics inasmuch as they have no protein precipitant action but, nevertheless, provide a low concentration of mercury ions. Likewise, it provides a basis of

$$(30) \quad R \overset{\displaystyle \diagup SH}{\underset{\displaystyle \diagdown SH}{}} + Hg^{++} \rightarrow R \overset{\displaystyle \diagup S}{\underset{\displaystyle \diagdown S}{}} Hg + 2H^+$$

Protein　　　　　　　Mercaptide
(inactivated mercury)

explanation for the proven antidotal action of Dimercaprol (31) (see also p. 538) against injected mercuric chloride as well as for the more recently discovered antidotal action of DL-penicillamine and N-acetyl-DL-penicillamine,[1] the latter two compounds having an advantage over Dimercaprol in that they are orally effective.

$$(31) \quad \begin{matrix} CH_2-SH \\ | \\ CH-SH \\ | \\ CH_2OH \end{matrix} + Hg^{++} \rightarrow \begin{matrix} CH_2-S \\ | \quad \diagdown \\ | \quad \quad Hg + 2H^+ \\ CH-S \diagup \\ | \\ CH_2OH \end{matrix}$$

Dimercaprol　　　　　　　Mercaptide
(inactivated mercury)

In general, however, the protein precipitating action of the mercuric ion is a contributing factor to the antiseptic action. It does not distinguish between bacterial and human protein and, therefore, is quite irritating when applied to the tissues. Its action is lowered by the very fact that it precipitates protein indiscriminately instead of being specific for bacterial protein. One might assume from the foregoing discussion that solutions of mercury salts would be excellent antiseptics for non-protein substances such as surgical instruments, etc. Their chief drawback in this application is that ionizable salts corrode metals badly and, therefore, their use is limited.

---

[1] Chem. and Eng. News, April 13, 1959, p. 43.

Mercurous chloride, probably acting *via* slow liberation of mercuric ion, is an excellent antiseptic and is used widely in about a 30 per cent ointment. Auto-oxidation-reduction of the mercurous ion has been suggested as an explanation for its properties. It is used almost exclusively in the prophylaxis of syphilis in the well-known Army and Navy prophylactics. It is said that almost 100 per cent protection from syphilis is obtained by applying the ointment to the affected parts within an hour after exposure.

3. *Antisyphilitic Action.*—Mercury and its salts have been used since the end of the fifteenth century in the prophylaxis and treatment of syphilis. As previously indicated, Calomel ointment is used as an efficient prophylactic. However, the use of mercurials in the treatment of syphilis has been largely superseded by more efficient medications, *e.g.*, arsenicals, bismuth compounds and antibiotics. One of the mercury preparations used in this connection was an ointment of metallic mercury which was applied by inunction (rubbing into the skin). It is vigorously rubbed into the skin in areas where it is most readily absorbed, *e.g.*, armpits, groins, etc. In this form of medication, the metallic mercury was gradually changed into more or less soluble compounds by the body.

Although mercury compounds, intramuscularly and intravenously, have not been used extensively, constant research has gone on in an effort to minimize the difficulties accompanying this type of medication. Intramuscular usage is desirable from the standpoint of slowing down absorption so that less frequent injections are necessary. Some of the organic mercurials have been important in connection with intramuscular use.

4. *Cathartic Action.*—Although this action is seldom used in modern therapy, at one time it was regarded as standard practice. (See Calomel.) The laxative effect is undoubtedly a function of the irritant properties of the mercuric ion which is slowly liberated from the insoluble mercurous chloride, the salt that is used almost exclusively. Mercuric ions are formed by oxidation-reduction of the mercurous ion which also yields free mercury. The principal therapeutic advantage of this cathartic over most other cathartics is that its action starts high in the small intestine giving a thorough cleansing but its disadvantage is that it must be removed by a saline cathartic to avoid possible mercurial poisoning.

5. *Parasiticidal and Fungicidal Action.*—At one time, metallic mercury in the form of "blue ointment" was used as an effective but untidy means of treating crab-louse infestation. It has been largely superseded by equally effective and more acceptable preparations. In a similar manner, dilute solutions of mercuric chloride in 50 per cent alcohol have been advocated for getting rid of head lice and crab lice. In the form of Ammoniated Mercury Ointment the effect of mercury is to act as an efficient antiseptic and fungicide, and is used largely in the treatment of impetigo contagiosa, ringworm infections, etc.

Uses.—*Mercury* (Hydrargyrum, Quicksilver), N.F. XI.—As previously pointed out, metallic mercury has been used by inunction in the treatment of the secondary cutaneous lesions of syphilis but the treatment is little used today. It is used to some extent today only in ointment form (*Mild Mercurial Ointment*, the so-called "blue ointment") as a parasiticide for the treatment of crab-louse infestation. Since this ointment is no longer official the N.F. ceased to recognize mercury officially.

A "water soluble mercury" used to treat urethral infections is a solid preparation containing mercury (10 to 20 per cent), cetyl alcohol (70 per cent), sodium laurylsulfate, dictyl sodium sulfosuccinate, glycerin, and water.

Aside from its medicinal uses, it is employed in the metallurgy of gold and silver. It is also used in making mercury compounds, amalgams, thermometers, barometers, mirrors, vermilion and various physical and chemical apparatus.

Toxicity of mercury vapor[1] is often overlooked and yet is a real danger. Poisoning may occur in workers exposed to mercury vapor or mercury compounds in dust, smoke, etc. Mercury has a low vapor tension but at 25° C. the equilibrium concentration in the air is over 200 mg. per 10 cubic meters. There is no sensory warning of the presence of mercury vapor. Therefore, well ventilated areas are necessary to handle the element.

OFFICIAL MERCURY COMPOUNDS

AMMONIATED MERCURY

Ammoniated Mercury, U.S.P. XVII

Formula, $HgNH_2Cl$; $\begin{array}{c} NH_2 \\ \diagdown \\ \diagup \\ Cl \end{array} Hg$. Molecular Weight, 252.07

Physical Properties.—Ammoniated Mercury occurs in white, easily powdered (pulverulent) pieces, or as a white, amorphous powder. It is odorless, and is stable in air, but is affected by light. It has a styptic, metallic taste. It is insoluble in water and in alcohol. Warm hydrochloric, nitric, and acetic acids readily dissolve it. Below red heat, Ammoniated Mercury is decomposed without fusion, and at red heat it is volatilized.

Chemical Properties.—As pointed out above, this compound decomposes without fusion (1) when heated and is sometimes known as "non-fusible white precipitate" to distinguish it from a related compound, $Hg(NH_3)_2Cl_2$ (fusible white precipitate).

---

[1] Circular D-Chem 17, National Safety Council, Chicago. See also ref. 1, p. 429.

Ammoniated Mercury is converted to soluble mercuric chloride by treating it with a hot ammonium chloride solution (2) or a cold solution of ammonium carbonate.

(1) $6HgNH_2Cl \overset{\Delta}{\rightarrow} 3Hg_2Cl_2 \uparrow + 4NH_3 \uparrow + N_2 \uparrow$

(2) $HgNH_2Cl + NH_4Cl \rightarrow HgCl_2 + 2NH_3 \uparrow$

Prolonged washing of the compound with water results in the formation of a yellow basic compound (3). Therefore, lotions using oil are available.

(3) $2HgNH_2Cl + H_2O \rightarrow NH_4Cl + H_2N(HgO)HgCl$

When the salt is heated with a solution of a fixed alkali hydroxide, yellow oxide of mercury is formed and ammonia is liberated (4).

(4) $HgNH_2Cl + NaOH \rightarrow HgO + NH_3 \uparrow + NaCl$
(yellow)

When Ammoniated Mercury is dissolved in nitric acid (5) and the liquid treated with a solution of potassium iodide, a red precipitate of mercuric iodide (soluble in an excess of the precipitant) is formed (6).

(5) $HgNH_2Cl + 2HNO_3 \rightarrow Hg(NO_3)_2 + NH_4Cl$

(6) $Hg(NO_3)_2 + 2KI \rightarrow HgI_2 \downarrow + 2KNO_3$

A cold solution of sodium thiosulfate (equal parts of the salt and water) readily dissolves the salt (7) with the evolution of ammonia. When this solution is heated for a short time, red mercuric sulfide is precipitated and turns black on long boiling (8).

(7) $HgNH_2Cl + 2Na_2S_2O_3 + H_2O \rightarrow NH_3 \uparrow + NaOH + Na_2[Hg(S_2O_3)_2] + NaCl$

(8) $Na_2[Hg(S_2O_3)_2] + 2H_2O \overset{\Delta}{\rightarrow} HgS \downarrow + Na_2S + 2H_2SO_4$

Ammoniated Mercury may be analyzed by dissolving it in acetic acid and adding granules of zinc to permit the mercury to deposit upon the granules. The zinc-mercury granules are dissolved in nitric acid and the mercuric ion is titrated with 0.1 N ammonium thiocyanate using ferric alum as an indicator.

Official Tests for Identity.—1. One Gm. of the compound is soluble in a cold solution of 5 Gm. of sodium thiosulfate in 5 ml. of water, evolving ammonia in the process (7). Heating of this solution for a short time will produce red mercuric sulfide which turns black on prolonged boiling.

2. When heated with sodium hydroxide T.S. the material becomes yellow due to formation of mercuric oxide and evolves ammonia (4).

3. A solution of Ammoniated Mercury in nitric acid (5) gives a red precipitate with potassium iodide T.S. (6). The precipitate is soluble in an excess of the reagent (9).

(9) $HgI_2 + 2KI \rightarrow K_2HgI_4$

4. A solution of Ammoniated Mercury in nitric acid gives a precipitate with silver nitrate T.S.

Commercial Manufacture.—A cold solution of mercuric chloride is poured slowly and with constant stirring into cold ammonia water (10). The solutions should be kept cold in order to minimize hydrolysis to basic compounds, as well as to prevent loss of ammonia. The precipitate is washed with very dilute ammonia water and finally dried in a dark place at a temperature not exceeding 30° C.

(10) $HgCl_2 + 2NH_4OH \rightarrow NH_2HgCl \downarrow + NH_4Cl + 2H_2O$

Uses.—*Ammoniated Mercury* (White Precipitate), U.S.P. XVII, contains not less than 98 per cent of $HgNH_2Cl$. This compound is occasionally used as a dusting powder against eczema and parasitic skin diseases and is classified as a local anti-infective. It has a useful effect against low-grade staphylococcal infections. Usually it is applied in the form of *Ammoniated Mercury Ointment* (5%) and *Ammoniated Mercury Ophthalmic Ointment* (3%). It is considered to be a fairly efficient treatment for impetigo contagiosa. It might be mentioned here that the French Précipité Blanc (white precipitate) is Calomel and *not* Ammoniated Mercury. Therefore, care should be exercised in the interpretation of a French prescription so as not to confuse these compounds.

Combinations of salicylic acid and Ammoniated Mercury are known to produce a synergistic effect in that skin irritation is increased. A study[1] of these two compounds indicates that when combined in equal quantities the following reaction occurs:

$$4HC_7H_5O_3 + 2HgNH_2Cl \rightarrow HgCl_2 + Hg (C_7H_5O_3)_2 + 2NH_4C_7H_5O_3$$

The corrosive sublimate formed is responsible for the irritant properties. In mixtures containing an excess of Ammoniated Mercury a less irritant basic mercuric salicylate $[Hg(OH)C_7H_5O_3]$ forms.

MERCURIC CHLORIDE

Mercury Bichloride, N.F. XII

Formula, $HgCl_2$. Molecular Weight, 271.50

Physical Properties.—Mercury Bichloride crystallizes in heavy, white, odorless, rhombic prisms. It occurs also in the form of large crystalline masses, or as a white powder having a specific gravity of 5.44 at 20° C. Water hydrolyzes it, yielding a slightly acid solution which may be made neutral by the addition of sodium chloride (1).

---

[1] Huyck, C. L., J. A. Ph. A. Pr. Ed., **10**, 568 (1949).

It is only feebly ionized. (In a normal solution at 18° C. only 0.01 per cent of $HgCl_2$ is ionized.)

One Gm. of Mercury Bichloride dissolves in 13.5 ml. of water, in 3.8 ml. of alcohol, in about 12 ml. of glycerin, and in 25 ml. of ether, at 25° C. Usually non-ionized inorganic salts are soluble in ether. (See chlorides of zinc, cadmium, and aluminum.)

One Gm. dissolves in 2.1 ml. of boiling water and in 1.6 ml. of boiling alcohol.

At about 277° C. the salt fuses to a colorless liquid which boils at about 300° C. and gives off dense, white vapors of $HgCl_2$.

Chemical Properties.—Mercury Bichloride in solution forms an auto-complex (1) similar to that of zinc chloride.

(1) $2HgCl_2 + 2H_2O \rightleftarrows (HgOH)^+ + (HgCl_4)^= + H_3O^+$

(2) $(HgCl_4)^= \rightleftarrows HgCl_2 + 2Cl^-$

(3) $Hg^{++} + 2H_2O \rightleftarrows (HgOH)^+ + H_3O^+$

The amount of $(HgCl_4)^=$ formed is small and also this auto-complex dissociates (2) quite readily (note that $HgI_4^=$ does not). Solutions are acid in reaction because the mercuric ion is hydrolyzed (3) liberating hydronium ions. Addition of a chloride (NaCl) increases the chloride ion on the right hand side of the equation and by common ion effect decreases the ionization of Mercury Bichloride and thereby decreases the acidity. Note that the solubility of mercuric chloride is not appreciably increased upon the addition of sodium chloride but sodium iodide does solubilize mercuric iodide ($HgI_4^=$ is very stable). The chemical properties of Mercury Bichloride are those of the mercuric ion (q.v.) and the chloride ion (q.v.).

Mercury Bichloride is assayed by treating a solution of the salt with excess hydrogen sulfide and weighing the precipitate of mercuric sulfide.

Official Tests for Identity.—1. A 1 in 20 aqueous solution responds to the tests for *Mercuric salts* (q.v.).

2. An aqueous solution also responds to all tests for *Chloride* (q.v.).

Commercial Manufacture.—1. Mercuric sulfate, made by heating mercury (4 parts) with sulfuric acid (5 parts) and drying, is thoroughly mixed with about one-half its weight of sodium chloride (4) and a small amount of manganese dioxide (an oxidizing agent to prevent mercurous salt formation) and placed in clay or glass vessels. These are heated on a sand-bath until the bichloride sublimes as white, rhombic crystals into the upper part of the vessel. The container is broken and the salt purified, if necessary, by resublimation.

(4) $HgSO_4 + 2NaCl \xrightarrow{300°} HgCl_2 \uparrow + Na_2SO_4$

2. Mercuric chloride is also obtained by direct union of the elements. About 50 pounds of mercury are heated nearly to boiling

in a large glass retort and subjected to the action of gaseous chlorine for from eight to ten hours. The bichloride that is formed sublimes and condenses on the cold, enlarged portion of the retort.

3. It is also made by dissolving mercuric oxide (HgO) in hydrochloric acid and evaporating the solution. The product is usually purified by sublimation.

Uses.—*Mercury Bichloride* (Corrosive Sublimate, Mercuric Chloride), N.F. XII, when dried over phosphorus pentoxide for 4 hours, contains not less than 99.5 per cent of $HgCl_2$. The N.F. cautions: *Mercury Bichloride is extremely poisonous!* The salt is used for its antiseptic action in *Mercury Bichloride Large Poison Tablets* (see below). In aqueous solution, mercuric chloride ionizes only slightly. (See chemical properties.) However, the speed with which it replaces its ions makes its chemical behavior simulate a very highly ionized compound and therefore it is thought to be an effective germicidal agent. It is used in concentrations of 1:1000 as a disinfectant hand wash. Proteins greatly lessen the activity of the salt. Because of its irritant action and also because of the toxic effects produced, its solutions are seldom used to irrigate wounds. Sodium chloride added to its solution reduces irritation. It is used very little internally, if at all, although when so employed it will exert a diuretic effect.

Mercury Bichloride and mercurials of the organic type are not as effective disinfectants as is commonly assumed. The mercurials do act as bacteriostatics but upon removal of the mercurial, the organism will resume growth and will again become infectious. Koch, in 1881, promoted $HgCl_2$ as an antiseptic but by 1891 Abbott stated "It is plain that for use in surgical practice the solutions of $HgCl_2$ do not possess all of the advantages hitherto attributed to them."

Mercury Bichloride Large Poison Tablets contain not less than 420 mg. and not more than 520 mg. of $HgCl_2$, with a sufficient quantity of a suitable excipient or diluent. Sodium chloride or ammonium chloride is sometimes used in the tablets to reduce irritation. *These tablets must be of a distinctive color, not white; they must be of an angular or irregular shape, not discoid. When the Tablets are sold in quantities of 100 or less, they must be dispensed in containers of a distinctive shape. On the exterior of each container must be placed a red printed label bearing the word "POISON" and a statement indicating the amount of mercury bichloride in each tablet.*

MERCURIC OXIDE

Yellow Mercuric Oxide, N.F. XII

Formula, HgO. Molecular Weight, 216.59

Physical Properties.—This oxide is a yellow to orange-yellow, heavy, impalpable powder which is odorless and stable in air. It is practically insoluble in water and in alcohol, but is readily soluble in diluted hydrochloric and nitric acids to form colorless solutions. It is converted to the red form by heating and remains red upon cooling. Light very slowly causes the red form to develop.

The red oxide occurs as heavy, orange-red crystalline scales, or as a crystalline powder. It acquires a yellow color when finely divided. It is odorless and has a slight metallic taste. Its solubilities are practically the same as those of the yellow form being, if anything, less water-soluble.

Although the two forms given above have identical chemical formulæ, they have different colors; the difference in color being ascribed to a difference in particle size (the red is coarse and the yellow is fine). Only the yellow oxide is official.

Chemical Properties.—Both of these oxides behave the same chemically. They are readily soluble in diluted acids, e.g., hydrochloric acid (1).

$$(1) \quad HgO + 2HCl \rightarrow HgCl_2 + H_2O$$

When either of the oxides is heated to red heat, it is decomposed into oxygen and vapors of metallic mercury (2).

$$(2) \quad 2HgO \overset{\triangle}{\rightarrow} 2Hg \uparrow + O_2 \uparrow$$

Mercuric oxide will react with oleic acid to form mercury oleate, a salt of an organic acid (3).

$$(3) \quad 2CH_3(CH_2)_7CH=CH(CH_2)_7COOH + HgO \rightarrow [CH_3(CH_2)_7-CH=CH(CH_2)_7COO]_2Hg + H_2O$$

Mercuric oxide is determined by dissolving it in nitric acid and titrating the mercuric ion with 0.1 N ammonium thiocyanate using ferric alum as an indicator.

Official Tests for Identity.—A solution of Yellow Mercuric Oxide prepared by mixing 1 Gm. of the compound with 20 ml. of water and adding enough hydrochloric acid to just dissolve it (1) will give all tests for *Mercuric salts* (q.v.).

Commercial Manufacture.—In the manufacture of Yellow Mercuric Oxide, all of the operations are carried on in the dark, thereby insuring a bright orange-yellow product. The absence of light is not too important because the yellow oxide is only very slowly transformed to the red form.

A concentrated solution of mercuric chloride is poured slowly and with constant agitation into a dilute solution of sodium hydroxide free from carbonate (4). The mixture is allowed to stand at room temperature for approximately one hour in order to permit of complete decomposition and to allow the precipitate to settle. Then the supernatant liquid is poured off and the precipitate repeatedly washed with water until the washings are free from alkali. The yellow precipitate is drained and dried on absorbent paper, in a dark place, at a temperature of about 30° C.

29

(4) $HgCl_2 + 2NaOH \rightarrow 2NaCl + Hg(OH)_2 \rightarrow HgO \downarrow + H_2O$
(yellow)

Uses.—*Yellow Mercuric Oxide* (Yellow Precipitate), N.F. XII, when dried at 105° for 2 hours, contains not less than 99.5 per cent of HgO. Because of its mild antiseptic effect, yellow oxide of mercury is used as *Yellow Mercuric Oxide Ointment* (1 per cent) in ophthalmology for treating a number of inflammatory eye conditions such as blepharitis and conjunctivitis. Yellow Mercuric Oxide Ointment should not be used in patients receiving iodide internally. Precautions should be observed in preparing this ointment so that it does not come in contact with metallic utensils or containers other than those made of stainless steel, tin, or tin-coated materials.

MERCUROUS CHLORIDE

Calomel, N.F. XII

Formula, HgCl. Molecular Weight, 236.04.

Physical Properties.—Calomel (mercurous chloride) is a heavy, white, impalpable powder that is insoluble in water, in alcohol, in ether, and in cold dilute acids. The salt is odorless and tasteless. It is permanent in air, but turns slightly gray when exposed to light, due to decomposition into mercury and mercuric chloride. This is due to an auto-oxidation-reduction, characteristic of mercurous compounds. When triturated with strong pressure, it becomes yellowish-white.

Chemical Properties.—When heated to about 383° C., Calomel is converted into a vapor having a density that corresponds to the formula, HgCl. However, at this temperature, it is decomposed into mercuric chloride and mercury (7), which recombine in the cold and, therefore, the constitutional formula of calomel is thought to be Hg_2Cl_2. X-ray studies indicate that most of the molecules may be represented by the following structure: Hg—Hg. In solution

$$\begin{array}{cc} | & | \\ Cl & Cl \end{array}$$

mercurous salts yield the Hg_2^{++} ion.

Because Calomel is insoluble in water it does not undergo very many chemical reactions. It does, however, react with lime water (see Black Lotion N.F. VIII). (1) and with solutions of alkali hydroxides and ammonia water (2) to give a black precipitate.

(1) $Hg_2Cl_2 + Ca(OH)_2 \rightarrow Hg_2(OH)_2 \downarrow + CaCl_2$
$Hg_2(OH)_2 \rightarrow Hg_2O + H_2O$
(2) $2Hg_2Cl_2 + 4NH_4OH \rightarrow HgNH_2Cl \downarrow + Hg \downarrow + 3NH_4Cl + Hg_2O \downarrow + 3H_2O$

Most reducing agents do not attack the mercurous ion but stannous chloride (3) and hypophosphorous acid (4) do reduce the ion.

(3) $Hg_2Cl_2 + SnCl_2 \rightarrow 2Hg \downarrow + SnCl_4$

(4) $2Hg_2Cl_2 + HPH_2O_2 + 2H_2O \rightarrow H_3PO_4 + 4Hg \downarrow + 4HCl$

When a mixture of equal parts by weight of mercurous chloride and reagent anhydrous sodium carbonate (chloride-free) is heated in a dry test-tube, metallic mercury sublimes and forms a gray mirror on the inner surface of the cold parts of the tube (5).

(5) $2Hg_2Cl_2 + 2Na_2CO_3 \overset{\triangle}{\rightarrow} 4NaCl + 2Hg_2CO_3$

$2Hg_2CO_3 \overset{\triangle}{\rightarrow} 2Hg_2O + 2CO_2 \uparrow$

$2Hg_2O \overset{\triangle}{\rightarrow} 4Hg \uparrow + O_2 \uparrow$

This decomposition is true of all compounds of mercury when heated with sodium carbonate. Sodium bicarbonate reacts in a similar way (6) to produce mercuric ion.

(6) $Hg_2Cl_2 + 2NaHCO_3 \rightarrow HgCl_2 + Hg \downarrow + Na_2CO_3 + CO_2 \uparrow + H_2O$

By heating under the proper conditions mercurous chloride is decomposed to metallic mercury and poisonous mercuric chloride (7) but may be cooled to form mercurous chloride again.

(7) $Hg_2Cl_2 \overset{\triangle}{\rightleftarrows} HgCl_2 + Hg$

Light has an action similar to heat, decomposing the salt to mercuric chloride and mercury.

The assay of Calomel depends upon the oxidation of mercurous to mercuric mercury with iodine and the product is then solubilized with potassium iodide (8). Exactly 50 ml. of 0.1 N iodine is used and back titrated with 0.1 N sodium thiosulfate using starch T. S. as an indicator.

(8) $Hg_2Cl_2 + 6KI + I_2 \rightarrow 2K_2HgI_4 + 2KCl$

Official Tests for Identity.—1. Calomel is blackened by contact with calcium hydroxide T.S. (1), with solutions of alkali hydroxides, or with ammonia T.S. (2).

2. It decomposes to yield free mercury when heated in a test-tube with an equal weight of anhydrous sodium carbonate (5). The mercury condenses on the wall of the tube. When the residue in the tube is treated with nitric acid, filtered, and silver nitrate added to the filtrate a white, curdy precipitate of silver chloride is formed showing the presence of *Chloride* (*q.v.*).

Commercial Manufacture.—1. Calomel has been prepared by heating a mixture of mercurous sulfate and sodium chloride and condensing the vapors of mercurous chloride that result. To prepare the mercurous sulfate, a mixture of sulfuric acid and mercury are heated together until a dry salt, mercuric sulfate, is obtained (9). A quantity of mercury sufficient to convert the mercuric sulfate into mercurous sulfate is then extinguished in the dried salt (10) and the product intimately mixed with the necessary amount of sodium chloride. The mixture is then sublimed and the vapors condensed in such a manner as to produce a fine, amorphous product (11). This is done by mixing the vapors of mercurous chloride with steam or cold air just as they enter the condensing chamber.

The impure product thus obtained is thoroughly agitated and washed with water to remove any mercuric chloride. It is then washed repeatedly with dilute nitric acid to dissolve any unchanged mercury and, after removing all traces of nitric acid, the salt is finally resublimed.

(9) $Hg + 2H_2SO_4 \rightarrow HgSO_4 + SO_2 \uparrow + 2H_2O \uparrow$

(10) $HgSO_4 + Hg \rightarrow Hg_2SO_4$

(11) $Hg_2SO_4 + 2NaCl \overset{\triangle}{\rightleftarrows} Na_2SO_4 + Hg_2Cl_2 \uparrow$

2. Calomel may also be made by adding a solution containing the chloride ion to any soluble mercurous salt (12). This method is used in making the Précipité Blanc (white precipitate) of the French Codex. (See also Ammoniated Mercury.) The product is more active than that made by sublimation and hence is usually given in doses about one-third of the pharmacopoeial product. The greater activity is probably due to smaller particle size, which causes a greater surface to be exposed for a given weight of compound.

(12) $Hg_2(NO_3)_2 + 2NaCl \rightarrow Hg_2Cl_2 \downarrow + 2NaNO_3$

3. A technical grade of mercurous chloride is made by subliming an intimate mixture of mercuric chloride and the equivalent amount of mercury, or by passing sulfur dioxide into a solution of mercuric chloride.

4. Calomel is also made by the interaction of mercury vapor with an excess of chlorine gas. The product is washed free of poisonous mercuric chloride with hot water.

Uses.—*Calomel* (Mercurous Chloride), N.F. XII, when dried over phosphorus pentoxide for five hours, contains not less than 99.6 per cent of HgCl. An interesting article on the history of Calomel has been published by Dr. G. Urdang.[1]

The principal use of Calomel is as a cathartic in the form of *Calomel Tablets*. It is insoluble in the gastric juice and is not absorbed from the stomach or intestines. It is attacked in the intestines by the alkaline pancreatic and intestinal juices and is slowly dissoci-

---

[1] J. Am. Pharm. Assoc., Pr. Ed., **9**, 414 (1949).

ated into mercury and yellow mercuric oxide; the latter dissolving slowly and incompletely in the intestinal fluid. The cathartic action is generally attributed to the irritant action of very small quantities of mercuric ion. For maximum cathartic effect from a given dose, it is desirable to give the dose in several portions spaced at twenty to thirty minute intervals. This spreads the irritant effect over a longer portion of the intestine than would otherwise be affected by the same dose given at one time. For this purpose tablets of 6, 15, 30, and 60 mg. sizes are available. Because of the possibility of mercury poisoning, it is always advisable to follow the administration of Calomel by a saline cathartic within six hours. Calomel enjoyed a widespread popularity at one time because it was thought to stimulate the flow of bile. This belief was based upon the fact that the stools were colored green and that this color was due to increased bile secretion. The green coloration, however, has been shown to be due to the antiseptic effect of the mercury which prevents the normal conversion of biliverdin (green) to bilirubin by intestinal bacteria. There are very few instances in which the use of Calomel is indicated as a cathartic. The very fact that a saline cathartic is required to remove it from the intestine, complicates its use. Usual dose—120 mg.

Much more rational and based on a firmer scientific basis is the use of Calomel in an ointment as a prophylactic against syphilis. For maximum antiseptic effect it is desirable to have the Calomel in as fine a state of subdivision as possible. Ointments with 3 to 30 per cent Calomel are used topically, the formerly official *Mild Mercurous Chloride Ointment* being an example of the stronger form.

Non-Official Mercury Compounds

Red Mercuric Iodide N.F. XI, HgI_2 occurs in two microcrystalline modifications, *red* (tetragonal octahedra, stable below 127° C. at 760 mm.) and *yellow* (rhombic prisms, stable above 127° C. at 760 mm.). Its density is 6.28.

It is practically insoluble in water. One Gm. dissolves in about 115 ml. of alcohol, in about 910 ml. of chloroform, or in about 120 ml. of ether, at 25° C. (a property of covalently bonded salts), or in about 20 ml. of boiling alcohol. The salt dissolves in solutions of the soluble iodides, mercuric chloride, sodium thiosulfate, and in hot solutions of the alkali chlorides.

Because of its insolubility, mercuric iodide enters into few chemical reactions. However, it is soluble in an excess of potassium iodide solution due to the formation of a complex salt (1).

The same is also true of mercuric chloride solutions which dissolve mercuric iodide forming a soluble double salt (2).

(1) $HgI_2 + 2KI \rightarrow K_2HgI_4$ (soluble)
(2) $HgI_2 + 2HgCl_2 \rightarrow HgI_2 . 2HgCl_2$ (soluble)

Similar considerations are responsible for the solubility of the salt in solutions of sodium thiosulfate (3) and alkali chlorides (4).

$$(3)\ \ HgI_2 + 3Na_2S_2O_3 \rightarrow 2NaI + Na_4\,[Hg(S_2O_3)_3]$$

$$(4)\ \ HgI_2 + 2NaCl \rightarrow Na_2(HgI_2Cl_2)$$

Red Mercuric Iodide in potassium iodide solution produces a solution known as *Valser's reagent* which is widely used as a testing agent for alkaloids because it readily precipitates most alkaloids from solution. (See also Mayer's reagent.)

This salt is a powerful irritant poison. Its action is similar to that of mercuric chloride and it is similarly used as an antibacterial. It is used also externally as a stimulant for indolent ulcers, glandular swellings, etc.

Mercury Oleate, N.F. XI, $(C_{17}H_{33}COO)_2Hg$ (approx.) is a yellowish brown, somewhat transparent substance, ointment-like in consistency, and having the odor of oleic acid. It is affected by light and is darkened by hydrogen sulfide.

It is insoluble in water and only slightly soluble in alcohol or ether, but is freely soluble in fixed oils.

This compound is somewhat unstable and, on keeping, will convert partly to the mercurous state or even to mercury metal. It contains an excess of oleic acid and will show characteristic reactions of this unsaturated acid, namely the development of rancidity (through oxidation) and a yellow to brown color.

It is prepared by interacting Yellow Mercuric Oxide in a finely pulverized condition with excess oleic acid. (1) The reaction is carried out at a temperature not exceeding 50° C.

$$(1)\ \ 2C_{17}H_{33}COOH + HgO \rightarrow (C_{17}H_{33}COO)_2Hg + H_2O$$

About 10 per cent excess oleic acid is provided for in this formulation. N.F. XI cautions: *Mercury Oleate must not be dispensed if globules of mercury have separated.*

It has been used as a pharmaceutical necessity in *Mild Mercurial Ointment* N.F. XI to aid in the complete dispersion of mercury into a finely divided form.

BORON, ALUMINUM AND THE METALS OF GROUP III

In the next five chapters, boron, aluminum and the metals in the subgroups of Group III will be considered although by far the greatest interest to the pharmacist attaches itself to the first two named. The short period elements of Group III are boron and aluminum. Aside from these two elements, the group contains two subgroups of metallic elements which are neither well known nor abundant. The elements of subgroup A are scandium, yttrium, lanthanum and a large number of elements having atomic numbers from 58 to 71 inclusive. known as the *rare earth elements*. Subgroup B contains the elements gallium, indium and thallium. In comparison with other groups of elements the entire group is approximately twice as large as any other group. Only one of these elements, aluminum, can be considered to be abundant and, in fact, it is the most common metal and third most common element in the earth's crust. Only oxygen and silicon are more abundant.

The first so-called "typical element", boron, is a non-metal but is sometimes termed a *metalloid* in reference to its somewhat hybrid behavior as a borderline element possessing both metallic and non-metallic character. Comparison of the electronic structures of the elements reveals that boron is the only element with less than 4 electrons in its valence shell that is not a metal. Once again (see p. 348) we find the diagonal relationship of an element with the element to its right in the next period when we consider the many similarities of boron to silicon.

In general, the tendency to form covalent bonds in Group III is greater than in the preceding groups as a result of the small ion size and the greater charge, both of which result in greater ability to deform anions (a measure of covalency). Boron almost invariably forms covalent linkages whereas aluminum is on the borderline but with a strong tendency toward covalency. The tendency toward covalent bond formation is even greater in aluminum than it is in beryllium with which it has a diagonal relationship in the Periodic Table and which is also a borderline case with respect to covalency and electrovalency. The strong tendency toward covalency of boron as compared to aluminum is not too surprising in view of the fact that the ionic radius ratio of boron to aluminum is approximately $\frac{2}{3}$ and the ionic volumes have a ratio of approximately $\frac{1}{16}$. The A subgroup elements have an increasing metallic character as the atomic number increases with less tendency toward covalency. An illustration of this is the increasing basicity and decreasing degree of hydrolysis of the hydroxides. Indeed, boron trihydroxide (boric acid) is a weak acid, aluminum hydroxide is a weak amphoteric base, scandium hydroxide is a weak base, yttrium hydroxide is a stronger base, etc. On the other hand, the basicity of the rare earth metals decreases as the atomic number increases. This may be ascribed to the peculiarity in this series of elements known as the "lanthanide contraction."[1] It is described as the small but consistent decrease in the trivalent ion size of each succeeding rare earth element (La = 1.22 Å → Lu = 0.99 Å). Naturally, as the ion size decreases it has greater deforming power (tendency to hold the oxygen of the OH⁻ more firmly) and thus would decrease the ionization.

The electron structure of the Group IIIA elements is probably a result of the change following calcium (2–8–8–2) in which the nuclear charge becomes large enough to permit the addition of electrons in the 3d-subgroup of the third quantum group (M shell) to build up to the maximum complement of 18 electrons. Thus, instead of the expected structure for scandium of 2–8–8–3 we have, instead, 2–8–(8 + 1)–2 and the process continues with titanium (2–8–(8 + 2)–2, etc. up to where gallium is reached and the fourth quantum group (N shell) has 3 electrons (2–8–18–3). This filling-in process is repeated again in the fourth quantum group starting with yttrium and ending with indium. However in the 5th period beginning with lanthanum, the fourth quantum group begins to grow toward its normal complement of 32 electrons which is reached with lutetium. Then the fifth quantum group (O shell) begins to fill to the maximum of 18 and finally with thallium reaches the electron arrangement of 2–8–18–32–18–3. The elements involved in the growth of the fourth quantum group to its maximum of 32 (starting from 18) electrons are termed the *rare earth elements* and may be considered to be a side growth from the normal A and B subgroup arrangements. Because the (8 + 1)–2 grouping of the 5th and 6th quantum groups does not change during the whole series, the entire group is placed in Group III. The normal valence for these elements is three but there are certain of them which have abnormal valencies of 2 or 4. Of particular interest to the pharmacist is cerium which exhibits valence states of 3 (cerous) and 4 (ceric), although praseodymium and terbium also can be tetravalent. Among the elements forming divalent ions are samarium, europium and ytterbium. The chemical behavior of these elements lies between that of aluminum and the alkaline earth metals. The solubilities of many of the comparable salts are similar.

The IIIB group of elements is not of importance in pharmacy. They exhibit the normal valence of three, but they also show a marked tendency to deviate from this group valence. For example, gallium can be divalent and indium and thallium monovalent. The

---

[1] See also Douglas, B. E., J. Chem. Education, **31**, 598 (1954).

PROPERTIES OF GROUP III AND IIIA ELEMENTS

Properties	Boron	Aluminum	Scandium	Yttrium	Rare Earth Metals*
Atomic Number	5	13	21	39	57 → 71
Atomic Weight	10.811	26.9815	44.956	88.905	138.91 → 174.97
Isotopes	10, 11	27	45	89	(138–9) → (175)
Electrons	2–3	2–8–3	2–8–(8+1)–2	2–8–18–(8+1)–2	2–8–18–18–(8+1)–2 to 2–8–18–32–(8+1)–2
Density	2.34 (amor.) 3.33 (cryst.)	2.7	2.5	5.51	6.15 → 9.74
M.P.	2300°	660°	1200°	1490°	860° → ?
B.P.	>2550°	1800°	2400°	2500°	1800° → ?
Common Oxidation States	0, +3	0, +3	0, +3	0, +3	0, +2, +3, +4
Radius (cov.), Å	0.80	1.25	1.51	1.8	1.87 → 1.74
Radius (ionic), Å	0.20	0.50	0.81	0.93	1.22 → 0.99
Ionization Potential, first, volts	8.28	5.96	6.7	6.5	5.6 → ?

* The elements here included represent the atomic numbers 57 (lanthanum) to 71 (lutetium) inclusive. The outside limits of this large group are given. Other information concerning these elements will be found in various reference texts such as the Handbook of Chemistry and Physics published by the Chemical Rubber Co., Cleveland, Ohio.

deviations in the case of In and Tl are explainable on the basis of some sort of stability or "inertness" associated with the two electrons in the s-subgroup of the respective quantum groups of the elements as contrasted to the evident lability of the single electron in the p-subgroup. The stability of the monovalent ion is much greater in thallium than in indium as evidenced by the ready disproportionation of monovalent indium to free metal and trivalent ion which is in contrast to the marked stability of thallous ion. The divalent character of gallium has no ready explanation. The metals of this group are readily oxidized when heated in air although they are stable at ordinary temperatures. The oxides are readily reduced

PROPERTIES OF SUBGROUP IIIB ELEMENTS

Properties	Gallium	Indium	Thallium
Atomic Number	31	49	81
Atomic Weight	69.72	114.82	204.37
Isotopes	69, 71	113, 115	203, 205
Electrons	2–8–18–3	2–8–18–18–3	2–8–18–32–18–3
Density	5.91	7.31	11.85
M.P.	29.8°	156.4°	300 ±3°
B.P.	2070°	>1450°	1460°
Common Oxidation States . .	0, +2, +3	0, +1, +3	0, +1, +3
Radius (cov.), Å	1.26	1.44	1.47
Radius (ionic), Å (trivalent) .	0.62	0.81	0.95
Ionization Potential, first, volts	6.00	5.785	6.106
Oxidation Potential, volts, $M \rightarrow M^{+++}$	+0.52	+0.38	+0.336*

* for $Tl \rightarrow Tl^+$

back to the free metal. The metals react readily with sulfur and the halogens. The hydroxides of the IIIB group exhibit an amphoteric character in the case of gallium and indium (form gallates and indates) but not with thallium. It will be recalled that the hydroxides of the IIIA group all lacked amphoteric character although aluminum possessed this property. The property thus seems to relate aluminum more closely with gallium and indium than with the IIIA group. This, in spite of the fact that on the basis of ionic radii the members of both groups would be expected to exert approximately equal attraction for the oxygen of the OH group. However, the amphoteric character of gallium and indium hydroxides can probably be related to the increased effectiveness of the nuclear attraction on the valence electrons because of the non-inert-gas kernel (see p. 12).

27

Boron and Boron Compounds

BORON

Symbol, B.   Valence, 3.   Atomic Weight, 10.811; Atomic Number 5

History and Occurrence.—J. Gay-Lussac and L. Thénard isolated the impure element in 1808 by heating boron trioxide (*q.v.*) with potassium carbonate in an iron retort.   Sir Humphrey Davy obtained it about the same time from boric acid.

The American development of the borax industry is one of intensive pioneering, successes, disappointments and daring investment.   Although borax is associated by many with Death Valley and "20 Mule Teams" it was actually discovered first in a mineral spring near Red Bluff, California, by J. A. Veatch who developed it in 1862 and caused a sharp drop in foreign imports.   Following this, William Troup utilized "cottonballs" (borate crust) in the deserts of Nevada and boiled them with sodium carbonate.   Francis Smith, however, discovered the first rich borax find at Teel's Marsh, a Nevada alkali flat, and, after many tribulations, established the origins of the now important Pacific Coast Borax Co.   The discovery of borax in Death Valley is credited to Aaron Winters, a desert prospector, in 1881 although Isadore Daunet had actually found specimens six years earlier but attached no commerical importance to the finding.   Searles Lake, Calif., has also been an important source of boron chemicals since approximately 1870 when John Searles worked that deposit.

Boron does not occur free in Nature.   In combinations containing oxygen, it is found as boric acid, borax, tincal, boracite, borocalcite, colemanite, etc.   (See Boric Acid, Sodium Tetraborate.)

Physical Properties.—Pure boron is an amorphous, brown powder having a density of 2.34.   The crystalline form of boron (density, 3.33), also known, is in the form of brown or brownish-black, exceedingly hard, friable, lustrous crystals which are insoluble in the usual solvents.   The hardness of the crystalline form makes it of value as a substitute for diamond in glass cutting and gem polishing. It is stable in air.

Chemical Properties.—With a few possible exceptions, boron is trivalent and its oxide and hydroxide are acidic.   The chemical behavior of boron resembles that of silicon, and the chemical properties of its compounds bear a close relationship to those of both silicon and carbon.   It has a strong tendency to form covalent

(447)

bonds. The element sublimes in the electric arc and burns on very strong ignition, producing boron trioxide (B_2O_3) and boron nitride (BN). At ordinary temperatures, boron is a poor conductor of electricity but as the temperature rises its electrical conductivity rapidly increases. As previously stated, the chemical behavior of boron closely resembles that of silicon. Concentrated nitric or sulfuric acids oxidize it to boric acid. It burns in oxygen at 700° C. Fluorine combines with it at ordinary temperatures. Chlorine, bromine and sulfur unite with it at 410° C., 700° C., and 600° C., respectively. It does not combine with iodine. When heated to redness with magnesium, it forms a boride. At higher temperatures, the borides of other metals are also formed. It unites with carbon at the temperature of the electric arc to form boron carbide. It does not react with the alkali metals, but forms alkali borates with fused fixed alkalies. It reduces many metallic oxides (PbO, CuO, etc.) and, at red heat, decomposes water, carbon dioxide, sulfur dioxide, and nitric oxide.

Commercial Manufacture.—In 1909, Weintraub prepared the first absolutely pure boron by reducing boron trichloride with hydrogen (1).

$$(1) \quad 2BCl_3 + 3H_2 \rightarrow 6HCl + 2B$$

H. Moissan[1] prepared the element by heating 3 parts of boron trioxide with 1 part of magnesium powder (2). The resulting dark brown powder was then washed with water, hydrochloric acid, hydrofluoric acid and finally calcined with boron trioxide or with borax, the mass being protected during the operation by a layer of powdered charcoal.

$$(2) \quad B_2O_3 + 3Mg \xrightarrow{\triangle} 3MgO + 2B$$

Boron may be made by heating a mixture of potassium borofluoride (KBF_4) and metallic sodium in a magnesia-lined crucible, through which a stream of hydrogen is being passed.

Boron trioxide may be readily reduced by heating with aluminum (3).

$$(3) \quad B_2O_3 + 2Al \xrightarrow{\triangle} 2B + Al_2O_3$$

Uses.—The largest consumers of boron products in the U.S. are the glass and ceramic industries although fiber glass has become an important user. Porcelain enamel as well as agriculture is consuming substantial quantities of production. In recent years, boron fuels for rocket propulsion have consumed an increasing amount of the mineral.

OFFICIAL BORON COMPOUNDS

Boric Acid (H_3BO_3).—(See p. 122.)
Sodium Tetraborate ($Na_2B_4O_7 . 10H_2O$).—(See p. 209.)
Sodium Perborate ($NaBO_3 . 4H_2O$).—(See p. 253.)

[1] Ann. Chem. Phys., **6**, 296 (1895).

28

Aluminum and Aluminum Compounds

ALUMINUM

Aluminum, U.S.P. XVII

Symbol, Al. Valence, 3. Atomic Weight, 26.9815
Atomic Number, 13

History.—In 1754, Marggraf showed that *alumina* (aluminum oxide, Al_2O_3) was not identical with lime. In 1825, Hans Christian Oersted obtained the metal by reducing aluminum chloride with sodium amalgam. In 1827, Wöhler reduced the chloride with metallic potassium (1) and obtained the metal.

(1) $AlCl_3 + 3K \rightarrow Al + 3KCl$

Occurrence.—Aluminum *per se* is not found in Nature, although in combination, it constitutes about 7.3 per cent of the earth's crust. In combination, it is found extensively as the oxides, silicates and hydrated oxides. As the oxide, it is native as *corundum* [Al_2O_3] containing 52.9 per cent of aluminum and as *emery* [Al_2O_3, associated with black oxide of iron]. As the silicate, it is found in rocks, clays [*kaolin,* $Al_2O_3.2SiO_2.2H_2O$ or $Al_2Si_2O_7.2H_2O$, containing 20.9 per cent of aluminum] and shales. (See Talc.) As *cryolite,* a double fluoride, Na_3AlF_6, it occurs notably in Greenland. *Bauxite* [$Al_2O(OH)_4$], [$Al_2O_3.2H_2O$], or [$AlO(OH).Al(OH)_3$], is a hydrated oxide mixed with ferric oxide. It contains 39.1 per cent of aluminum. It is found in the United States, chiefly in Georgia, Alabama, Tennessee and Arkansas. It is found also in France and in British Guiana. Two other hydrated oxides of aluminum, *diaspore* [$Al_2O_3.H_2O$, containing 45 per cent of aluminum] and *gibbsite* [$Al_2O_3.3H_2O$, containing 34.6 per cent of aluminum] are commonly present in bauxite ores. Aluminum is always present in the ashes from bird feathers (Gonnermann, 1918). *Spinel* [$Mg(AlO_2)_2$] is a naturally occurring mineral and seems to be a salt of metaluminic acid. It is representative of an entire group of minerals collectively called *the spinels.* Other trivalent metals may replace the aluminum, and other bivalent metals may take the place of magnesium to give isomorphous compounds. Some members of the spinels are *gahnite* [Zn(AlO$_2$)$_2$], *chrysoberyl* [Be(AlO)$_2$], *franklinite* [Zn(FeO$_2$)$_2$], *magnetite* [Fe(FeO$_2$)$_2$], *chromite* [Fe(CrO$_2$)$_2$], etc.

Physical Properties.—Aluminum is a silver-white metal, having a density of 2.7. It is ductile and malleable. When it is heated between 100° C. and 150° C., it can be worked into thin sheets, drawn into wire, punched, stamped, or spun into any desired form. It melts at 660° C. and boils at 1800° C. Weight for weight, it is as good a conductor of electricity as copper. Pure aluminum cannot be worked on a lathe or polished, but when it is alloyed with about 2 per cent of magnesium, it is admirably adapted for such purposes.

The official form of Aluminum is a very fine, free-flowing, silvery powder, free from gritty or discolored particles.

Chemical Properties.—*Aluminum metal* is a very active element. Although tarnishing only slightly in air, aluminum has a great affinity for oxygen and displaces the metals below it in the electromotive series from their heated oxides. Its stability in air may be explained by the fact that a superficial layer of oxide (Al$_2$O$_3$) protects the metal from being further attacked by the oxygen of the atmosphere. Aluminum is not attacked by sulfuric acid, and only slowly by nitric acid. These are oxidizing acids which immediately form a protective layer of aluminum oxide and thus inhibit their action upon the metal. Both dilute and concentrated hydrochloric acid rapidly act upon it (2). Being of an amphoteric character, aluminum readily dissolves in alkali hydroxides with the evolution of hydrogen and the formation of alkali metaluminates (3).

$$(2)\ 2Al + 6HCl \rightarrow 2AlCl_3 + 3H_2 \uparrow$$

$$(3)\ 2Al + 2NaOH + 2H_2O \rightarrow 2NaAlO_2 + 3H_2 \uparrow$$

The chemical properties of the *aluminum ion* are largely a result of its rather small size which in turn is due to its high nuclear charge. This results in a strong tendency to associate with dipoles such as water molecules to form complex ions. Most estimates, based on the relative sizes of the aluminum cation and water molecules, suggest that six molecules of water are associated with each aluminum ion (4). This high tendency toward hydration is evident in the

$$(4)\ Al^{+++} + 6H_2O \rightarrow Al(6H_2O)^{+++}$$

crystals of the salts wherein water molecules are found interspersed in the crystal lattice. The six water molecules arrange themselves around the aluminum ion at the corners of a circumscribed octahedron which persists in the crystal form. Examples of this are found in the hexahydrates of the aluminum halides, aluminum chlorate, etc. In the alums, which contain 12 molecules of water of crystallization, six are known to be associated with the aluminum and the other six are thought to be near the univalent ion. The fact that these water molecules already exist within the crystal lattice undoubtedly aids in the water solubility of these salts in great measure.

One of the properties of aluminum ions that is of importance is that of hydrolysis which results in acidic aqueous solutions of the strong acid salts. The hydrolytic process may be considered as the formation of hydroxyl complexes by successive ionization of the water molecules (5). The process of hydrolysis proceeds to the

$$(5)\ Al(H_2O)_6{}^{+++} + H_2O \rightleftarrows Al(H_2O)_5OH^{++} + H_3O^+$$
$$Al(H_2O)_5OH^{++} + H_2O \rightleftarrows Al(H_2O)_4(OH)_2{}^+ + H_3O^+$$
$$Al(H_2O)_4(OH)_2{}^+ + H_2O \rightleftarrows Al(H_2O)_3(OH)_3 + H_3O^+$$
$$Al(H_2O)_3(OH)_3 \rightleftarrows Al(OH)_3 \downarrow + 3H_2O$$

stage where $Al(OH)_3$ precipitates only if the hydronium ions are continually removed and kept small in concentration (e.g., by addition of basic substances). However, this also takes place if the acid anion combined with the aluminum is from a weak acid which accounts for the fact that when alkali carbonates or soluble sulfides are added to a solution of an aluminum salt, aluminum hydroxide (soluble in an excess of either precipitant) is precipitated (6, 7).

$$(6)\ 2Al^{+++} + 3CO_3^- + 3H_2O \rightarrow 2Al(OH)_3 \downarrow + 3CO_2 \uparrow$$
$$(7)\ 2Al^{+++} + 3S^- + 6H_2O \rightarrow 2Al(OH)_3 \downarrow + 3H_2S \uparrow$$

This precipitation of the weak and insoluble base, aluminum hydroxide, is common to all aluminum salts of weak acids and is further accentuated in the case of volatile acids by heating the solution in order to remove the acid by volatilization.

In a similar manner we can explain the formation of the white, gelatinous precipitate of aluminum hydroxide when ammonia is added to a solution of an aluminum salt (8). It is customary to

$$(8)\ Al^{+++} + 3NH_3 + 3H_2O \rightarrow Al(OH)_3 \downarrow + 3NH_4{}^+$$

neglect the six water molecules associated with the aluminum ion (as we have done in 6, 7 and 8) in writing equations to avoid needless complications and, because, in many cases the exact degree of hydration is not known.

With alkali hydroxides (but not with ammonia) the precipitation of aluminum hydroxide is followed by the dissolution of the precipitate in an excess of the reagent. Because of its amphoteric character, it is evident that aluminum hydroxide can dissociate in two ways (9 and 10).

$$(9)\ Al(OH)_3 \rightleftarrows Al(OH)_2{}^+ + OH^-$$
$$Al(OH)_2{}^+ \rightleftarrows Al(OH)^{++} + OH^-$$
$$Al(OH)^{++} \rightleftarrows Al^{+++} + OH^-$$
$$(10)\ Al(OH)_3 \rightleftarrows AlO_2{}^- + H_3O^+$$

The formation of metaluminates, as indicated by equation 10, accounts for the solubility of aluminum hydroxide in excess fixed base as the water-soluble alkali metaluminate.

Aluminum salts formed with the highly electronegative ions such as F^-, NO_3^- and SO_4^- are ionic compounds. With the less electronegative halides (Cl^-, Br^-, and I^-) the tendency is towards progressively more covalent type of bonding. Among the halides, the fluoride is quite inert and insoluble which is probably due to the fact that the small aluminum cation can approach closely to the small, highly electronegative fluoride ion. Even though this compound is ionic the interionic forces are so strong as to prevent hydration of the ions and subsequent solution. All of the other halides are water-soluble. Virtually all of the aluminum salts with univalent anions are water-soluble as well as many of the bivalent anion salts. However, interionic forces become quite strong with trivalent aluminum and trivalent phosphate ion and, as a consequence, the salt ($AlPO_4$) is insoluble.

Official Tests for Identity of Aluminum Ion.—Aluminum salts when treated with ammonia T.S. produce a gelatinous white precipitate which is insoluble in an excess of reagent (8). With sodium hydroxide T.S. or sodium sulfide T.S. the hydroxide formed is soluble in an excess of reagent (formation of metaluminate).

Commercial Manufacture.—As previously pointed out, Wöhler was the first to produce metallic aluminum by the reduction of its oxide with metallic potassium (1). The cost of the metal prepared by this method was very high (about $545 a pound) and it was not until 1854, when Deville devised the first working process for the manufacture of aluminum, that the cost dropped to about $34 a pound. Deville's method consisted in reducing the double chloride of sodium and aluminum with metallic sodium.

In 1886, Charles Hall made the metal by the electrolysis of aluminum oxide dissolved in molten cryolite (Na_3AlF_6, melting-point $1000°$ C.). About the same time, Heroult, a Frenchman, working independently, devised the same method for making metallic aluminum. These methods have been successful commercially and, as a result, the cost of the metal has steadily declined.

In recent years the electrolysis of aluminum oxide has been the most widely used method. A process for obtaining aluminum oxide is as follows: Bauxite, $AlO(OH).Al(OH)_3$ is refined by the Boyer process. It is converted to a powder and treated with a hot solution of sodium hydroxide (12). This mixture is filtered, leaving behind the insoluble impurities. As the filtrate cools, carbon dioxide is passed through the solution to acidify it and causes the precipitation of $Al(OH)_3$ (12). A pure grade of aluminum oxide is obtained by heating the hydroxide (13).

$$(11)\ AlO(OH).Al(OH)_3 + 2NaOH \xrightarrow{\Delta} 2NaAlO_2 + 3H_2O \text{ or}$$
$$AlO(OH).Al(OH)_3 + 2NaOH \rightarrow 2NaAlO(OH)_2 + H_2O$$

(12) $NaAlO(OH)_2 + CO_2 + H_2O \rightarrow NaHCO_3 + Al(OH)_3 \downarrow$

(13) $2Al(OH)_3 \overset{\triangle}{\rightarrow} Al_2O_3 + 3H_2O \uparrow$

The electrolysis is conducted in cells lined with carbon, acting as the cathode. A series of carbon rods serve as the anode and are so arranged that they may be lowered into the fused electrolyte. The cell is partly filled with cryolite and the heat generated by the current is sufficient to melt it. The current is then reduced to between 5 and 6 volts, which is sufficient to maintain the temperature of the melt (875° to 950° C.), and also to cause decomposition. Aluminum oxide is added from time to time. The molten aluminum sinks to the bottom of the cell where it is tapped off, whereas part of the evolved oxygen escapes and part combines with the carbon anodes. The decomposition of purified bauxite (Al_2O_3) by an electric current is more than likely accompanied by some complex reactions. Nevertheless, in its simplest form, the decomposition may be represented by equation (14).

(14) $2Al_2O_3 \rightarrow 4Al + 3O_2 \uparrow$

Pharmacological Action of Aluminum Ion.—Dilute solutions of the soluble salts of aluminum, when applied topically, have the property of constricting the blood vessels. More concentrated solutions precipitate proteins and, therefore, are not only astringent but also antiseptic. The soluble salts of all of the heavy metals are astringent but, in concentrations slightly greater than that required to produce vasoconstriction, they are destructive to tissue and hence irritating and even escharotic. The soluble salts of aluminum, lead and zinc differ from the salts of the other heavy metals by retaining their astringent action over a broad solution-concentration range. The astringent action of the aluminum salts is taken advantage of in the formulation of many antiperspirant preparations. The principal drawback to these salts has been their rather high acidity (as a result of hydrolysis) which often causes deterioration of clothing and skin irritation. These effects may be counteracted by buffering the preparations but usually this leads to decreased astringent activity. It is also possible to minimize the acidity by using aluminum salts of weak (organic) acids or by using partially hydrolyzed complexes (*e.g.*, aluminum chlorhydroxide complex). An additional advantage is that the antiseptic action associated with aluminum can help to reduce body odors due to bacterial decomposition of perspiration.

Aluminum ion is practically unabsorbed from the alimentary tract and hence large oral doses given over an extended period of time will produce nothing more than local inflammation. The element is excreted in the feces, principally as the phosphate.

The action of diluted acids upon aluminum cooking utensils is so slight as to be negligible. The use of ammonium alum in baking powders for the purpose of liberating carbon dioxide from sodium bicarbonate (15) is considered by some to be a most serious objection to the use of the so-called "alum baking powders." No doubt some of the aluminum hydroxide formed during the reaction is dissolved by the hydrochloric acid and proteins in the stomach. On the other hand, the Referee Board of 1914 was unable to detect any aluminum in the blood after orally administering 1 Gm. of alum per day for four days.

$$(15)\ 2NH_4Al(SO_4)_2 + 6NaHCO_3 \rightarrow 2Al(OH)_3 \downarrow + 3Na_2SO_4 + (NH_4)_2SO_4 + 6CO_2 \uparrow$$

Uses.—*Aluminum*, U.S.P. XVII, is officially recognized in order to provide standards for its use in *Aluminum Paste*, a protective which is used primarily to prevent irritation around intestinal fistulæ. The Aluminum prevents the digestive effects of the intestinal contents on the surrounding skin. Official Aluminum Paste contains 10 per cent Aluminum. Another formula, containing one-third by weight of aluminum powder in a similar base of liquid petrolatum and zinc oxide ointment is known as *Ladd's Paste*.

Aluminum powder (and also alumina) has been used as an inhalation in the treatment of silicosis. It has been claimed that when the fine powder is inhaled it coats the silica particles to prevent any further solubility which, in turn, is said to prevent further progress of the disease. However, Brown and Van Winkle in a report to the Councils of Industrial Health and Pharmacy and Chemistry[1] pointed out that there is no conclusive proof of value, although it has been used extensively, in both a prophylactic and treatment capacity. However, it does seem that inhalations are not particularly harmful, although tubercular patients should not be permitted this type of therapy.

A thin aluminum foil has been used in burn treatment with remarkable results. The foil not only protects the burn and conserves fluid but also seems to stimulate tissue growth.

OFFICIAL COMPOUNDS OF ALUMINUM

ALUMINUM CHLORIDE

Aluminum Chloride, N.F. XII

Formula, $AlCl_3.6H_2O$.   Molecular Weight, 241.43

Physical Properties.—Aluminum Chloride is a white or yellowish-white crystalline powder. It is odorless and has a sweetish, very astringent taste. It is deliquescent.

---

[1] Brown, E. W., and Van Winkle, W., J. Am. Med. Assn., **140**, 1024 (1949).

One Gm. of the salt is soluble in about 0.9 ml. of water and in about 4 ml. of alcohol, at 25° C. It is soluble also in ether or glycerin.

Chemical Properties.—When the hexahydrate is heated, it decomposes into hydrogen chloride and aluminum oxide (1).

(1) $2AlCl_3 . 6H_2O \triangleq 6HCl \uparrow + Al_2O_3 + 9H_2O \uparrow$

The chemical properties of a solution of the salt are due to the aluminum ion (*q.v.*) and the chloride ion (*q.v.*).

Aluminum chloride (anhydrous) is a Lewis acid and in contact with molecular groups that are capable of strongly donating electrons, will form molecular complexes such as those obtained from trimethylamine (2) and carbonyl compounds (3).

(2) $AlCl_3 + (CH_3)_3N \rightarrow (CH_3)_3N:AlCl_3$

$$(3) \quad \begin{matrix} R \\ \diagdown \\ C=O + AlCl_3 \rightarrow \\ \diagup \\ R \end{matrix} \quad \begin{matrix} R \\ \diagdown \quad + \quad - \\ C=O-AlCl_3 \longleftrightarrow \\ \diagup \\ R \end{matrix} \quad \begin{matrix} R \\ \diagdown + \quad - \\ C-O-AlCl_3 \\ \diagup \\ R \end{matrix}$$

This salt, in common with most soluble aluminum salts, hydrolyzes in aqueous solution to give somewhat acidic solutions.

The covalent character of the aluminum chloride bonding is reflected by its solubility in ether, a characteristic of many covalently bonded molecules.

Most aluminum salts are assayed as is Aluminum Chloride by residual titration of excess standard disodium ethylenediaminetetraacetate solution with standard zinc sulfate solution using dithizone as indicator.

Official Tests for Identity.—A solution of Aluminum Chloride responds to the tests for *Aluminum* (*q.v.*) and *Chloride* (*q.v.*).

Commercial Manufacture.—1. When aluminum or its hydroxide is treated with hydrochloric acid, aluminum chloride is formed. Upon concentrating the liquid and allowing it to cool, crystals of the hexahydrate separate out (4).

(4) $Al(OH)_3 + 3HCl + 3H_2O \rightarrow AlCl_3 \cdot 6H_2O$

2. Anhydrous aluminum chloride ($AlCl_3$) may be made by subjecting heated metallic aluminum to a current of dry chlorine (5), or by passing chlorine over a mixture of aluminum oxide and carbon at red heat (6).

(5) $2Al + 3Cl_2 \triangleq 2AlCl_3$

(6) $Al_2O_3 + 3C + 3Cl_2 \triangleq 2AlCl_3 + 3CO \uparrow$

Uses.—*Aluminum Chloride*, N.F. XII, when dried over silica gel for 4 hours, contains not less than 95 per cent and not more than 102 per cent of $AlCl_3.6H_2O$. It is employed externally as a general astringent and antiseptic. Solutions of Aluminum Chloride (10 to 25 Gm./100 ml.) are used as antiperspirants and deodorants.

A dermatological astringent, Chlorhydrol (aluminum chlorohydroxide), is available that is less acid in solution, less corrosive, and less irritating.

Anhydrous aluminum chloride is used industrially as a catalytic agent and in petroleum refining. It is also used in various organic syntheses (Friedel and Crafts' reaction).

ALUMINUM HYDROXIDE

Aluminum Hydroxide Gel, U.S.P. XVII

Dried Aluminum Hydroxide Gel, N.F. XII

Formula, $Al(OH)_3$.   Molecular Weight, 78.00

Physical Properties.—The gel is a white, viscous suspension, translucent in thin layers, from which small amounts of water may separate on standing. The dried gel is a white, odorless, tasteless, amorphous powder. Aluminum hydroxide is insoluble in water but readily soluble in acids and fixed alkali.

Chemical Properties.—Aluminum Hydroxide Gel is amphoteric in character. It slightly affects both red and blue litmus paper, but does not affect phenolphthalein T.S. When it is heated to redness, it decomposes into water and aluminum oxide. The hydroxide reacts readily with acids, such as hydrochloric acid, forming water and the aluminum salt (1). In this connection, however, it may be pointed out that it has been suggested that aluminum hydroxide acts as an antacid not so much by chemical neutralization as by physical adsorption of the acid molecules. When the gel (with acid) passes into the intestine the acid is released.

(1) $Al(OH)_3 + 3HCl \rightarrow AlCl_3 + 3H_2O$

Aluminum Hydroxide Gel is assayed like Aluminum Chloride after a solution in hydrochloric acid (1) is obtained.

Official Tests for Identity.—A hydrochloric acid solution of Aluminum Hydroxide Gel responds to the tests for *Aluminum* (*q.v.*).

Commercial Manufacture.—A hot solution of potassium alum is added slowly to a hot solution of sodium carbonate (2). The precipitated aluminum hydroxide is then washed thoroughly with hot water until it is free of sulfate ion and the gel is adjusted to the requisite strength with distilled water.

(2) $3Na_2CO_3 + 2KAl(SO_4)_2 + 3H_2O \rightarrow 3Na_2SO_4 + K_2SO_4 + 2Al(OH)_3\downarrow + 3CO_2\uparrow$

It will be noted that the alum solution is *added to* the solution of sodium carbonate. It has been observed that aluminum hydroxide, prepared by adding the carbonate solution to that of the alum, persistently retains the alkali sulfate and hence is difficult to wash. *Hot* water, not *boiling* water, should be used to wash the precipitate because the latter tends to decompose the aluminum hydroxide.

It may seem odd that the reaction of a carbonate with alum gives a hydroxide instead of a carbonate. However, a stepwise consideration of the probable sequence of reactions may help to clarify the matter. If the alum is looked upon as a double salt, $K_2SO_4 \cdot Al_2(SO_4)_3$, instead of $2KAl(SO_4)_2$ it is apparent that only aluminum sulfate will react with the sodium carbonate to give an insoluble precipitate (3). However, the aluminum carbonate precipitate is so unstable that it immediately hydrolyzes to give aluminum hydroxide and carbon dioxide (4). Also it should be remembered that aluminum hydroxide is less soluble than aluminum carbonate and should be precipitated first in the alkaline sodium carbonate solution.

(3) $Al_2(SO_4)_3 + 3Na_2CO_3 \rightarrow Al_2(CO_3)_3 \downarrow + 3Na_2SO_4$

(4) $Al_2(CO_3)_3 + 3H_2O \rightarrow 2Al(OH)_3 \downarrow + 3CO_2 \uparrow$

Uses.—1. *Aluminum Hydroxide Gel* (Colloidal Aluminum Hydroxide), U.S.P. XVII, is a suspension containing the equivalent of not less than 3.6 per cent and not more than 4.4 per cent of aluminum oxide (Al_2O_3), in the form of aluminum hydroxide and hydrated oxide. It is a white viscous suspension, translucent in thin layers, from which small amounts of water may separate on standing.

The Pharmacopeia permits a sufficient amount of oil of peppermint, glycerin, sucrose, or saccharin to be added for flavoring and other purposes. Sodium benzoate or benzoic acid in an amount not to exceed 0.5 per cent may be used as a preservative.

During the preparation, some aluminum subcarbonate [$Al(OH)CO_3$] may form and, due to the adsorptive properties of aluminum hydroxide, some carbonate will adhere to the gelatinous precipitate. For this reason a slow effervescence takes place between the gel and an acid.

Colloidal aluminum hydroxide is used as an antacid and protective in treating peptic ulcers. Because its insolubility precludes excessive alkalinization, and because the aluminum ion formed by its solution in the hydrochloric acid of the stomach makes it astringent and also antiseptic, colloidal aluminum hydroxide has a distinct advantage over soluble alkalies. Because of this astringent action there is a tendency to constipation which may be overcome by administering magnesium trisilicate simultaneously.

Intestinal bacteria are also adsorbed by the aluminum hydroxide not dissolved in the stomach. It is used in cases of marked hyperacidity. It decreases the secretion of total and free acid and few ill-effects have been observed as a result of its use. However, continued use will cause a phosphate deficiency because insoluble AlPO₄ is formed in the intestine.

Depending upon the severity of the lesion in cases of peptic ulcer, it may be administered orally in divided doses totalling 1 to 5 fluid-ounces of the gel daily. It is also administered effectively against the hyperchlorhydria of ulcer patients by the so-called continuous intragastric drip method. It acts principally by buffering against the excess acid. A teaspoonful will neutralize in one hour over $1\frac{1}{2}$ fluidounces of gastric juice containing 0.36 per cent hydrochloric acid.

The adsorptive properties of aluminum hydroxide have been shown to remove almost 100 per cent of aureomycin from its solutions. Aureomycin given orally in this combination did not exhibit any stomach distress but its antibiotic effect was virtually nil. Usual dose—10 ml. four times a day with a range of 5 to 30 ml.

2. *Dried Aluminum Hydroxide Gel*, N.F. XII, yields not less than 50 per cent of Al₂O₃. Dried Aluminum Hydroxide Gel is a white, odorless, tasteless, amorphous powder, which is insoluble in water and in alcohol. It is soluble in diluted mineral acids and in solutions of fixed alkalies.

Dried Aluminum Hydroxide Gel may be suspended in Purified Water to make the official Aluminum Hydroxide Gel. Dried Aluminum Hydroxide Gel is used externally as a mild astringent and desiccant and internally as an antacid and protective. It is infrequently used in the treatment of diarrhea and cholera, externally as a dusting powder for desiccating foul wounds, etc. It is a constituent of some foot powders.

In silicosis therapy, inhalation of powdered aluminum hydroxide for a few minutes per day over a period of several weeks has been claimed to give improvement.

Usual dose—390 mg., the equivalent of 300 mg. of aluminum hydroxide, 0.3 Gm. four times a day to hourly.

ALUMINUM PHOSPHATE

Aluminum Phosphate Gel, N.F. XII*

Formula, AlPO₄. Molecular Weight, 121.95

Physical Properties.—Aluminum Phosphate Gel is a white, viscous suspension from which small amounts of water may separate on standing. Aluminum phosphate is insoluble in water but readily soluble in acids. The pH of the gel at 25° C. is between 6 and 7.2.

Chemical Properties.—Aluminum Phosphate Gel reacts with nitric or hydrochloric acids to form a clear solution. These acid solutions respond to the reactions of the phosphate ion (*q.v.*) and the aluminum ion (*q.v.*), respectively.

* Patented. See N.F. XII, p. ii.

In assaying Aluminum Phosphate Gel the sample is first dissolved in nitric acid and then the phosphate radical is precipitated as $(NH_4)_3PO_4 \cdot 12MoO_3$ by the addition of excess ammonium molybdate T.S. This precipitate is dissolved in exactly 50 ml. of 0.5 N sodium hydroxide (1) and the excess sodium hydroxide titrated with 0.5 N sulfuric acid using phenolphthalein as an indicator (2).

(1) $(NH_4)_3PO_4 \cdot 12MoO_3 + 27NaOH \rightarrow 3NH_3 \uparrow + Na_3PO_4 + 12Na_2MoO_4 + 15H_2O$

(2) $Na_3PO_4 + NaOH + H_2SO_4 \rightarrow Na_2HPO_4 + Na_2SO_4 + H_2O$

Official Tests for Identity.—1. A solution of Aluminum Phosphate Gel in hydrochloric acid responds to the tests for *Aluminum* (*q.v.*).

2. A solution of the gel in diluted nitric acid responds to the tests for *Phosphate* (*q.v.*).

Commercial Manufacture.[1]—"Thirty-six (36) pounds of aluminum chloride are dissolved in any suitable vessel in twenty (20) gallons of water. Twenty-one (21) pounds of dried dibasic sodium phosphate are dissolved in twenty-two and one-half ($22\frac{1}{2}$) gallons of water and this second solution added slowly to the solution of aluminum chloride in water previously formed. When the reaction (3) of forming the aluminum phosphate is complete the combined solution is neutralized with diluted ammonia water to a pH of between 6.8 to 7.4 (4).

(3) $AlCl_3.6H_2O + Na_2HPO_4 \rightarrow AlPO_4 \downarrow + 2NaCl + HCl + 6H_2O$

(4) $HCl + NH_4OH \rightarrow NH_4Cl + H_2O$

The mixture is strained and washed until it is practically free from soluble salts when sufficient water is removed so that the mixture shows a strength of 4 per cent of aluminum phosphate. In order to make the product more palatable sweetening agents such as glycerin, sugar, or saccharin may be added and a flavor such as oil of peppermint additionally incorporated, if desired.

The product of the above example in the fluid form having a strength of 4 per cent of aluminum phosphate is the preferred product which has given the best results. A partially or totally dried product, or one containing a higher concentration of aluminum phosphate may be prepared by control of the dehydration step, in order to give convenience of administration or greater strength of aluminum phosphate, as desired."

For a discussion of the reason why the normal aluminum phosphate precipitates in preference to a secondary phosphate when Na_2HPO_4 is used see Phosphoric Acid, p. 143.

Uses.—*Aluminum Phosphate Gel*, N.F. XII, is a water suspension containing not less than 4 per cent and not more than 5 per cent

[1] U.S. patent 2,294,889 September 8, 1942.

of AlPO$_4$. This preparation is commercially obtainable as Phosphaljel.[1]

The N.F. permits a sufficient amount of oil of peppermint, glycerin, sucrose, or saccharin to be added for flavoring and other purposes. Sodium benzoate or benzoic acid may be added in an amount not to exceed 0.5 per cent as a preservative.

Aluminum Phosphate Gel possesses antacid, astringent and demulcent properties analogous to those of Aluminum Hydroxide Gel, and it provides an effective and safe method of promoting the healing of peptic ulcer, but, unlike Aluminum Hydroxide Gel, it does not interfere with the absorption of phosphates from the intestines. This gel is of particular value for the management of peptic ulcer in the presence of a relative or absolute deficiency of pancreatic juice, diarrhea or a low phosphorus diet.

Usual dose—15 ml. six times daily with a range of 15 ml. to 30 ml.

ALUMINUM SILICATES

1. *Bentonite*, U.S.P. XVII

Physical Properties.—Bentonite is native colloidal, hydrated aluminum silicate. It is a very fine, odorless, pale buff or cream-colored powder. It possesses a slight earthy taste and is free from grit.

The most common type is Volclay bentonite composed of about 90 per cent montmorillonite [Al$_2$Si$_4$O$_{10}$(OH)$_2$·nH$_2$O] which is a clay mineral of unique characteristics. The remainder is mostly feldspar (K$_2$O.Al$_2$O$_3$.6SiO$_2$).

Particle size of bentonite is about 44 microns or will pass through a 325 mesh sieve. One cubic inch of bentonite is estimated to contain 9500 billion particles having a total surface area of more than an acre.

Bentonite has a specific gravity of 2.75 and an index of refraction of 1.55. It is slightly harder than talc. In water suspensions the medium has a pH of 9 to 10. It is insoluble in water and organic solvents.

It should always be added *to* water rather than adding water to it when suspensions are to be made.

In contact with water each flake of bentonite attempts to surround itself with a layer or shell of water. This creates a particle several times larger than the original bentonite flake. Swelling of mass results and bentonite can be expected to absorb up to five times its weight of water and increase from twelve to fifteen times its bulk. The more or less round "balls" of bentonite-water particles give the product a smooth slippery feeling. Repeated wetting and drying

[1] Wyeth Laboratories, Philadelphia, Pa.

of bentonite does not alter its properties. Dilutions as great as 1 to 5000 do not settle out upon standing.

Bentonite suspensions are thixotropic, meaning that they are liquid when agitated but solid when at rest.

Chemical Properties.—Analysis shows it to be an alumino-silicate containing SiO_2, Al_2O_3, Fe_2O_3, CaO, MgO, and some sodium and potassium. In acid solution the metallic ions are exchangeable for hydrogen ions and for this reason bentonite is not readily maintained in acid media.[1]

It can be assumed that bentonite is chiefly a silicate containing sodium as the primary exchangeable ion. Using sodium silicate the reaction in water may be illustrated as (1):

$$(1)\ Na_2SiO_3 + 2H_2O \rightarrow H_2SiO_3 + 2NaOH$$

Silicic acid is non-ionized allowing the highly ionized sodium hydroxide to maintain an alkaline medium (pH 8.5 to 10).

The "ion exchange" property of bentonite has been studied and shows that certain ions will replace the sodium in bentonite.[2] These ions in the order of their replacing ability are $H < Ca < Mg < K < Na$. The calcium and magnesium bentonites have only slight swelling properties. It follows that all dispersions of bentonite are affected by electrolytes. The higher the valence of the cation, the greater the effect. In combining an electrolyte with bentonite the order of mixing is important. When the electrolyte is added to a suspension of bentonite, no noticeable change may occur; but if the dry bentonite is added to a solution of an electrolyte, the suspension is usually thinner than if pure water were used.

Official Tests.—A gel prepared from 6 Gm. of Bentonite and 300 mg. of Magnesium Oxide in 200 ml. of water is agitated for one hour. One hundred ml. of the mixture is transferred to a 100 ml. cylinder, and allowed to remain undisturbed for twenty-four hours. Not more than 2 ml. of supernatant liquid should appear on the surface.

Swelling power: when 2 Gm. of Bentonite is added to 100 ml. of water in a 100 ml. cylinder, the mass occupies an apparent volume of not less than 24 ml. in 2 hours.

Fineness of powder: when an aqueous suspension is passed through a No. 200 standard mesh sieve, no grit is felt when the fingers are rubbed over the wire mesh of the sieve.

When dried at 110° C. to constant weight, Bentonite loses not less than 5 per cent and not more than 8 per cent of its weight.

Commercial Manufacture.—Bentonite is mined as such in different parts of the United States but most of it comes from Wyoming and South Dakota.

[1] Martin, B. and Guth, E. P., J. Am. Pharm. Assoc. Sci. Ed., **39**, 646 (1950).
[2] Barr, M., and Guth, E. P.: J. Am. Pharm. Assoc. Sci. Ed., **40**, 9 (1951).

Uses.—*Bentonite,* U.S.P. XVII, is a native, colloidal, hydrated aluminum silicate. It is also known as "soap clay" or "mineral soap." It is used to stabilize emulsions, as a detergent in cleaners, as a clarifying agent, as an adsorbent for coloring matter, and as a suspending agent.

Bentonite Magma is a preparation containing 5 per cent (w/v) of Bentonite in suspension in distilled water. It is used where the suspending properties of Bentonite are desired.

A brand of bentonite containing iron oxide is named *Neutracolor* and is used as a coloring agent to impart a skin color to suspensions intended for external application.

2. *Kaolin,* N.F. XII

Physical Properties.—Kaolin is a native hydrated aluminum silicate, powdered, and freed from gritty particles by elutriation. It occurs as a soft, white or yellowish-white powder, or as lumps. It has a clay-like or earthy taste and, when moistened with water, assumes a darker color and develops a marked clay-like odor. It is insoluble in water, in cold dilute acids and in solutions of the alkali hydroxides.

Chemical Properties.—Kaolin is chemically inert since it is insoluble in all of the common solvents.

When treated with sulfuric acid and strongly heated, aluminum sulfate and silicon dioxide form (1).

Nearly all igneous rocks contain aluminum silicate ($Al_2O_3.2SiO_2.-2H_2O$) in some combined form, *e.g.,* the double silicates of aluminum and the alkali metals [*feldspar,* $(SiO_3)_2AlK.SiO_2$; *lencite* $(SiO_3)_2AlK$; etc.]. Weathering permits the alkali silicates to be removed by rain, leaving large deposits of relatively pure aluminum silicate. When the material is pure and white, it is known as *kaolin* or *kaolinite* and, as indicated, is the principal product of weathering of aluminum minerals such as the feldspars and micas. Aluminum silicate (principally *kaolinite,* $Al_2Si_2O_7.2H_2O$ or $Al_2O_3.2SiO_2.2H_2O$, or a very similar colloid) containing impurities of calcium, magnesium, iron oxides, fragments of quartz, etc., is known as *clay.* A pure, finely divided clay possesses some very definite properties, *viz.,* it takes up water to form a plastic mass that is capable of being molded (the plasticity probably being due to colloidal materials or "*gels*" that it contains); a molded form becomes very hard, retains its shape and contracts from 20 to 40 per cent on burning in suitable furnaces; it loses all of its plasticity upon burning. Because of these inherent properties, clay and kaolin are the principal materials used for the manufacture of bricks, pottery and porcelainware in the ceramic industry.

Official Tests for Identity.—Mix 1 Gm. of Kaolin with 10 ml. of water and 5 ml. of sulfuric acid in a porcelain dish. Evaporate the mixture until the excess of water is removed, and further heat the residue until dense white fumes of sulfur trioxide appear (1); then cool, add cautiously 20 ml. of distilled water, boil for a few minutes, and filter. A gray residue (SiO_2) remains on the filter. The filtrate responds to the tests for *Aluminum (q.v.)*.

(1) $Al_2Si_2O_7.2H_2O + 4H_2SO_4 \xrightarrow{\Delta} Al_2(SO_4)_3 + SO_3 \uparrow + 6H_2O$
    $\uparrow + 2SiO_2 \downarrow$

Kaolin loses not more than 15 per cent of its weight upon ignition at 550 to 600° C. It does not give a test for carbonate or iron and is less than 0.02 per cent soluble in diluted hydrochloric acid.

Commercial Manufacture.—Kaolin is present in Nature as clays, the three specific classes being *kaolinite, dickite* and *nacrite*. Deposits are found widely distributed over the surface of the earth. Elutriation of the crude clay removes the larger particles of quartz, mica, etc., but in some cases not all of the fine grit. Official Kaolin differs a great deal in properties and state of firmness. To obtain a finer state of subdivision, the clay is peptized in water by adding the proper quantity of a suitable electrolyte (sodium pyrophosphate). This charges the particles, maintaining the finer ones in suspension whereas the heavier ones settle out. The peptized suspension is then flocculated with another electrolyte and the colloidal kaolin collected.

The plastic and adsorptive properties of kaolin samples usually vary widely. To insure a uniform product both the source and purification must be controlled.

Uses.—*Kaolin*, N.F. XII, "is a native hydrated aluminum silicate, powdered and freed from gritty particles by elutriation." Kaolin is used internally for its adsorptive properties as well as its ability to coat irritated intestinal mucosa. It is useful in diarrhea where the cause is food poisoning or organisms causing dysentery. In cases of intestinal fermentation it helps by adsorbing gases, toxins and bacteria. A useful preparation for this purpose is *Kaolin Mixture with Pectin*.

Externally it is used as a dusting powder, absorbent in ulcers and moist infections, and in cataplasms as a carrier of heat.

3. *Pumice*, N.F. XII

Physical Properties.—Pumice occurs as a gritty, grayish powder or as very light, hard, rough, porous grayish masses. It is tasteless and odorless, and is permanent in air. It is insoluble in all of the usually used solvents. In the large masses, pumice will float on water but due to its porous structure gradually absorbs water and sinks. The specific gravity of pumice is 2.3.

It is available in three powder forms:

1. "Pumice Flour" or "Superfine Pumice" is a finely divided form of which not less than 97 per cent will pass through a 200 mesh sieve.

2. "Fine Pumice" is a little coarser powder in that not less than 95 per cent passes through a 200 mesh sieve, and not more than 75 per cent passes through a 150 mesh sieve.

3. "Coarse Pumice" are particles that will permit not less than 95 per cent to pass through a 60 mesh sieve, yet not more than 5 per cent will pass through a 200 mesh sieve.

Chemical Properties.—Pumice is chemically inert. It is not attacked by acids or alkalies. It is composed of 70 to 75 per cent of silica (SiO_2), 15 to 20 per cent of iron and aluminum oxides, and traces of calcium, magnesium, potassium and sodium compounds.

Official Tests.—When 10 Gm. of Pumice is boiled with 50 ml. of water for thirty minutes and then filtered, the reaction is neutral to litmus paper and one-half of the filtrate yields upon evaporation not more than 10 mg. of residue.

When 1 Gm. is boiled with 25 ml. of diluted hydrochloric acid for thirty minutes and filtered, the residue from the filtrate yields not more than 60 mg. of acid-soluble ash.

Commercial Manufacture.—Pumice is found in volcanic areas and mined. There are deposits in Italy and in the western part of the United States in Nebraska and Oregon.

Uses.—*Pumice*, N.F. XII, is a substance of volcanic origin, consisting chiefly of complex silicates of aluminum, potassium, and sodium. It is used as a distributing agent for slowly soluble substances. Because of its hardness, some use is found for it in dental preparations and cleaners.

ALUMINUM SULFATE

Aluminum Sulfate, U.S.P. XVII

Formula, $Al_2(SO_4)_3.18H_2O$.   Molecular Weight, 666.42

Physical Properties.—Aluminum Sulfate occurs in the form of a white crystalline powder, in shining plates, or in crystalline fragments. It is odorless and has a sweetish, astringent taste. It is stable in air, but hydrolyzes in solution.

One Gm. of aluminum sulfate is soluble in about 1 ml. of water at 25° C., and 11.3 Gm. are soluble in about 1 ml. of boiling water. It is insoluble in alcohol.

When the salt is gradually heated to about 200° C., it loses its water of hydration (about 48.6 per cent) and at 770° C., it decomposes.

Chemical Properties.—An aqueous solution is acid to litmus paper (pH = 2.9). Aluminum sulfate in solution has the chemical properties of the aluminum ion and the sulfate ion.

It is assayed by the method used for Aluminum Chloride (*q.v.*).

Official Tests for Identity.—The salt in solution (1 to 10) responds to the tests for *Aluminum* (*q.v.*) and for *Sulfate* (*q.v.*).

Commercial Manufacture.—1. A very pure grade of aluminum sulfate can be made by dissolving aluminum hydroxide in sulfuric acid (1). When the solution is concentrated and allowed to crystalize, aluminum sulfate with 18 molecules of water of hydration, $Al_2(SO_4)_3.18H_2O$, separates out.

$$(1) \quad 2Al(OH)_3 + 3H_2SO_4 + 12H_2O \rightarrow Al_2(SO_4)_3.18H_2O$$

2. Aluminum sulfate for industrial uses is made either by the action of sulfuric acid on bauxite (2), or by digesting clay (impure aluminum silicate) or kaolin (pure, white aluminum silicate) in sulfuric acid (3).

$$(2) \quad Al_2O_3.2H_2O + 3H_2SO_4 \rightarrow Al_2(SO_4)_3 + 5H_2O$$

$$(3) \quad H_2Al_2(SiO_4)_2 + 3H_2SO_4 \rightarrow Al_2(SO_4)_3 + 2H_2SiO_3 \downarrow + 2H_2O$$

In the latter case, the silicic acid is removed by filtration and the filtrate evaporated to crystallization. During the solidification, the liquid is stirred continuously with wooden paddles to keep the salt from "caking."

Uses.—*Aluminum Sulfate*, U.S.P. XVII, contains an amount of $Al_2(SO_4)_3$ equivalent to not less than 99.5 per cent and not more than 112 per cent of $Al_2(SO_4)_3.18H_2O$. It is never used internally in pharmacy. Solutions (5 to 25 per cent) of the salt are antiseptic and astringent. Its principal use is in the preparation of Alum and Aluminum Subacetate Solution. It is also the astringent component of some deodorant preparations. Amebic cysts may be removed from water by adding about 0.5 Gm. per gallon, allowing to settle for an hour, and filtering.

Aluminum Sulfate is used in the manufacture of *Aluminum Subacetate Solution*. Precipitated Calcium Carbonate is gradually added to an aqueous solution of Aluminum Sulfate (4). Acetic acid is then added, and the mixture set aside for 24 hours (5). The clear liquid is filtered off and after the magma has been washed, sufficient water is poured through it to make the required volume. This preparation is used in much the same manner as Aluminum Acetate Solution.

$$(4) \quad Al_2(SO_4)_3 + 3CaCO_3 + 3H_2O \rightarrow Al(OH)_3 \downarrow + 3CaSO_4 \downarrow + 3CO_2 \uparrow$$

$$(5) \quad 2Al(OH)_3 + 4CH_3COOH \rightarrow 2Al(CH_3COO)_2OH + 4H_2O$$

The product is a clean, colorless, or faintly yellow liquid, possessing an odor of acetic acid and having an acid reaction. On standing, the aluminum subacetate is subject to hydrolysis with the precipitation of a more basic salt. The solution yields, from each 100 ml., not less than 2.30 Gm. and not more than 2.60 Gm. of aluminum oxide (Al_2O_3), and not less than 5.43 Gm. and not more than 6.13 Gm. of acetic acid ($C_2H_4O_2$). To prevent hydrolysis and maintain a clear solution 0.9 per cent of boric acid may be added. A pH of about 5 is thereby established.

For external astringent use this solution should be diluted with 20 to 40 volumes of water. It is applied in the form of wet dressings.

Aluminum Acetate Solution (Burow's Solution) may be prepared by adding glacial acetic acid (15 ml.) to Aluminum Subacetate solution (545 ml.) and making up to one liter with Purified Water. The solutions are well mixed and filtered if necessary. The finished solution should have a specific gravity of about 1.022 at 25° C., and should be dispensed only when clear.

It is permissible to stabilize the preparation by adding not more than 0.6 per cent of boric acid. Basic salts of aluminum are thus prevented from forming and a pH of 3.6 to 4.4 is maintained.

In the average dilution with 10 to 40 volumes of water, this preparation is used as a wet dressing on the skin for its mild astringent and antiseptic action. The 5 per cent solution is said to possess definite germicidal properties, and a 1 per cent dilution is still considered a good antiseptic.

A Burow's Solution Base Powder[1] is available. It is composed of aluminum subacetate that is soluble in water and may be used to prepare Burow's Solution or Aluminum Subacetate Solution U.S.P. Only the addition of water is necessary to prepare the subacetate solution but to obtain Burow's Solution, the addition of acetic acid is required.

Burow's Solution may also be prepared with Domeboro[2] (tablets or powder) containing aluminum subacetate, aluminum sulfate, calcium acetate and subacetate, and aluminum acetate. The product dissolved in water forms aluminum acetate solution with a pH of approximately 4.2. In addition a fine calcium sulfate precipitate is formed.

Aluminum acetate in colloidal suspension is marketed under the name Hydrosal[3] in a solution and an ointment.

Another use of aluminum acetate has been to buffer products such as Acid Mantle Creme and Acid Mantle Lotion to provide a pH compatible with the normal skin pH of 4.0 to 6.6 or, in other words, to provide an "acid mantle" that protects the skin from bacterial infection. This hypothesis is said to be largely incorrect by Pillsbury *et al.*[4] and Nelson and McCarthy[5] maintain that the mechanical keratin barrier, sebum and perspiration are more effective antibacterial mechanisms than the pH of the skin.

[1] Irving Wise and Co., N.Y.
[2] Dome Chemicals Inc., N.Y.
[3] Hydrosal Co., Cincinnati, Ohio.
[4] "Dermatology" by D. M. Pillsbury, W. B. Shelley, and A. M. Kligman, Philadelphia, W. B. Saunders Co., 1957, p. 122.
[5] Nelson, C. T., and J. T. McCarthy, Med. Clin. of North Amer., **43**, 871 (1959).

The N.F. VII gave a method of preparing the solution by inter-action of lead acetate and aluminum sulfate that has the disadvantage of requiring more time, and results in having lead as an impurity (exceeding heavy metals limit of 10 parts per million).

ALUM

Alum, N.F. XII

Formula, $AlNH_4(SO_4)_2 . 12H_2O$.   Molecular Weight, 453.33;

$AlK(SO_4)_2 . 12H_2O$.   Molecular Weight, 474.39

Physical Properties.—Alum occurs in the form of large, colorless, octahedral crystals, in crystalline fragments, or as a white powder. It is odorless and has a sweetish, strongly astringent taste.

One Gm. of Ammonium Alum dissolves in 7 ml. of water at 25° C. and in 0.3 ml. of boiling water. One Gm. of Potassium Alum dissolves in 7.5 ml. of water at 25° C., and in 0.3 ml. of boiling water. Both Ammonium and Potassium Alum are freely but slowly soluble in glycerin, but insoluble in alcohol.

When Potassium Alum is heated, it melts at 92° C., and loses all of its water at 200° C., forming *burnt alum*. Ammonium Alum melts at 95° C., and, besides water, loses some ammonia and sulfuric acid upon ignition (1). Either Alum, however, may be used to prepare *Dried Alum* N.F.

$$(1) \ 2NH_4Al(SO_4)_2 . 12H_2O \xrightarrow{\Delta} 2NH_3 \uparrow + 4H_2SO_4 + Al_2O_3 + 21H_2O$$

Chemical Properties.—Solutions of alum are acid to litmus paper. The alums are not complex compounds, since the ions of the component salts are formed in solution. Solutions of either alum give the chemical reactions for the aluminum ion (*q.v.*) and sulfate ion (*q.v.*), and for ammonium or potassium ion (*q.v.*).

An alum is a double salt of a trivalent and a univalent element containing 12 molecules of water of hydration. All alums form isomorphous crystals. The trivalent element may be aluminum, iron, chromium, manganese, cobalt, indium, gallium, vanadium, etc., whereas, the univalent radical may be any one of the alkali metals, ammonium, silver or thallous thallium. The most common alums are double sulfates, although double selenates (with the radical, SeO_4) are also considered as alums. Potassium or ammonium-aluminum sulfates are the two best known alums. Not infrequently their composition is expressed by the formulas, $K_2SO_4 . Al_2(SO_4)_3 .-24H_2O$ and $(NH_4)_2SO_4 . Al_2(SO_4)_3 . 24H_2O$, respectively.

Double salts such as $Na_2SO_4 . MgSO_4 . 6H_2O$ or $ZnSO_4 . K_2SO_4$ are not to be confused with alums.

Both Alums are assayed in the same way as is Aluminum Chloride (*q.v.*), *i.e.*, by use of excess standard disodium ethylenediaminetetraacetate with the excess being determined with standard zinc sulfate solution using a dithizone indicator.

Official Tests for Identity.—1. Sodium hydroxide T.S. added to a solution of Ammonium Alum (1 in 20) at first produces a precipitate which completely dissolves in an excess of the reagent and ammonia is evolved (2, 3, and 4).

$$(2) \ AlNH_4(SO_4)_2 + 4NaOH \rightarrow Al(OH)_3 \downarrow + NH_4OH + 2Na_2SO_4$$
$$(3) \ NH_4OH \rightarrow NH_3 \uparrow + H_2O$$
$$(4) \ Al(OH)_3 + NaOH \rightarrow NaAlO_2 + 2H_2O$$

2. Potassium Alum undergoes similar reactions to (2) and (4).

3. An aqueous solution of Potassium Alum responds to all tests for *Aluminum* (*q.v.*), *Potassium* (*q.v.*) and *Sulfate* (*q.v.*).

4. An aqueous solution of Ammoinum Alum responds to all tests for *Aluminum* (*q.v.*), *Ammonium* (*q.v.*) and *Sulfate* (*q.v.*).

Commercial Methods of Manufacture.—The various methods now used to make alum are dependent upon the aluminum-containing materials employed. A cursory description of each process is given below:

1. *Alum stone* (alumite) is an abundant mineral occurring in large quantities in Italy. It is a basic alum having the approximate composition $KAl(SO_4)_2 . Al(OH)_3$. First, the alum stone is roasted at 500° C. to convert the aluminum hydroxide to insoluble Al_2O_3 and then the alum is extracted with hot water. When the liquid is concentrated and cooled, large pure cubes of the so-called "*Roman Alum*" crystallize out.

2. Both *bauxite* ($Al_2O_3 . 3H_2O$) and *cryolite* (Na_3AlF_6) are used in making alum. When either one of these minerals is fused with sodium carbonate, soluble sodium metaluminate is formed. When carbon dioxide is passed into a solution of the latter, aluminum hydroxide is precipitated. (See commercial production of aluminum.) The hydroxide is converted into aluminum sulfate by the action of sulfuric acid (5) and the solution is mixed with either potassium sulfate or ammonium sulfate to form the respective alums (6, 7). Crystals of the alum are obtained by concentrating and cooling.

$$(5) \ 2Al(OH)_3 + 3H_2SO_4 \rightarrow Al_2(SO_4)_3 + 6H_2O$$
$$(6) \ Al_2(SO_4)_3 + K_2SO_4 + 24H_2O \rightarrow 2AlK(SO_4)_2.12H_2O$$
$$(7) \ Al_2(SO_4)_3 + (NH_4)_2SO_4 + 24H_2O \rightarrow 2AlNH_4(SO_4)_2.12H_2O$$

Alum may be made also by adding a solution of potassium sulfate or ammonium sulfate to a solution of "alum cake,"[1] and then concentrating the solution to crystallization.

---
[1] Impure aluminum sulfate made by the action of sulfuric acid on bauxite.

Uses.—*Alum,* N.F. XII, contains not less than 99.5 per cent of $AlNH_4(SO_4)_2.12H_2O$ or not less than 99.5 per cent and not more than 105 per cent of $AlK(SO_4)_2.12H_2O$. The label of the container must indicate whether the salt is Ammonium Alum or Potassium Alum. Alum precipitates proteins and may, therefore, cause irritant or caustic effects. It is used externally for its astringent properties. In this capacity it is often used in soluble footbath preparations to harden the skin. Infrequently, Alum is orally administered in doses of about 5 grains to remedy a diarrheal condition. One to 5 per cent solutions are used as gargles (somewhat injurious to the teeth) and 0.5 to 1 per cent solutions are employed as urethral injections or as skin lotions. A 2 per cent solution may be employed to reduce excessive perspiration. It is also the active ingredient in the common styptic pencil for stopping the bleeding of small cuts.

The protein-precipitation property is used in preparing alum precipitated diphtheria toxoid, alum precipitated diphtheria and tetanus toxoids, and alum precipitated tetanus toxoid.

Dried Alum (Exsiccated Alum, Burnt Alum), N.F. XII, when recently dried at 200° for 4 hours, contains not less than 96.5 per cent of $AlNH_4(SO_4)_2$ or of $AlK(SO_4)_2$. It is made by heating Ammonium Alum at about 250° C. or Potassium Alum at about 200° until a nearly anhydrous residue is obtained. It is a white, odorless powder having a sweetish, astringent taste. It absorbs moisture upon exposure to air. One Gm. is very slowly and usually incompletely soluble in about 20 ml. of water at 25° C. It is soluble in about 2 ml. of boiling water. It is insoluble in alcohol. As in the case of Alum, the label of the container must indicate whether it is Dried Ammonium Alum or Dried Potassium Alum. It is used as a mild caustic.

Industrially, alum is sometimes substituted for aluminum sulfate for purposes mentioned in the discussion of the latter.

Alum is also used in the textile and paper industries, for hardening Plaster of Paris and in the so-called "alum baking powders."

DIHYDROXYALUMINUM AMINOACETATE

Dihydroxyaluminum Aminoacetate, N.F. XII

Formula, $H_2NCH_2COOAl(OH)_2.xH_2O$
Molecular Weight (anhydrous), 135.06

Physical Properties.—Dihydroxyaluminum Aminoacetate occurs as an impalpable, white, odorless powder with a faintly sweet taste.

It is insoluble in water and in organic solvents but mixes readily with water to form fairly permanent suspensions. The pH of a 1 in 25 suspension is almost neutral (pH, 7.4) at room temperature.

31

The salt dissolves readily in dilute mineral acids and in solutions of fixed alkalies to form cloudy solutions which clarify on heating.

Chemical Properties.—The solubility of the product in mineral acids may be accounted for most readily by assuming formation of soluble aluminum chloride and the salt of aminoacetic acid (1).

(1) $H_2NCH_2COOAl(OH)_2 + 4HCl \rightarrow H_2NCH_2COOH.HCl + AlCl_3 + 2H_2O$

Solubility of the salt in fixed alkalies is probably a result of hydrolysis of the salt to provide aluminum hydroxide and water-soluble sodium aminoacetate (2). The formed aluminum hydroxide would behave normally with excess fixed alkali to yield water-soluble sodium metaluminate (3). These reactions, of course, indicate the amphoteric properties of the compound.

(2) $H_2NCH_2COOAl(OH)_2 + NaOH \rightarrow H_2NCH_2COONa + Al(OH)_3$

(3) $Al(OH)_3 + NaOH \rightarrow NaAlO_2 + 2H_2O$

Perhaps the most important chemical property of dihydroxy-aluminum aminoacetate is its ability to neutralize and/or buffer acid solutions. The official requirements for this product require conformity to acid-consuming capacity, acid-neutralizing capacity and prolonged neutralization. It should consume not less than 140 ml. of 0.1N hydrochloric acid and it should be able to keep the pH of a solution, to which 25 ml. of 0.1N hydrochloric acid is added per 200 mg. of compound, above a pH of 3. Finally, when a specified amount of the compound and artificial gastric juice are kept at 38° C. and tested periodically over a period of 2 hours the pH should show a rapid rise above 3.5 and maintain a pH above 3 for the entire period.

It has been suggested that the immediate neutralization shown by the salt is due to the amino group of the compound (4).

(4) $H_2NCH_2COOAl(OH)_2 + HCl \rightarrow H_2NCH_2COOAl(OH)_2.HCl$

The delayed neutralization is accounted for by removal of the aluminum moiety as $AlCl_3$ (5). To account for the mild astringency

(5) $H_2NCH_2COOAl(OH)_2.HCl + 3HCl \rightarrow AlCl_3 + 2H_2O + H_2NCH_2COOH.HCl$

of the compound it is suggested that ionization into aluminum ions is responsible (6).

(6) $AlCl_3 \rightleftarrows Al^{+++} + 3Cl^-$

The assay of Dihydroxyaluminum Aminoacetate is unlike those employed for the other aluminum salts in that it depends on precipitation of the contained aluminum as the hydroxide which is subsequently ignited to provide Al_2O_3. All of the other aluminum salts use the more effective method of adding excess standard disodium ethylenediaminetetraacetate to the assay solution followed by determination of the excess with standard zinc sulfate solution using dithizone as the indicator.

Commercial Manufacture.—This compound is made by the interaction of aluminum isopropylate with glycine in isopropanol solution (7). The mixture is heated on a steam bath and, since glycine

$$\left[\begin{array}{c} CH_3 \\ \diagdown \\ \quad CHO \\ \diagup \\ CH_3 \end{array} \right]_3 Al + H_2NCH_2COOH + 2H_2O \rightarrow$$

(7)

$$H_2NCH_2COOAl(OH)_2 + 3 \quad \begin{array}{c} CH_3 \\ \diagdown \\ CHOH \\ \diagup \\ CH_3 \end{array}$$

is not readily soluble in any common solvent except water, this cannot be excluded from the reaction and, therefore, the basic rather than the normal salt is obtained. The precipitated salt is easily separated from glycine by washing with water.

Uses.—*Dihydroxyaluminum Aminoacetate* (Basic Aluminum Glycinate), N.F. XII, dried to a constant weight at $130°$, contains not less than 35.5 per cent and not more than 38.5 per cent of aluminum oxide (Al_2O_3). It may contain small amounts of aluminum oxide and of aminoacetic acid. This salt acts as a gastric antacid when taken orally and is, therefore, useful in the control of hyperacidity when treating peptic ulcer. In many ways it resembles aluminum hydroxide but, because it contains from 50 to 60 per cent less aluminum, the formation of astringent aluminum chloride in the intestine is theoretically reduced. This would be expected to cause less constipation but apparently this difference has not proven to be too convincing clinically. Likewise, the slightly more prompt buffering action over aluminum hydroxide preparations has been deprecated by some authorities. A number of commercial preparations make use of this chemical, among them being Alglyn, Dialminate, and Robalate. Officially it is recognized in the form of *Dihydroxy-Aminoacetate Magma* and *Dihydroxyaluminum Aminoacetate Tablets*. The former contains an amount of Al_2O_3 equal to not less than 28.5 per cent and not more than 35 per cent of the labeled amount of dihydroxyaluminum aminoacetate. The tablets usually contain about 500 mg. of the compound.

Usual dose—500 mg. with the usual regimen being one or two 500 mg. tablets or an equivalent amount of the magma being given after meals and at bedtime.

NON-OFFICIAL ALUMINUM COMPOUNDS

Aluminum Carbonate ($Al_2(CO_3)_3$).—Aluminum carbonate is completely hydrolyzed by water at the moment of its formation (1). Therefore, when a soluble carbonate is added to a solution of an aluminum salt, the *hydroxide* and *not* the *carbonate* is precipitated (2).

(1) $Al_2(CO_3)_3 + 3H_2O \rightarrow 2Al(OH)_3 \downarrow + 3CO_2 \uparrow$

(2) $Al_2(SO_4)_3 + 3Na_2CO_3 + 3H_2O \rightarrow 2Al(OH)_3 \downarrow + 3Na_2SO_4 + 3CO_2 \uparrow$

A commercial product is "Basaljel,[1]" which is a basic aluminum carbonate gel. This product may be obtained by using a solution of sodium carbonate which has sufficient sodium bicarbonate present to retard the hydrolysis of the carbonate ion and thus decrease the concentration of the hydroxide ion.

$Na_2CO_3 + 2H_2O \rightleftarrows 2NaOH + H_2CO_3$
$H_2CO_3 + H_2O \rightleftarrows HCO_3^- + H_3O^+$

The addition of sodium bicarbonate forces the reactions to the left and therefore decreases the concentration of hydroxide ions. Sodium carbonate is still ionized sufficiently to supply carbonate ions. Upon the addition of aluminum sulfate a basic carbonate or a mixture of aluminum carbonate and aluminum hydroxide precipitates.

$Al^{+++} + OH^- + CO_3^= \rightarrow Al(OH)CO_3 \downarrow$
(excess)

Also a basic carbonate may be prepared from a solution of sodium carbonate saturated with carbon dioxide.

The gel of basic aluminum carbonate is suggested for the management of phosphatic urinary calculi. It functions very much like aluminum hydroxide in this capacity in that dietary phosphate is excreted in the feces as aluminum phosphate.

Fuller's Earth.—This aluminum magnesium silicate, also known as "floridin," is a low plasticity clay-like material quite similar to kaolin. It has a high water content and, like clay, is produced by weathering of aluminum-bearing rocks. It is principally montmorillonite [$Al_2Si_4O_{10}(OH)_2 \cdot xH_2O$]. Originally, this mineral was found in Germany and, until the turn of the century, was imported into the U.S. At that time a superior type of Fuller's Earth was discovered in northern Florida, largely displacing the German import. The mineral has much the same properties and has found extensive use in the decolorization of oils and other liquids, especially when pretreated with diluted acids. It has also been used as a filtering medium and as a rubber filler.

[1] Wyeth Laboratories, Philadelphia, Pa.

Exploration of the geological formation that produced the American Fuller's Earth referred to above revealed that it could also be found in southern Georgia near the small town of Attapulgus and that the clay found there (*i.e.*, *attapulgite*) was of a particularly useful quality. This clay when heated, in contrast to kaolin, experienced an increase in its adsorptive properties. The properties of the heated clay have led to its use as an ingredient in numerous pharmaceutical preparations because of its claimed greater adsorptive capacity over kaolin. Attapulgite was found to adsorb diphtheria toxin as well as certain bacteria (*Staph. aureus*) at least five times better than kaolin and, particularly interesting from the standpoint of its use in antidiarrheal preparations, it showed excellent adsorption of the endotoxins of certain strains of *Escherichia coli* and even one of the dysentery (*Shigella*) group. Since these bacteria may be associated with diarrheal diseases the superior adsorptive properties exhibited could be of value. Examples of commercial preparations making use of this new adsorptive agent in antidiarrheal preparations are Quintess and Polymagma. Each of these is marketed with or without added antibiotics.

29

Scandium and Yttrium and Their Compounds

SCANDIUM

Symbol, Sc. Valence, 3. Atomic Weight, 44.956
Atomic Number, 21

History and Occurrence.—Many of the properties of scandium were predicted by Mendeléeff. He chose to call this undiscovered element "*eka-boron.*" About ten years later (1879) the element was discovered by Nilson in the mineral *euxenite*. Its name is derived from Scandinavia, the place where it was first obtained and the native country of its discoverer.

Scandium is widely distributed in Nature, but in very small amounts. Its richest minerals, *wiikite* and *anorthite*, are found in Finland. It has a density of 2.5, melts at 1200° C., and boils at 2400° C.

Compounds.—Its hydroxide, $Sc(OH)_3$, or $ScO.OH$, is less basic than the corresponding compounds of the family, including the rare earths. Scandium oxide (Sc_2O_3) is more basic than aluminum oxide, as is evidenced by the fact that the carbonate $[Sc_2(CO_3)_3]$ exists. Scandium chloride has the formula $ScCl_3.12H_2O$. Like boron it yields both the simple and complex fluorides, such as ScF_3 and Na_3ScF_6. The nitrate, $Sc(NO_3)_3.4H_2O$, and the sulfate, $Sc_2(SO_4)_3$, are known. The double sulfate, $Sc_2(SO_4)_3.3K_2SO_4$, is not an alum.

YTTRIUM

Symbol, Y. Valence, 3. Atomic Weight, 88.905;
Atomic Number, 39

History and Occurrence.—Yttrium was the first of the elements of this family, rare earths included, to be discovered. The oxide was obtained by the Finnish chemist, Gadolin, in 1794 from *gadolinite*, a mineral occurring near Ytterby, a town in Sweden. Cleve obtained the metal as a dark gray powder of metallic luster by the

(474)

electrolysis of the double chloride of sodium and yttrium. Gadolinite contains, in addition to yttrium, other members of the yttrium family.

Physical Properties.—Yttrium melts at 1475° C. and has a density of 5.51.

Chemical Properties.—It is slowly converted into the oxide (Y_2O_3) by cold water, but more rapidly by hot water. Its oxide is the most basic of the yttrium family which consists of dysprosium, holmium, erbium, thulium, ytterbium, lutetium, and yttrium. It is a weaker base than lanthanum oxide. The hydroxide $Y(OH)_3$ will absorb carbon dioxide to form the carbonate. It will also liberate ammonia from ammonium salts. The salts of yttrium are colorless.

Compounds.—Yttrium salts, when treated with hydrofluoric acid, yield the fluoride, $2YF_3.H_2O$. The chloride is obtained by passing chlorine over a heated mixture of the oxide and carbonate. It forms the hydrate $YCl_3.H_2O$. Yttrium nitrate, $Y(NO_3)_3.2H_2O$, is freely soluble in water. Some of the other salts are the phosphate $YPO_4.-2H_2O$, the sulfide Y_2S_3, the carbonate $Y_2(CO_3)_3.3H_2O$ and the carbide YC_2.

Although unimportant in medicine, the oxide has found some use as a ceramic, particularly in electric resistance furnaces.

30

Gallium, Indium and Thallium and Their Compounds

GALLIUM

Symbol, Ga. Valences, 2, 3. Atomic Weight, 69.72;
Atomic Number, 31

History.—In 1869, Mendeléeff predicted the existence of an element having an atomic number of 31. He called this undiscovered element "*eka-aluminum*" and described its properties with remarkable accuracy. In 1875, Lecoq de Boisbaudran discovered the spectroscopic lines of the element in a sample of zinc blende (*sphalerite*) and named it *gallium* after his native country, France (Gallia).

Occurrence.—Gallium is a rare element and is found in small amounts in most samples of zinc blende (sphalerite).

Physical Properties.—Gallium is a white, lustrous and tough metal, that may be cut with a knife. It melts at 29.8° C. and, because it remains super-cooled, is often considered to be a liquid element like bromine and mercury. It has a density of 5.91.

Chemical Properties.—It does not react with water and only slightly with nitric acid. It dissolves in hydrochloric acid and in alkalies. With aluminum, it forms liquid alloys which readily decompose water.

Commercial Manufacture.—This metal has been obtained by the electrolysis of an ammoniacal solution of its sulfate.

Compounds.—Gallium oxide [Ga_2O_3], gallium hydroxide [$Ga(OH)_3$], gallium chloride [$GaCl_3$], and gallium sulfate [$Ga_2(SO_4)_3$] have been prepared and have similar physical and chemical properties to the corresponding aluminum compounds. Gallium forms a true alum, $Ga(NH_4)(SO_4)_2 . 12H_2O$. The gallium salts are all hydrolyzed by water, and gallium hydroxide, like the hydroxide of aluminum, is amphoteric.

Uses.—Gallium has been used little in medicine or in the industries, it being mainly of scientific interest. Its chief use, up to now, has been in thermometers to measure high temperatures. A potentially important use may be as a dental alloy. A mixture of nickel, silicon and gallium is said to be nontoxic yet it wets the tooth and forms a filling that adheres tightly to dental cavities. Radioactive gallium, obtained by cyclotron bombardment of zinc, may be useful for detecting bone cancers.

INDIUM

Symbol, In.   Valences, 1, 3.   Atomic Weight, 114.82;
Atomic Number, 49

History.—In 1863, Reich and Richter discovered this element when they observed its spectroscopic lines in the spectrum of zinc blendes obtained from Freiberg. They named it *indium* from the two remarkably characteristic and brilliant indigo-blue lines of its spectrum.

Occurrence.—Indium is found in small quantities in zinc blende, and in tungsten, tin, and iron ores.

Properties.—Indium is a grayish-white metal that is softer than lead. It has a density of about 7.31 and fuses at 156.4° C.

It is permanent in air. When heated, it burns with a dark blue flame to form the oxide, In_2O_3. The metal is more readily attacked by nitric acid than by either hydrochloric or sulfuric acids.

Commercial Manufacture.—The metal is made by the reduction of the oxide.

Compounds.—The oxides (InO, In_2O_3, In_3O_4) and hydroxide [In(OH)$_3$] of indium resemble the analogous compounds of aluminum. Although amphoteric, their basic character is much more pronounced than that of either aluminum oxide or hydroxide. Indium hydroxide is nearly insoluble in excess of alkali hydroxide. Indium chloride ($InCl_3$) is not hydrolyzed by hot water. However, water acts upon both indium monochloride (InCl) and indium dichloride ($InCl_2$) to form indium trichloride ($InCl_3$) and free indium (1).

(1) $3InCl_2 \rightarrow 2InCl_3 + In$

Indium sulfate forms a true alum with ammonium sulfate.

Uses.—Like gallium, indium is never used in medicine.

THALLIUM

Symbol, Tl.   Valences, 1, 3.   Atomic Weight, 204.37;
Atomic Number, 81

History.—Thallium was discovered in 1861 by Crookes, who observed its brilliant green line in the spectrum obtained in the spectroscopic analysis of flue dust secured from a sulfuric acid plant in the Harz Mountains. He named the element *thallium* from the

Greek *thallos*, meaning a "green twig." While investigating the sludges of lead chambers, Lany, working independently, discovered the same element one year later.

Occurrence.—Thallium is rather widely distributed in Nature and is more abundant than either gallium or indium. The principal thallium-bearing minerals are Swedish *crooksite* [(CuTlAg)$_2$S; about 17 per cent Tl], *lorandite* [TlAsS$_2$; about 60 per cent Tl], and *vrbaite* [TlAs$_2$Sb$_5$; about 30 per cent Tl]. Small amounts of the elements are found in pyrites, zinc blende, hematite, and traces are found in sylvine and carnallite at Stassfurt and in some mineral springs.

Physical Properties.—Thallium is a leaden-colored metal with a hardness about equal to that of sodium. It has a density of 11.85 and fuses at 300 ± 3° C. Its vapor density indicates the formula, Tl$_2$.

Chemical Properties.—The metal is oxidized in moist air, but is permanent when kept under water. It burns with a green flame It is attacked by nitric acid and by sulfuric acid. It is only slightly soluble in hydrochloric acid, because it soon becomes covered with thallous chloride (TlCl) which is difficultly soluble.

Commercial Manufacture.—The metal is obtained by dissolving the aforementioned flue dust or sludge in sulfuric acid and precipitating the metal as thallous iodide with hydriodic acid. When the iodide is heated with sodium, sodium iodide (soluble) and metallic thallium (insoluble) result.

Compounds.—Thallium forms two series of compounds, *viz.*, thallous compounds, in which the metal is univalent, and thallic compounds, in which the element is trivalent.

Thallous compounds have properties that are similar to those of analogous compounds of silver and of potassium. Thus, the *halides*, *cyanides* and *sulfides* of thallous thallium are insoluble and, in this respect, are like the corresponding compounds of silver. *Thallous sulfate* and *carbonate*, like the corresponding salts of potassium with which they are isomorphous, are soluble in water; the former also yields true alums, whereas the latter is readily hydrolyzed, giving an alkaline reaction to its solution. *Thallous hydroxide* (TlOH) is a highly ionized base like potassium hydroxide, and a black *thallous oxide* (Tl$_2$O) may be obtained by heating it in the absence of air.

Compounds of the *thallic* series markedly resemble the compounds of aluminum and also show some properties that are like the auric compounds. Thus, *thallic hydroxide* [Tl(OH)$_3$] is a stronger base than aluminum hydroxide. Thallic oxide [Tl$_2$O$_3$], like aluminum oxide, is formed when the hydroxide is heated. *Thallic chloride* [TlCl$_3$] and *thallic sulfate* [Tl$_2$(SO$_4$)$_3$] are highly ionizable salts and thus possess properties that lie between those of similar aluminum and auric compounds. Thallic sulfate forms a double sulfate with potassium sulfate (K$_2$SO$_4$.Tl$_2$(SO$_4$)$_3$.8H$_2$O] but, on account of its having only 8 molecules of water of hydration, it is not a true alum. Like trivalent gold, thallium forms definite and stable complex ions.

Uses.—Thallium acetate has been used in creams as a depilatory. However, it has very toxic effects[1] and may be absorbed through the skin and exert a systemic action. In such cases or when taken orally it causes the loss of body hair. Thallium is very toxic and its use in medicine is unnecessary. The chemotherapy of thallium poisoning by the use of Trihexyphenidyl and Dimercaprol has been suggested by Stein and Perlstein.[2] The Tridihexyphenidyl is given for tremors which are an early sign of thallium poisoning. The Dimercaprol acts as the detoxifying agent.

The value of thallium salts in the control of various rodents was suggested in 1924. In the manufacture of refractive optical glass, it is sometimes used in place of lead.

[1] For a brief but informative discussion of thallium poisoning, its clinical signs, diagnosis and treatment see "Thallium Poisoning." Pfizer Spectrum, Vol. **6**, p. 558 (1958).

[2] Stein, M. D., and Perlstein, M. A., J. Dis. Child. **98**, 80 (1959).

31

The Rare-Earth Metals

IT is customary to designate the metals having atomic numbers of 57 to 71 as the *rare earths*. This name is not accurate in describing these substances because they are metals and not earths and they are not especially rare. The name "earths" was given to them because they were first known in the form of their oxides which resembled the then known alkaline earths (lime, magnesia, etc.). With respect to their rarity, the element cerium, for example, is more abundant in the earth's crust than tin, silver, gold, cadmium mercury, antimony, tungsten or platinum. Rich pockets of most of these metals are found in many parts of the world. No doubt, the "rare" designation resulted from the fact that they are so alike chemically that their separation is a tremendous task. Nevertheless, they are exciting considerable interest today with simultaneous development of commercial processes for their separation. Although no large scale industrial uses have yet been developed it is safe to predict that the current demand created by the Atomic Energy Commission will eventuate in broader commercial utilization. The accompanying table gives many of the presently known properties of these interesting elements.

Occurrence.—Rare-earth metals are currently obtained chiefly from the mineral monazite, an orthophosphate mineral found in Africa, India, Brazil, and in this country in the beach sands of Florida and the Carolinas as well as in the river sands of Idaho. The monazite sands produce principally cerium and thorium. A number of other minerals are also good sources of the rare earths; they occur in Texas, North Carolina and Colorado and, abroad in Scandinavia, Greenland, Brazil, Australia and the Urals.

Properties.—The most common form in which the rare-earth metals was found until the recent interest in the pure metals was as an alloy containing about 70 per cent cerium and smaller amounts of the other metals. This is known as *Mischmetal* and, because of its pyrophoric nature (gives sparks when scraped) has been used in cigarette lighter flints. Some of the other properties are found in the accompanying table.

The remarkable similarity of the rare-earth metals is based on the peculiarity of their atomic structure which has previously been discussed. As we know, the energy states of electrons in the outer-

(480)

most valence shell are the determinants in the chemical activity of an atom. Ordinarily, the usual energies (heat, moderate voltages of electricity, chemical reactions) available in laboratories are unable to affect any but these outer electron shells and do not affect the shielded inner shells. Thus, because these elements all have three electrons in the outer shell, and in fact are identical in their outer shell arrangement, they have a strong chemical similarity. The differences in these elements lie deeper than the valence shell and, as we have noted (see Chap. 1), occur in the 4f subgroup. All the other shells are identical and, because there are 14 places to

PROPERTIES OF RARE EARTHS

Name	Symbol	Atomic Number	Density*	Melting Point	Atomic Diameter, Å	Color of Salts
Lanthanum	La	57	(α) 6.194	860°	3.741	White
			(β) 6.18			
Cerium	Ce	58	(α) 6.78	770-800°	3.64	White
			(β) 6.81			
Praseodymium	Pr	59	(α) 6.776	940-960°	3.65	Green
			(β) 6.805			
Neodymium	Nd	60	(α) 7.004	800-900°	3.63	Reddish-violet
Promethium	Pm	61	——	——	——	——
Samarium	Sm	62	6.93	1350°	——	Yellow
Europium	Eu	63	5.244	1100-1200°	4.08	Pink
Gadolinium	Gd	64	7.948	——	3.59	White
Terbium	Tb	65	8.332	——	3.54	White
Dysprosium	Dy	66	8.562	——	3.54	Yellow
Holmium	Ho	67	8.764	——	3.52	Yellow
Erbium	Er	68	9.164	1250° (?)	3.50	Pink
Thulium	Tm	69	9.346	——	3.48	Green
Ytterbium	Yb	70	7.01	1800° (?)	3.87	White
Lutetium	Lu	71	9.74	——	3.47	White

* Indicates two different forms of the elements when the Greek letters are used.

be filled in the 4f shell, there are 14 rare earths. Actually, lanthanum is not a true rare earth because it has no electrons in the 4f shell but it is so similar to the others that it is always included with them. It is natural, then, to expect marked similarities in this series of elements wherever the differences lie only in the shielded (from ordinary energy and chemical effects) 4f shell and where the valence shell is identical in each element. The principal differences have been in the radius which shrinks as the atomic number increases, the so-called "lanthanide contraction." This is due to the variation in size of the nucleus with the increasing weight of the nucleus being associated with a greater positive charge. The increasing positive charge results in a greater attraction of the electrons causing the shells to shrink. Thus, in general, the heavier elements have smaller radii and the densities are greater.

Many of the salts of these metals are colored and these may be referred to in the table

Separation of the Rare Earths.—Because of their likeness in chemical behavior, the rare-earth metals are not separated easily by the usual methods. This is responsible for special methods that have been used. Among these are:

(a) Fractional decomposition of the nitrates by ignition.
(b) Fractional crystallization of salts, a process still in active use by some commercial concerns.
(c) Fractional precipitation of various salts.
(d) Fractional precipitation by bases of different strengths.
(e) Ion-exchange separations using synthetic resin columns. This procedure will undoubtedly become one of the important commercial processes. It is one of the newest and depends on passing a solution of the rare-earth metals through an ion-exchange resin. As the solution progresses down the column literally thousands of exchanges take place and, because they progress at different rates, a separation takes place. The heaviest rare earth is the first to emerge, then the next heaviest, etc.

Uses.—The only rare-earth compound that has found any medicinal application is cerium oxalate as an antiemetic and even this has been dropped from official recognition.

CERIUM

Symbol, Ce.   Valences, 3, 4.   Atomic Weight, 140.12;
Atomic Number, 58

History.—In 1803, Berzelius and Hisinger simultaneously discovered the oxide (CeO_2) of a new element in a Swedish mineral. Hisinger called the oxide *ceria* and the element *cerium* in allusion to the planet, Ceres, which had but recently been discovered. Mosander obtained the element in 1826, and found that *ceria* was a mixture of the oxides of cerium, lanthanum and "didymium."

Occurrence.—Cerium, together with lanthanum, praseodymium, neodymium and samarium, is found as silicate in the minerals *cerite* and *allanite*. The mineral *monazite*, which is the chief source of thorium oxide, also contains cerium.

Physical Properties.—Cerium is an iron-gray, ductile and malleable metal. It has a density of 6.78–6.81, fuses at 770–800° C., and boils at 1400° C. The metal is insoluble in water but soluble in acids.

Chemical Properties.—Cerium forms two series of compounds: (1) cerous salts (CeX_3) and (2) ceric salts (CeX_4).

The cerous salts are colorless and stable. In these, cerium has a valence of 3. A cerous salt heated with a volatile acid such as nitric or oxalic, results in the formation of cerium dioxide (CeO_2). The cerous oxide (Ce_2O_3) may be obtained by reducing the dioxide with calcium. Solutions of cerous salts, when treated with an alkali, form a white precipitate of cerous hydroxide (1).

(1) $Ce(NO_3)_3 + 3NaOH \rightarrow Ce(OH)_3 \downarrow + 3NaNO_3$

This hydroxide is readily oxidized on exposure to air, to red, violet and finally yellow ceric hydroxide ($Ce(OH)_4$). From solutions of cerous salts, ammonium sulfide precipitates cerous sulfide which is immediately hydrolyzed to the hydroxide.

The ceric salts color their solutions an orange-red. They are readily reduced by most reducing agents such as ferrous salts and hydroquinones to cerous salts. Ceric salts form insoluble carbonates and hydroxides.

Commercial Manufacture.—Metallic cerium is obtained with a small amount of lanthanum and other rare earths mixed with it, by the electrolysis of cerium chloride. It may also be made by the reduction of the oxide with magnesium powder.

Pharmacological Action of Cerium Ion.—Cerium salts injected intravenously depress the heart and thus affect the circulation. When soluble salts are ingested they cause blood to effuse from the wall of the stomach and intestine. The use of insoluble salts such as cerium oxalate caused no effect since they are unabsorbed.

Uses.—Metallic cerium finds little use as such and is employed mostly for preparing its salts.

Cerium (about 70 per cent) and iron (about 30 per cent) form one of the principal *pyrophoric* alloys. It is often called *"misch metal."* When particles of this alloy are torn off by a file, they catch fire in the air and will ignite illuminating gas and vapors of benzine, alcohol, etc.; hence the use of this alloy in making gas lighters, cigar lighters, etc.

The N.F. IX recognized *Cerium Oxalate*, $Ce_2(C_2O_4)_3$, as a remedy for vomiting, especially during the early stages of pregnancy. It has been superseded by other more effective agents.

GROUP IV ELEMENTS

Carbon and silicon belong in the second and third so-called "short periods" of the Periodic Table. Both of these elements are characteristically nonmetallic in chemical behavior and, like all other members of this group have a maximum valence of 4. Carbon, but not silicon, can exhibit a valence of 2. This bivalency is also noted among other members of this family. The members of subgroup IVA are titanium, zirconium and hafnium. Cerium and thorium also often are considered with this group but, having been considered elsewhere, will be omitted here. The members of subgroup IVB are germanium, tin and lead

In general, the properties of group IV take on a different chemical character than those of groups I, II and III. These elements now are able to make up the valence octet without the use of coordination. From the standpoint of electronic configurations of the atoms, when the four possible covalent bonds are formed, we find that the first two elements (C and Si) and the elements of the B subgroup possess the same arrangement of electrons as in the next inert gas. This is not true of the A subgroup and, as a result, the resemblance of the "typical" elements is nearer to that of the B group than the A group. This has not been true of previous groups but is increasingly true of all succeeding groups until, in the halogen series, the resemblance of the B group to the typical elements is marked. The elements of both subgroups are classed among the metals although the typical elements are nonmetals. It is primarily in the lower valence states where the metallic character is most pronounced and it is in these states where the greatest differences in the two subgroups occur. Actually, because of the small size and high charge on the tetravalent ions, the bonding is predominantly covalent in all cases although with the divalent ions the bonding has considerable ionic character. The ionic character, naturally, increases with the size of the ion.

The importance of carbon both in the elemental state and in combined forms can scarcely be overestimated. By far the greatest importance attaches itself to its function as the basic building unit of organic chemical compounds. These, of course, will not be discussed in this textbook although the principal applications of elemental carbon will be discussed in the following chapter. One is often tempted to draw analogies between carbon and silicon to the point where a system of *silanes* (covalent Si-Si bonds) is considered in a manner analogous to the well-known alkanes. However, whereas carbon seems able to make chains of indefinite length, at present

(485)

PROPERTIES OF GROUP IV AND IVA ELEMENTS

Properties	Carbon	Silicon	Titanium	Zirconium	Hafnium
Atomic Number	6	14	22	40	72
Atomic Weight	12.0115	28.086	47.90	91.22	178.49
Isotopes	12, 13	28–30	46–50	90–2, 94, 96	174, 176–80
Electrons	2–4	2-8-4	2-8-(8 + 2)-2	2-8-18-(8 + 2)-2	2-8-18-32-(8 + 2)-2
Density	2.22	2.33	4.51	6.53	11.4
M.P.	3700 ± 100°	1420°	1725°	1857°	1700°
B.P.	4830°	2300°	5100°	3577°	5390°
Common Oxidation States	−4 to +4	−4 to +4	0, +2, +3, +4	0, (+2), (+3), +4	0, (+2), (+3), +4
Radius (cov.), Å	0.771	1.17	1.32	1.45	1.48
Radius (ionic), Å	0.15	0.41	0.68	0.80	0.87
Ionization Potential, first, volts	11.264	8.149	6.82	6.84	ca. 5.5
Oxidation Potential, volts, $M \rightarrow MO^{++}$	—	—	+0.95	+1.53	+1.68

the length of the silicon chains that have been made and characterized cannot be said to exceed six. Thus, the stability of the silicon
systems does not seem to approach that of carbon systems.

The elements of IVA are transitional in character. Hafnium is
so similar to zirconium in all respects that whatever applies to
zirconium in a chemical way also applies to hafnium. Because of
the electron arrangement, the valences of the elements in this
group can vary from 2 to 4 by making use of the electrons from the
next outermost shell in addition to the valence electrons. In the
A subgroup the lower valence forms are less stable than the tetravalent form. Trivalent titanium is of importance although the

PROPERTIES OF GROUP IVB ELEMENTS

Properties	Germanium	Tin	Lead
Atomic Number	32	50	82
Atomic Weight	72.59	118.69	207.19
Isotopes	70, 72–3, 76	112, 114–20, 122, 124	204, 206–8
Electrons	2-8-18-4	2-8-18-18-4	2-8-18-32-18-4
Density	5.323	7.31	11.34
M.P.	936°	231.9°	327.4°
B.P.	2700°	2260°	1740°
Common Oxidation States	0, +2, +4	0, +2, +4	0, +2, +4
Radius (cov.), Å	1.22	1.40	1.74
Radius (ionic), Å, tetravalent	0.53	0.71	0.84 1.21 (+2)
Ionization Potential, first, volts	8.09	7.30	7.38
Oxidation Potential, volts, M → M++	——	+0.13	+0.12

divalent form is mostly a curiosity. The trivalent states of zirconium and hafnium exist but are not of importance. In general,
compounds containing the tetravalent form of the elements do not
exhibit color in their compounds whereas the lower valence states
are associated with color. This is frequently the case among ions
of transitional elements (and their complexes) where the d-subgroup is
only partially filled and the color is thought to result from the raising
of these d-electrons to higher energy states by absorption of light.
The cation in this group are not the normal type but instead are
oxo-ions of the type TiO^{++} and ZrO^{++}. The halides of titanium and
zirconium both behave as acids in the Lewis sense, forming adducts
with nucleophilic organic oxygen derivatives (alcohols, ethers,
phenols, esters, etc.). Although they already possess complete
octets the central atoms are capable of holding more electrons than
the normal octet. Tetravalent titanium and zirconium also form
stable complexes with halogens with the hexafluoride (TiF_6^- or
ZrF_6^-) being the most important.

The IVB subgroup elements exhibit valences of either 2 or 4. The divalent form implies the presence of an "inert" pair of electrons. The stability of the divalent character increases with the atomic number. Divalent germanium is a good reducing agent whereas tetravalent lead (*e.g.*, PbO_2) is a good oxidizing agent. Indeed, the stability of the divalent form of lead is such that frequently it is assumed to be its characteristic oxidation state. Although germanium is classed as a metal its metallic character only slightly exceeds its nonmetallic character so that it can properly be called a metalloid. Nonmetallic character even extends to tin inasmuch as one of its allotropic forms (low temperature form) is definitely nonmetallic and the other form is the familiar metallic tin. Lead, on the other hand, is definitely metallic. The activity increases as we progress down the group in the Periodic Table with lead being the most active. The tetrahalides are volatile (except SnF_4) and are mainly of the covalent type. In the tetravalent state the only element in the series that forms compounds of stability with oxyacids is lead, with one of the most important ones being lead tetraacetate, a good oxidizing agent. Here again the behavior is that of a covalent compound rather than a salt. The hydroxides in the tetravalent state of IVB elements are all very weak acids.

32

Carbon and Carbon Compounds

CARBON

Activated Charcoal, U.S.P. XVII

Symbol, C.   Valence, 4.   Atomic Weight, 12.01115
Atomic Number, 6

Occurrence.—This non-metallic element is found in the free condition as the diamond in Brazil, Venezuela, India and South Africa, as graphite (plumbago) in the United States, Germany, Spain, Siberia, Canada, Ceylon and Bohemia, and as coal which is very widely distributed.

Carbon is the fundamental constituent of all animal and vegetable tissue and of coal and petroleum. In the form of carbonates, it enters the composition of many minerals such as *chalk, dolomite, calcite, witherite, calamine,* and *spathic* iron ore. Combined with oxygen it is found to a small extent as carbon dioxide in the atmosphere. In combination with hydrogen it occurs as methane or marsh gas.

Allotropic Modifications.—Carbon exists in two *crystalline* modifications, *viz.,* diamond and graphite. So-called "amorphous" carbon is in reality a mass of very minute crystals, which have the identical crystalline structure of graphite.

Diamond.—Diamond is the purest native form of uncombined carbon. It occurs in colorless, tinted or black crystals belonging to the regular system. Diamond has a density of 3.50 to 3.56. It is one of the hardest known substances (10 on Mohs' scale) and must be "cut" and polished with diamond dust. It has a high index of refraction (2.417 for sodium light). It is a good conductor of heat but a poor conductor of electricity. The diamond resists the action of most chemicals. When it is burned in oxygen, carbon dioxide and a trace of ash result.

Colorless or tinted diamonds are "cut" into those shapes that secure the greatest light reflection and refraction. When these are polished, they form gems having remarkable brilliance and luster. Black diamonds (carbonado) and those that cannot be cut into gems because of flaws, are used for cutting glass or for pointing rock drills.

(489)

Artificial diamonds of microscopic size were prepared by Moissan in 1893 by suddenly cooling molten iron containing dissolved carbon and then dissolving the iron in acid.

Graphite.—This variety of crystalline carbon occurs native in Ceylon, the United States, Germany, Spain, Siberia, and elsewhere. Its physical properties are markedly different from those of diamond. It is a soft, unctuous, black or dark lead-colored, shiny solid which is composed of crystalline scales belonging to the hexagonal system. It has a density of 2.09 to 2.23 and is a good conductor of electricity. Like diamond, it resists the action of chemicals at ordinary temperatures. When heated in oxygen, it is converted into carbon dioxide.

Large quantities of artificial graphite are now being manufactured by the Acheson process at Niagara Falls.

Graphite is very soft and leaves a black mark on paper and other objects when drawn across them, hence the name "graphite" from the Greek meaning "to write." "Lead" pencils are made by extruding a paste of powdered graphite and varying quantities of grit-free clay through perforated plates. The small rods of "lead" are dried, cut into desired lengths and baked to remove all moisture. They are then glued in wooden cases to complete the pencil.

Because intense heat does not affect graphite, it is used to make stove polish and protective paints. It is also employed for making electrodes for use in electro-chemical industries. Crucibles, (plumbago crucibles) made from graphite and clay are used in making crucible steel (*q.v.*).

The unctuous property of graphite, together with its great resistance to heat, makes it suitable as a lubricant for machinery running at high temperatures. Unlike lubricating oils, graphite is not absorbed by wood, and therefore is used to reduce the friction between moving wooden parts of machines.

Coal.—These natural deposits are the result of slow decomposition of vegetable matter in the presence of water, the absence of air, and under pressure. Coal consists of carbon, carbon compounds, mineral matter, and moisture. There are many varieties of coal but only two general kinds, *viz.*, *anthracite* or *hard* coal and *bituminous* or *soft* coal. The former contains about 90 per cent of carbon and about 6 per cent of volatile matter. It ignites with some difficulty and burns without appreciable smoke or flame, giving off a large quantity of heat. It is used extensively for domestic heating purposes, for making producer gas, coke, tar, and in electric furnace reductions. *Bituminous* or soft coal contains about 70 per cent of carbon with large quantities of volatile matter. Soft coal burns with a smoky flame. Soft coal is used for both domestic and industrial heating and for the manufacture of illuminating gas, coke and tar.

Other Forms of Carbon.—There are numerous other kinds of carbon, *e.g.*, (1) charcoal, (2) lampblack and carbon black, (3) coke and (4) gas carbon. These forms of carbon are amorphous and are obtained by the destructive distillation of many carbon compounds. The various kinds of amorphous carbon differ greatly as to purity and physical properties; their properties depending upon the substances from which they are made. As previously stated, none of these well-known forms is *pure* carbon because they contain variable amounts of other elements or their compounds.

Physical Properties.—*Activated Charcoal* is a fine, black, odorless, tasteless powder free from gritty matter and is insoluble in water. When dried for 4 hours at 120° C. it loses not more than 15 per cent of its weight. Upon incineration the residue does not exceed 4 per cent of its weight.

Activated Charcoal is an active adsorbent of various substances. As an example, the U.S.P. requires a certain minimum adsorptive capacity for strychnine solutions, in that a solution containing 100 mg. of strychnine sulfate has all of the alkaloidal salt removed by shaking with 1 Gm. of Activated Charcoal. It is also required to adsorb a definite minimum amount of methylene blue from solution.

It is characterized by its power to adsorb various gases. One volume at 0° C. and 760 mm. pressure will adsorb 171.7 ml. of ammonia, 86.3 ml. of nitrous oxide, 67.7 ml. of carbon monoxide, 21.2 ml. of carbon dioxide, 17.9 ml. of oxygen, 15.2 ml. of nitrogen and 4.4 ml. of hydrogen.

Chemical Properties.—The aqueous filtrate from a boiled suspension of Activated Charcoal is colorless and neutral to litmus paper.

At ordinary temperatures, carbon is an inactive element, but its activity rapidly increases with rising temperatures until, at about 3500° C., it becomes very active. At elevated temperatures, it has a great affinity for oxygen and forms carbon dioxide and carbon monoxide. The different forms of carbon are variously affected by the most active oxidizing agents (*e.g.*, nitric acid, chromic oxide, potassium permanganate and potassium chlorate). For example, diamond is scarcely attacked by them, graphite is but slowly oxidized, and charcoal is rapidly oxidized. At the temperature of the electric furnace, carbon unites with many metals and some non-metals to form carbides, such as calcium carbide (CaC_2), aluminum carbide (Al_4C_3), and silicon carbide or carborundum (SiC), etc. When heated with the various metallic oxides, *e.g.*, zinc oxide, copper oxide, iron oxide, etc., carbon reduces them to the metal and carbon monoxide, carbon dioxide, or a mixture of the two, depending upon the amount of charcoal used. Carbon will unite with hydrogen in the presence of finely divided nickel at a temperature of 250° C. to form methane (CH_4). A number of molten metals will dissolve at least small quantities of carbon, which generally cause a deterioration in metallicity. Iron, however, gains in elasticity and tensile strength with only slight loss of plasticity.

Official Tests for Identity.—The official compendium does not provide specific tests for identification. All of the monograph requirements lend themselves to identifying the product.

Commercial Manufacture.—Activated Charcoal is obtained by the destructive distillation of plant substances. The materials mostly used are wood, waste liquor from wood pulp, paper, molasses, fruit stones, nut shells, corn cobs and straw. An activated form of charcoal may be produced by (1) mixing pumice with the plant material and distilling, (2) adding a salt such as zinc chloride and distilling at a low temperature, or (3) by heating carbon at high temperatures in the presence of steam.

Uses.—*Activated Charcoal*, U.S.P. XVII, is the residue from the destructive distillation of various organic materials, treated to increase its adsorptive power.

Official recognition of Activated Charcoal is for its use as a general-purpose antidote against a variety of poisonous substances. This is a well-known property of the product and, of course, is based on its exceptionally effective adsorptive capacity for these substances. Strangely enough, in spite of a literature on the use of Activated Charcoal the use of the most common antidotal preparation, *i.e.*, "Universal Antidote," had not been subjected to a critical analysis until that of Picchioni *et al.*[1] in 1966. These workers discovered that the combination of 2 parts Activated Charcoal in combination with magnesium oxide (1 part) and tannic acid (1 part) was inferior to the use of Activated Charcoal alone. Their studies were carried out *in vivo* and *in vitro* using pentobarbital, strychnine and malathion as the representative chemical toxic agents. Indeed, their studies indicate that the presence of magnesium oxide and tannic acid actually interferes with the activity of Activated Charcoal as a detoxicant. Dreisbach[2] recommends the use of Activated Charcoal in all cases where Universal Antidote has been used previously. It should also be noted that "burned toast" is useless as a substitute for Activated Charcoal[3] and it is remarkable that even certain current compendia describing treatment for emergency poisoning continue to recommend its use. The usual dose for antidotal purposes is 10 Gm. with an allowable usual dose range of 5 to 50 Gm.

It has been used for its adsorptive properties in the treatment of stomach and intestinal disorders where chemicals, enzymes or toxins are to be removed. When wet, Activated Charcoal will not adsorb gases and therefore its use for "gas on the stomach" is irrational.

[1] Picchioni, A. L., Chin, L., Verhulst, H. L. and Dieterle, B.: "Activated Charcoal vs. Universal Antidote as an Antidote for Poisons," Toxicol. Appl. Pharmacol., **8**, 447 (1966).

[2] Dreisbach, R. H.: Handbook of Poisoning-Diagnosis and Treatment, 5th ed., Lange Medical Publications, Los Altos, California, 1966.

[3] Lehman, A. J., Assoc. Food Drug Officials U.S. Quart. Bull., **21**, 210 (1957); see also, Lehman, A. J., Am. Prof. Pharm., **29**, 75 (1963).

Depending on the conditions being treated, the dose may vary from 0.6 to 6 Gm. and even higher.

It has been used to some extent as a dressing for foul-smelling wounds. Charcoal chewing gums have not been accepted by the A.D.A. as dental remedies.

CARBON COMPOUNDS

The natural and synthetic compounds of carbon already described in the literature number well over 1,000,000 and are more numerous than the known compounds of any other element. This vast number is not difficult to account for when one considers that carbon derivatives are the chief components of all plants and animals. The natural sources of carbon compounds quite logically lead to the use of the name *organic* to differentiate them from *inorganic* or mineral substances. Carbon compounds bear a definite relationship to one another but differ markedly in general behavior from the compounds of other elements. In fact, they form a distinct group, the consideration of which constitutes the interesting study of *Organic Chemistry*. Only a few of the simpler compounds of carbon will be considered here.

OFFICIAL COMPOUND OF CARBON AND OXYGEN

CARBON DIOXIDE

Carbon Dioxide, U.S.P. XVII

Formula, CO_2. Molecular Weight, 44.01

Physical Properties.—Carbon Dioxide is a colorless, odorless gas. An aqueous solution of the gas has a faintly acid taste. It is about one and a half times heavier than air, 1 liter weighing 1.977 Gm. at 760 mm. and at 0° C. At 25° C. and 760 mm. pressure, it is soluble in about its own volume of water. For pressures up to about 4 atmospheres, the gas conforms to Henry's law.[1] By subjecting the gas to a pressure of about 59 atmospheres, it is rather easily converted into a colorless liquid which freezes at −57.7° C. The vapor pressure of solid carbon dioxide is 760 mm. at −79° C., hence upon exposure to air the solid evaporates without melting. The rapid evaporation of liquid carbon dioxide (from cylinders) absorbs sufficient external heat to convert the remainder to a crystalline mass (carbon dioxide "snow"). It is used to produce low temperatures. So-called "dry ice" is CO_2-snow pressed into forms.

---

[1] The concentration of a saturated solution of a given gas is proportional to the concentration or pressure at which the gas is supplied.

Chemical Properties.—As evidenced by the extinguishing of a burning taper in the gas (air containing 2.5 per cent of CO_2), carbon dioxide does not support combustion. Between 1200° C. and 1300° C., it is slightly decomposed into carbon monoxide and oxygen (1).

(1) $2CO_2 \overset{\triangle}{\rightleftarrows} 2CO + O_2$

At 2000° C., 1.8 per cent of carbon dioxide is decomposed. It will be noted that the reaction is a reversible one and, therefore, the products of the decomposition reunite when the temperature is lowered. However, in the presence of a combustible substance, all of the carbon dioxide is reduced to monoxide. Burning magnesium ribbon continues to burn in an atmosphere of carbon dioxide, reduces the latter to carbon, and forms the oxide of the metal (2).

(2) $2Mg + CO_2 \rightarrow 2MgO + C$

When carbon dioxide is passed over heated sodium or potassium, the carbonates of the metals and carbon are formed (3).

(3) $4K + 3CO_2 \overset{\triangle}{\rightleftarrows} 2K_2CO_3 + C.$

Carbonic Acid and Its Salts.—As previously stated, carbon dioxide is soluble in water and produces a liquid which contains the very weak acid known as carbonic acid. This acid reddens blue litmus paper and is a very poor conductor of electricity. Being a dibasic acid, it characteristically ionizes in steps, although the secondary ionization is very slight (4) and (5).

(4) $H_2CO_3 + H_2O \rightleftarrows H_3O^+ + HCO_3^-$ ($K_1 = 5.0 \times 10^{-7}$)

(5) $HCO_3^- + H_2O \rightleftarrows H_3O^+ + CO_3^=$ ($K_2 = 4.6 \times 10^{-11}$)

Carbonic acid forms both acid (hydrogen) and normal salts. Thus, when carbon dioxide is passed into a solution of a fixed alkali, the hydrogen salt or bicarbonate is formed (6) which, contrary to expectations, does not give an acid solution because the small ionization of the HCO_3^- (5) is somewhat less than the amount of hydrolysis (7) of HCO_3^-. When an equivalent amount of fixed alkali is added to a solution of the bicarbonate, the normal carbonate is formed (8). Due to the somewhat reversible character of this reaction, solutions of alkali carbonates are alkaline in reaction.

(6) $NaOH + H_2CO_3 \rightleftarrows NaHCO_3 + H_2O$

(7) $HCO_3^- + H_2O \rightleftarrows H_2CO_3 + OH^-$

(8) $NaHCO_3 + NaOH \rightleftarrows Na_2CO_3 + H_2O$

The carbonates and bicarbonates of ammonium and the alkali metals are soluble, whereas the carbonates of other metals are almost insoluble. When carbon dioxide is passed into a solution of calcium hydroxide (lime water) or barium hydroxide (baryta water), a white precipitate of calcium or barium carbonate is formed (9) (test for CO_2). If an excess of carbon dioxide is employed, the precipitates dissolve because of the formation of the respective hydrogen carbonates or bicarbonates (10). Thus, when a natural water containing carbon dioxide in solution trickles over limestone (normal calcium carbonate), some of the latter is dissolved as calcium bicarbonate (see temporary hard water, p. 40). If the solution is heated, carbon dioxide is evolved and the normal calcium carbonate is reprecipitated (10).

(9) $Ca(OH)_2 + CO_2 \rightleftarrows CaCO_3 \downarrow + H_2O$

(10) $CaCO_3 + H_2O + CO_2 \rightleftarrows Ca(HCO_3)_2$

Carbon Dioxide is assayed officially by determining its absorption in 50 per cent potassium hydroxide solution (11). The residual gas from 100 ml. of carbon dioxide should not exceed 1 ml. (1 per cent by volume).

(11) $2KOH + CO_2 \rightarrow K_2CO_3 + H_2O$

Official Tests for Identity.—1. Carbon Dioxide extinguishes a flame (*q.v.*).

2. A precipitate of barium carbonate is formed when the gas is passed through a solution of barium hydroxide.

Commercial Manufacture.—Carbon dioxide occurs in small quantities in the atmosphere (about 0.03 to 0.04 per cent), in the earth, and in the waters of some springs and wells. Some gas wells produce gas which is nearly pure carbon dioxide. It is invariably produced when any compound containing carbon (*e.g.*, wood, coke, coal, oil, gas, etc.) is burned in excess of oxygen. Carbon dioxide is one of the products of chemical change (*e.g.*, decay, fermentation) in organic matter (12). Carbon dioxide is also formed by the slow combustion of foods in the body (digestion).

(12) $C_6H_{12}O_6$ (a sugar) $\rightarrow 2C_2H_5OH$ (alcohol) $+ 2CO_2 \uparrow$ (carbon dioxide)

Preparation.—1. When coke is burned in air, an impure gas containing nitrogen results. When this product is forced under pressure into a concentrated solution of potassium carbonate, only the carbon dioxide is absorbed forming potassium bicarbonate (13). When the pressure is reduced and the solution heated, carbon dioxide, free from nitrogen, is obtained (13). The carbon dioxide under high pressure may be dissolved in cold water to form H_2CO_3. When the pressure is released the carbon dioxide is again liberated. This is compressed in iron cylinders.

(13) $H_2CO_3 + K_2CO_3 \rightleftarrows 2KHCO_3$

2. An unusual process for the preparation of carbon dioxide has recently been announced. This method represents a short cut over older methods. In the process powdered coke and iron ore are mixed together and form a "Fluidized Powder" by means of blowing a stream of pure CO_2 through them. The mixture bubbles like a liquid and the coke is converted to CO_2 by stripping oxygen from the iron oxide. The iron is converted back to the oxide with oxygen from the air. The CO_2 obtained this way is said to be of an exceptional grade of purity without further refining.

3. Carbon dioxide may be obtained by heating sodium bicarbonate (14). A large number of normal carbonates are also decomposed by heat to oxide and carbon dioxide (15).

(14) $2NaHCO_3 \xrightarrow{\Delta} Na_2CO_3 + CO_2 \uparrow + H_2O$

(15) $CaCO_3 \xrightarrow{\Delta} CaO + CO_2 \uparrow$

4. When a carbonate is treated with an acid, carbon dioxide is evolved. This method is employed for generating carbon dioxide for laboratory use. Calcium carbonate (small lumps of marble) is placed in a Kipp generator and dilute hydrochloric acid is allowed to act upon it (16). The unstable carbonic acid produced by the reaction immediately decomposes into water and carbon dioxide (17).

(16) $CaCO_3 + 2HCl \rightarrow H_2CO_3 + CaCl_2$

(17) $H_2CO_3 \rightleftarrows H_2O + CO_2 \uparrow$

5. A relatively high quality "dry ice," suitable for use in refrigeration of foods, has been obtained from natural gas containing gaseous to heavy crude oil hydrocarbons.

Uses.—*Carbon Dioxide* (Carbonic Acid Gas), U.S.P. XVII, contains not less than 99 per cent by volume of CO_2. For convenience it is usually supplied in compressed form in gray metallic cylinders.

Inhalations of oxygen containing 5 to 7.5 per cent of carbon dioxide are efficacious as a respiratory stimulant in the treatment of poisoning by carbon monoxide, alcohol, methanol, morphine and, in fact, all cases of depressed respiration (anesthesia accidents, etc.). The carbon dioxide stimulates the vasomotor as well as the respiratory center.

An unusual use of carbon dioxide[1] as an inhalant has been reported by various workers. Inhalations of a mixture composed of 70 per cent oxygen and 30 per cent carbon dioxide are administered as a treatment for various nervous disorders especially linked with emotional upsets. This group consists of alcoholics, stutterers, asthmatics and those with allergic dermatoses. Therapy with this agent is said to require no accompanying psychotherapy. Although

[1] See *Carbon Dioxide Therapy, A Neurophysiological Treatment of Nervous Disorders* by L. J. Meduna, pub. by C. C Thomas, Springfield, Ill., 1950.

the mechanism for the beneficial action seems to be unclear it is theorized that neuroses are essentially caused by altered function of brain cells and can be changed by physical or chemical rather than psychologic technics. Carbon dioxide acts as a powerful narcotic when inhaled in sufficient quantity. Animals exposed to the gas have become completely anesthetized. In addition, it is said to act as an antagonist to convulsions produced by electrical stimulation of the cerebral cortex. In its effect on the brain it produces changes in motor, sensory, emotional, perceptual, and vegetative function and the state of consciousness. Treatments are usually given 3 times a week until from 20 to 150 treatments have been given using 25 or more respirations per treatment. It seems to be best suited for the psychoneuroses and psychosomatic disorders. It is of little value in psychoses.

Carbon dioxide is used in the manufacture of various chemicals, *viz.*, sodium bicarbonate (baking soda), normal sodium carbonate (washing soda), basic lead carbonate (white lead), etc. Soda water (carbonated water) is made by charging water with the gas under a pressure of 3 to 4 atmospheres. When carbonated water is administered orally, it hastens absorption in the stomach, increases the secretion of acid gastric juice (Chiari, 1915) and acts as a carminative. It is used to relieve nausea. It is used pharmaceutically to mask the disagreeable taste of certain medicines. The U.S.P. permits the air in the container of certain pharmaceuticals to be replaced by carbon dioxide.

Carbon dioxide snow for correcting many skin disorders has been known as an effective remedy since its introduction in 1905 by Pusey.[1] It has been used successfully in the treatment of such skin conditions as acne, angiomas, corns and callouses, eczema, moles, psoriasis and warts. A convenient apparatus for making small quantities of carbon dioxide snow is available.[2]

NON-OFFICIAL COMPOUND OF CARBON AND OXYGEN

Carbon Monoxide (CO). — Carbon monoxide is a colorless gas having a very faint pungent odor and a slightly metallic taste. It is only slightly soluble in water (3 ml. in 100 ml. water at about 0° C., 760 mm.) with which it does not form a compound. Liquid carbon monoxide boils at −193° C. and freezes at about −200° C.

Carbon monoxide is an unsaturated compound and therefore combines directly with oxygen, chlorine and the metals (*viz.*, nickel, iron), to form additive products. At high temperatures, carbon monoxide has a great affinity for combined oxygen (oxides), a fact that is utilized in the recovery of the various metals from their

[1] J. Am. Med. Assn., **49**, 1954 (1907).
[2] Central Scientific Company, Chicago 13, Illinois.

respective ores.   Because of the increasing number of accidental and suicidal deaths due to carbon monoxide poisoning, this compound is of great toxicological interest.   The affinity of hemoglobin for carbon monoxide is said to be about two hundred and ten times greater than it is for oxygen.   Thus, a very low concentration of carbon monoxide in the air (0.2 to 0.4 per cent) is generally fatal. It produces a very stable, cherry-red "carbonic oxide hemoglobin," which prevents the hemoglobin from uniting with oxygen (oxyhemoglobin) and asphyxia results.   Asphyxia produced by carbon monoxide is the same as ordinary asphyxia, except that the skin and mucous membranes are colored a bright red due to CO-hemoglobin instead of being cyanotic (blue), a fact of great diagnostic importance.   The treatment consists of artificial respiration or forced inhalations of oxygen, and warmth.   Blood transfusions also have proven very efficacious.   Over the years, a large number of deaths have resulted from carbon monoxide produced by allowing automobile engines to run in poorly ventilated garages.

Carbon monoxide constitutes 4 to 10 per cent of ordinary *coal* or *illuminating gas* and 30 to 40 per cent of *water gas* (*q.v.*).   It is their principal toxic constituent.

33

Silicon and Silicon Compounds

SILICON

Symbol, Si. Valence, 4. Atomic Weight, 28.086,
Atomic Number, 14

History and Occurrence.—Silicon was discovered by Berzelius in 1823. This non-metallic element does not occur in the uncombined condition in Nature. In combination with other elements it is, with the exception of oxygen, the most widely distributed and abundant of all the elements. When united with oxygen as silicon dioxide (silica), it occurs in the form of quartz, flint, sand, etc. In this form or in that of the silicates, it is the principal constituent of nearly all rocks and likewise of the soil resulting from their disintegration. Silica is found also in the normal ashes of many plants, in the feathers of birds and in the hairs of animals.

Physical Properties.—Silicon exists in two allotropic forms: the *amorphous* and the *crystalline*. *Amorphous* silicon is a dark brown powder having a density of 2.33. When heated to dull redness in an atmosphere of oxygen, it burns with a brilliant flame and forms the dioxide. *Crystalline* or semi-metallic silicon occurs as large, silvery octahedral crystals having a density of 2.49. It melts at 1420° C. and boils at about 2300° C. It will scratch glass. Unlike the amorphous variety, it does not inflame in oxygen even when heated to a white heat. It burns in chlorine or fluorine.

Chemical Properties.—It resists attack by all acids except hydrofluoric, which, when mixed with nitric acid and heated, slowly dissolves it. Hot concentrated solutions of sodium or potassium hydroxides dissolve silicon with the evolution of hydrogen (1).

$$(1) \quad Si + 2NaOH + H_2O \rightarrow Na_2SiO_3 + 2H_2 \uparrow$$

Silicon is tetravalent in all of its compounds. Chemically, it closely resembles carbon with which it unites at the temperature of the electric furnace to form compounds that are known as silicides, *e.g.*, carbon silicide (carborundum CSi).

At red heat, silicon decomposes ammonia into hydrogen and a compound containing silicon and nitrogen. Silicon reduces many metallic and non-metallic oxides. When fused with alkaline carbonates and hydroxides, it is converted into silicon dioxide which dissolves in the molten alkali to form soluble alkali silicates.

Tests for Identity.—The element, silicon, can be recognized by its physical and chemical properties. Silicates can be identified by first converting them into silicon dioxide by fusion with a mixture of sodium and potassium carbonates and then digesting the mass first, with hot water and then with hydrochloric acid. The thoroughly washed precipitate of SiO_2 is then warmed in a lead or platinum dish with calcium fluoride and sulfuric acid (hydrofluoric acid may be used) and the gaseous silicon tetrafluoride (SiF_4) passed into water in which it hydrolyzes into gelatinous silicic acid and fluosilicic acid (2).

$$(2)\ 3SiF_4 + 8H_2O \rightarrow H_4SiO_4 + 2SiF_6^= + 4H_3O^+$$

Commercial Manufacture.—1. *Amorphous silicon* may be prepared by (*a*) the reduction of $SiCl_4$ with sodium at a high temperature (3) and (*b*) by heating powdered sand with magnesium powder (4) and then digesting the mass with hydrochloric acid (5) to remove magnesium oxide and any magnesium silicide (Mg_2Si); (*c*) by reducing SiO_2 in an electric furnace with coke. The temperature is very carefully controlled.

$$(3)\ SiCl_4 + 4Na \xrightarrow{\triangle} Si + 4NaCl$$

$$(4)\ SiO_2 + 2Mg \xrightarrow{\triangle} 2MgO + Si$$

$$(5)\ Mg_2Si + 4HCl \rightarrow 2MgCl_2 + Si + 2H_2 \uparrow$$

2. *Crystalline silicon* may be prepared by dissolving amorphous silicon in molten zinc and allowing the melt to cool slowly. The zinc is removed by treatment with hydrochloric acid.

It may be made either by reducing Na_2SiF_6 or SiO_2 with an excess of Al, or by heating SiO_2 with carbon in an electric furnace.

Pharmacological Action of Soluble Silicates.—Very small quantities of silicates are found in nearly all tissues. When orally administered, soluble silicates act as mild alkalies. Soluble sodium silicate (water glass) is readily absorbed from the alimentary tract and is excreted by the urine. Large doses cause lesions of the capillaries with interstitial inflammation of the organs, especially the liver. Cases of acute poisoning by sodium silicate have been reported.

In the form of magnesium trisilicate the liberated silicic acids and colloidal SiO_2 function as protective substances.

Intravenous injections of sodium silicate produce intravascular coagulation of the blood.

Uses.—Silicon is used in the manufacture of silicon tetrachloride (*q.v.*) and various alloys, *e.g.*, silicon bronze (composed of copper, tin and silicon and used for telephone and telegraph wires), ferrosilicon, etc. Silicon (also ferrosilicon) is sometimes used in the production of hydrogen for filling balloons.

When coke, silica and ferric oxide (Fe_2O_3) are heated together in an electric furnace, a gray, crystalline compound known as *ferrosilicon* is formed. This alloy of iron and silicon is used in making special steels (*e.g.*, duriron, corrosiron, etc.) which are very resistant to the action of acids (especially nitric acid). Silicon and ferrosilicon are used as "scavengers" (*q.v.*) in the steel industry.

OFFICIAL COMPOUND OF SILICON

Purified Siliceous Earth, SiO_2, is an amorphous, very fine, white, light gray or pale buff powder. It is gritty, readily absorbs moisture, and retains about four times its weight of water without becoming fluid. It is insoluble in water, acids, or in dilute solutions of the alkali hydroxides.

Purified Siliceous Earth has little chemical reactivity, a property which recommends it for pharmaceutical uses.

There are no tests for identity. The physical properties of the product and the characteristic appearance of the diatom fragments are sufficient for identification.

Certain ocean creatures (diatoms) develop a siliceous skeleton, and these skeletons accumulate on the ocean floor when the organisms die. Collections of these siliceous skeletons occur in deposits many hundred feet in thickness in the United States, left there in prehistoric times. The frustules and fragments of these diatoms are purified by boiling with hydrochloric acid, washing, and finally calcining the residue.

Although official in U.S.P. XV with full monographic treatment this valuable pharmaceutical aid since has been placed in the category of "Adjuncts and Clinical Reagents" and, specifically, in the group of Filtering Media. Most of the former requirements for purity, etc. are still in effect, however.

Purified Siliceous Earth (Terra Silicea Purificata, Purified Kieselguhr, Purified Infusorial Earth) is used in pharmacy as an absorbent, filtering medium, and clarifying agent. If mixed with soap and soda ash it makes an excellent scouring powder. It is also used to make soluble glass, cement and dynamite (nitroglycerin absorbed in siliceous earth and molded into sticks).

Bentonite.—(See p. 460.)

Kaolin.—(See p. 462.)

Pumice.—(See p. 463.)

Talc.—(See p. 370.)

The Silicic Acids.—When silicon tetrachloride is treated with water, orthosilicic acid (H_4SiO_4) is thrown down as a gelatinous precipitate which is a good example of a *hydrogel* or *gel*. Orthosilicic acid, formed by the interaction of sodium silicate (dilute solution) and hydrochloric acid, remains in the colloidal state and is known as a *hydrosol* or *sol*. Orthosilicic acid cannot be prepared from its anhydride (silicon dioxide) and water, but must be made as previously described. When one molecule of orthosilicic acid loses a molecule of water, it is converted into metasilicic acid (H_2SiO_3). A number of other silicic acids in the form of their simple or mixed salts are found in Nature. These acids may be considered as condensed or polysilicic acids and are formed by the loss of water from *more than* 1 molecule of orthosilicic acid (1 to 8).

(1) H_4SiO_4 (zircon—$ZrSiO_4$; garnet—$Ca_3Al_2(SiO_4)_3$)

(2) $H_4SiO_4 - H_2O \rightarrow H_2SiO_3$ (metasilicic acid) (enstatite—$MgO.SiO_2$; beryl—$3BeO.Al_2O_3.6SiO_2$)

(3) $2H_4SiO_4 - H_2O \rightarrow H_6Si_2O_7$ (orthodisilicic acid) (kaolinite—$Al_2Si_2O_7.2H_2O$; hardystonite—$Ca_2ZnSi_2O_7$)

(4) $2H_4SiO_4 - 2H_2O \rightarrow H_4Si_2O_6$ (dimetasilicic acid) (rhodonite—$Mn_2Si_2O_6$; spodumene—$AlLiSi_2O_6$)

(5) $2H_4SiO_4 - 3H_2O \rightarrow H_2Si_2O_5$ (metadisilicic acid) (rivaite—$Ca_2Na_2(Si_2O_5)_3$)

(6) $3H_4SiO_4 - 2H_2O \rightarrow H_8Si_3O_{10}$ (orthotrisilicic acid) (melilithe—$Ca_4Si_3O_{10}$)

(7) $3H_4SiO_4 - 3H_2O \rightarrow H_6Si_3O_9$ (trimetasilicic acid) (wollastonite—$Ca_3Si_3O_9$)

(8) $3H_4SiO_4 - 4H_2O \rightarrow H_4Si_3O_8$ (trisilicic acid) (meerschaum—$Mg_2Si_3O_8.2H_2O$; orthoclase—$AlKSi_3O_8$)

Salts of Polysilicic Acids.—Purified forms of native aluminum polysilicate (Kaolin, $Al_2Si_2O_7.2H_2O$) and of native magnesium polysilicate [Talc, $Mg_3H_2(SiO_3)_4$ or $3 MgO.4SiO_2.H_2O$] are recognized by the N.F. XII and the U.S.P. XVII, respectively.

34

Titanium and Zirconium and
Their Compounds

TITANIUM

Symbol, Ti.   Valences, 2, 3, 4.   Atomic Weight, 47.90;
Atomic Number, 22

In 1789, the Rev. William Gregor discovered a new metal in
ilmenite ($FeTiO_3$). Six years later Klaproth studied the composition
of *rutile* and named the metal it contained, *titanium*. Subsequently,
he found the same metal in *ilmenite*. The name of the element
signifies the "sons of the earth" (the mythical Titans).

According to Clarke's table of the abundance of the elements,
titanium (9th most plentiful on earth) stands just above chlorine.
It occurs in a greater amount than either phosphorus or carbon. It
is found as the dioxide, TiO_2, in the minerals *rutile, brookite* and *ana-
tase*, all three possessing different crystalline forms. Another important mineral is *ilmenite*. Magnetic iron ores frequently contain
titanium.

The metal is difficult to obtain in the pure state. Its dioxide is
reduced by sodium or magnesium (1).

(1) $TiO_2 + Na \rightarrow Ti + NaO_2$

Podszus describes a method of making almost pure titanium by
heating the tetrachloride with sodium in a steel bomb filled with
hydrogen or carbon dioxide (2).

(2) $TiCl_4 + 4Na \rightarrow Ti + 4NaCl$

Titanium is a steel-gray, brittle metal having a density of 4.51.
It melts at about 1725° C. It burns brilliantly in oxygen and unites
with nitrogen with great vigor. Its alloys with steel are of some
importance.

TITANIUM DIOXIDE

Titanium Dioxide, U.S.P. XVII

Formula, TiO_2. Molecular Weight, 79.90

Physical Properties.—Titanium Dioxide occurs as a white, amorphous, tasteless, odorless, infusible powder. A suspension of Titanium Dioxide (1 in 10) in distilled water is neutral to litmus paper. It is insoluble in water, in hydrochloric acid, in nitric acid, and in dilute sulfuric acid.

Because the pharmaceutical use of Titanium Dioxide depends on its whiteness and opacity it is of some interest to know that the best particle size for these properties is approximately 1/125,000 of an inch. The property of opacity is due to Titanium Dioxide's high refractive index (2.70).

Chemical Properties.—Titanium dioxide dissolves in hot concentrated sulfuric acid, and in hydrofluoric acid. It is rendered soluble by fusion with potassium bisulfate or with alkali hydroxides or carbonates.

Hydrogen peroxide reacts with titanium dioxide in dilute sulfuric acid to produce an orange-red color of titanium peroxide (TiO_3).

The dioxide is reduced to metallic titanium when heated with carbon, calcium, sodium or magnesium.

Titanium Dioxide is assayed officially by dissolving it in sulfuric acid with the aid of ammonium sulfate to form a soluble double salt (1). The titanium sulfate solution is then passed through a reducing column containing zinc amalgam to effect reduction of the titanic sulfate to titanous sulfate (2). The titanous sulfate solution is oxidized immediately back to the titanic state by running it into a solution of ferric ammonium sulfate (3). The ferrous sulfate formed by this reaction is titrated with standard potassium permanganate solution (4) to give a measure of the amount of titanium dioxide originally present.

(1) $TiO_2 + 2H_2SO_4 + (NH_4)_2SO_4 \rightarrow Ti(SO_4)_2 . (NH_4)_2SO_4 + H_2O$

(2) $2Ti(SO_4)_2 + H_2 \rightarrow Ti_2(SO_4)_3 + H_2SO_4$

(3) $Ti_2(SO_4)_3 + 2FeNH_4(SO_4)_2 \rightarrow 2Ti(SO_4)_2 + (NH_4)_2SO_4 + 2FeSO_4$

(4) $2KMnO_4 + 10FeSO_4 + 8H_2SO_4 \rightarrow 5Fe_2(SO_4)_3 + 2MnSO_4 + K_2SO_4 + 8H_2O$

Official Tests for Identity.—Titanium Dioxide is dissolved in sulfuric acid with the aid of heat. This solution is diluted and filtered. An orange-red color of titanium peroxide develops upon the addition of a few drops of hydrogen peroxide.

Commercial Preparation.—Titanium dioxide occurs in Nature (*q.v.*) but a better product is obtained by treating ilmenite (FeTiO₃) with hydrogen chloride and chlorine (5).

(5) $2FeTiO_3 + 4HCl + Cl_2 \triangleq 2FeCl_3 + 2TiO_2 + 2H_2O$

Uses.—*Titanium Dioxide*, U.S.P. XVII, contains not less than 99 per cent of TiO_2 calculated on the dried basis. It is used as a white pigment in creams and paints. The refractive characteristic makes it useful to ward off light rays and it is used for this purpose in sun-tan preparations. The official recognition is as a solar ray protectant to be applied topically in the form of a 15 to 25 per cent ointment or lotion as required.

It does not react with hydrogen sulfide, is very stable to weather conditions and spreads well when mixed with a suitable paint base. These properties make it useful for special paints.

ZIRCONIUM

Symbol, Zr. Valences, 2, 4. Atomic Weight, 91.22;
Atomic Number, 40

In 1789, Klaproth discovered a new earth in the mineral *zircon* to which he assigned the name "zirconia." The metal was first prepared by Berzelius as a gray powder by heating potassium zirconofluoride with potassium. The metal was obtained in a state of purity of a little more than 99 per cent by heating the oxide, ZrO_2, with shavings of calcium in an evacuated vessel. One of the chief difficulties associated with the metallurgy of zirconium has been its reactivity with oxygen and nitrogen (more so than titanium) and the presence of even small amounts of these contaminants renders the metal useless for most purposes. On the other hand, the great resistance of the metallic zirconium to corrosion by concentrated acids (nitric, hydrochloric or sulfuric) recommends it for many purposes. Zirconium has a density of 6.53 and melts at about 1857° C.

Compounds.—Zirconium is found in Nature as the silicate, *zircon* ($ZrSiO_2$) and as the oxide, *baddeleyite* (ZrO_2). Zirconia, ZrO_2, is obtained from *zircon*, $ZrSiO_2$, by heating the latter with potassium hydrogen fluoride. Potassium zirconofluoride, K_2ZrF_6, is formed. This compound is decomposed with sulfuric acid and the zirconia is precipitated with ammonium hydroxide from the resulting solution. The oxide is both basic and acidic. It dissolves in acids to form salts such as the nitrate, $Zr(NO_3)_4$, and the sulfate, $Zr(SO_4)_2$. When the oxide is fused with basic oxides or carbonates of the metals, zirconates are formed. Meta- and ortho-zirconates such as Na_2ZrO_3 and Na_4ZrO_4 are known. Polyzirconates also have been prepared. The metal acts almost entirely with the valence of 4, yet the oxide, Zr_2O_3, and the hydride, ZrH_2, are given in the literature. Their existence is questionable. It acts like silicon by forming compounds such as K_2ZrO_6. The halides, such as $ZrCl_4$, hydrolyze easily to form basic salts, such as $ZrOCl_2$.

Uses.—Zirconium or its salts have found little use in medicine. It has been recommended for use in sutures and dental equipment because it does not corrode easily. Zirconium silicate has been found to have properties similar to titanium dioxide for cosmetic preparations. It possesses slightly less covering power but has a good degree of slip and high clinging power to the skin.

Zirconium carbonate and oxide have been claimed to be effective in combating the effects of urushiol in poison ivy dermatitis although there is very little in the literature to support the claims. A number of preparations are on the market that include local anesthetics or antihistamines. Other uses include poison oak eruptions, athlete's foot, industrial dermatitis, and as an anti-perspirant.

35

Germanium and Tin and Their Compounds

GERMANIUM

Symbol, Ge.   Valences, 2, 4.   Atomic Weight, 72.59;
Atomic Number, 32

History and Occurrence.—In 1871, Mendeléeff predicted this element and gave it the name *eka-silicon*. Winkler discovered it in 1886 in the mineral *argyrodite* (5 to 7 per cent Ge), which is a sulfide of germanium and silver ($GeS_2.3Ag_2S$) mined at Freiburg, Saxony, and Ormo, Bolivia. He found the properties of this new element to be in close agreement with those predicted by Mendeléeff for the hypothetical element, eka-silicon. It is also found in *euxenite* in Sweden.

Physical Properties.—Germanium is a soft, white, lustrous metal. It has a density of 5.323 and melts at 936° C. When the fused metal is slowly cooled, it crystallizes in the regular system. It is stable in air.

Chemical Properties.—The metal is insoluble in hydrochloric acid. It is readily attacked by nitrohydrochloric and sulfuric acids to form $GeCl_4$ and $Ge(SO_4)_2$, respectively. Nitric acid oxidizes the element to white germanic oxide (GeO_2). It is insoluble in concentrated solutions of the alkali hydroxides but dissolves with incandescence in molten alkali hydroxides.

Germanium forms two series of compounds. In one of these the metal is bivalent (germanous series) and in the other quadrivalent (germanic series). It unites directly with the halogens.

Germanium forms two oxides, GeO and GeO_2, from which are derived two series of compounds, *viz.*, the germanous and the germanic. Germanous compounds are rather unstable, whereas the germanic compounds are characterized by their greater stability. *Germanous chloride* ($GeCl_2$) is a strong-smelling liquid obtained by heating the metal in an atmosphere of hydrogen chloride. It boils at 72° C. *Germanic chloride* ($GeCl_4$) is a liquid resembling germanous chloride. It is made by the action of chlorine upon the metal. It boils at about 86° C., and is easily hydrolyzed by water.

(507)

Germanium salts give almost no characteristic reactions with the different reagents. In general behavior, it lies between tin and silicon. White germanic sulfide (GeS_2) is precipitated by hydrogen sulfide from strongly acid solutions of germanium salts. The precipitate is soluble in ammonium sulfide.

Commercial Manufacture.—The pulverized mineral, *argyrodite* (approximately 5 to 7 per cent of germanium) is thoroughly mixed with equal weights of sodium carbonate and sulfur and then fused. When cooled, the mass is extracted with water in which the germanium goes into solution as a thio-compound. The arsenic and antimony are separated by neutralizing the solution with sulfuric acid. The filtered solution is made distinctly acid with hydrochloric acid and the germanium precipitated with hydrogen sulfide as white germanic sulfide (GeS_2). The metal is obtained either by reducing the sulfide with hydrogen, or the oxide, GeO_2, with hydrogen, carbon or magnesium.

Uses.—Germanium dioxide has been used to increase the formation of red blood cells, and for the treatment of anemia. It is not in general use.

TIN

Symbol, Sn.   Valences, 2, 4.   Atomic Weight, 118.69;
Atomic Number, 50

History.—This element is found as a component of prehistoric bronzes and therefore must have been used by man as a metal many thousands of years before the dawn of history.[1] In his writings, Herodotus spoke about the Cassiterides or "tin islands." It is evident that tin was imported from the British Isles (Cornwall) into Italy after, if not before, the conquest of Britain by Julius Caesar. Pliny's writings indicate that in his time the Romans did not differentiate between tin and lead, because he refers to the former as *plumbum album* and to the latter as *plumbum nigrum.*

Occurrence.—Small quantities of the free metal are found in the gold ores of Siberia, Guiana and Bolivia. The principal ore of tin is *cassiterite* or *tinstone,* which is almost pure, crystallized SnO_2. It occurs in its matrix in veins or disseminated through rock masses and is known as *vein-* or *mine-tin.* The disintegration of these rocks gives rise to alluvial gravels (found in stream-beds) in which *tinstone* is found in the form of lumps or grains and is called *stream-tin.* Most of the tinstone is obtained from the Malay Peninsula, the islands of Banka and Billiton, the Dutch East Indies, Bolivia, Cornwall, and Australia. In the United States, tin is found in South Dakota and in South Carolina.

[1] The early Greek alchemists named the metal Hermes and during the sixth century, it was called Zensor Jupiter and designated by the symbol ℞.

Physical Properties.—At ordinary temperatures, tin is a white, lustrous metal having a density of 7.31 and a crystalline form belonging to the tetragonal system. It is a good conductor of heat and electricity. It is pliable and malleable, and may be rolled into very thin sheets (tin-foil). When tin is bent, a peculiar sound is heard. This is sometimes called the "cry of tin," and is caused by the friction of its crystalline particles. At 161° C. *tetragonal tin* changes to *rhombic tin*, which is brittle and has a density of 6.56. *Rhombic tin* melts at 231.9° C. and distils at 2260° C. The transition of *tetragonal tin* to *gray tin* takes place either at low temperature (−40° C.) or when gray tin is present and, when the conversion is once initiated, it proceeds rapidly. The metal modifies its structure and becomes a gray powder having a specific gravity of 5.85 at 15° C. The transition temperature is 18° C., and the phenomenon is known as "tin-disease" or "tin-plague."

Chemical Properties.—At ordinary temperatures, tin is only slightly changed by air and by water. As the temperature is increased, a film of oxide (SnO) forms on the surface, and at white heat the metal is converted to the dioxide (SnO_2), which is yellow when hot and white when cold.

Tin is slowly attacked by dilute acids, yielding stannous salts and hydrogen. Concentrated nitric acid converts it into β-stannic acid (meta-stannic acid). The metal resists weak alkalies, but dissolves in hot concentrated alkalies to form meta-stannates and hydrogen.

Tin unites directly with most of the non-metals. It forms also a number of very useful alloys, *e. g.*, *pewter* (Sn, 80 per cent; Pb, 20 per cent), *solder* (Sn, 50 per cent; Pb, 50 per cent), *type metal* (Sn, 25 per cent; Pb, 50 per cent; Sb, 25 per cent), *gun metal* (Sn, 10 per cent; Cu, 90 per cent), *Rose's metal* (Sn, 25 per cent; Pb, 25 per cent; Bi, 50 per cent), *bronze, bell metal, britannia metal,* etc. Tin forms an amalgam which is used largely for silvering mirrors.

The chemical properties of the stannous and stannic ions are expressed in the following reactions. 1. When hydrogen sulfide is passed through a not too acid solution of a stannous salt, brown stannous sulfide (1) which is soluble in ammonium sulfide (2) is precipitated.

(1) $Sn^{++} + H_2S + 2H_2O \rightarrow SnS \downarrow + 2H_3O^+$

(2) $SnS + (NH_4)_2S_2 \rightarrow (NH_4)_2SnS_3$

With a solution of a stannic salt, hydrogen sulfide precipitates yellow stannic sulfide, which is soluble in ammonium sulfide (3).

(3) $Sn^{++++} + 2H_2S + 4H_2O \rightarrow SnS_2 \downarrow + 4H_3O^+$

2. Sodium or potassium hydroxide added to a solution of a stannous salt, produces a white precipitate of stannous hydroxide (4), which is easily soluble in alkalies to form stannites (5).

$$(4) \; Sn^{++} + 2OH^- \rightarrow Sn(OH)_2 \downarrow$$

$$(5) \; Sn(OH)_2 + OH^- \rightarrow HSnO_2^- + H_2O$$

With stannic salts, the alkali hydroxides precipitate white stannic hydroxide (6) which is soluble in an excess of the alkali to form stannate (7).

$$(6) \; Sn^{++++} + 4OH^- \rightarrow Sn(OH)_4 \downarrow$$

$$(7) \; Sn(OH)_4 + 2OH^- \rightarrow [Sn(OH)_6]^{=} \; or \; SnO_3^{=} + 3H_2O$$

3. When metallic zinc is placed in an acidified (HCl) solution of a tin salt, metallic tin is deposited (8).

$$(8) \; Zn° + Sn^{++} \rightleftarrows Zn^{++} + Sn°$$

When tin is dissolved in boiling hydrochloric acid, the solution gives a white or gray precipitate with mercuric chloride test solution (9).

$$(9) \; Sn^{++} + 2Cl^- + 2Hg^{++} \rightarrow Sn^{++++} + Hg_2Cl_2$$

4. Acid tin solutions are reduced to stannous ion by the addition of aluminum or antimony. When a drop of this solution is added to a saturated aqueous solution of cacothelin on drop-reaction paper, a violet to red coloration shows presence of tin.

Commercial Manufacture.—Cassiterite is crushed to a coarse powder and most of the gangue separated by gravity, flotation, or by magnetic methods. The "concentrated" ore, now containing from 83 to 88 per cent of SnO_2, is roasted in a furnace with a revolving hearth, during which operation the sulfur and arsenic are eliminated. The residue is usually lixiviated with water or a dilute muriatic acid to separate the iron, copper and bismuth. The washed material is mixed with powdered anthracite coal (10) and a little lime to facilitate the formation of a slag and reduced in a reverberatory furnace.

$$(10) \; SnO_2 + 2C \rightarrow Sn + 2CO \uparrow$$

or

$$SnO_2 + C \rightarrow Sn + CO_2 \uparrow$$

The impure tin that collects in a separate vessel at the bottom of the furnace is refined by *liquation*, repeated fusion, or electrolytically until a product of about 99.75 per cent purity is obtained. The *liquation* process consists in heating the ingots just sufficiently to melt the tin but not the more difficultly fusible metals (iron, copper, etc.). The tin is then "flowed off." Tin is purified also by agitating the molten metal, skimming off the lighter impurities from the surface, and pouring off the purified tin from the heavier metals that settle on the bottom. Tin is sometimes purified by stirring the molten metal with sticks of green wood and skimming off the impurities that collect on the surface of the melt.

Pharmacological Action of Tin Ion.—Repeated oral administrations of tin salts result in the absorption of tin ion. Poisoning is rare because of the lack of cumulative tendency. When solutions of tin salts are hypodermically injected, they stimulate the central nervous system and paralysis subsequently takes place. The symptoms of tin poisoning resemble those of lead, *viz.*, inflammation of the stomach and intestines with marked injury to the kidneys and paresis of the heart. Tin is retained principally by the skin and the liver. Elimination slowly takes place by way of the alimentary tract and to a lesser degree by the kidneys.

Tin has a marked germicidal effect against staphylococci. It has been observed that persons who work in tin mines are rarely if ever afflicted with furunculosis. This has led to the use of metallic tin and also tin oxide in the treatment of acne, furunculosis, etc. Local applications of dilute solutions of the chloride are said to be of value in treating slow-healing infected wounds.

Uses.—On account of its resistance to very weak acids and alkalies, tin is used for household utensils, chemical apparatus (still coils), etc. *Tinplate* is employed in making "tin cans," etc. It is made by immersing thin sheets of iron that have been washed with hydrochloric or sulfuric acids in baths of molten tin. Fabricated articles of solid tin are said to be made of "block tin" in order to distinguish them from those made from tinplate. Tin is used in alloys (*q.v.*), solder, coins, piping, and for preparing tin salts. Metallic tin is incorporated in pills and tablets that are used for acne and furunculosis.

COMPOUNDS OF TIN

Stannic Oxide (SnO_2).—Stannic oxide occurs in Nature as *cassiterite* (*q.v.*). It may be prepared by burning the metal in air or by igniting the hydroxide. It is a white, amorphous substance which is insoluble in acids or alkalies, and fuses at the temperature of the electric furnace. Its density is 6.95. Stannic oxide is amphoteric; its acidic property, however, being more pronounced. It is the tin compound most commonly used in tablet form for internal administration. A 5 per cent tin oxide ointment is available for external use in staphylococcal infections. Stannic oxide has been employed as the abrasive and polishing agent in dentifrices.

Stannous Fluoride (SnF_2).—This salt occurs as colorless, monoclinic, lamellar plates. It is freely soluble in water up to concentrations of approximately 30 per cent. Aqueous solutions are acidic (ca. pH 3) as a result of hydrolysis and, on standing, slowly develop a fine, white precipitate of stannous hydroxide. Because of this hydrolysis, the salt should never be made up into a stock solution and the salt itself should be stored in tight containers. Handling of the dry salt in an excessively humid atmosphere should be

avoided. In addition, excessive exposure of the salt to air should
be avoided because of the tendency for it to be oxidized to stannic
fluoride or to stannic oxyfluoride (SnOF$_2$). Both of these forms are
less anticariogenic than stannous fluoride, thus reducing the clinical
usefulness of the salt.

Stannous fluoride is a valuable adjunct in the prevention of
caries[1] and seems to have a definite superiority over the older
sodium fluoride for two reasons: (1) simplified application and
(2) greater effectiveness. The first advantage derives from the
fact that only a single application of 8 per cent aqueous stannous
fluoride solution to the tooth surfaces is necessary every 6 months to
1 year. In contrast to this, 2 per cent sodium fluoride solution is
applied four times during a 10 day period. The second advantage
is based on the finding that stannous ion enhances the anticariogenic
action of fluoride ion so that both ions contribute to clinical effectiveness.

The commercial development[2] of stannous fluoride into a suitable
dentifrice (Crest toothpaste) bears the distinction of providing the
first toothpaste bearing the American Dental Association's stamp
of approval as a useful caries preventive. One of the major problems
in developing a suitable paste was to find compatible abrasives and
binders—the development of calcium pyrophosphate and carboxy-
methylcellulose providing answers to both problems.

Tin Proteinates.—Tin combines with proteins to form insoluble
tin complexes similar to those of silver, etc. Several such compounds are marketed for the internal administration of tin. One
is a 6 per cent solution of sclero-sulfhydryl proteins organically
combined with tin for intramuscular use.

[1] "Dental Use of Stannous Fluoride" by Paul E. Norris, J. Am. Pharm. Assoc.
(Pract. Ed.), **20**, 86 (1959).
[2] Chem. and Eng. News, p. 26, Feb. 20, 1961; see also *ibidum*, p. 40, Aug. 1, 1960.

36

Lead and Lead Compounds

LEAD

Symbol, Pb.   Valences, 2, 4.   Atomic weight, 207.19;
Atomic Number, 82

History.—This metallic chemical element has been known since the earliest historic time. It is mentioned in the Old Testament (Job and Numbers). It was used extensively by the Romans for making conduits. Pliny describes a solder made of *plumbum nigrum* (lead) and *plumbum album* (tin), and it is quite evident that these two elements were considered as being varieties of the same substance. Dioscorides fully described a compound that evidently was litharge. White lead was known to Geber in the eighth century. Pliny called red lead by the name *minium*. As was the custom of the alchemists, this metal was associated with Saturn and designated by the sign of this planet.

Occurrence.—Very small quantities of uncombined lead are found in Nature. The principal lead ores are *galena* (PbS), *cerusite* ($PbCO_3$) and *anglesite* ($PbSO_4$). Galena, the principal primary ore of lead, is by far the most important and widely distributed. It occurs in a great many geological formations, *e.g.*, veins in the cambrian clay slate, in beds or nests within sandstones and limestones, etc. Most of the galena that is connected genetically with igneous rocks is argentiferous or auriferous or both. The most important deposits of lead in the United States are located in Missouri, Oklahoma (Mississippi Valley District), Colorado, Nevada, Idaho and Utah (Rocky Mountain District). Lead ores are also mined in Cumberland and Cornwall, England, Wales, Scotland, Mexico, Germany, Austria and in the southern provinces of Spain.

Until the discovery of the large deposits of cerusite (native lead carbonate) in Colorado and Nevada, this ore was not considered of much metallurgical value. It is quite evident that originally this native carbonate was galena, as the latter is always present in admixture. The crude ore contains about 30 per cent of lead and from 0.2 to 2 per cent of silver.

Anglesite is a native lead sulfate and generally may be considered as an alteration product of galena. Large quantities are found in France, Spain, Sardinia and Australia. This ore is poor in silver and only occasionally is mined for itself.

Physical Properties.—Lead is a bluish-gray, feebly lustrous metal, having a density of 11.34. It is very soft and plastic and hence may be cut or rolled with ease. It is nearly devoid of elasticity. When warmed, lead is especially plastic and may be "squirted" through dies to form tubes or wire. While in this plastic condition it may be "wiped" on a connection of two pipes to form a joint. Lead crystallizes in two forms, *viz.*, octahedral and monoclinic. It melts at 327.4° C., vaporizes at a bright red heat and boils at a temperature of 1740° C. Lead readily forms alloys, the better known ones being solder, pewter, type metal, Rose's metal, Babbitt metal, etc.

Chemical Properties.—1. *Metallic Lead.*—Lead tarnishes rapidly in moist air. When fused in the presence of air, it quickly forms lead monoxide (PbO). The rate of this oxidation increases with the temperature. In the absence of air, pure water does not attack lead. However, when air is present, lead hydroxide [$Pb(OH)_2$], which is appreciably soluble in water, is formed. The presence in water of bicarbonate ions or sulfate ions (hard water) effects the precipitation of any lead ions as an insoluble basic carbonate or sulfate which further inhibit the action of the water upon the metal. Lead pipes are dangerous to use as conduits for soft waters, but hard waters that have passed through lead pipes may be imbibed with impunity.

Lead unites directly with fluorine, chlorine and sulfur. By virtue of its position in the electromotive series of the metals, lead is precipitated from solutions of its salts by zinc, tin and iron.

Almost all acids react with metallic lead to form the corresponding salts. However, unless the salt which forms is soluble in the acid, it deposits on the surface of the metal and quickly stops further action of the acid on the metal. Sulfuric acid (1) reacts readily with lead to form lead sulfate, but under ordinary conditions the lead sulfate coats the lead, preventing further reaction. This is the reason that lead chambers can be used in the sulfuric acid process. However, from experience it has been found that if the concentration of the sulfuric acid in the lead chambers exceeds 78 per cent, it begins to react with the lead sulfate to form lead bisulfate which is soluble (2). If this happens the lead will be rapidly dissolved.

(1) $Pb + H_2SO_4 \rightarrow PbSO_4 + H_2 \uparrow$

(2) $PbSO_4 + H_2SO_4 \rightarrow Pb(HSO_4)_2$

Dilute nitric acid is the best solvent for lead (3), converting the lead to lead nitrate. The concentrated acid is not a desirable solvent because lead nitrate is not very soluble in it.

(3) $Pb + 2HNO_3 \rightarrow Pb(NO_3)_2 + H_2 \uparrow$

2. Lead Ion.—Lead exists in two states of oxidation, (a) the divalent (Pb^{++}) and (b) the tetravalent (Pb^{++++}). The former is the more important and is usually spoken of as the "lead ion" or "plumbous ion," the other form being referred to as the "plumbic" form of lead. We will consider only the chemistry of the plumbous ion.

Hydrogen sulfide and soluble sulfides precipitate brownish-black lead sulfide (4) from acid, alkaline or neutral solutions of lead salts. The precipitate is insoluble in dilute acids, in alkali hydroxides, in carbonates, and in sulfides.

(4) $Pb^{++} + H_2S + 2H_2O \rightleftarrows PbS \downarrow + 2H_3O^+$

Sulfuric acid and soluble sulfates precipitate white lead sulfate (5) from acid or neutral solutions of lead salts. It is insoluble in water and in diluted hydrochloric or nitric acids. The precipitate is completely soluble in warm sodium hydroxide T.S. and in ammonium acetate solution.

(5) $Pb^{++} + SO_4^= \rightarrow PbSO_4 \downarrow$

Hydrochloric acid and soluble chlorides precipitate white lead chloride (6) from solutions of lead salts. It is soluble in *hot* water.

(6) $Pb^{++} + 2Cl^- \rightarrow PbCl_2 \downarrow$

Fixed alkalies precipitate white lead hydroxide [$Pb(OH)_2$] from solutions of lead salts (7). The precipitate is soluble in an excess of the precipitant to form *plumbites* (8).

(7) $Pb^{++} + 2OH^- \rightarrow Pb(OH)_2 \downarrow$ (or H_2PbO_2)
(8) $Pb(OH)_2 + 2OH^- \rightarrow PbO_2^- + 2H_2O$

Chromic acid and soluble chromates (K_2CrO_4 and $K_2Cr_2O_7$) precipitate bright yellow lead chromate ($PbCrO_4$) from solutions of lead salts (9, 10). The solutions should be free or nearly free from mineral acids. The precipitate is insoluble in ammonium hydroxide and in acetic acid but readily dissolves in fixed alkali hydroxides to form *plumbites* (11).

(9) $Pb^{++} + CrO_4^= \rightarrow PbCrO_4 \downarrow$
(10) $2Pb^{++} + Cr_2O_7^= + 3H_2O \rightarrow 2PbCrO_4 \downarrow + 2H_3O^+$
(11) $PbCrO_4 + 4OH^- \rightarrow CrO_4^= + PbO_2^- + 2H_2O$

Official Tests for Identity.—1. Solutions of lead salts yield a precipitate of lead sulfate with diluted sulfuric acid (5). This precipitate is insoluble in diluted hydrochloric or nitric acids, but is completely soluble in warm sodium hydroxide T.S. or ammonium acetate solution.

2. With potassium chromate T.S., solutions of lead salts will precipitate yellow lead chromate (9, 10) provided the solution is free or nearly free of mineral acids. This precipitate is insoluble in acetic acid, but is soluble in sodium hydroxide T.S. (11).

Commercial Manufacture.—Lead is made from galena by roasting the ore at a moderate temperature in a blast furnace. During this initial roasting a part of the lead sulfide is oxidized to oxide (12) and a part to sulfate (13). This ore is then charged with coke and fluxes in alternate layers to the top of the lead blast furnace which is ordinarily about 35 feet high, 20 feet long, and 10 feet wide, and has 8 or 10 tuyeres along each side. The lead runs out of the furnace through a siphon into a forehearth (14) and (15), while the matte and slag are tapped. The matte contains most of the silver, gold, and copper in the ore, and is subsequently refined. The solidified but impure lead is called "hard lead" and is ready to be purified by various methods.

(12) $2PbS + 3O_2 \rightarrow 2PbO + 2SO_2 \uparrow$

(13) $PbS + 2O_2 \rightarrow PbSO_4$

(14) $PbS + 2PbO \rightarrow 3Pb + SO_2 \uparrow$

(15) $PbS + PbSO_4 \rightarrow 2Pb + 2SO_2 \uparrow$

The *hard lead* is carefully heated until most of the copper, arsenic and antimony are oxidized and removed. The lead still contains silver, gold, and bismuth and, depending upon the amount of silver present, is desilvered in one of three ways.

1. *Pattinson Process.*—This method consists in gradually cooling the molten metals and removing with perforated ladles the pure lead which crystallizes out. By repeated crystallizations, not only is a very pure lead obtained but also a residual metal rich in silver. The latter may be cupellated.

2. *Parkes Process.*—This process is based upon the facts that molten lead and zinc are not miscible in all proportions and that gold and silver are much more soluble in melted zinc than in lead. Therefore, when zinc is added to a molten argentiferous lead, it melts and, having effected the solution of the gold and silver, it rises to the top of the molten mass and may be skimmed off or allowed to solidify. The zinc is then distilled off in retorts, leaving a residue of impure silver. The zinc distillate is used over again to extract silver and gold from molten lead.

3. *Betts Process.*—This is an electrolytic process. A sheet of pure lead (cathode) and a plate of impure lead (anode) are immersed in an electrolyte of lead fluosilicate. When the current is turned on, lead dissolves from the anode and is deposited on the cathode. Any iron that is present goes into solution, whereas, gold and silver remain on the anode. The impure lead is often poled before purifying it electrolytically.

Pharmacological Action of Lead Ion.—Aub and his collaborators have shown that lead is stored in the bones, and is mobilized in the circulation by the administration of ammonium chloride, acid sodium phosphate and acid-producing (carbohydrate-free) diets. Administration of potassium iodide also brings the lead into the circulation and, if this occurs too rapidly, toxic phenomena and mania may set in. It is stabilized in the bones by administration of sodium bicarbonate, disodium hydrogen phosphate and alkali-producing diets.

Soluble lead salts precipitate proteins and hence, act as topical astringents. In fact, they are not only one of the most astringent of all of the soluble salts of the metals but they are also the least destructive of tissue. Lead ion is toxic and, although absorption is rather slow, its action is cumulative and chronic poisoning is produced by continued intakes even of small quantities of lead compounds. Although absorption from intact skin is practically *nil*, lead ion is absorbed in sufficient quantities from denuded or chapped skin to cause lead poisoning.

The toxicity of insoluble lead salts depends upon their solubilities in the digestive fluids. In the stomach, insoluble lead salts are converted into lead chloride of which 21.85 millimols dissolve in a liter of 0.2 per cent (0.063 normal) hydrochloric acid. Peptone also facilitates solution of lead salts, probably in protein combination or as lead albuminate.

The inhalation of white-lead dust, fumes from molten lead (consisting chiefly of oxides), atomized spray used in painting, etc., will cause lead poisoning. The symptoms of poisoning appear more quickly when the compounds are inhaled. This is due in part to the fineness of the particles. Absorption takes place from the lungs and nasopharynx and, to a greater degree, from the stomach into which the lead compound is introduced by swallowing the dust. Lead is excreted both in the feces and in the urine.

Ten Gm. of the soluble lead salts have produced death and recoveries from 30 Gm. have been reported. The antidotal treatment consists of large doses of magnesium or sodium sulfates (1 or 2 per cent solution) and emptying the stomach. Milk, eggs, and coffee are of value after the stomach is empty. A cathartic should be given to cause rapid elimination of any lead sulfide formed in the bowels.

Lead poisoning (*i.e.*, plumbism) was formerly treated by procedures designed to encourage deposition of the lead in the bones of the body. This was accomplished as indicated above by administration of sodium bicarbonate, disodium hydrogen phosphate and alkali-producing diets. Since the discovery of Rubin *et al.*[1] that calcium disodium edetate enhances the excretion of lead from

[1] Rubin, M., Gignac, S., Bessman, S. P. and Belknap, E. L., Science, **117**, 659 (1953).

34

humans the above treatment has become outmoded and the chelation procedure has taken precedence. The calcium disodium edetate chelates the lead ion into a non-dissociated form enabling it to be excreted more readily. However, in some conditions it appears to exacerbate the symptoms (*e.g.*, lead encephalopathy) initially for reasons that are not entirely clear at present. In order to avoid this difficulty, some physicians are initially treating the patient with Dimercaprol in order to complex the free lead ion in the blood and then following this with an intravenous dose of the edetate with each subsequent dose of Dimercaprol. Incidentally, although Dimercaprol is effective in complexing the lead ion in the blood, it is unable to promote its loss from the bones and, therefore, it is only used as an adjunct to the edetate chelation procedure rather than as the sole treatment. Oral administration of calcium disodium edetate is valueless and, indeed, may be toxic. Oral penicillamine, however, may prove to be an effective treatment.[1]

Uses.—Because of its property of resisting the action of air, water and acids, lead is employed for making a large variety of articles, *e.g.*, water pipes, chemical and electrical apparatus, linings for acid-proof vessels (sulfuric acid chambers), valves, insulators for cables, etc. It is also used in making lead salts, lead pigments, white lead, etc. Its use in solders and alloys has been mentioned previously.

Large quantities of lead are used in making *ordinary storage batteries*.

NON-OFFICIAL LEAD COMPOUNDS

Lead Acetate N.F. X $(CH_3COO)_2Pb.3H_2O$, crystallizes with 3 molecules of water in colorless, shining, transparent, monoclinic prisms or plates, or in heavy, white, crystalline masses, or granular crystals. It has a faint odor of acetic acid and a sweet taste, effloresces, and absorbs carbon dioxide from the air. Its density is about 2.55.

One Gm. of lead acetate dissolves in 1.6 ml. of water and in about 30 ml. of alcohol, at 25° C. One Gm. dissolves in 0.5 ml. of boiling water. It is freely soluble in glycerin.

The salt becomes anhydrous when heated at 40° C. At 75° C. it dissolves in its own water of hydration and at temperatures above 280° C. it decomposes into finely divided metallic lead and lead oxide.

When acidified, lead acetate is decomposed into acetic acid and the lead salt of the acid, *e.g.*, with hydrochloric acid (1). If the acidified solution is warmed, the acetic acid is volatilized to give an odor of "vinegar."

$$(1) \quad (CH_3COO)_2Pb + 2HCl \rightarrow 2CH_3COOH + PbCl_2 \downarrow$$

[1] Goldberg, A., Smith, J. A. and Lochhead, A. C., Br. Med. J., **1**, 1270 (1963).

Solutions of lead salts have a strong tendency to precipitate out a white carbonate when in contact with the CO_2 of the air. Although the composition of the carbonate is probably not represented accurately by the formula, $PbCO_3$, this will serve to illustrate the precipitation (2).

$$(2) \quad Pb^{++} + 3H_2O + CO_2 \rightarrow PbCO_3\downarrow + 2H_3O^+$$

For this reason, it is desirable to use only recently boiled distilled water to dissolve lead acetate, because the boiling process effectively removes dissolved CO_2.

In all of its other reactions lead acetate exhibits the usual reactions of the plumbous ion (q.v.) and of the acetate ion (q.v.).

This salt is made by the action of acetic acid upon metallic lead or litharge. Large quantities of lead acetate are made by allowing concentrated acetic acid to trickle over lead coils or sheets contained in large, open, stone cylinders. During the operation, the lead goes into solution in the form of basic lead acetate (3). In order to obtain the normal salt, the liquid is made slightly acid with acetic acid (4), concentrated and crystallized. Pharmaceutical lead acetate in small granular crystals is prepared by dissolving the large crystals in water, filtering and evaporating the filtrate with constant stirring.

$$(3) \quad 2Pb + 2CH_3COOH + O_2 \rightarrow Pb_2O(CH_3COO)_2 + H_2O$$

$$(4) \quad Pb_2O(CH_3COO)_2 + 2CH_3COOH + 5H_2O \rightarrow 2Pb(CH_3COO)_2 . 3H_2O$$

Lead acetate is also made by dissolving litharge (PbO) in acetic acid (5). The resulting solution is made acid with acetic acid (to prevent carbonate formation), concentrated and crystallized.

$$(5) \quad PbO + 2CH_3COOH + 2H_2O \rightarrow Pb(CH_3COO)_2 . 3H_2O$$

Internally, lead acetate is used very rarely as an astringent in diarrheal and catarrhal inflammations because there is definite danger of acute lead poisoning. *Externally*, lead acetate is used for its astringent properties either as a lotion, or as an injection into the urethra, vagina, etc. The use of lead acetate as a wash in the treatment of poison ivy poisoning is contraindicated. Its use for the treatment of poison ivy was based on the observed fact that lead precipitates the phenolic substances present in poison ivy. However, research has shown that the lead precipitate is just as, if not more, active than the original phenolic substances.

Lead Subacetate Solution, N.F. X (Liquor Plumbi Subacetatis, Goulard's Extract), was an aqueous solution containing in each 100 ml., lead subacetate, approximately $Pb_2O(CH_3COO)_2$, equivalent to not less than 22.5 Gm. of Pb. It was made by allowing lead monoxide (litharge, PbO) to stand for seven days in contact with a solution of lead acetate, or by boiling the mixture of lead acetate, lead monoxide and water for one-half hour, cooling and filtering[1] (6, 7, 8).

(6) $PbO + H_2O \rightleftarrows Pb(OH)_2$

(7) $Pb(CH_3COO)_2 + H_2O \rightleftarrows Pb(OH)(CH_3COO) + CH_3COOH$

(8) $Pb(OH)_2 + CH_3COOH \rightarrow Pb(OH)(CH_3COO) + H_2O$

Two moles of the basic lead acetate may combine and split out a molecule of water to form: $Pb_2O(CH_3COO)_2$.

A diluted form of Lead Subacetate Solution was official as *Diluted Lead Subacetate Solution* N.F. X (Liquor Plumbi Subacetatis Dilutus, Lead Water). It was prepared by diluting 35 ml. of Lead Subacetate Solution with sufficient recently boiled distilled water to make 1000 ml. of finished product.

The solution described above has been used for the astringent and antiseptic properties connected with lead subacetate.

Lead Monoxide, N.F. X (Litharge), PbO, occurs as a heavy, yellowish or reddish powder, or as minute scales, without odor or taste. This variation in color is due to the fact that it occurs in two forms, namely yellow litharge and red massicot. On exposure to air, it slowly absorbs moisture and CO_2. When it is heated it becomes darker in color but goes back to its original color when cooled again. It fuses at red heat.

The oxide is almost insoluble in water, although it imparts a faintly alkaline reaction to the water. It is insoluble in alcohol but is soluble in acetic acid, diluted nitric acid, and warm solutions of the alkali hydroxides.

Lead monoxide is reduced to free lead when it is heated in contact with charcoal (1).

(1) $PbO + C \overset{\triangle}{\rightarrow} Pb + CO \uparrow$

Its solubility in acids, such as nitric acid (2), is a reaction characteristic of most oxides of metals.

(2) $PbO + 2HNO_3 \rightarrow Pb(NO_3)_2 + H_2O$

Its solubility in alkali hydroxides is due to the formation of the plumbite ion. The solubility in sodium hydroxide is characteristic. A stepwise consideration of the reactions involved will serve to better clarify this solubility. The first reaction is undoubtedly the hydration of the oxide to form a small amount of lead hydroxide (3). The lead hydroxide then reacts with sodium hydroxide to form the plumbite (4). As the equilibrium between the unhydrated lead oxide and the hydroxide is disturbed by withdrawing the hydroxide, more of the oxide is hydrated until it is all in solution.

---

[1] See also G. F. Cahill *et al.*, J. A. Ph. A., Pr. Ed. **9,** 490 (1948).

(3) $PbO + HOH \rightarrow Pb(OH)_2$

(4) $Pb(OH)_2 + 2NaOH \rightarrow Na_2PbO_2 + 2H_2O$

When litharge is mixed with glycerin in the proper proportions, a reaction takes place in which heat is given off and the mixture sets to a hard, cement-like mass. Use is made of this property by plumbers to cement pipe joints together.

Lead Monoxide is not used medicinally as such but has been used to prepare various other pharmaceutical preparations such as *Lead Subacetate Solution* N.F. X.

GROUP V AND VB: THE NITROGEN FAMILY

Introduction.—Nitrogen and phosphorus are the short period elements of Group V. The members of the A subgroup are vanadium niobium (columbium) and tantalum but the members of the B subgroup (arsenic, antimony and bismuth) are usually classified with nitrogen and phosphorus as the "nitrogen family." The relationship of the short period elements with the B subgroup is in the fact that they all possess five valence electrons in the outer shell. As the atomic number increases, the number of electron shells as well as the atomic radius increases. The A subgroup has a different electronic arrangement with the outermost and next outermost shells having (8 + 3)–2 and (8 + 4)–1 electrons instead of the 8–5 or 18–5 arrangement. The short period elements will be considered with the B subgroup because they form a series with a better gradation of properties than the A subgroup.

Nitrogen and phosphorus are both nonmetallic elements, arsenic is a metalloid and antimony and bismuth are usually classed as metals. However, antimony has some nonmetallic character and could be classed as a metalloid. Nitrogen is a somewhat nontypical member of this family and, because of its many unique properties, has already been discussed in the early part of this text. Suffice it to point out that, in combination with carbon, oxygen and hydrogen it is usually a covalent bonding. In the nitride form ($N^\equiv$) its bonding may be considered ionic. Nitrogen compounds usually have three covalent bonds (a covalency of 3) and an unshared electron pair. It is also quite able to act as a donor of its unshared electron pair to cations or neutral atoms to form 4-covalent compounds or radicals (*e.g.*, NH_4^+, $R_3N{\rightarrow}O$). This type of bonding also occurs with other elements in this family. Although the covalency of 5 is not found with nitrogen, which might be expected because of its 5-valence electrons, it is found with other elements of Group V and VB. However, the 3 and 4 covalent states, common with nitrogen, are found among some of the other members of the group as a typical type of bonding. It is believed that two of the electrons often behave as an "inert pair" analogous to that previously outlined for the IVB subgroup. Nitrogen also seems to form the triple bond (*e.g.*, $N^\equiv$) quite readily which accounts for its great stability to oxidation or reduction and its relatively nonpolar character. This triple link is not found in the later elements of the group, where the P_4 and As_4 molecules are found in a tetrahedral arrangement instead.

(523)

Although N, P, and As in the oxidation state of $+3$ act almost exclusively as the oxyacids or their derivatives, Sb and Bi may exist as positive ions of the type SbO^+ and BiO^+. The typical oxidation states for this family are -3, 0, $+3$ and $+5$ which are normal for elements with five electrons in the valence shell. The -3 state is found in such compounds as NH_3, PH_3, AsH_3, Li_3N, etc. where the bonding occurs because of combination with three other electrons to form the nitride anion or to form three covalent bonds with less electronegative elements. In the $+3$ state, the "inert pair" is apparent and bonding occurs with three other more electronegative elements as in H_3PO_3, PCl_3, $AsCl_3$, etc. The highest oxidation state of $+5$ utilizes all five electrons to form covalent bonds as in H_3PO_4, PCl_5, H_3AsO_4, etc. Although nitrogen does not enter into the 5-covalent state, the other elements can expand their shells beyond the usual octet (*i.e.*, to ten) of electrons. The oxyanions from acids such as nitric, phosphoric and arsenic all have equivalent oxygen bonds although we conventionally show them as possessing one coordinate covalence which might indicate that, as an anion, there is something different about one oxygen as contrasted to the others. The explanation for this is that in the anion form they must have equivalent bonds that are intermediate between single and multiple covalent bonds, a phenomenon called *resonance*. As we proceed down the group to higher atomic numbers the negative oxidation state becomes less stable. Likewise, as the electronegativity increases in going down the group and the electropositivity increases, the tendency to form cations, already cited, is evident. It is interesting to note the increase in the number of oxygens associated with the central element in this group. These are $N=3$, P and $As=4$, Sb and $Bi=6$. Thus, it follows that as the central atom gets larger it is possible for more oxygens to get close enough to form stable bonds.

All of the elements in this family form hydrides which are analogous to ammonia. The tendency to form hydrides from the binary combinations with metals (*e.g.*, Mg_3P_2) by the action of water or dilute acids decreases as the atomic number increases. All of them, except NH_3, tend to be inflammable and are poisonous. The elements react readily with the halogens to form covalent tri- and pentahalides. These tend to hydrolyze readily with water to the hydrogen halides and oxyacids in the case of P and As and to hydroxy and oxychlorides (*e.g.*, BiOCl) in the case of Sb and Bi. All of them form oxides with oxygen and sulfides with sulfur to give a number of different combinations. As the atomic number increases, the oxides in this group are less acidic and, in fact, become somewhat basic (or at least amphoteric) in the last members of the group. The sulfides are highly colored and have, historically, been used as pigments. With active metals, these elements readily form binary combinations known as phosphides, arsenides, etc.

PROPERTIES OF GROUP V AND VB (The Nitrogen Family)

Properties	Nitrogen	Phosphorus	Arsenic	Antimony	Bismuth
Atomic Number	7	15	33	51	83
Atomic Weight	14.0067	30.9738	74.9216	121.75	208.980
Isotopes	14, 15	31	75	121, 123	209
Electrons	2-5	2-8-5	2-8-18-5	2-8-18-18-5	2-8-18-32-18-5
Density	0.81 ($-195°$)	1.83 (wh.) 2.34 (red)	2.0 (yellow) 3.70 (amor.) 5.727 (met.)	6.68	9.78
M.P.	$-209.9°$	44.1°	818°	631°	271°
B.P.	$-195.8°$	280°	Sublimes	1380°	1438°
Common Oxidation States	$0, -3, +3, +5$	$0, -3, +3, +5$	$0, -3, +3, +5$	$0, -3, +3, +5$	$0, -3, +3, +5$
Radius (cov.), Å	0.70	1.10	1.21	1.41	1.52
Radius (ionic), Å, M^{5+} (Pauling)	0.11	0.34	0.47	0.62	0.74
Ionization Potential, first, volts	14.54	11.10	10.5	8.5	8.0
Electronegativity (after Pauling)	3.0	2.1	2.0	1.8	
Physical State	Gas	Solid	Solid	Solid	Solid
Color	Colorless	White	Gray	Shiny gray	Shiny gray

PROPERTIES OF GROUP VA

Properties	Vanadium	Niobium (Columbium)	Tantalum
Atomic Number	23	41	73
Atomic Weight	50.942	92.906	180.948
Isotopes	51	93	181
Electrons	2-8-(8 + 3)-2	2-8-18-(8 + 4)-1	2-8-18-32-(8 + 3)-2
Density	6.11	8.57	16.69
M.P.	1717°	2415°	2996°
B.P.	3000°	>3300°	6100°
Common Oxidation States	0, +2, +3, +4, +5	0, +3, +4, +5	0, +4, +5
Radius (cov.), Å	1.22	1.34	1.34
Radius (ionic), Å, M^{5+}	0.40	0.70	0.73
Ionization Potential, first, volts	6.71	6.77	ca. 6
Oxidation Potential, volts, $M \rightarrow M^{++}$	+1.5	ca. +1.1 ($M \rightarrow M^{+++}$)	———

The elements of group VA do not show much relationship to the other group V elements except insofar as the electronic structure relates them. These elements have their valence electrons in both the outermost and next outermost shells. The difference of niobium from vanadium and tantalum as regards the distribution of the valence electrons does not appear to bring about any significant differences. As the accompanying table shows, they exhibit variable valences but with a principal oxidation state of +5. In some respects the resemblance to the IVA group is noticeable, especially in the differences between the first member and the second and third members. For all practical purposes the resemblance of niobium and tantalum is identical to that of zirconium and hafnium. As we have previously noted, the lower valence states become less stable as the atomic number increases. The acidity of the oxides decreases with progressing atomic number, with vanadium being amphoteric to a notable degree in its highest oxidation state. The basicity of the hydroxides decreases with the increasing oxidation state. In the +5 state vanadium has some resemblance to phosphorus but there are numerous differences as well. The oxides are more acidic than the comparable IVA elements as expected on the basis of increased nuclear charge. Hydrolysis of the covalent halides takes place readily in aqueous solution. The compounds of these elements, in the lower oxidation states, are usually colored which is in keeping with their character as transition metals. In the lower oxidation states vanadium is basic and forms ionic bonds. However, in the higher oxidation states the bonding becomes more covalent together with increasing volatility of the compounds.

These metals show a *passivity* unless finely divided. That is, although they show on the basis of oxidation potentials a good reducing action, for all practical purposes they are inert to chemical action. It is this property of tantalum which permits it to be used for corrosion-resistant applications in medicine (*e.g.*, screens, plates and wires to be left in the body).

37

Phosphorus and Phosphorus Compounds

PHOSPHORUS

Symbol, P. Valences, 3, 5. Atomic Weight, 30.9738;
Atomic Number, 15

History.—The name phosphorus (Greek, φῶς, light, φέρω, I bear) was given originally to all phosphorescent substances, *i. e.*, those having the power of shining in the dark, but now its use is restricted to a non-metallic element which was first known as "phosphorus mirabilis" or "phosphorus igneus." This element was obtained in 1669 by Brand, a Hamburg alchemist, by evaporating urine to dryness and distilling the residue with sand. Krafft bought the secret of its preparation from its originator and in 1677 exhibited specimens of phosphorus in England, where it caused great excitement among chemists. Working independently, Kunckel, in 1678, and Boyle, in 1680, succeeded in obtaining the element. In 1769, Gahn showed that bones were composed largely of calcium phosphate, and in 1771 Scheele prepared phosphorus by treating bone ash with nitric acid, precipitating the calcium as calcium sulfate, filtering, evaporating and distilling the residue with charcoal. Later, the Scheele process was improved by Nicolas and Pelletier, who decomposed the bone ash directly with sulfuric acid.

Occurrence.—This element is never found as such in Nature, but occurs in combination as native *calcium phosphate* (generally known as *phosphorite* or "*phosphate rock*") in large deposits in Georgia, Florida, Tennessee, Utah, Idaho, Montana, Wyoming, Alabama, the Carolinas and Algeria. A mineral known as *apatite*, $Ca_3(PO_4)_2.$-CaF_2, is found in large quantities in Canada. Phosphorus is essential to animal and vegetable life. It occurs in bones and teeth (58 per cent calcium phosphate), blood, urine and in considerable quantities in the nervous, muscle and brain tissue as complex organic compounds called *phosphoproteins*.

Physical Properties.—Commercial phosphorus may be obtained in two forms, *viz.*, white phosphorus and red phosphorus.

White Phosphorus.—White phosphorus, as usually prepared, is a pale yellow, transparent, waxy solid, having a density of 1.83, melting at 44.1° C., and boiling at 280° C. It is thought that the

(527)

yellow color of phosphorus is occasioned by the presence of small quantities of red phosphorus. The pure white element may be obtained by heating the yellow phosphorus with chromic acid solution, washing, and drying it in a vacuum, first at 40° C. and then at 80° C. The element will remain colorless if kept in vacuum tubes in the dark, but upon exposure to light it rapidly turns yellow. The fracture of phosphorus is distinctly crystalline; large, regular, duodecahedral or octahedral lustrous crystals being obtained by crystallization from carbon disulfide or by sublimation in the absence of air.

Phosphorus is nearly insoluble in water. At 25° C., 1 Gm. of phosphorus dissolves in 0.9 ml. of carbon disulfide, about 400 ml. of anhydrous alcohol, about 40 ml. of chloroform, 102 ml. of anhydrous ether, 31.5 ml. of benzene, in sulfur chloride, and it is sparingly soluble in fixed oils and oil of turpentine. *It is very poisonous,* 0.15 Gm. being the lethal dose. Exposure to phosphorus vapors produces necrosis. It is a non-conductor of electricity. Molten phosphorus boils at 280° C. and forms colorless vapors which, at approximately the boiling-point, correspond in density to a tetra-atomic molecule, P_4. Biltz and Meyer, working at higher temperatures (1500° to 1700° C.), found dissociation into P_2 molecules. Beckmann obtained P_4 molecules from the boiling-points of carbon disulfide solutions, and Hertz arrived at the same conclusion from the lowering of the freezing-point in benzene solution.

Red Phosphorus.—Red phosphorus occurs as a dark purplish-red to violet, microcrystalline, non-poisonous (when pure) powder which is insoluble in all solvents. Its density varies from 2.05 to 2.34. The variability of its heat of combustion, together with its other non-constant physical properties, preclude its being considered as a simple allotropic form of phosphorus. It is thought to be a more or less pure *solid solution* of scarlet phosphorus in metallic or black phosphorus. It is stable in air and light. Under a pressure of 43 atmospheres, it melts at 590° C. It crystallizes in the regular system. On account of its stability and its non-poisonous property, it is produced in large quantities for consumption in the match industry.

Allotropic Modifications of Phosphorus.—A number of modifications of phosphorus are said to exist. Besides ordinary *white phosphorus* there seem to be three rather well-defined forms, all of which are claimed to be true allotropic modifications. In 1905, R. Schenck obtained a *scarlet amorphous powder* by boiling a solution of white phosphorus in either phosphorus tribromide or tri-iodide, or in the sulfide. The powder may be obtained also by heating phosphorus tribromide with mercury at 240° C. This *scarlet phosphorus* is non-poisonous. When heated, it is converted into red phosphorus. When mixed with potassium chlorate, it is used in the match industry. *Violet phosphorus* is obtained by heating white phosphorus with a minute quantity of sodium to 200° C. under very high pressure. Hittorf prepared *metallic* or *black phosphorus* by heating phosphorus with lead in a sealed tube at 530° C., and recovering the lead by boiling the product with nitric or hydrochloric acid. It occurs as minute, lustrous, black, rhombohedral crystals.

Chemical Properties.—*White phosphorus* combines directly with most of the elements, and hence is a very chemically active substance. Moistened phosphorus is slowly oxidized in air to ozone, phosphorous and phosphoric acids. It is oxidized so rapidly in air that it takes fire at about 35° C. and burns with a bright, white flame to form dense, snow-white clouds of phosphorus pentoxide. Shells and hand grenades containing white phosphorus (W. P.) have been used for incendiary and screening purposes. It is also easily oxidized by oxidizing agents, *e.g.*, nitric acid (1) to form phosphoric acid and nitric oxide.

$$(1)\ 3P + 5HNO_3 + 2H_2O \rightarrow 3H_3PO_4 + 5NO \uparrow$$

When phosphorus or solutions of it in some essential oils, chloroform, etc., are exposed to the air, the element undergoes slow combustion which is revealed by a greenish-white phosphorescence when viewed in the dark. The glowing is always accompanied by the evolution of hydrogen dioxide and ozone (pungent odor). Many theories have been advanced to explain this action, but most investigations lend support to the view that it is due either to the combustion of an oxide more volatile than phosphorus or, that the chemical energy transformed in connection with the oxidation of the phosphorus is partly converted into radiant energy instead of heat.

Red Phosphorus.—The equation (7) representing the reaction that takes place in the manufacture of red phosphorus from white phosphorus clearly shows that the former contains much less internal energy than the latter, and hence is less active chemically. Only when heated to 240° C. or above does red phosphorus unite with the oxygen of the air and ignite.

Tests for Identity.—1. By its phosphorescence.

2. When white phosphorus is placed in a flask from which the air has been displaced by coal gas (to prevent an explosion), a 30 per cent sodium hydroxide solution run in through a dropping funnel, and the mixture heated, phosphine is evolved and sodium hypophosphite is formed (2). The phosphine made in this way contains a trace of the spontaneously inflammable (liquid) dihydrogen phosphide (P_2H_4). If the gaseous mixture is passed through water, the bubbles, upon coming in contact with the air, are immediately oxidized to phosphorus pentoxide (white smoke) and a mist of phosphoric acid.

$$(2)\ 4P + 3OH^- + 3H_2O \rightarrow 3PH_2O_2^- + PH_3 \uparrow$$

3. When phosphorus is treated with nitric acid, orthophosphoric acid and NO are produced (1). The former may be identified by appropriate tests for phosphate ion.

Commercial Manufacture.—*White Phosphorus.*—Formerly, all of the phosphorus of commerce was made from bone-ash, but now the less expensive calcium phosphate (phosphorite) of fossil origin is used. Bone-ash or calcium phosphate is treated with sulfuric acid (specific gravity, 1.5 to 1.6), heated with steam and stirred in a wooden vat. During the heating, the larger part of the calcium is converted into calcium sulfate, and phosphoric acid is obtained (3).

$$(3)\ Ca_3(PO_4)_2 + 3H_2SO_4 \rightarrow 2H_3PO_4 + 3CaSO_4 \downarrow$$

The mixture is filtered and the weak phosphoric acid solution concentrated in leaden pans. During the concentration most of the remaining calcium sulfate is deposited. The syrupy crude phosphoric acid is then mixed with charcoal, coke or sawdust and dried in a muffle furnace. Stourbridge clay retorts, arranged in a galley furnace, are then heated to a bright red heat and charged with the mixture. At red heat, the phosphoric acid loses water and is converted into metaphosphoric acid (4).

$$(4)\ H_3PO_4 \rightarrow H_2O + HPO_3$$

As the temperature of the retorts is gradually raised to a white heat, the metaphosphoric acid is reduced by the carbon to phosphorus which distils (5). The vapors are led through malleable iron pipes into condensing troughs containing cold water.

$$(5)\ 2HPO_3 + 6C \xrightarrow{\triangle} H_2 \uparrow + 6CO \uparrow + 2P \uparrow$$

Most phosphorus is now made by continuously charging a mixture of calcium phosphate, silica (sand) and coke into an electric furnace[1] provided with a close-fitting cover having an outlet leading to a condenser. The discharging of an alternating current between carbon electrodes produces a very high temperature. At the temperature of the furnace the silica attacks the calcium phosphate and forms calcium silicate ($CaSiO_3$) and phosphorus pentoxide (P_2O_5). (See p. 146.) The latter is reduced by the carbon to carbon monoxide and phosphorus, which pass over to the condensers (6).

$$(6)\ Ca_3(PO_4)_2 + 3SiO_2 + 5C \xrightarrow{\triangle} 3CaSiO_3 + 5CO \uparrow + 2P \uparrow$$

The impure phosphorus,[2] obtained by either process, is purified by melting under water and filtering, first, through animal black and then, through chamois skin. The molten phosphorus is sometimes

---

[1] See also, Phosphoric Acid, page 146.

[2] The Monsanto Chemical Company claims that by their improved electrothermal process they are able to reduce phosphate rock and subsequently condense elemental phosphorus of better than 99.9 per cent purity.

purified by washing with a weak solution of potassium dichromate and sulfuric acid. By this treatment, the impurities rise to the surface as a scum and may be removed. At one time, workmen sucked up the molten phosphorus in glass tubes in which it was allowed to solidify. On account of the danger to the health of the operators, this method of casting has been replaced by a continuous process, whereby the molten phosphorus is drawn off by suction into cooled tin tubes, where it solidifies as a continuous rod.

Red Phosphorus.—Red phosphorus is made by a continuous process in which white phosphorus is continuously fed to an electrically heated reactor in which it is retained for 5 to 6 hours at its boiling point. This effects a conversion of about 30 to 50 per cent of the white form to the red form. The slurry of red phosphorus in white phosphorus is then passed to a vaporizer in which heated carbon monoxide gas vaporizes the white phosphorus leaving the red. The red phosphorus is then made into a slurry with water, boiled with soda ash to remove traces of white phosphorus and finally is treated with hot 5 per cent sulfuric acid to remove traces of iron. The red phosphorus is then dried and coated with aluminum hydroxide to stabilize it against atmospheric oxygen.

(7) P (white) → P (red) + 4200 calories

Uses.—Phosphorus and its preparations (Elixirs, and Phosphorated Oil), official in N.F. VII, were deleted from subsequent editions of the N.F. This was no doubt due to the fact that its therapeutic value is very questionable. It was defined as a yellow allotropic form of phosphorus (P). When taken internally in small doses ($\frac{1}{100}$ grain) the only noticeable effects are an increased formation of bony and connective tissue. It is supposed to exert a gentle stimulating action upon the nervous system. It has been used in cases of nervous exhaustion, sexual impotency, rickets and in other disorders of the nervous and bony systems characterized by poor development. *In large doses it is a lethal poison.* A solution of copper sulfate (0.5 Gm. $CuSO_4$ in 120 ml. of H_2O) is an excellent antidote for phosphorus poisoning. Any free particles or globules of free phosphorus are coated with a layer of metallic copper (8). On account of the formation of turpentine-phosphoric acid, old turpentine or French oil of turpentine is said to be an effective antidote. Usual dose—Metric, 0.6 mg.; Apothecaries, $\frac{1}{100}$ grain.

(8) $6CuSO_4 + 2P + 8H_2O \rightarrow Cu(H_2PO_4)_2 + 5Cu \downarrow + 6H_2SO_4$

Aside from its medicinal uses, phosphorus has been used in rat poisons, which have been named "Electric Rat Paste," etc., because of their phosphorescence.

38

Arsenic and Arsenic Compounds

ARSENIC

Symbol, As. Valences, 3, 4, 5. Atomic Weight, 74.9216;
Atomic Number, 33

History.—This non-metallic element was known to the ancients
in the form of its native sulfides, *realgar* and *orpiment*. Aristotle
(384–322 B.C.) called these sulfides *sandarace*. Later, Theophrastus
(372–287 B.C.) gave them the name, *arsenicon*. The Greek alchemist, Olympiodorus, made *white arsenic* (As_2O_3) by roasting the sulfides of arsenic. This compound was known to Geber and the later
alchemists. About 1250, Albertus Magnus obtained the free element as did Schröder in 1694. In 1733 G. Brandt showed that
white arsenic was an oxide of this element which he was possibly
the first to obtain in pure form.

Occurrence.—Uncombined arsenic is found in Nature in the form
of gray colored masses or acicular crystals (rare). In combination,
arsenic is widely distributed. Its principal minerals are *realgar*
(As_2S_2), *orpiment* (As_2S_3), *tennantite* ($As_2S_3 . 4Cu_2S$), *enargite* (Cu_3-
AsS_4) and *arsenopyrite* or *mispickel* (FeAsS). *Cobalt glance* (CoAsS)
and *nickel glance* (NiAsS) also contain arsenic in combination. Copper and gold ores are usually associated with one or more arsenic
minerals. Traces of arsenic-bearing minerals are found in nearly
all naturally occurring metallic sulfides, especially zinc and iron.

Physical Properties.—Arsenic is a steel-gray, brittle solid having
a distinct metallic luster. It crystallizes in rhombohedrons, has a
density of 5.727 and is a good conductor of electricity. It
is insoluble in water. Arsenic sublimes at about 615° C. (760 mm.)
without melting, the vapors having a yellow color and a garlic-like
odor. Fusion takes place only when the element is heated under a
pressure of 36 atmospheres. It then melts at approximately 818° C.
At 644° C., the vapors have a density that corresponds to a formula As_4, but at 1700° C. the vapor density drops considerably
in value due to the dissociation of the As_4, and then corresponds to
As_2. Arsenic resembles phosphorus by existing in one or more allotropic modifications. There are two well-known forms. When
arsenic is sublimed in a current of hydrogen or when arsine (AsH_3)

(532)

is heated, a black *amorphous* form of arsenic is deposited. When the yellow vapors of arsenic are condensed, a grayish-white *crystalline* form of arsenic is obtained. The amorphous variety of arsenic may be converted to the crystalline form by heating it to about 360° C.

Chemical Properties.—The chemical properties of arsenic and its compounds present a somewhat complex picture. They will be discussed as (1) elemental arsenic, (2) trivalent arsenic, and (3) pentavalent arsenic.

1. *Arsenic* is permanent in dry air but tarnishes in moist air. It ignites at about 180° C., burns with a bluish flame and evolves white clouds of arsenic trioxide (1).

(1) $4As + 3O_2 \overset{\triangle}{\rightarrow} 2As_2O_3$

In an atmosphere of chlorine or bromine, arsenic ignites and forms the trichloride (2) or tribromide, as the case may be.

(2) $2As + 3Cl_2 \rightarrow 2AsCl_3$

However, the presence of water causes chlorine (3) or bromine to oxidize arsenic to orthoarsenic acid.

(3) $2As + 5Cl_2 + 8H_2O \rightarrow 2H_3AsO_4 + 10HCl$

Acids do not attack arsenic readily unless the acid has oxidizing properties, *e. g.*, dilute nitric acid (4), concentrated nitric acid (5), or hot concentrated sulfuric acid (6).

(4) $As + HNO_3 + H_2O \rightarrow H_3AsO_3 + NO \uparrow$

(5) $As + 5HNO_3 \rightarrow H_3AsO_4 + 5NO_2 \uparrow + H_2O$

(6) $2As + 3H_2SO_4 \rightarrow As_2O_3 + 3SO_2 \uparrow + 3H_2O$

Arsenic is also readily reacted upon by sodium hypochlorite solution (7).

(7) $2As + 5NaClO + 3H_2O \rightarrow 2H_3AsO_4 + 5NaCl$

2. *Trivalent arsenic* is one of the common forms of this element. Although arsenic is classified as a non-metal, it has the ability to form a limited number of compounds in which it acts as a cation. Of these, the halides, *e.g.*, arsenic trichloride ($AsCl_3$), are the outstanding examples. Even in these cases it is best regarded as an acid chloride because it is decomposed quantitatively by excess water to form orthoarsenous acid (8).

(8) $AsCl_3 + 3H_2O \rightleftarrows 3HCl + H_3AsO_3$

The above reaction is a reversible one in that if the concentration of HCl is increased the reaction is forced to the left and the solution will contain mostly arsenic trichloride. It is interesting to note

35

that a hydrochloric acid solution of orthoarsenous acid, when evaporated, gives off vapors of arsenic trichloride until no arsenic remains. This is not true of a hydrochloric acid solution of ortho-arsenic acid in which arsenic exists in the pentavalent form.

Graphic formulæ show the relationships of the oxides, sulfides and acids of arsenic much better than the conventional molecular formulæ. For example, arsenic trioxide may be considered as the product of dehydration of orthoarsenous acid (9).[1]

(9)

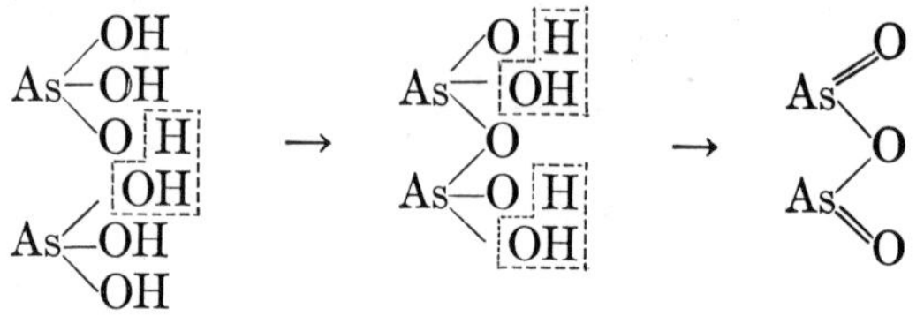

Orthoarsenous acid   Pyroarsenous acid   Arsenic trioxide

The above may be regarded as an *intermolecular* dehydration. On the other hand, one may consider *intramolecular* dehydration, wherein metarsenous acid is formed (10).

(10) HO—As ... → HO—As=O + H₂O

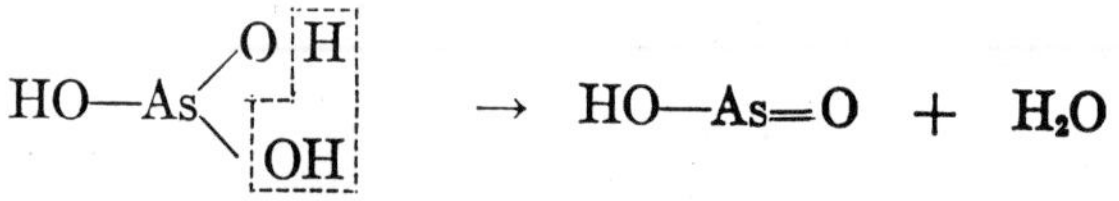

Orthoarsenous acid   Metarsenous acid

Arsenic trisulfide is exactly analogous to arsenic trioxide and is formed by the *intermolecular* removal of H_2S from two molecules of the orthothioarsenous acid (11).

(11)

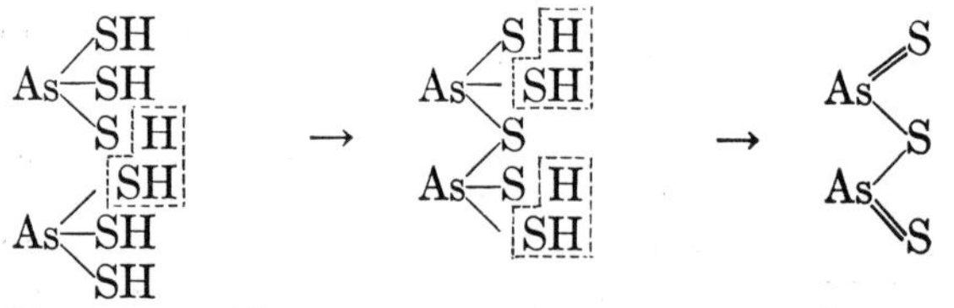

Orthothioarsenous acid   Pyrothioarsenous acid   Arsenic trisulfide

When hydrogen sulfide is passed into an acidulated (HCl) aqueous solution of an arsenous compound, yellow arsenous sulfide is precipitated (12). The precipitate is insoluble in concentrated hydrochloric acid, but dissolves in the hydroxides (13), carbonates (14) and sulfides (15) of sodium, potassium and ammonium.

[1] The true molecular formula for arsenic trioxide is As_4O_6 rather than As_2O_3. However, we shall continue to use the As_2O_3 formula in conformity to the N.F. XI in which it was last official. Likewise, the As_2O_5 formula for arsenic pentoxide is actually As_4O_{10}. Similar considerations are true for the corresponding oxides of phosphorus.

(12) $2AsCl_3 + 3S^= \rightarrow As_2S_3 \downarrow + 6Cl^-$

(13) $As_2S_3 + 6OH^- \rightarrow AsO_3^\equiv + AsS_3^\equiv + 3H_2O$

(14) $As_2S_3 + 3CO_3^= \rightarrow AsO_3^\equiv + AsS_3^\equiv + 3CO_2 \uparrow$

(15) $As_2S_3 + 3S^= \rightarrow 2AsS_3^\equiv$

With neutral solutions of soluble arsenites, silver nitrate produces a yellow precipitate of silver orthoarsenite (16), which is soluble in an excess of ammonium hydroxide or in diluted nitric acid.

(16) $AsO_3^\equiv + 3Ag^+ \rightarrow Ag_3AsO_3 \downarrow$
     (yellow)

Copper sulfate precipitates from neutral solutions of arsenites, green cupric hydrogen arsenite (17) (*Scheele's green*), which is soluble in ammonium hydroxide and in acids. The precipitate turns red when boiled with sodium hydroxide T.S. (18)

(17) $HAsO_3^= + Cu^{++} \rightarrow CuHAsO_3 \downarrow$

If copper sulfate and an excess of alkali hydroxide are added to a solution of an arsenite, cuprous oxide (red-brown) is precipitated and an alkali arsenate is formed (18).

(18) $AsO_3^\equiv + 2Cu^{++} + 4OH^- \rightarrow AsO_4^\equiv + Cu_2O \downarrow + 2H_2O$

When copper acetate is added to a boiling solution of an arsenite, a green precipitate of copper aceto-arsenite is produced.

Pentavalent arsenic is of primary interest only in that it forms certain well-defined acids, an oxide and a sulfide. Arsenic pentoxide may be considered as the anhydride of orthoarsenic acid (19) in the same way that arsenic trioxide is the anhydride of orthoarsenous acid.

(19)

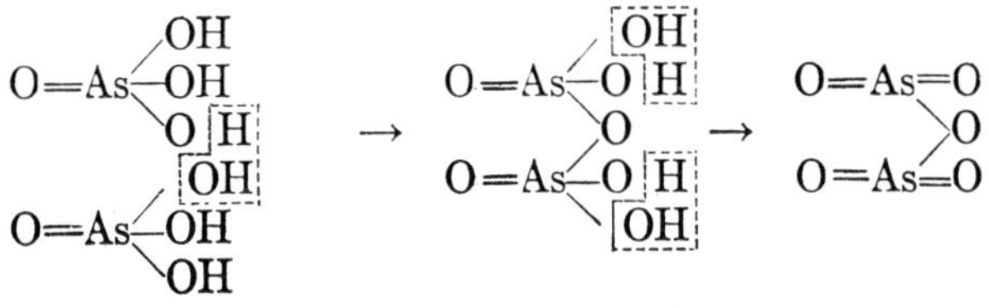

Orthoarsenic acid   Pyroarsenic acid   Arsenic pentoxide

The sulfur acid, namely orthothioarsenic acid, is analogous to its trivalent counterpart (20).

(20)

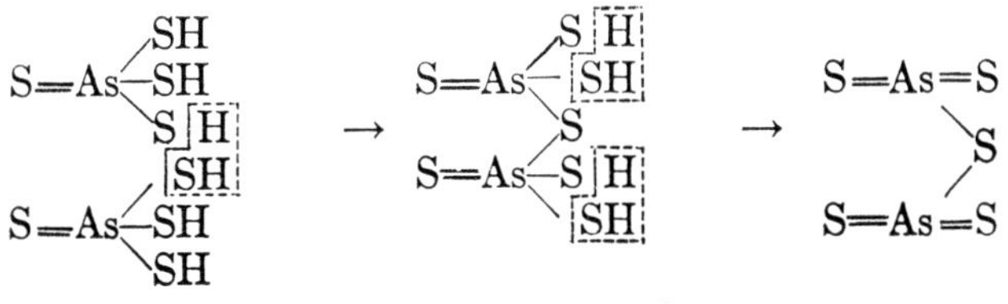

Orthothioarsenic acid   Pyrothioarsenic acid   Arsenic pentasulfide

When hydrogen sulfide is passed into a hot acidulated solution of an arsenate, a yellow precipitate of arsenic pentasulfide is formed (21). The precipitate is soluble in the reagents in which arsenic trisulfide is soluble (12, 13, 14, 15).

$$(21)\ 2H_3AsO_4 + 5H_2S \rightarrow As_2S_5 \downarrow + 8H_2O$$

Silver nitrate, when added to a solution of an arsenate, precipitates a reddish-brown silver arsenate (22), which is soluble in ammonium hydroxide or in diluted nitric acid.

$$(22)\ AsO_4^{\equiv} + 3Ag^+ \rightarrow Ag_3AsO_4 \downarrow$$
$$\text{(reddish-brown)}$$

When a nitric acid solution of ammonium molybdate is warmed with a solution of an arsenate, there is produced a yellow precipitate of ammonium arsenomolybdate (23). Arsenites do not give a precipitate with this reagent.

$$(23)\ AsO_4^{\equiv} + 3NH_4^+ + 12MoO_4^{=} + 24H_3O^+ \rightarrow (NH_4)_3AsO_4.\text{-}$$
$$12MoO_3 + 36H_2O$$

When a small quantity of a solution of an arsenate is shaken with a clear solution of magnesium chloride, ammonium chloride, and ammonium hydroxide, a white precipitate of ammonium magnesium arsenate is formed (24). The precipitate is soluble in hydrochloric acid.

$$(24)\ AsO_4^{\equiv} + Mg^{++} + NH_4^+ \rightarrow NH_4MgAsO_4 \downarrow$$

Note in the above reactions (22, 23, 24) how closely they compare with those of orthophosphoric acid (*q.v.*).

Tests for Identity.—A. *Arsenate.*—1. With silver nitrate T.S. the soluble arsenates yield a reddish-brown precipitate (22).

2. A white precipitate is obtained from arsenates with magnesia mixture T.S. (24).

This precipitate is converted to orthoarsenic acid on treatment with hydrochloric acid. This acid solution yields a precipitate of arsenic pentasulfide with hydrogen sulfide, the precipitate being soluble in ammonium sulfide T.S.

B. *Arsenite.*—1. With silver nitrate T.S. neutral solutions of arsenites yield a yellow precipitate (16).

2. Copper sulfate T.S. yields a green precipitate (17). When boiled with sodium hydroxide T.S. the precipitate becomes red in color (18).

3. Hydrogen sulfide precipitates yellow arsenic trisulfide from acidified (with HCl) solutions of arsenites (12).

Special Tests.—Because arsenic at one time was used quite extensively for criminal poisoning, its detection has received much attention and numerous special tests have been devised.[1] The only one that has achieved official status is related to the Gutzeit test and is used to detect excessive quantities of arsenic in many of the official chemicals. The procedure is described in detail in the U.S.P. XVII[2] together with the required apparatus and need not be repeated here. Suffice it to say that a dilute solution of the chemical substance is treated with sulfuric acid to convert it to either arsenous (25) or arsenic (26) acid. This solution is further treated with sulfurous acid (27) to reduce any arsenic acid formed to the trivalent arsenous state in which form it is necessary for the successful production of arsine. The sample is introduced into a mixture of potassium iodide solution and acid stannous chloride solution, both reducing agents, to which is then added granulated reagent zinc. The mixture produces hydrogen (28) which reduces the arsenous acid present to arsine (29). The arsine is carried through the apparatus by the flow of hydrogen and finally reacts with mercuric bromide saturated strips of paper to produce an orange-yellow stain. The length and intensity of the stain produced should not exceed that produced by a standard solution of arsenic which represents a concentration of not more than 10 parts per million of arsenic trioxide in the substance being tested.

$$(25) \quad 2M_3AsO_3 + 3H_2SO_4 \rightarrow 2H_3AsO_3 + 3M_2SO_4$$

$$(26) \quad 2M_3AsO_4 + 3H_2SO_4 \rightarrow 2H_3AsO_4 + 3M_2SO_4$$

$$(27) \quad H_3AsO_4 + H_2SO_3 \rightarrow H_3AsO_3 + H_2SO_4$$

$$(28) \quad Zn + H_2SO_4 \rightarrow ZnSO_4 + H_2 \uparrow$$

$$(29) \quad H_3AsO_3 + 3H_2 \rightarrow AsH_3 + 3H_2O$$

(M = any univalent metal, although a divalent metal could be used with appropriate adjustment).

The N.F. XII[3] recognizes a related test for arsenic which, in a sense, is a Gutzeit test but in which the quantitative detection of evolved arsine has been modified from a paper strip impregnated with mercuric bromide to a spectrophotometric procedure employing silver diethyldithiocarbamate (AgDDC). The fact that AgDDC formed a red color complex with arsine was reported by Vasak and Sedivek in 1953[4] although its utility as a qualitative and quantitative reagent for arsenic with a sensitivity of 0.2 mcg. of As was not reported until 1961.[5] Both official compendia considered the method for inclusion in the latest revisions but only the N.F. adopted it.

[1] A more extensive discussion of several of the tests will be found in earlier editions of this textbook.
[2] U.S.P. XVII, page 868.
[3] N.F. XII, p. 435.
[4] Vasak, V. and V. Sedivek: Chem. listy, **46**, 341 (1952); through Chem. Abstr., **47**, 67 (1953).
[5] Morrison, J. I.: J.A.O.A.C., **44**, 740 (1961).

The advantage of the method, of course, is that it permits a spectrophotometric estimation of the intensities of colors obtained with both the sample under consideration and a standard preparation, the absorbancies being determined at 525 mμ in a suitable spectrophotometer or colorimeter. This method, with further experience, will probably be adopted by the U.S.P. in future revisions as well.

Commercial Manufacture.—Arsenic is prepared by roasting arsenopyrite out of contact with air (30). The vapors are condensed between rolls of sheet iron and collected in an earthenware receiver. A residue of iron sulfide is left in the retorts.

(30) $4FeAsS \xrightarrow{\Delta} 4FeS + 4As \uparrow$

In the smelting of copper ores, arsenic trioxide collects as a dirty powder in the flues. When this is mixed with powdered coke and heated, arsenic sublimes (31).

(31) $2As_2O_3 + 6C \xrightarrow{\Delta} 4As \uparrow + 6CO \uparrow$

Arsenic may be purified by sublimation with powdered charcoal.

Pharmacological Action of Arsenic Ions.—Compounds of arsenic injure or destroy all cells and, therefore, are protoplasmic poisons. As early as 1878 it was noted that inorganic arsenicals were able to lower the leukocyte (white blood cell) count in cases of chronic myeloid leukemia, a disease characterized by excessive white cell production by the bone marrow. Although treatment with arsenic (as arsenic trioxide or as potassium arsenite solution) is effective and of unquestionable value, other methods of treatment have largely displaced it or relegated it to an adjuvant type of treatment. The repressive action on the bone marrow is also useful in the treatment of polycythemia vera, a disease characterized by overproduction of red blood cells by the bone marrow.

The difference in toxicity of inorganic compounds containing arsenous ions and arsenic ions is not great for mammals, but for protozoa, bacteria and yeasts the former (As^{III}) is generally much more toxic than the latter (As^{V}). This is also true of organic compounds containing ionizable arsenic. The toxicity of arsenic upon cells has been shown quite conclusively to be due to a "tying up" effect that it has on —SH (sulfhydryl) groups in the tissues. These sulfhydryl compounds, of which *thioglycollic acid* and *glutathione* are typical examples, are essential to normal oxidation-reduction in the tissues.

| Free sulfhydryl groups | "Tied up" sulfhydryl groups | Thioglycollic acid | BAL |

This knowledge gave research workers the idea that possibly the use of simple dithiol compounds (those which contain sulfhydryl groups) as competitors for the arsenic might serve to prevent a toxic reaction. This idea proved to be successful and subsequent work brought out 2,3-dimercapto-propanol (also known as Dimercaprol or BAL which is the abbreviation of British Anti-Lewisite) as an effective neutralizing agent for arsenical war gases, e.g., "lewisite." Following its use for this purpose, the compound was used with marked success in the treatment of arsenic poisoning from other causes. Its use has been extended to the treatment of gold and mercury poisoning with encouraging results.

The fact, brought out above, that protozoa are much more susceptible to trivalent arsenic than are mammals, explains the onetime widespread use of arsenic in the treatment of syphilis, a protozoan infection. It will be noted that the inorganic arsenicals were unsuited for syphilitic treatment because they could not be administered in sufficient quantity to kill the protozoa without harming the host. Furthermore, it is important to note that pentavalent arsenicals must be reduced to the trivalent form in order to exert the characteristic arsenic effects.

Arsenic is eliminated from the system by the urine, feces, perspiration, milk and epithelium. Long-continued use of arsenic results in a resistance of the intestinal mucosa to the inflammatory action of arsenic. Consequently, there is much less absorption. Individuals who have developed such a tolerance for the drug can take with impunity doses which would produce very serious toxic reactions in ordinary persons.

Inorganic arsenic compounds cause dilatation and increased permeability of the capillaries, particularly in the visceral region. This action results in circulatory changes which disturb the normal functions of various organs. Small doses of arsenic compounds induce these reactions in a very mild form and, therefore, may be stimulating to the formation of new tissue. Hence, arsenic preparations have been used for their supposed alterative or tonic effects and in the treatment of anemias, skin diseases, etc.

Because arsenicals are not precipitants for albumin, local applications produce only slight irritation. However, the cells are slowly killed by continuous exposure to them. These facts are responsible for the use of arsenicals to kill nerves in teeth and for the treatment of epitheliomas, rodent ulcers, warts, etc.

Uses.—Arsenic is used in making drugs, dyes and glass. It forms alloys with many metals. Lead containing about 0.5 per cent of arsenic has been used for making harder and more spherical shot.

NON-OFFICIAL ARSENIC COMPOUNDS

Arsenic Trioxide, N.F. XI, As_2O_3 (Arsenous Acid, White Arsenic) occurs as a white powder, or in irregular masses of two varieties, viz.:

(1) amorphous, transparent, colorless, odorless, glassy masses, some-times called the "vitreous" or "glassy" variety; and (2) crystalline (octahedral), opaque, white, odorless masses known as the "porce-lain" variety. When the "glassy" variety is exposed to moist air, it gradually becomes opaque, due to crystallization. At 800° C., the vapor density of arsenic trioxide corresponds to the formula As_4O_6, but for convenience and because this molecule dissociates into As_2O_3 at 1800° C., the formula is written As_2O_3.

Arsenic trioxide is very poisonous, hence, great care should be exercised in tasting and handling it.

All forms of arsenic trioxide are slowly soluble in water. The amorphous variety is slightly more soluble than the crystalline variety, 1 part of the former dissolving in about 27 parts of water, whereas 1 part of the latter dissolves in about 59 parts of water. Because of the formation of orthoarsenous acid (1), both solutions give faintly acid reactions to litmus. Arsenic trioxide is slightly solu-ble in alcohol and in ether, and freely dissolves in glycerin. Hydro-chloric acid (2) and solutions of alkali hydroxides (3) and carbonates dissolve arsenic trioxide.

(1) $As_2O_3 + 3H_2O \rightleftarrows 2H_3AsO_3$

(2) $As_2O_3 + 6HCl \rightleftarrows 2AsCl_3 + 3H_2O$

(3) $As_2O_3 + 6NaOH \rightarrow 2Na_3AsO_3 + 3H_2O$

Arsenic trioxide is usually obtained as a by-product in the roasting of copper, tin, cobalt and nickel ores. The fumes are passed through a series of chambers in which the arsenic trioxide collects as a dirty powder. It is purified by resublimation from iron vessels, connected by flues with condensing chambers. The arsenous oxide condenses in the first part of the apparatus as the amorphous variety and in the chamber as a crystalline powder.

Arsenic trioxide is employed as a tonic and antileukemic. Usual dose—2 mg. (approximately $\frac{1}{30}$ grain) of Arsenic Trioxide.

Potassium Arsenite Solution (Fowler's Solution) is made by boiling potassium bicarbonate and arsenic trioxide with distilled water until solution is effected. A small amount of alcohol is added and the solution made up to volume with distilled water. This preparation is used for the therapeutic effect of the arsenic present, and may be used, because it is alkaline, wherever incompatibility exists with an acid solution.

Sodium Cacodylate, N.F. X, $(CH_3)_2AsOONa.3H_2O$, occurs in white crystals, or as a white granular powder. It is odorless and deli-quescent.

One Gm. of the salt dissolves in about 0.5 ml. of water and in about 2.5 ml. of alcohol, at 25° C.

When heated to 60° C., it melts in its water of hydration and at 120° C. it becomes anhydrous. When ignited, the salt burns with a bluish flame and evolves fumes having a garlic-like odor.

Sodium cacodylate, being a salt of a strong base and a weak acid, gives aqueous solutions which are alkaline to litmus paper. However, they are nearly neutral to phenolphthalein.

Sodium cacodylate in solution is readily reduced with hypophosphorous acid (1) to yield cacodyl.

$$(1)\ 4(CH_3)_2AsOONa + 3HPH_2O_2 \rightarrow 2\ \begin{matrix}(CH_3)_2As \\ | \\ (CH_3)_2As \\ \text{(cacodyl)}\end{matrix} + Na_2HPO_4 +$$

$$2NaH_2PO_4 + 2H_2O$$

It has been used in the treatment of anemia, psoriasis, and leukemia. Usual oral dose—60 mg.

Disodium Hydrogen Orthoarsenate (Exsiccated Sodium Arsenate, N.F. VIII, Dried Sodium Arsenate, Na_2HAsO_4).—This salt is an odorless, amorphous, white powder. It is slightly hygroscopic.

One Gm. of Exsiccated Sodium Arsenate is soluble in about 3.5 ml. of water at 25° C. and in about 1.5 ml. of boiling water. The salt is slightly soluble in alcohol at 25° C., and is nearly insoluble in boiling alcohol.

Sodium arsenate may be crystallized in colorless, transparent, odorless, monoclinic prisms having 7 molecules of water of crystallization. In dry air the crystals effloresce, and in a moist atmosphere they deliquesce slightly.

Because of its *very poisonous character, the salt should be tasted with caution.* At high temperatures the dried salt fuses and is gradually converted into sodium pyroarsenate (1).

$$(1)\ 2Na_2HAsO_4 \overset{\triangle}{\rightarrow} Na_4As_2O_7 + H_2O$$

Because it is a salt of a strong base and a relatively weak acid, solutions of it have a slightly alkaline reaction due to hydrolysis.

For a more extended discussion of the reactions of the arsenate ion see page 535.

To prepare it, finely powdered arsenic trioxide, sodium nitrate, and dried sodium carbonate are thoroughly mixed and heated to dull redness in a large, clay crucible provided with a cover (2). When effervescence has ceased and complete fusion has taken place, the melt is poured on stone slabs to cool. While still warm the solidified mass is dissolved in hot water and the solution boiled with constant stirring (3). The solution is filtered and allowed to crystallize. The crystals are separated from the mother liquor and washed in a centrifuge with a fine spray of water, and rapidly dried. The crystals are heated to constant weight at 150° C. to remove the water of crystallization (4).

$$(2)\ As_2O_3 + 2NaNO_3 + Na_2CO_3 \overset{\triangle}{\rightarrow} Na_4As_2O_7 + N_2O_3 \uparrow + CO_2 \uparrow$$

$$(3)\ Na_4As_2O_7 + 15H_2O \rightarrow 2Na_2HAsO_4.7H_2O$$

$$(4)\ Na_2HAsO_4.7H_2O \overset{\triangle}{\rightarrow} Na_2HAsO_4 + 7H_2O \uparrow$$

This salt represents a pentavalent inorganic arsenic compound, but in all likelihood the arsenic is reduced in the body to the trivalent form prior to exerting its action.

Because of its poisonous nature, sweetened solutions of the salt are used to kill flies and ants.   Usual dose—3 mg. (approximately $\frac{1}{20}$ grain).

Lead Arsenate.—($PbHAsO_4$).   This is a white compound which occurs as monoclinic leaflets or more commonly as an amorphous, heavy powder.   It is insoluble in water, but soluble in nitric acid and in solutions of alkali hydroxides.

When heated to about 280° C. it is converted to lead pyroarsenate (1) through loss of 1 molecule of water.

$$(1)\ 2PbHAsO_4 \xrightarrow{\Delta} Pb_2As_2O_7 + H_2O \uparrow$$

It is prepared commercially by the interaction of litharge, arsenic pentoxide, and acid (2).

$$(2)\ As_2O_5 + 2PbO + H_2O \xrightarrow{acid} 2PbHAsO_4$$

This is the salt referred to whenever "lead arsenate" is mentioned without qualification.   F. C. Moulton, a chemist employed by the Gypsy Moth Commission in Massachusetts, was the first to suggest this compound as an insecticide against the gypsy moth (*Porthetria dispar*).   Subsequent experience has shown it to be very effective and as a result it has come into widespread use as an insecticide.

39

Antimony and Antimony Compounds

ANTIMONY (STIBIUM)

Symbol, Sb. Valences, 3, 5. Atomic Weight, 121.75;
Atomic Number, 51

History.—This metallic chemical element, in the form of its sulfide (Sb_2S_3), has been known from very early times. It is quite evident that, aside from using the sulfide as a cosmetic, the metal itself was obtained by the Chaldeans and used for making ornamental vessels. The Arabic and Hebrew name for native antimony sulfide was *kohl*, and Pliny mentions it as *stibium*. Geber and Basil Valentine called it *antimonium*. About the middle of the fifteenth century, Valentine not only described the metal and its method of preparation, but also discussed a number of its compounds. He also described some of the alloys of this metal and indicated the use of antimony compounds in medicine.

Occurrence.—Native free antimony is occasionally found in lamellar or granular masses in limestone or in mineral veins often associated with silver ores. The principal source of antimony is *antimony glance* or *stibnite* (Sb_2S_3). Other antimony minerals are *cervantite* (Sb_2O_4), *senarmontite* (Sb_2O_3) and *valentinite* (Sb_2O_3). Many of the native sulfides of copper, nickel, lead, and silver contain small amounts of antimony. Most of the world's supply of antimony comes from China. Mexico, Bolivia, Czechoslovakia and France each produce a small amount of the metal.

Physical Properties.—Antimony is a silvery-white, crystalline brittle solid, having a high metallic luster. It crystallizes in rhombohedrons and its granular or coarsely laminated crystalline structure accounts for its brittleness. When molten antimony or its alloys are allowed to cool, they crystallize and, in doing so, expand; hence, their use in making type or sharp castings. Antimony has a density of 6.68, melts at 631° C. and boils at 1380° C. Its vapor density at 1640° C. corresponds to the formula Sb_2, but at lower temperatures it is apparently a mixture of Sb_2 and Sb_4 molecules.

Antimony exists in several allotropic forms. These are (1) the metallic form just described, (2) amorphous (or explosive) antimony, (3) black antimony, and (4) yellow antimony. The *amorphous* antimony results from the electrolysis of a solution of antimony trichloride in hydrochloric acid using an antimony anode and a copper or platinum cathode. This allotropic modification is so unstable that when it is scratched, it instantaneously and with explosive violence passes into the more stable metallic form. This change is accompanied by the evolution of a large quantity of heat.

$$Sb \text{ (amorphous)} \rightarrow Sb \text{(metallic)} + 2400 \text{ cal.}$$

Black antimony is produced spontaneously from the yellow allotrope by rapidly cooling antimony vapor, or reacting oxygen and stibine, SbH_3, at $-40°$. This form is more reactive than the metallic form. *Yellow* antimony is prepared by reacting stibine with oxygen at $-90.°$ This form is highly unstable and is easily converted to black antimony.

Chemical Properties.—At ordinary temperatures antimony is quite stable in air. When heated in air or oxygen, it burns, evolving white fumes of the trioxide (Sb_2O_3). Water does not act upon the metal but when the latter is heated to redness, it decomposes steam. Antimony combines directly with sulfur, phosphorus, and the halogens. Because antimony is below hydrogen in the electromotive series it is not affected by dilute hydrochloric or sulfuric acids. Hot *dilute* nitric acid reacts with antimony to give a white precipitate of Sb_2O_3 (1), the precipitate being soluble in concentrated hydrochloric acid due to the formation of complex ions such as $[SbCl_4]^-$ (2). It is also soluble in tartaric acid solution because of the formation of a complex antimonyl tartrate ion (3), or in excess alkali hydroxides (4).

(1) $2Sb + 2HNO_3 \rightarrow Sb_2O_3 + 2NO \uparrow + H_2O$

(2) $Sb_2O_3 + 8HCl \rightarrow 2[SbCl_4]^- + 2H_3O^+ + H_2O$

(3) $Sb_2O_3 + 2C_4H_4O_6^= + 2H_3O^+ \rightarrow 2[(SbO)C_4H_4O_6]^- + 3H_2O$

(4) $Sb_2O_3 + 2OH^- + 3H_2O \rightarrow 2[Sb(OH)_4]^-$ or $2[SbO_2^- + 2H_2O]$

Hot *concentrated* nitric acid causes the formation of a precipitate of Sb_2O_5 (5) which is soluble in concentrated hydrochloric acid to form $(SbCl_6)^-$ (6), as well as in tartaric acid (7), and excess alkali hydroxides (8).

(5) $2Sb + 10H_3O^+ + 10NO_3^- \rightarrow Sb_2O_5 + 10NO_2 \uparrow + 15H_2O$

(6) $Sb_2O_5 + 12HCl \rightarrow 2[SbCl_6]^- + 2H_3O^+ + 3H_2O$

(7) $Sb_2O_5 + 2C_4H_4O_6^= + 2H_3O^+ \rightarrow 2[(SbO_2)C_4H_4O_6]^- + 3H_2O$

(8) $Sb_2O_5 + 2OH^- + 5H_2O \rightarrow 2[Sb(OH)_6]^-$ or $2[SbO_3^- + 3H_2O]$

Antimony forms two series of compounds, namely, the *antimonous* (Sb^{3+}) and the *antimonic* (Sb^{5+}) compounds. Antimonous compounds are of the type formed in equations 1, 2, 3 and 4, whereas the antimonic compounds are represented by the type formed in equations 5, 6, 7, and 8. Antimony in its trivalent state acts both as a metal and as a non-metal, whereas in the pentavalent condition, it acts almost exclusively as a non-metal. The oxides and hydroxides of antimony are amphoteric, those of trivalent antimony having more pronounced basic properties than those of the pentavalent element.

Antimonous compounds in solution exhibit the following types of reactions: (*a*) When hydrogen sulfide is passed through a solution of an antimonous compound (*e.g.*, $SbCl_3$), an orange-red precipitate of Sb_2S_3 is formed (9). This precipitate is soluble in hydrochloric acid (10), and in fixed alkali hydroxides (11).

(9) $2Sb^{+++} + 3S^{=} \rightarrow Sb_2S_3 \downarrow$

(10) $Sb_2S_3 + 8HCl + 2H_2O \rightarrow 2[SbCl_4]^- + 2H_3O^+ + 3H_2S \uparrow$

(11) $2Sb_2S_3 + 4OH^- \rightarrow [Sb(OH)_4]^- + 3SbS_2^-$

(*b*) In the presence of ammonia the antimonous compounds are precipitated as antimonous acid [$Sb(OH)_3$ or H_3SbO_3] (12), a product which gradually changes to meta antimonous acid (13), $HSbO_2$, and finally to the oxide, Sb_2O_3 (14). The precipitate is

(12) $Sb^{+++} + 3NH_3 + 3H_2O \rightarrow 3NH_4^+ + Sb(OH)_3 \downarrow$ (or H_3SbO_3)

(13) $Sb(OH)_3 \rightarrow HSbO_2 + H_2O$

(14) $2HSbO_2 \rightarrow Sb_2O_3 + H_2O$

insoluble in excess ammonia, but is soluble in excess alkali hydroxides. Alkali hydroxides, themselves, will first precipitate antimonous acid (15) but an excess of alkali will redissolve the precipitate (16).

(15) $Sb^{+++} + 3OH^- \rightarrow Sb(OH)_3 \downarrow$

(16) $Sb(OH)_3 + OH^- \rightarrow [Sb(OH)_4]^-$

(*c*) A solution of antimonous chloride will undoubtedly contain some of the antimonyl ion (SbO^+), present because of hydrolysis of the antimonous ion (17). The presence of high concentrations

(17) $Sb^{+++} + 3H_2O \rightarrow SbO^+ + 2H_3O^+$

of hydrochloric acid tends to minimize this formation and instead the antimonous ion is present in the form of complex ions such as [$SbCl_4$]$^-$. When an antimonous compound is converted into the trichloride and the resulting solution concentrated and poured into water, a white, almost insoluble precipitate of antimonous oxychloride is formed (18). This is due to the hydrolysis of the trichloride. This hydrolysis is incomplete as long as any hydrochloric acid is present.

The addition of more water causes further hydrolysis (19). When this latter precipitate is boiled with water, it changes to antimonous oxide (20).

(18) $SbCl_3 + 3H_2O \rightleftarrows SbOCl \downarrow + 2H_3O^+ + 2Cl^-$

(19) $4SbOCl + 3H_2O \rightarrow Sb_4O_5Cl_2 \downarrow + 2H_3O^+ + 2Cl^-$

(20) $Sb_4O_5Cl_2 + 3H_2O \rightarrow 2Sb_2O_3 \downarrow + 2H_3O^+ + 2Cl^-$

(d) The addition of iron to a solution of antimony trichloride produces a brownish-black precipitate of metallic antimony (21). When

(21) $2Sb^{+++} + 3Fe \rightarrow 2Sb \downarrow + 3Fe^{++}$

a solution of tartaric acid and a few drops of nitric acid are added, soluble antimonyl tartrate is formed. When this solution is diluted with water to the point where the nitric acid will not oxidize hydrogen sulfide, and hydrogen sulfide passed into the solution, an orange-red precipitate of antimony trisulfide is produced. This test also gives a positive reaction with pentavalent antimony.

(e) Sb^{+++} is reduced in acid solution by tin (or copper) and forms a coal-black metal scale which is not soluble in freshly prepared NaBrO reagent.

Antimonic compounds in solution behave in a similar manner to the antimonous compounds, exhibiting the following types of reactions: (a) Hydrogen sulfide precipitates an orange precipitate of Sb_2S_5 (23), soluble in hot hydrochloric acid (24) and alkali hydroxides (25). Note that in strongly acidic solution the antimonic chloride forms complex ions just as does the trichloride (22).

(22) $SbCl_5 + Cl^- \rightleftarrows [SbCl_6]^-$

(23) $2[SbCl_6]^- + 5S^= \rightarrow Sb_2S_5 \downarrow + 12Cl^-$

(24) $Sb_2S_5 + 12HCl + 2H_2O \rightarrow 2[SbCl_6]^- + 2H_3O^+ + 5H_2S \uparrow$

(25) $Sb_2S_5 + 6OH^- \rightarrow SbS_4^= + SbO_3S^= + 3H_2O$

(b) Ammonia precipitates a hydroxide (26) insoluble in excess reagent, but the alkali hydroxides precipitate the same hydroxide (27) soluble in excess of the fixed alkali hydroxide (28).

(26) $[SbCl_6]^- + 5NH_3 + 6H_2O \rightarrow HSb(OH)_6 \downarrow + 6Cl^- + 5NH_4^+$

(27) $[SbCl_6]^- + 5OH^- + H_2O \rightarrow HSb(OH)_6 \downarrow + 6Cl^-$

(28) $HSb(OH)_6 + OH^- \rightarrow [Sb(OH)_6]^- + H_2O$

(c) Antimonic chloride will form a precipitate of SbO_2Cl when diluted with water (29), the precipitation being more complete with a large excess of water.

(29) $SbCl_5 + 6H_2O \rightarrow SbO_2Cl \downarrow + 4H_3O^+ + 4Cl^-$

(*d*) With metallic iron the antimonic salts will also precipitate metallic antimony just as was the case with antimonous chloride (30).

(30) $3[SbCl_6]^- + 5Fe \rightarrow 3Sb \downarrow + 5Fe^{+++} + 18Cl^-$

Official Test for Identity.—Antimonous compounds may be identified by their characteristic precipitation of an orange precipitate of antimony sulfide (9), insoluble in ammonia but soluble in ammonium sulfide T.S. (31).

(31) $Sb_2S_3 + (NH_4)_2S \rightarrow 2NH_4SbS_2$

Pentavalent antimony (no official test) may be identified by the use of potassium iodide. About 0.5 Gm. of the material is dissolved in 10 ml. of hydrochloric acid and the mixture warmed for several minutes at 60° to 100° C. The material is filtered and the filtrate evaporated to a volume of about 0.5 ml. The concentrated liquid is mixed thoroughly with 5 ml. of water, the precipitate allowed to settle (18), and then separated by filtration. The oxychloride is dissolved in a small amount of hydrochloric acid and a few drops of a solution of potassium iodide are added to the resulting solution (32). If pentavalent antimony is present, iodine will be set free (distinction from stannic tin) (33). Trivalent antimony will not liberate iodine in the above solution because it cannot be further reduced.

(32) $KI + HCl \rightarrow HI + KCl$

(33) $SbCl_5 + 2HI \rightarrow SbCl_3 + 2HCl + I_2$

Commercial Manufacture.—1. Antimony is obtained by reducing finely powdered stibnite (Sb_2S_3) with scrap iron. The molten metal is drawn off from beneath the slag of ferrous sulfide (34).

(34) $Sb_2S_3 + 3Fe \rightarrow 2Sb + 3FeS$

2. Large quantities of antimony are obtained by roasting the ore in air to remove sulfur and to convert the antimony into its oxides (Sb_2O_3 and Sb_2O_4). The oxides, in turn, are reduced by fusion with coal or charcoal (35).

(35) $2Sb_2O_3 + 3C \xrightarrow{Na_2CO_3} 4Sb + 3CO_2 \uparrow$

3. Sulfide ores are often reduced by fusion with sodium carbonate and coke (36).

(36) $2Sb_2S_3 + 6Na_2CO_3 + 3C \rightarrow 4Sb + 6Na_2S + 9CO_2 \uparrow$

Pharmacological Action of Antimony Ion.—Antimony differs in its action from arsenic by being less readily absorbed and by producing topical irritation. Otherwise, the actions of antimony very closely resemble those of arsenic. It is more caustic to the skin than arsenic, causing papular eruptions which develop into vesicular and pustular sores. The irritant action is also exerted upon the gastro-intestinal mucosa, and this results in an emetic action. When given orally in small quantities it exhibits an expectorant and a nauseant action. The salivary and bronchial glands are reflexly stimulated. Although antimony compounds are toxic and are dangerous to use as expectorants, they have been present in some official preparations.

Inorganic antimonials are not used in medicine. In organic combination, e.g., *Antimony Potassium Tartrate*, *Stibophen*, Antimony Sodium Thioglycollate, and Antimony Thioglycollamide, antimony is used in the treatment of protozoan infections, schistosomiasis, leishmaniasis (kala azar), etc. These organic combinations have been found to be less toxic and less irritating than antimony potassium tartrate. Although the trivalent antimony compounds are more effective than the pentavalent in the treatment of schistosomiasis, the latter seem to be of value in filariasis and leishmaniasis.

Uses.—Antimony is used in the preparation of its compounds, some of which (*e.g.*, tartar emetic) are used in medicine. By far the largest amount of antimony is used in the form of its alloys, of which type metal (Pb, 82 per cent; Sb, 15 per cent; Sn, 3 per cent), Babbitt metal (Sn, 80 per cent; Sb, 20 per cent), pewter (*q.v.*) and antifriction metal (Sn, 75 per cent; Sb, 12.5 per cent; Cu, 12.5 per cent) are examples. Black metallic antimony obtained by the action of zinc upon solutions of antimony trichloride is called *antimony-black* and is used to give a metallic iron or steel appearance to plaster of Paris or papier maché figures.

OFFICIAL ANTIMONY COMPOUND

ANTIMONY POTASSIUM TARTRATE

Antimony Potassium Tartrate, U.S.P. XVII

Formula, $KOOC.CHOH.CHOH.COO(SbO).\frac{1}{2}H_2O$

Molecular Weight, 333.93

Physical Properties.—Antimony Potassium Tartrate occurs as colorless, odorless, transparent crystals, or as a white powder. The crystals effloresce upon exposure to air. One Gm. of Antimony Potassium Tartrate is soluble in 12 ml. of water and in about 15 ml. of glycerin, at 25° C. One Gm. of it is soluble in about 3 ml. of boiling water. It is insoluble in alcohol.

Chemical Properties.—In aqueous solution the salt turns litmus paper red (acid). This solution responds to the tests for trivalent antimony (*q.v.*) and for tartrate ion (see potassium bitartrate).

Antimony Potassium Tartrate is officially assayed by treating an aqueous solution of a weighed sample with sodium bicarbonate and then titrating the solution with standard iodine solution. The iodine oxidizes the trivalent antimony (1) to pentavalent antimony (metantimonic acid, $HSbO_3$) with simultaneous formation of hydriodic acid. The sodium bicarbonate prevents the interaction of metantimonic acid and hydriodic acid (2) by converting both to the sodium salts (3).

(1) $K(SbO)C_4H_4O_6 + I_2 + 2H_2O \rightarrow HSbO_3 + 2HI + KHC_4H_4O_6$

(2) $HSbO_3 + 2HI \rightarrow H_3SbO_3 + I_2$

(3) $HSbO_3 + 2HI + 3NaHCO_3 \rightarrow NaSbO_3 + 2NaI + 3H_2O + 3CO_2 \uparrow$

Official Tests for Identity.—1. Antimony Potassium Tartrate chars when heated, develops an odor of burning sugar, and leaves a blackened residue. This residue contains potassium carbonate and antimony trioxide and imparts an alkaline reaction to water. A piece of the residue held in a non-luminous flame produces a violet color due to the potassium.

An acidic solution of the salt gives the insoluble orange-red antimony trisulfide with hydrogen sulfide [see p. 545, equation (9)].

Method of Manufacture.—It is prepared by boiling a mixture of antimony trioxide and potassium bitartrate with water for some time. The solution is filtered, concentrated and crystallized.

Uses.—*Antimony Potassium Tartrate* (Tartar Emetic), U.S.P. XVII, contains not less than 99 per cent and not more than 103 per cent of $C_4H_4KO_7Sb \cdot \frac{1}{2}H_2O$.

When employed as an emetic, the action (which is largely reflex) is slow and marked depression follows. For these reasons, its former extensive use to produce emesis has been almost discontinued. It is used largely as a depressant expectorant in an oral dose of 3 mg. The nauseant dose is about one-tenth that of the emetic dose. For its expectorant properties it is employed in the official (N.F.) *Brown Mixture*.

The U.S.P. does not recognize this salt for its emetic or expectorant properties, however, and simply designates it as an anti-schistosomal. Intravenous injections are of value in the treatment of kala-azar, schistosomiasis, and some other tropical diseases. The usual intravenous dose is 40 mg., initially; repeat every 2 days, increasing each dose by 20 mg. until 140 mg. is reached, then 140 mg. every 2 days for a total dose of 2 Gm. The usual range per dose is 40 to 140 mg.

36

40

Bismuth and Bismuth Compounds

BISMUTH

Symbol, Bi.   Valences, 3, 5.   Atomic Weight, 208.980;
Atomic Number, 83

History. — In 1450, Basil Valentine described this metallic chemical element, and referred to it by the name of "wismut." Because of its brittleness, Paracelsus later designated it as a "semi-metal" and called it "wissmat." In 1546, Georgius Agricola described bismuth, suggested it as a true metal and used the names "wissmuth" and "bisemutum" and "plumbum cineareum" to designate it. Because the elementary character of bismuth was not clearly understood, it was confused with a number of other better known metals, *e.g.*, lead, zinc, tin, antimony, etc. The investigations of Johann Heinerich Pott (1739) and the accurate descriptions by Torbern Olof Bergman definitely placed the element among the metals and gave a fairly clear idea of its reactions.

Occurrence. — Bismuth occurs free in Nature. The element, both free and in combination, is found disseminated in pegmatite veins and in some contact-metamorphic deposits. Most of the bismuth is obtained from the muds produced in the refining of blister copper (*q.v.*). Some of the more important bismuth minerals are *bismuth ocher* or *bismite* [$Bi_2O_3 + (H_2O)_n$], usually containing $3H_2O$, *bismutite* ($Bi_2O_3 . CO_2 . H_2O$), *bismuthinite* or *bismuth glance* (Bi_2S_3) and *tetradymite* (Bi_2Te_2S). The United States produces very little bismuth. One of the world's most important deposits is located near Schneeberg, Saxony, where the bismuth is associated with cobalt minerals. Bolivia is the principal producer, although England, France, Scandinavia, Australia, United States, and Hungary also produce some of the metal.

Physical Properties. — Bismuth is a hard, brittle, lustrous, grayish-white metal having a reddish tint. It is usually covered with a superficial film of bismuth oxide. It has a density of 9.78, melts at 271° C. and boils at 1438° C. When the molten metal is cooled it crystallizes in cube-like rhombohedrons; while doing so it expands quite materially. This expansion is due to the fact that crystals of bismuth are lighter (density, 9.78) than the molten metal (density,

(550)

10.07). Therefore, they must occupy a greater volume than that occupied by the same weight of the fused metal. On account of its internal crystalline structure, the metal can be powdered easily. Bismuth is a good conductor of electricity, but a poor conductor of heat.

Chemical Properties.—Only a thin film of oxide is formed when bismuth is exposed to moist air. However, when bismuth is heated in air, it is converted into the trioxide (Bi_2O_3). The metal decomposes steam and combines directly with the halogens and sulfur. Only the oxidizing acids attack metallic bismuth to form salts (1). Solutions of bismuth exhibit the following types of reactions.

$$(1)\ Bi + 6H_3O^+ + 3NO_3^- \rightarrow Bi^{+++} + 3NO_2 \uparrow + 9H_2O$$

1. When a bismuth salt is dissolved in the least amount of diluted nitric or hydrochloric acids and water added, a white precipitate of the basic chloride or nitrate is produced (2) (3). Basic bismuth chloride loses water and is converted into the oxychloride (4). The precipitate dissolves upon the addition of acids. The presence of citric, tartaric, acetic, or other organic acids prevents the precipitation of Bi^{+++} when water is added in excess.

$$(2)\ BiCl_3 + 4H_2O \rightleftarrows Bi(OH)_2Cl \downarrow + 2H_3O^+ + 2Cl^-$$

$$(3)\ Bi(NO_3)_3 + 4H_2O \rightleftarrows Bi(OH)_2NO_3 + 2H_3O^+ + 2NO_3^-$$

$$(4)\ Bi(OH)_2Cl \rightarrow BiOCl + H_2O$$

2. When hydrogen sulfide is passed into an acid solution of a bismuth salt, a brownish-black precipitate of bismuth sulfide is formed (5). This is soluble in a warm mixture of equal parts of nitric acid and water (6).

$$(5)\ 2Bi^{+++} + 3H_2S + 6H_2O \rightarrow Bi_2S_3 \downarrow + 6H_3O^+$$

$$(6)\ Bi_2S_3 + 8H_3O^+ + 2NO_3^- \rightarrow 2Bi^{+++} + 2NO \uparrow + 12H_2O + 3S \downarrow$$

3. Alkali hydroxides precipitate white bismuth hydroxide (Bi[OH]_3) from solutions of bismuth salts (7). The precipitate is insoluble in an excess of the precipitant.

$$(7)\ Bi^{+++} + 3OH^- \rightarrow Bi(OH)_3 \downarrow$$

Because bismuth solutions tend to hydrolyze to yield bismutho or bismuthyl ions (BiO^+) (8) the addition of alkali hydroxides also causes the precipitation of $BiOOH$ (9).

$$(8)\ Bi^{+++} + 3H_2O \rightarrow BiO^+ + 2H_3O^+$$

$$(9)\ BiO^+ + OH^- \rightarrow BiOOH \downarrow$$

4. When potassium or sodium hydroxide is added in excess to a solution of stannous chloride, potassium or sodium stannite is

formed. When an excess of this solution is added to a solution of a bismuth salt, a black precipitate of metallic bismuth is produced (10).

$$(10)\ 3SnO_2^= + 2Bi^{+++} + 6OH^- \rightarrow 3H_2O + 3SnO_3^= + 2Bi \downarrow$$

5. Solutions of soluble iodides precipitate brownish-black bismuth tri-iodide from solutions of bismuth salts (11). When the precipitate is boiled with water, it is converted into the scarlet-red basic iodide (12).

$$(11)\ Bi^{+++} + 3I^- \rightarrow BiI_3$$

$$(12)\ BiI_3 + 3H_2O \rightarrow BiOI \downarrow\ + 2H_3O^+ + 2I^-$$

Official Tests for Identity.—1. Bismuth salts, when dissolved in a slight excess of either nitric or hydrochloric acids, give a white precipitate of the basic salt when diluted with water (2,3,4).

2. If hydrogen sulfide is passed into the precipitated solution the precipitate assumes a dark color because of bismuth sulfide formation (5), but this dark precipitate is soluble in a mixture of equal parts of nitric acid and water (6).

Commercial Manufacture.—1. Native bismuth is obtained from its ore by heating the latter in inclined iron pipes. The easily fusible metal (271° C.) runs off into suitable receiving vessels.

2. Oxide and sulfide ores usually contain one or more of the following impurities: arsenic, antimony, sulfur, selenium, cobalt, nickel, iron, tin, lead, copper, etc. Such ores are first roasted to drive off sulfur and then heated in small furnaces with iron (to combine with the remaining sulfur), charcoal (to reduce the oxides) and a flux to facilitate the operation. Metallic bismuth melts and is drawn off from underneath the lighter materials. This impure metal is usually purified by fusing it with a flux of sodium nitrate or a mixture of sodium carbonate and potassium chlorate, whereby the As, Sb, Fe, Pb, S, etc., are removed.

3. Bismuth is usually present as an impurity in lead ores, from which it is separated by an electrolytic process. All of the metallic bismuth produced in the United States is a by-product from the manufacture of electrolytic lead.

Pharmacological Action of Bismuth Ion.—Soluble, inorganic bismuth compounds are protoplasmic poisons and, therefore, are not used in medicine. Although bismuth can combine with sulfhydryl groups, as shown by its successful antagonism with Dimercaprol, it has not been conclusively determined that this is responsible for any of its therapeutic values.

Because of their fineness, insolubility, and density, the insoluble bismuth compounds adhere to mucous surfaces and inflamed areas. They are employed as protectives. When taken internally, a very small amount of the bismuth goes into solution and then exerts a mild astringent and antiseptic action. The basic bismuth salts are useful, non-irritant intestinal antiseptics. Intestinal hydrogen sulfide acts upon basic bismuth salts to form bismuth sulfide; hence the black stools during bismuth treatment. The slight astringent and antiseptic properties, together with the protective action, make the insoluble basic carbonate and nitrate helpful in the treatment of diarrhea, gastritis, hyperacidity, etc. There is no evidence to show that bismuth is constipating to normal individuals.

The employment of bismuth as an adjunct to arsenical treatment of syphilis has been largely discontinued although the use of the combination in the form of *Glycobiarsol* persists for the treatment of certain protozoal infections such as amebiasis.

Because of their opacity, basic bismuth salts were once used for Roentgen-ray diagnosis. They have been largely displaced by barium sulfate (*q.v.*).

Insoluble bismuth compounds are used as dusting powders or in the form of ointments (30 per cent) on irritated and inflamed mucous membranes or open wounds. When applied in this manner, the secretions are absorbed and the wound heals under an aseptic protective coating.

Bismuth compounds are useful in the removal of warts (*verrucae*). This was first proposed by Luris in 1932 who injected bismuth sub-salicylate in oil intramuscularly and noted a significant number of cures. A few years later, however, Shellow recommended intra-cutaneous injection of 0.5 to 2 minims of a one and one-half per cent solution of bismuth sodium tartrate toward the base of the wart. His results showed a high per cent of cures against a salt solution control. Numerous other dermatoses are also treated, often as a last resort, with bismuth preparations. Among these are lupus erythematosus (non-disseminated), lichen planus, scleroderma, vitiligo and Boeck's sarcoidosis.

Uses.—Bismuth is used in the preparation of its compounds and for making alloys. Colloidal metallic bismuth in an isotonic, sterile medium is available for use as an antisyphilitic. Alloys containing bismuth are distinctive in that they are rather hard and fusible, and expand when changing from the liquid to the solid state. The latter property makes them admirably adapted for use as type metal, for taking impressions of molds and for stereotyping. The low melting-points of bismuth alloys are easily understood when it is recalled that "solutions (alloys) freeze below the freezing-point of the pure solvent." In the case of bismuth alloys ("solid solutions"), the metallic bismuth may be considered as the "solvent," whereas the other constituents of the alloy are "solutes." Thus, *Wood's metal*, containing 50 per cent of bismuth (melting-point, 71° C.), 25 per cent of lead (melting-point, 327.5° C.), 12.5 per cent of tin (melting-point, 231.8° C.) and 12.5 per cent of cadmium (melting-point, 320.9° C.), melts at 60.5° C., or *considerably* below the boiling-point of water. Other similar alloys are *Rose's metal* (melting-point, 93.75° C.), *Lipowitz alloy* (melting-point, 65° C.) and *Newton's alloy* (melting-point, 94.5° C.).

BISMUTH SUBCARBONATE

Bismuth Subcarbonate, U.S.P. XVII

Approximate Formula, $[(BiO)_2CO_3]_2 \cdot H_2O$.   Molecular Weight, 1037.96

Physical Properties.—Bismuth Subcarbonate is a white or pale yellowish-white, odorless and tasteless powder having a density of 6.86. It is permanent in air but is slowly affected by light.

It is insoluble in water and in alcohol, but dissolves with copious effervescence in nitric and hydrochloric acids.

When ignited, the salt decomposes into yellow bismuth trioxide, carbon dioxide and water (1).

Chemical Properties.—The salt is of indefinite chemical composition and, therefore, the purity rubric is based upon Bi_2O_3. It is practically insoluble but shows the expected effervescence of carbonates when treated with acids. The resulting acid solutions contain the bismuth ion and will produce reactions which are characteristic of bismuth.

Bismuth Subcarbonate is assayed by igniting a weighed sample to yield bismuth trioxide (1) as a residue. However, Bismuth Subcarbonate Tablets (N.F.) are assayed by a method identical to that employed for the assay of Bismuth Potassium Tartrate (*q.v.*).

(1) $[(BiO)_2CO_3]_2 \cdot H_2O \overset{\triangle}{\rightarrow} 2Bi_2O_3 + 2CO_2 \uparrow + H_2O \uparrow$

Official Tests for Identity.—1. Bismuth Subcarbonate is completely soluble in nitric or hydrochloric acid with copious effervescence.

2. The solution in nitric acid or hydrochloric acid yields a white precipitate when diluted with water (2).

(2) $BiCl_3 + 4H_2O \rightarrow Bi(OH)_2Cl \downarrow + 2H_3O^+ + 2Cl^-$

3. When hydrogen sulfide is passed into an acid solution of a bismuth salt, a brownish-black precipitate of bismuth sulfide is formed (3).

(3) $2Bi^{+++} + 3H_2S + 6H_2O \rightarrow Bi_2S_3 \downarrow + 6H_3O^+$

This black sulfide is soluble in a warm mixture of equal parts of nitric acid and water (4).

(4) $Bi_2S_3 + 8H_3O^+ + 2NO_3^- \rightarrow 2Bi^{+++} + 2NO \uparrow + 12H_2O + 3S \downarrow$

Commercial Manufacture.—Bismuth subcarbonate is made by adding an acid solution of a bismuth salt (normal bismuth nitrate) with constant stirring to a warm (not hot) solution of sodium carbonate

(5). The precipitate is washed with an equal volume of cold water and dried at a temperature not above 60° C. Repeated washing of the precipitate will decompose the subcarbonate into hydroxide and therefore, should be avoided.

(5) $4Bi(NO_3)_3 + 6Na_2CO_3 + H_2O \rightarrow [(BiO)_2CO_3]_2 \cdot H_2O \downarrow + 12NaNO_3 + 4CO_2 \uparrow$

Uses. — *Bismuth Subcarbonate* (Basic Bismuth Carbonate), U.S.P. XVII, is a basic salt which yields on ignition not less than 90 per cent of Bi_2O_3, calculated on the dry basis.

This salt is officially recognized as a protectant for external application as a dry powder or in the form of lotions or ointments to relieve dermal and mucous membrane irritation. Internally, Bismuth Subcarbonate has been employed in a usual dose of 1 Gm. four times a day (range 1 to 4 Gm.) for gastric disorders, ulcers, diarrhea, dysentery, etc. This usage is based on a presumed protective action on the irritated gastrointestinal mucosa. It is quite safe to use and is superior to Bismuth Subnitrate (*q.v.*) which has much the same properties but which can produce nitrite by biological reduction. Use of this salt as an antacid ignores the fact that it is at best extremely weak in this respect and that any beneficial effects may be attributed to the protective function.

BISMUTH SUBNITRATE

Bismuth Subnitrate, N.F. XII

Approximate Formula, $4Bi(OH)_2NO_3 \cdot BiO(OH)$. Molecular Weight, 1461.99 (approx.)

Physical Properties. — Bismuth Subnitrate is a white, amorphous, slightly hygroscopic powder. It is nearly insoluble in water and insoluble in alcohol. It is dissolved by hydrochloric or nitric acids.

When Bismuth Subnitrate is heated to redness, it is decomposed into yellow bismuth trioxide and oxides of nitrogen (1). The official assay procedure is based upon this reaction.

(1) $2[Bi(OH)_2NO_3]_4 \cdot BiO(OH) \overset{\triangle}{\rightarrow} 5Bi_2O_3 + 8HNO_3 \uparrow + 5H_2O \uparrow$

Chemical Properties. — Bismuth subnitrate is a basic bismuth nitrate of unknown composition. The product must be fairly constant, however, since ignition of various batches of the salt yield between 79 and 82 per cent of Bi_2O_3.

When moistened blue litmus paper is brought in contact with basic bismuth nitrate, it turns a faint pink. This is caused by the further hydrolysis of the salt to the hydroxide and free nitric acid (2). A hydrochloric or nitric acid solution exhibits the reactions of the bismuth ion (*q.v.*).

(2) $[Bi(OH)_2NO_3]_4 \cdot BiO(OH) + 4H_2O \rightarrow 5Bi(OH)_3 + 4HNO_3$

When the compound is heated with sulfuric acid and metallic copper, brownish-red fumes (NO_2) are evolved. A hydrochloric acid solution of the salt gives the tests for the nitrate ion (See Nitric Acid).

Bismuth subnitrate has a well recognized incompatibility with tragacanth in which tragacanth precipitates as a hard mass in the presence of the salt. An interesting paper[1] in connection with this incompatibility points out that the difficulty may be overcome by the protective action of sodium biphosphate or trisodium phosphate. These authors feel that because tragacanth is a negative colloid, the adsorption of the positive bismuth ion (without corresponding adsorption of the negative nitrate ions) tends to precipitate the colloid. The use of phosphates is based on their supplying the lacking negative ions that may then be adsorbed by the tragacanth, stabilizing the colloid.

Bismuth Subnitrate is assayed by igniting a weighed sample in exactly the same way as Bismuth Subcarbonate (1).

Official Tests for Identity.—Bismuth Subnitrate responds to all tests for *Bismuth* (*q.v.*) and for *Nitrate* (*q.v.*).

Commercial Manufacture.—One part of bismuth trinitrate is rubbed to a smooth paste with 4 parts of water, and then added with constant stirring to 20 parts of boiling water (3). The white precipitate is allowed to subside and the supernatant liquid decanted. The precipitate is washed with an equal volume of cold water. The mixture is filtered and the basic bismuth nitrate dried at a temperature of 30° C. If repeatedly washed with water, bismuth subnitrate will be converted into bismuth hydroxide (2).

$$(3)\ 5Bi(NO_3)_3 + 10H_2O \rightleftarrows [Bi(OH)_2NO_3]_4 \cdot BiO(OH) \downarrow + 11HNO_3$$

Uses.—*Bismuth Subnitrate* (Basic Bismuth Nitrate), N.F. XII is a basic salt which, when dried at 105° C. for two hours, yields upon ignition not less than 79 per cent of bismuth oxide (Bi_2O_3). Like bismuth subcarbonate, the subnitrate is a non-irritant intestinal astringent with antiseptic properties. Its astringent action probably results from a small amount of ionized bismuth. By virtue of a purely protective mechanical action, it has a marked healing effect on inflamed mucous surfaces and hence, it is used as a dusting powder for wounds. It is employed in treating gastric ulcers, etc. (see Bismuth Subcarbonate). Because bismuth subnitrate is slowly converted to the nitrite form by the intestinal bacteria it can cause hypotension as well as cause production of methemoglobin for which reasons it may be desirable to use the subcarbonate instead. Usual dose—1 Gm.

A rather novel use for bismuth subnitrate is in the form of an *x*-ray shielding putty.[2] In treating dermatologic lesions with *x*-rays it is necessary to shield the normal skin around the lesion. Sheet

---

[1] R. E. Schmitz and J. S. Hill, J. Am. Pharm. Assoc., Pract. Ed., **9**, 493 (1948).
[2] See "*X*-ray Shielding Putty," Am. Prof. Pharm., **17**, 1089 (1951).

lead is usually used but has some drawbacks. The bismuth sub-nitrate putty contains 84 per cent of the chemical in 15 per cent wool fat. It is about one-third to one-fourth as radiopaque as sheet lead but is more easily handled and is quite effective in the recommended thicknesses of 5 to 6 mm.

Bismuth Magma (Milk of Bismuth, Bismuth Cream), N.F. XII contains bismuth hydroxide and bismuth subcarbonate in suspension in water, and yields not less than 5.2 per cent and not more than 5.8 per cent of Bi_2O_3. Bismuth Subnitrate is converted to an acidulated solution of normal bismuth nitrate which is added to a solution of ammonium carbonate in diluted ammonia solution (5) (6) (7) (8). The magma is then washed with distilled water until free of ammonium nitrate and ammonium hydroxide.

(5) $NH_4NH_2CO_2 \cdot NH_4HCO_3 + NH_4OH \rightleftharpoons 2(NH_4)_2CO_3$
(6) $3(NH_4)_2CO_3 + 2Bi(NO_3)_3 \rightarrow Bi_2(CO_3)_3 \downarrow + 6NH_4NO_3$
(7) $2Bi_2(CO_3)_3 + H_2O \rightarrow [(BiO)_2CO_3]_2 \cdot H_2O + 4CO_2 \uparrow$
(8) $Bi(NO_3)_3 + 3NH_4OH \rightarrow Bi(OH)_3 \downarrow + 3NH_4NO_3$

It is used internally as an astringent and antacid similarly to the subcarbonate but, as a rule, is less effective. Usual dose—5 ml.

As a protective and astringent it is also found in *Compound Resorcinol Ointment*.

NON-OFFICIAL BISMUTH COMPOUNDS

Bismuth Potassium Tartrate, N.F. X, is a granular, white, odorless powder, having a sweetish taste. It darkens on exposure to light. One Gm. is soluble in 2 ml. of water. It is insoluble in alcohol, in ether, in chloroform and is decomposed by mineral acids.

A solution of the salt in water will give the reactions of the potassium ion (q.v.) and the bismuth ion (q.v.). Silver nitrate T.S. added to a solution of the compound produces a white precipitate $(Ag_2C_4H_4O_6)$. When the mixture is boiled the precipitate darkens and a silver mirror is formed. (See Potassium Sodium Tartrate.)

This compound of indefinite molecular composition may be prepared either by treating a mixture of bismuth nitrate and tartaric acid with sufficient potassium hydroxide solution to dissolve the precipitate that has formed, or by dissolving bismuth tartrate in the correct amount of potassium hydroxide solution. In either case, the solution is carefully evaporated to crystallization. The N.F. X required that the product contain the equivalent of not less than 60 and not more than 64 per cent of Bi.

It has been used in the form of an oil or water injection intramuscularly for treatment of syphilis. The usual dose is 100 mg.

Bismuth Subgallate, N.F. XI, $C_6H_2(OH)_3 \cdot COO(BiO) \cdot H_2O$, (Dermatol) is an amorphous, bright yellow powder. It is odorless and tasteless, and is stable in the air.

Bismuth subgallate is practically insoluble in water, in alcohol, and in ether. It is readily dissolved with decomposition by warm, moderately dilute hydrochloric, nitric, or sulfuric acid, but is insoluble in very dilute mineral acids. It is readily dissolved by solutions of alkali hydroxides, forming a clear, yellow liquid, which rapidly assumes a deep red color. When ignited it chars, leaving a yellow residue of Bi_2O_3.

Bismuth subgallate is a compound of indefinite composition containing bismuth and gallic acid (3, 4, 5-trihydroxybenzoic acid). Acid solutions will respond to the reactions for bismuth ion. By treating the compound in water with hydrogen sulfide a small amount of bismuth sulfide is precipitated, releasing some gallic acid. The filtrate will give the characteristic purplish-blue color of the tannin test when ferric chloride T.S. is added.

It may be made by adding a warm aqueous solution of gallic acid to a solution of normal bismuth nitrate in glacial acetic acid.

It is used similarly to bismuth subcarbonate as an astringent, antacid and protective, but is employed when greater astringent action is needed. Internally it finds some application in treating diarrhea. It has some antacid action also. Usual dose—1 Gm.

Bismuth Subsalicylate, U.S.P. XVI, $C_6H_4(OH) \cdot COO(BiO) \cdot H_2O$, is a white or nearly white, amorphous, or microcrystalline, odorless powder. It is stable in air, but is affected by light. It is practically insoluble in cold water. When heated it becomes soft and chars, leaving a residue of yellow Bi_2O_3.

Bismuth subsalicylate is a basic salt having an indefinite structure of bismuth and salicylic acid. When mixed with water and particularly hot water, a slow hydrolysis takes place that liberates salicylic acid and forms a more basic salt. The salicylic acid thus formed will give a deep violet-blue color upon the addition of a few drops of ferric chloride T.S. Alcohol and glycerin cause a similar reaction. If the bismuth oxide, Bi_2O_3, that results after ignition is dissolved in nitric acid, the solution exhibits all the reactions of the bismuth ion (*q.v.*).

It is made by precipitating bismuth hydroxide from a solution of the trinitrate with ammonium hydroxide and then digesting the precipitate with salicylic acid on a water-bath (1, 2).

(1) $Bi(NO_3)_3 + 3NH_4OH \rightarrow Bi(OH)_3 + 3NH_4NO_3$

(2) $Bi(OH)_3 + C_6H_4(OH).COOH \rightarrow C_6H_4(OH).COO(BiO) + 2H_2O$

It is marketed as a sterile suspension in a suitable fixed oil and is used intramuscularly for the suppressant effect of the bismuth against lupus erythematosus. Usual dose—Intramuscular, in oil, 100 to 200 mg. weekly. The intramuscular route is preferable because of the toxicity associated with intravenous injections of bismuth compounds.

41

Vanadium, Niobium and Tantalum and Their Compounds

VANADIUM

Symbol, V. Valences, 2 to 5. Atomic Weight, 50.942; Atomic Number, 23

History.—A. M. del Rio (1801) showed the existence of a new metal in a lead ore found at Zimapan, Mexico. He called it *erythronium*, because its salts became red when heated with acids. Four years later, Collet-Descotils suggested that Rio had obtained an impure oxide of chromium. The element was rediscovered and first described by Sefström in 1830. He found it in an iron ore occurring in Sweden and named it *vanadium* from Vanadis, a cognomen of the goddess Freia. A year afterward he published the results of his investigation, described a large number of compounds of vanadium and called attention to the similarity in chemical behavior of this element to that of chromium and molybdenum.

Occurrence.—Vanadium is somewhat rare and forms the main part of but few minerals. It, however, is fairly widely distributed in the earth's crust and its presence has been shown in some meteorites and in the sun. The chief vanadium minerals are *patronite*, a complex vanadium sulfide, *vanadinite* ($3Pb_3(VO_4)_2.PbCl_2$), *dechenite* (Pb, Zn) ($VO_3)_2$, *descloizite* ($Pb_2V_2O_7$) and several others. The principal commercial source is Minas Ragra in the Peruvian Andes.

Physical Properties.—Pure vanadium is a grayish powder or crystalline mass having a silver-white luster. The metal takes an excellent polish and is permanent in air. It does not decompose water at ordinary temperatures, but the powdered metal burns like iron when heated in oxygen. Vanadium has a density of 6.11, melts at 1717° C. and boils at 3000° C. It is the hardest of all metals (about 7 on Moh's Scale).

Chemical Properties.—Solutions of vanadates yield with ammonium sulfide T.S. a brown precipitate which is moderately soluble in an excess of the reagent to produce a reddish-brown solution (NH_4VS_3).

Vanadium forms five compounds with oxygen. These are V_2O, VO (gray), V_2O_3 (black), VO_2 (dark blue), and V_2O_5 (dark red to orange-red). Each of these oxides forms salts. The first three are entirely basic, the last two are acidic, but also possess weak basic qualities. Metavanadic acid (HVO_3) was first obtained by Gerland. It is a yellow pigment, sometimes called *vanadium bronze*, and is used instead of gold bronze. It results as fine golden or orange scales when copper vanadate is treated with sulfurous acid. Vanadium bronze is obtained also by the action of copper sulfate, containing an excess of ammonium chloride, on ammonium vanadate. Vanadium also forms *pyrovanadic acid* ($H_2V_2O_7$) and *hexavanadic acid* ($H_4V_6O_7$). Salts of all these acids are known, as are also the salts of *orthovanadic acid*, such as Na_3VO_4.

Vanadium forms three chlorides, VCl_2, VCl_3 and VCl_4, and also the oxychlorides VOCl, $VOCl_2$ and $VOCl_3$. Some of the corresponding compounds of the other halogens are known. The vanadyl compounds, such as $(VO)_2(SO_4)_3$, have been prepared. Vanadium forms the nitrides VN and VN_2 and the carbide VC.

Commercial Manufacture.—Vanadium in the pure state was first obtained by reducing its dichloride with pure hydrogen, but it is very difficult to prepare it by this method. The metal, usually in the form of an alloy, *ferrovanadium* (from 30 to 40 per cent V), is obtained by introducing the sulfide ore mixed with iron into an electric furnace, where carbon reduces the V_2S_5 to V, which combines with the molten iron to form the alloy. It is also obtained by roasting the sulfide ore to drive off sulfur, fusing with sodium carbonate and leaching out the sodium vanadate so formed. By the addition of concentrated sulfuric acid, the pentoxide is precipitated, mixed with iron and, at a very high temperature, reduced to ferrovanadium.

Uses.—Vanadium salts have been recommended for the treatment of anemia, chlorosis, etc. The most recent experimental application of vanadium salts has been on the basis that it may have blood cholesterol lowering properties. Such studies, few in number, have indicated that vanadium may be a very mild inhibitor of cholesterol biosynthesis with the medium for administration of vanadium being gelatin prepared from imported bones (contains 2 ppm). This treatment is too recent for any definitive results. Vanadium, in general, is very rarely, if ever, used medicinally.

It belongs to the group of metals known as the *steel elements*. It is used in making vanadium steel, which has a high tensile strength. It is employed also in the form of its compounds ($V_2O_2Cl_4.5H_2O$ $VOSO_4.2H_2O$) in the dyeing industry.

NIOBIUM (COLUMBIUM) AND TANTALUM

Symbols, Nb and Ta

Nb: Valences 2, 3, 4 and 5. Atomic Weight, 92.906; Atomic Number, 41

Ta: Valences 2, 3, 4 and 5. Atomic Weight, 180.948; Atomic Number, 73

History.—In the year 1801 Hatchett, an English chemist, reported to the Royal Society the results of his studies of a black mineral from Connecticut. He believed it contained a new metal which he named *columbium*. The newer name, however, is *niobium*. A year later Ekeberg, in Sweden, investigated a mineral from Finland, and found an element which resembled titanium, tin, and tungsten, but still was somewhat unlike any one of them. He suggested the name *tantalum* for the metal. Wollaston showed that the same element was found by both Hatchett and Ekeberg. The distinction between the two elements, niobium and tantalum, came in 1865 as a result of the work of Hermann, Blomstrand, and Marignac.

Occurrence.—Both niobium and tantalum are widely distributed in Nature. A few deposits are of commercial importance, such as the *samarskite* mineral in North Carolina. The metals occur chiefly as intimate mixtures of niobates and tantalates, $Fe(NbO_3)_2$ and $Fe(TaO_3)_2$. The ores are mined mainly for tantalum, since there is but little use for niobium.

Physical Properties.—Metallic niobium is about as hard as wrought iron, has a steel-gray color and when polished, possesses a brilliant metallic luster. It melts at 2415° C. and has a density of 8.57.

Metallic tantalum is somewhat like platinum in appearance but not so bright. It is ductile, very tough, and has a tensile strength about two and one-half times that of platinum. It melts at 2996° C. and has a density of 16.69. The pure metal is almost as soft as copper, but may be hardened by heat treatment, so that it will hold a cutting edge.

Chemical Properties.—The elements are so much alike in their chemical properties that they have been considered together. Niobium is pentavalent in most of its compounds and next most frequently is trivalent. It has a strong tendency to form oxysalts. Tantalum acts almost entirely as a pentavalent element and is more basic than niobium.

Niobium forms three oxides. They are the monoxide (NbO or Nb_2O_2), the dioxide (NbO_2 or Nb_2O_4) and the pentoxide (Nb_2O_5). The first two are prepared from the last by reducing it with sodium and hydrogen, respectively. The pentoxide is a white, infusible powder, formed by heating niobic acid.

Niobic acid ($HNbO_3$) results as a white precipitate when potassium hexaniobate is treated with sulfuric acid. Niobates of the formulas K_3NbO_4, $KNbO_3$, $K_4Nb_2O_7$ and $K_8Nb_6O_{19}$ are known. Perniobic acid ($HNbO_4$) is formed by treating $HNbO_3$ with H_2O_2.

Normal and oxyfluorides, such as NbF_5 and $NbOF_3$ are known. Salts of the type K_2NbF_7 and K_2NbOF_5 have been prepared. Likewise, normal and oxychlorides are known.

Tantalum forms compounds similar in composition to those of niobium.

Commercial Manufacture.—Niobium may be obtained by the thermit process, by the electrolysis of a solution of fluoxy-niobate, or by reduction of the chloride ($NbCl_4$) with hydrogen.

Tantalum is obtained by the electrolysis of fused K_2TaF_6 or of a tantalum salt in a 3 per cent solution of sulfuric acid. The metal is obtained as a powder which is purified by repeated extraction with water and acids. It is then pressed into bars, heat-treated and finally fused in a vacuum furnace.

Uses.—In recent years metallic tantalum has found a new use in surgical repair of large abdominal hernias. It is used by implanting a fine tantalum mesh in the wound and then suturing the mesh in place with tantalum wire. The strength of the repair is not due so much to the mesh as it is to the fibrous tissues that build up, through, and around it forming a strong abdominal wall. No toxic reactions were noted. Tantalum screen is also used in the repair of nasal deformities. Before the introduction of tungsten, tantalum was largely used as filaments for electric lamps. It finds use at present as a substitute for platinum for making standard weights and chemical apparatus, as electrodes which are not attacked appreciably by aqua regia, and as points for steel pens. Because of its valve effect, i.e., giving a pulsating direct current when connected in alternating lighting circuits, it is used in rectifiers for charging storage batteries. Certain of its alloys, such as ferrotantalum and nickel and tantalum, show promise of industrial use.

Tantalum oxide has been used as a surgical dusting powder. It is said to be nontoxic and chemically inert. It replaces gauze and sterile "Vaseline" in surgical wounds, forming a crust and accelerating healing.

GROUP VI

Introduction.—Oxygen and sulfur are the short period (typical) elements in Group VI. Oxygen has been discussed early in the text because it has so many properties that set it apart from the rest of the elements in the group. Sulfur, together with the elements of subgroup B (selenium, tellurium and polonium) constitute a family with a gradation of properties that merits the name of "sulfur family" as well as consideration as a unit. Polonium, being the product of radioactive change, will not be discussed here. Subgroup A, composed of chromium, molybdenum, tungsten (wolfram) and uranium, differs greatly from the other subgroup. This difference is characteristic of groups occurring late in the Periodic Table. The principal similarity between the two subgroups stems from the fact that they all have six valence electrons and it is only when these are all involved that similarities are found (*e.g.*, sulfates and chromates).

The typical elements and the B subgroup will be treated first. The accompanying table shows that the melting and boiling points, densities and atomic volumes increase with atomic number. As indicated above, the principal difference in this particular family is between oxygen and sulfur, the relationships of the rest of the elements being rather close. These latter elements exist in different allotropic forms and have oxidation states of -2, 0, $+2$, $+4$ and $+6$ whereas oxygen has only the oxidation states -2, -1, and 0. It is to be noted that, in common with VB elements, the negative oxidation states are less important as the atomic number increases. These elements are among the most electronegative in the Periodic Table with oxygen being, except for fluorine, the most electronegative of all elements. The electronegativity decreases down the group as expected. This decrease in electronegativity, concomitant with a decrease in oxidizing activity, is attributed to the fact that the nuclear attraction for an incoming electron is decreased as the distance to the outer shell is increased. Although the nucleus has an increasing charge as the atomic number increases, the additional electrons in the larger atoms have an additional repelling effect that reinforces the distance factor. The typical elements are nonmetallic with oxygen being a gas and sulfur a solid. The solid character of the later members of the group is attributed to the fact that they exist in chain structures whereas oxygen exists as a diatomic molecule. Sulfur, for example, has the S_8 molecule which permits a greater amount of intermolecular attraction than that in the smaller molecules and thus tends to raise the melting and boiling points. Selenium and tellurium are best characterized as metalloids although tellurium has considerably more metallic character than selenium. The general rule is that the metallic character increases in progressing down the group. These elements are the first mentioned that can form monatomic anions (oxide, sulfide, etc.) and, for this reason, can exist in both ionic as well as covalent bonding. The formation of covalent bonds is limited to two for oxygen but may rise to 3, 4 and 6 with the other elements. In general, it may be stated that, in binary combinations of these elements, they tend to be in the -2 oxidation state except for the oxides which, like ternary combinations, usually assume the higher oxidation states. Wherever the binary combinations involve nonmetals (*e.g.*, SeS) the negative oxidation state is assigned to the most electronegative elements (in this case, S).

This group forms hydrides of the general type RH_2 (*i.e.*, H_2O, H_2S, etc.) which decrease in stability and increase in acidity as the molecular weight increases. The hydrides are all gaseous with the exception of H_2O which, of course, is liquid and reflects the fact that strong association exists between the dipole molecules. This association is not evident with the hydrides of the other elements. With the exception of water the hydrides are all highly odoriferous and poisonous. The sulfides, selenides and tellurides of alkali and alkaline earth metals are water-soluble but the corresponding salts of the other metals are highly water insoluble. Although several oxides of these elements are known, the most common are those characterized by the general formulæ RO_2 and RO_3 which are the anhydrides of the acids represented by H_2RO_3 and H_2RO_4. Sulfurous acid (H_2SO_3) and sulfuric acid (H_2SO_4) may be cited as examples. Selenium and tellurium form similar acids. The salts of the "ous" acids have the familar "ite" ending and the salts of the "ic" acids have the "ate" ending. The acidity of the oxyacids of a given element in this group is always greatest when the oxidation number is highest. Thus, sulfuric acid (oxidation number = 6) will be more acidic than sulfurous acid (oxidation number = 4). This is related to the relative covalent characters of the oxides wherein we recognize that the most covalent oxides are the ones with the highest oxidation numbers. That the size of the central ion influences the relative acidity of the corresponding oxyacids in this group (as well as other groups) is to be noted in the fact that sulfurous acid is a slightly stronger acid than selenous acid. This is ascribed to the fact that sulfur is smaller than selenium. Thus, we find a combination of small size and high charge on the central ion contributing to high acidity.

The members of subgroup VIA are chromium, molybdenum, tungsten (wolfram) and uranium as previously mentioned. They are all distinctly metallic and form oxides of which those of higher molecular weight are acidic. These oxides form a series of com-

PROPERTIES OF GROUPS VI AND VIB

Properties	Oxygen	Sulfur	Selenium	Tellurium	Polonium
Atomic Number	8	16	34	52	84
Atomic Weight	16.000	32.064	78.96	127.60	210
Isotopes	16–8	32–4, 36	74, 76–8, 80, 82	120, 122–6, 128, 130	—
Electrons	2–6	2–8–6	2–8–18–6	2–8–18–18–6	2–8–18–32–18–6
Density	1.14 (−184°)	1.96–2.06	4.3–4.8	6.25	—
M.P.	−218.8°	214.5°	217°	450°	—
B.P.	−183°	444.6°	685°	1390°	—
Common Oxidation States	−2, −1, 0	−2, 0, +2, +4, +6	−2, 0, +4, +6	−2, 0, +4, +6	—
Radius (cov.), Å	0.74	1.04	1.17	1.45	—
Radius (ion), N^-, Å	1.45	1.95	2.02	2.21	—
Ionization Potential, first, volts	13.61	10.36	9.75	8.96	—
Electronegativity (after Pauling)	3.5	2.5	2.4	2.1	—
Physical State	Gas	Solid	Solid	Solid	Solid
Color	Colorless	Yellow	Gray	Gray	—
Oxidizing Ability	→ → → → → → → → → Decreasing → → → → → → → → →

37

pounds, such as the chromates, the molybdates, etc. In this respect they resemble the B subgroup. The metals of this group have a tendency to unite with oxygen and in such combination (CrO^{++}, MoO_2^{++}, UO_2^{++}) replace the hydrogen of acids to form salts. This property increases with the atomic number. Chromium forms two basic hydroxides, $Cr(OH)_2$ and $Cr(OH)_3$, which are the parent substances of a great many chromous and chromic salts. Molybdenum and tungsten are distinctly acidic, whereas uranium is both acid and base-forming. The similarity in the properties of successive horizontal elements in the Periodic Table is here particularly in evidence. For example, vanadium, chromium and manganese are closely related to one another by virtue of very similar physical and chemical properties. Molybdenum and columbium, and also tungsten and tantalum, exhibit close relationships.

PROPERTIES OF GROUP VIA

Properties	Chromium	Molybdenum	Tungsten
Atomic Number	24	42	74
Atomic Weight	51.996	95.94	183.85
Isotopes	50, 52–4	92, 94–8, 100	180, 182–4, 186
Electrons	2–8–(8 + 5)–1	2–8–18–(8 + 5)–1	2–8–18–32–(8 + 4)–2
Density	7.14	10.2	19.35
M.P.	1900°	2622°	3410°
B.P.	2480°	4510°	5900°
Common Oxidation States	2, 3, 6	2, 3, 4, 5, 6	2, 4, 5, 6
Radius (cov.), Å	1.17	1.29	1.30
Radius (ion), A	0.52	0.62	0.62
Ionization Potential, first, volts	6.77	7.38	7.98

42

Sulfur, Selenium and Tellurium and Their Compounds

SULFUR

Precipitated Sulfur, U.S.P. XVII
Sublimed Sulfur, N.F. XII

Symbol, S. Valences, 2, 4, 6. Atomic Weight, 32.064;
Atomic Number, 16

History and Occurrence.—This non-metallic element has been known since remotest time. The origin of the name "sulfur" is uncertain although it is said that it is derived from the Sanskrit *shulbari*, meaning "enemy (*ari*) of copper (*shulba*)." On account of its inflammable nature, the early alchemists considered it the "principle of combustibility" or phlogiston. In 1777, Lavoisier classed it among the elements.

Free sulfur is found in the volcanic regions of Sicily (provinces of Caltonisetta and Girgenti), in Chile and Peru, in the United States (Utah, Colorado, California, Nevada, Idaho, Texas and Wyoming) and, in fact, in all of the volcanic regions of the world. In Louisiana, there is a deposit more than $\frac{1}{2}$ mile in diameter. Formerly, it was believed that such deposits were of volcanic origin, but it is now generally held that they were formed either by the deposition of sulfur from sulfur-bearing waters or by the action of organic agencies upon *gypsum* ($CaSO_4.2H_2O$). In combination, the element occurs chiefly as sulfides or sulfates. The sulfides, *e. g.*, *copper pyrites* ($CuFeS_2$), *galena* (PbS), *zinc blende* (ZnS) and *cinnabar* (HgS) are commercially important on account of their metals. The sulfates, *e.g.*, *gypsum* ($CaSO_4.2H_2O$), *barytes* ($BaSO_4$), *celestite* ($SrSO_4$) and *kieserite* ($MgSO_4.(H_2O)_n$), are very plentiful and useful. The element occurs also in the animal and vegetable kingdom as a constituent of hair and wool, volatile oils of mustard and garlic, and in albuminous bodies.

Physical Properties.—Sulfur may appear in two distinct and characteristic *solid* forms, in two different *liquid* forms, and as a vapor. These allotropic modifications differ markedly from one another in physical properties. The physical properties of each allotrope are given as follows:

1. *Rhombic Sulfur or α-Sulfur.*—When carbon disulfide is allowed to evaporate spontaneously from a solution of commercial sulfur in this solvent, rhombic crystals of sulfur are formed. X-ray studies have shown these crystals to exist as rings of 8 sulfur atoms, Sα. These crystals have a density of 2.07 and melt at 112.8° C. to form Sλ. They are nearly insoluble in water and in alcohol. One Gm. dissolves slowly and usually incompletely in 2 ml. of carbon disulfide. One Gm. is soluble in about 70 ml. of chloroform, in 150 ml. of ether, and in 100 ml. of olive oil. Rhombic sulfur is a very poor conductor of electricity and becomes negatively electrified on friction. It ignites in air at a temperature of 363° C., and burns with a blue flame, forming quantities of sulfur dioxide. It is stable at temperatures below 96° C. Roll sulfur and most "flowers of sulfur" are crystalline in structure and are examples of this form of the element.

2. *Monoclinic Sulfur or β-Sulfur.*—This form of sulfur may be obtained by partially cooling molten sulfur, piercing the crust that forms, and pouring off the still liquid portion. The interior of the vessel will be found lined with needles of this crystalline form. These needles are nearly colorless, have a density of 1.957, melt at 119.25° C. to form Sλ, and are different from the rhombic variety in all physical respects. This form is stable from 96° C. to 119.25° C. but upon cooling it reverts to the rhombic sulfur, *e.g.*, monoclinic S_8 ⇌ rhombic S_8 at 96° C.

3. *Liquid Sulfur.*—When sulfur is heated above its melting-point, several interesting phenomena are observed. At approximately 160° C. a noticeable change takes place. The pale yellow, mobile liquid (Sλ) gradually darkens and becomes more viscous until at about 180° C. the product is dark brown in color and has reached a maximum viscosity (Sμ). The heating process is assumed to break down the S_8 rings to give filaments which become entangled and thus increase the viscosity. On continued heating the viscosity becomes less, until at 444.6° C. the liquid boils and sulfur vapors are evolved. These vapors correspond to the S_8 ring structure again. When the λ-sulfur is allowed to slowly cool, either α-sulfur or β-sulfur result, both of which are soluble in carbon disulfide. However, when the viscous variety is rapidly cooled or the more highly heated sulfur poured into water, an elastic substance (resembling rubber) insoluble in carbon disulfide is obtained. This variety is often called *plastic sulfur* and is considered to be a supercooled liquid. This substance becomes hard and brittle upon standing for several days and is then found to contain about 70 per cent of rhombic sulfur, soluble in carbon disulfide, and 30 per cent of another variety which is very nearly insoluble in any solvent. This latter is called *amorphous sulfur.* Molten sulfur is regarded

as a mixture of two isomers, $S\lambda$ and $S\mu$, in dynamic equilibrium. $S\lambda$ is light yellow in color and mobile, whereas $S\mu$ is dark brown and viscous. At the lower temperatures of molten sulfur, $S\lambda$ predominates, but as the higher temperatures are reached $S\mu$ increases ($\lambda \rightleftarrows S\mu$). This change from $S\lambda$ to $S\mu$ is reversible, as shown when sulfur at its boiling-point is allowed to cool slowly.

The physical properties of the *official* forms of sulfur may be summarized as follows:

Precipitated Sulfur.—This is a very fine, pale yellow, amorphous or microcrystalline powder, without odor or taste.

One Gm. is practically insoluble in water, and nearly insoluble in alcohol. One Gm. dissolves slowly and usually incompletely in about 2 ml. of carbon disulfide. One Gm. dissolves in about 100 ml. of olive oil.

Sublimed Sulfur.—This form is a fine, yellow, crystalline powder having a faint odor and taste. Its solubility is the same as that of Precipitated Sulfur.

Chemical Properties.—Under reduced pressure and at low temperatures, the formula of sulfur vapor is S_8. The freezing-point depressions of solutions of sulfur also indicate S_8. At 1000° C., however, the formula is S_2. Sulfur is a very active element. It unites with most metals (1) and non-metals (2) to form sulfides. When sulfur is treated with oxidizing agents in the presence of water, sulfuric acid is formed.

(1) $2Cu + S \rightarrow Cu_2S$

(2) $C + 2S \rightarrow CS_2$

When sulfur is oxidized with oxygen (burned), it evolves suffocating fumes of sulfur dioxide (3).

(3) $S + O_2 \xrightarrow{\triangle} SO_2 \uparrow$

When boiled with a solution of calcium hydroxide, sulfur is dissolved with the formation of calcium thiosulfate and calcium pentasulfide (4). It can easily be precipitated from such a solution by acidification. (See preparation of Precipitated Sulfur, p. 572.)

(4) $3Ca(OH)_2 + 12S \rightarrow 2CaS_5 + CaS_2O_3 + 3H_2O$

Its solubility in calcium hydroxide is very similar to its solubility in hot solutions of the alkali hydroxides, *e.g.*, potassium hydroxide (5).

(5) $6KOH + 8S \rightarrow 2K_2S_3 + K_2S_2O_3 + 3H_2O$

Part of its solubility in alkali hydroxides is probably due to the fact that it is also soluble in solutions of alkali sulfides such as sodium sulfide (6). Thus, it is reasonable to expect that the reaction does not contain only the products shown in equation (5) but also sulfides of sodium containing more sulfur such as are shown in equation (6).

(6) $Na_2S + S \rightarrow Na_2S_2$

or

$Na_2S + 4S \rightarrow Na_2S_5$

Sulfur reacts readily with the alkali cyanides (7) to form thiocyanates.

(7) $NaCN + S \underset{\triangle}{\rightleftharpoons} NaSCN$

Finally, sulfur reacts with sulfites to form thiosulfates (8).

(8) $Na_2SO_3 + S \rightarrow Na_2S_2O_3$

The official assay of sulfur (*i.e.*, official forms) requires that the sulfur first be solubilized by boiling with alcoholic potassium hydroxide solution (5), the alcoholic solution being preferred to an aqueous solution because sulfur is more easily wetted by alcohol. The solution of potassium sulfide and potassium thiosulfate is then oxidized with hydrogen peroxide (9) to potassium sulfate. The sulfate is estimated by conversion to insoluble barium sulfate (10) which is washed, dried and weighed.

(9) $K_2S_2O_3 + K_2S_3 + 6KOH + 14H_2O_2 \rightarrow 5K_2SO_4 + 17H_2O$

(10) $K_2SO_4 + BaCl_2 \rightarrow BaSO_4 \downarrow + 2KCl$

Official Test for Identity.—Sulfur is identified by burning it in air to yield sulfur dioxide (3) identifiable by its characteristic odor.

Commercial Production of Sulfur.—The recovery of sulfur from mixtures with limestone, clay, gypsum, etc., depends upon the liquefaction of the sulfur either by its own heat of combustion or by heat from other sources. In Sicily, sulfur is recovered in a crude furnace called a "calcarone." These "calcarones" are semicircular, stone-walled pits, 35 feet in diameter and 10 feet deep, dug into the side of a hill. As the quarried sulfur rock is packed in the calcarone, vertical air-passages are constructed by means of which the temperature of the crude furnace is regulated. The kilns are fired from the top and the heat generated by burning some of the sulfur is sufficient to liquefy the remainder. The molten sulfur is drawn off at the base of the furnace into square stone receptacles from which it is ladled into damp poplar wood molds. The truncated cones of sulfur thus produced weigh from 100 to 130 pounds. On account of the amount of sulfur consumed by combustion, the yield is approximately 50 per cent. Because of the destruction of crops by the immense volume of sulfur dioxide evolved, these calcarones are rigidly restricted to certain areas. Other methods (Gill, Gritti, Orlando) of liquefying sulfur are also in use.

The sulfur obtained from these various kilns contains about 3 per cent of earthy material and must be refined to meet commercial requirements. The refinery consists of a large stone chamber with a safety valve. This valve is usually located in the roof and is designed to take care of any developed pressure. The molten sulfur is contained in iron retorts (usually two) which communicate with the chamber. When the sulfur vapors first enter the stone chamber, they ignite and convert the air into nitrogen and sulfur dioxide. The next vapor diffuses through a mass of relatively cold gas and condenses on the walls and floors of the chamber in a fine crystalline form called *flowers of sulfur*. By conducting the sublimation so as not to raise the temperature of the condensing chamber, all of the sulfur may be converted to this form. If "roll sulfur" is desired, the rate of sublimation is increased. When the sulfur condenses in the chamber, it is immediately melted to a liquid which is run off from the bottom of the condenser and cast in molds.

The Louisiana deposits are worked by a process that was devised by Herman Frasch in 1891. A bore-hole is sunk some 700 to 1000 feet through clay, quicksand and rock until the sulfur bed is reached. Three concentric pipes of 8, 3 and 1 inch in diameter are then lowered into the hole. Superheated water (180° C.) is pumped down the outer pipe to the sulfur bed. When the sulfur is melted, compressed air is forced down the 1-inch pipe. The molten sulfur mixes with the air, its specific gravity is lowered and it then rises in the 3-inch tube and flows out above ground into large wooden enclosures in which it solidifies. This sulfur is about 98 per cent pure.

Sulfur may be obtained by heating sulfide ores, *e.g.*, iron pyrites, in closed retorts (11 or 12).

$$(11)\ 3FeS_2 \overset{\triangle}{\rightleftarrows} Fe_3S_4 + 2S$$

$$(12)\ 2FeS_2 \overset{\triangle}{\rightleftarrows} 2FeS + 2S$$

Although the Gulf Coast sulfur deposits (Louisiana, etc.) have been the principal sources of sulfur (Frasch process), these deposits are beginning to show signs of depletion. Therefore, it has become of interest in the national economy to utilize lower grades of sulfur deposits, heretofore unprofitable of operation. A process to meet this problem has been developed. Essentially, the process involves the grinding of sulfur bearing ores to a powder and then passing the pulverized ore through an autoclave to melt the sulfur and separate it from the gangue. This step is successful because of the high surface tension of the sulfur which prevents it from wetting the gangue particles. The molten sulfur is quenched in a water-bath to yield a crude product approximately 98 per cent pure. Further purification by remelting, flotation and filtration results in a 99.5 per cent sulfur.

Since some of the lower grade ores have been used a problem has arisen in that they contain appreciable amounts of selenium. The U.S.P. is cognizant of the problem and will probably establish limits for this contaminant in view of its potential toxicity in the internal use of sulfur.

The U.S. Pharmacoepia XVII recognizes one form of sulfur, *viz.*, Precipitated Sulfur. Sublimed Sulfur is recognized by the N.F. XII. Each one of these forms of sulfur, when dried for four hours over sulfuric acid, must contain not less than 99.5 per cent of sulfur.

1. *Sublimed Sulfur.*—Sublimed Sulfur or "flowers of sulfur" is made by the process previously described.

2. *Precipitated Sulfur.*—Precipitated Sulfur is a very fine amorphous or microcrystalline powder having a pale yellow color and no odor or taste. It is more readily and completely soluble in carbon disulfide than flowers of sulfur. It is prepared by boiling together sublimed sulfur and milk of lime for one hour. During the operation both calcium pentasulfide and thiosulfate are formed (13).

$$(13)\ 3Ca(OH)_2 + 12S \rightarrow 2CaS_5 + CaS_2O_3 + 3H_2O$$

The mixture is filtered and diluted hydrochloric acid added with constant stirring until the liquid is *nearly* neutralized but still retains an alkaline reaction to red litmus. The precipitated sulfur is collected on a strainer and washed with water until the washings are neutral to litmus and give no test for calcium with ammonium oxalate test solution. The product is then dried rapidly.

It will be noted that during the precipitation of the sulfur (14),

$$(14)\ CaS_5 + 2HCl \rightarrow CaCl_2 + H_2S \uparrow\ + 4S \downarrow$$

the liquid is kept alkaline and the addition of diluted hydrochloric acid is discontinued while the liquid is still alkaline to litmus. Although giving a lesser yield of precipitated sulfur than would be obtained if the liquid was made slightly acid, it is kept alkaline for several excellent reasons. Some sublimed sulfur contains a small amount of arsenic as the trisulfide, and when this is digested with hot milk of lime, calcium sulfarsenite $[Ca_3(AsS_3)_2]$ is formed. This is soluble in the alkaline liquid. However, if the liquid is made acid by the addition of hydrochloric acid, the calcium sulfarsenite is decomposed into the insoluble arsenic trisulfide which will again contaminate the precipitated sulfur. It is quite evident that the sulfides of calcium are very much more readily decomposed by hydrochloric acid than is calcium thiosulfate, the latter not being materially affected until all of the sulfides have been acted upon and only when the liquid is decidedly acid to litmus. Any sulfur precipitated by the decomposition of calcium thiosulfate is not only much coarser than that obtained from the sulfides but it is also insoluble in carbon disulfide; qualities that are most undesirable in Precipitated Sulfur.

Pharmacological Action of Sulfur.—Sulfur has been used therapeutically since antiquity and during that time, certain well-defined uses have emerged. These are (1) cathartic action, (2) parasiticide in scabies, (3) stimulant in alopecia, (4) fumigation, and (5) miscellaneous skin diseases. In addition, (6) sulfides have been used for many years as depilatories.

1. Sulfur exerts a mild cathartic (aperient) effect and therefore is used to soften the stools, particularly when the patient has hemorrhoids. The classical effect of "sulfur and molasses" is based largely on this action. The reason that it acts as a cathartic is because the sulfur reacts with protein to liberate, among other things, hydrogen sulfide which is mildly irritant to the intestinal tract. This action is very gradual, unless a finely divided form of sulfur, such as Precipitated Sulfur, is used.

2. Although sulfur is an insoluble and practically inert substance by itself, it has been shown that in contact with living tissue it forms hydrogen sulfide and an oxidation product, pentathionic acid, both of which have been shown experimentally to be germicidal and fungicidal. These products of interaction between sulfur and living tissue are responsible for the effectiveness of sulfur in the treatment of various skin conditions caused by fungus infections and parasites. For this type of action the sulfur should be in as finely a divided state as possible, which makes Precipitated Sulfur the one of choice. In the form of an ointment or as free sulfur, sulfur has been used a great deal for the treatment of scabies (itch). A novel method of administration is with the "sulfur foam" applicator in which the finely divided sulfur is applied to the skin as a soapy foam and allowed to dry. Since the itch mite eggs are not affected by sulfur, repeated application is necessary (usually for three successive days) to kill both the grown mites and the mites which hatch out. It is of utmost importance to prevent reinfection by wearing clean clothes and changing bedclothing. Other medications, e.g., benzyl benzoate, have largely superseded sulfur for this type of therapy.

3. Because sulfur also has a local stimulant and keratolytic action on the skin, it helps to overcome congestion and to soften horny elements and scaly formations. For this reason it has been used in the treatment of seborrheic alopecia (baldness). In the form of an ointment, it is applied to the scalp.

4. Because of the fact that sulfur forms sulfur dioxide when burned, it has been used for fumigating. Its use in this capacity has not proved too successful, but it has proven to be quite an effective insecticide for bedbugs, roaches, mosquitoes, etc. The procedure is to burn 2 to 3 pounds of sulfur per 1000 cubic feet of room space. Sulfur for this purpose is supplied in $\frac{1}{4}$ and 1 pound cakes, usually with a wick in the middle of the "candle." The sulfur cake should be placed on some non-inflammable object so that the floor does not burn. It works best when the air is saturated

with moisture, but at the same time it is well to remember that under these conditions sulfur dioxide is an effective bleaching agent. Therefore, objects that might be bleached should be removed from the room.

5. Because of its keratolytic and fungicidal action, sulfur has been used for a multiplicity of skin diseases such as psoriasis, acne, etc. In this connection, however, it is well to note that many allergists feel that sulfur is one of the elements that is most liable to cause dermatitis. Therefore, whenever it or its preparations are used, patients should be watched carefully for allergic manifestations.

6. The action of sulfides as depilatories is based on the reduction of the disulfide linkage in cystine. A strongly alkaline medium (pH 10 or better) is needed to facilitate the swelling process by reaction with the –SH groups formed. This seems to be a necessary precursor to complete depilation. The strontium and calcium sulfides seem to be the most popular today. Their biggest fault is the odor of hydrogen sulfide accompanying their use.

Uses.—*Precipitated Sulfur*, U.S.P. XVII, contains not less than 99.5 per cent of S, calculated on the anhydrous basis. This form of sulfur is also known as "lac sulfur" or "milk sulfur," these names being derived from the fact that formerly the precipitated sulfur of commerce was made by using sulfuric acid as a precipitant rather than hydrochloric acid. This resulted in a deposit of calcium sulfate in the sulfur which made it almost white. This form of sulfur is used largely for *external* application. Because of its fine state of subdivision, it should be used for compounding ointments. It occurs officially in *Sulfur Ointment* (10%S) for use as a scabicide to be applied topically every night for 3 nights.

This form of sulfur is also employed in *Compound Senna Powder* for its cathartic action.

Sublimed Sulfur (Flowers of Sulfur), N.F. XII, "dried over phosphorus pentoxide for 4 hours, contains not less than 99.5 per cent of S." This form of sulfur is sometimes used internally. It is also used in ointment form as a local irritant, parasiticide and scabicide. It is used in the preparation of *Sulfurated Lime Solution* (Vleminckx's Solution). This preparation is a scabicide and is made by boiling lime and sublimed sulfur (see eq. 13).

OFFICIAL SULFUR COMPOUND

SULFUR DIOXIDE

Sulfur Dioxide, U.S.P. XVII

Formula, SO_2.   Molecular Weight, 64.06

Physical Properties.—Sulfur Dioxide is a colorless non-inflammable gas possessing a characteristic pungent and irritating odor. It has a density of 2.264 (air=1). One volume of water at 0° C. (760 mm.) dissolves nearly 80 volumes of gas and at 25° C. (760 mm.) 32.8 volumes. The gas dissolves in alcohol and yields about a 26.5 per cent solution. The dry gas is neutral in reaction but its aqueous solutions are acid to litmus due to the formation of sulfurous acid.

The critical temperature is 157.2° C. and the critical pressure about 78 atmospheres. The gas is easily liquefied to a colorless liquid which boils at −10° C. This liquid is an excellent solvent for iodine, phosphorus and sulfur. Some inorganic salts dissolve in it to form addition products, such as $KI.4SO_2$, $KI.4I.SO_2$, etc. The rapid evaporation of liquid sulfur dioxide converts it into a white solid melting at −72.7° C.

Chemical Properties.—Sulfur dioxide is stable even at high temperatures. It does not burn or support combustion. Under the influence of a catalyst, it unites with oxygen to form sulfur trioxide. In the presence of camphor (catalyst) or in direct sunlight, SO_2 forms addition compounds with chlorine (1) and fluorine (2). Sulfur dioxide forms a hydrate containing 7 molecules of water ($SO_2.7H_2O$). This may be obtained by cooling a saturated aqueous solution of the gas.

Sulfur dioxide is a good reducing agent. For example, if it is passed into an aqueous solution of iodine, sulfuric and hydriodic acids are formed (3). In this case, the iodine is reduced, whereas the sulfur of the sulfur dioxide is oxidized. Sulfur dioxide also reduces permanganates to manganous salts (4), iodates to iodine (5), etc.

(1) $SO_2 + Cl_2 \rightarrow SO_2Cl_2$ (sulfuryl chloride)

(2) $SO_2 + F_2 \rightarrow SO_2F_2$ (sulfuryl fluoride)

(3) $I_2 + 2H_2O + SO_2 \rightarrow H_2SO_4 + 2HI$

(4) $2KMnO_4 + 2H_2O + 5SO_2 \rightarrow K_2SO_4 + 2MnSO_4 + 2H_2SO_4$

(5) $2KIO_3 + 4H_2O + 5SO_2 \rightarrow 2KHSO_4 + I_2 + 3H_2SO_4$

Tests for Identity.—1. Sulfur Dioxide may be detected by its characteristic acrid odor.

2. When a piece of paper moistened with a solution of potassium iodate and starch test solution is exposed to the gas, the starch turns blue, due to liberated iodine (5). Continued exposure of the paper to the gas will cause the blue color to disappear (3).

3. When moistened mercurous nitrate paper comes in contact with Sulfur Dioxide, it turns black due to the reduction of the mercurous nitrate to metallic mercury (6).

(6) $2HgNO_3 + SO_2 + 2H_2O \rightarrow 2Hg + 2HNO_3 + H_2SO_4$

Commercial Preparation.—Sulfur dioxide is produced when sulfur is burned in air or oxygen (7). A very small quantity of sulfur trioxide is also formed.

(7) $2S + 2O_2 \overset{\Delta}{\rightarrow} 2SO_2$

The gas is usually prepared for industrial purposes by roasting metallic sulfides (8) (9) (10). This roasting process is preliminary to the recovery of certain metals from their sulfide ores. (See copper, p. 320, and zinc, p. 408.)

(8) $Cu_2S + 2O_2 \overset{\Delta}{\rightarrow} 2CuO + SO_2 \uparrow$

(9) $2ZnS + 3O_2 \overset{\Delta}{\rightarrow} 2ZnO + 2SO_2 \uparrow$

(10) $4FeS_2 + 11O_2 \overset{\Delta}{\rightarrow} 2Fe_2O_3 + 8SO_2 \uparrow$

It may be obtained by reducing concentrated sulfuric acid with carbon (11), sulfur (12), or metals (13).

(11) $2H_2SO_4 + C \rightarrow 2SO_2 \uparrow + CO_2 \uparrow + 2H_2O$

(12) $2H_2SO_4 + S \rightarrow 3SO_2 \uparrow + 2H_2O$

(13) $2H_2SO_4 + Cu \rightarrow SO_2 \uparrow + CuSO_4 + 2H_2O$

Sulfur dioxide is formed when sulfites are decomposed with dilute acids (14).

(14) $NaHSO_3 + H_2SO_4 \rightarrow NaHSO_4 + SO_2 \uparrow + H_2O$

Uses.—*Sulfur Dioxide*, U.S.P. XVII, was introduced into the U.S.P. to provide standards for its use as a preservative in certain easily oxidized preparations (*i.e.*, injections). Thus, it may be characterized as an antioxidant pharmaceutical aid. Its action depends on its strong reducing action, this action, however, being so powerful that it is not used either in or on the body except in the very small amounts in these oxidizable preparations. Very dilute concentrations have been used with variable results in the treatment of colds. It finds extensive industrial use for bleaching wool, straw and wood pulp; for fumigating; for arresting fermentation, and in the manufacture of sugar. Its principal use is in the manufacture of sulfuric acid.

SELENIUM AND TELLURIUM

Symbols, Se and Te. Valences, 2, 4, 6. Atomic Weight: Se, 78.96; Te, 127.60; Atomic Number: Se, 34; Te, 52

History.—Berzelius (1817) discovered a new element which he called selenium (Gr. selene = "moon"), because of its close chemical relationship to tellurium (L. tellus = "earth"), discovered by Reichenstein in 1782 and named by Klaproth in 1798. Selenium was first obtained by its discoverer in the slime at the bottom of lead chambers used for making sulfuric acid.

Occurrence.—A small amount of tellurium occurs native. It is usually found in combination with silver, gold, lead and bismuth. Considerable amounts could be recovered during the refining of these metals and also of copper.

Selenium, on the other hand, is usually associated with sulfur and the sulfide ores. In the form of the selenides it may be recovered from the flue dust of pyrite burners and also in the electrolytic refining of copper (*q.v.*).

Properties.—Like sulfur, selenium and tellurium have the property of existing in different forms or allotropic modifications. A red, monoclinic, crystalline form of selenium having a density of 4.42 and a melting-point of 144° C. may be prepared. When this variety is heated between 200° and 230° C. for some time, it changes into the gray variety of metallic selenium having a density of 4.8. The electrical conductivity of this form especially is very small in the dark or at ordinary temperatures but increases markedly when exposed to light or elevations in temperature. This property is the basis for the action of the very sensitive selenium photoelectric cell. Selenium is used also in making red glass and in the rubber industry. The allotropism of tellurium is the lesser marked of the two elements, but it does occur in different forms. The fused element is metallic in appearance and has a density of 6.25. It is a good conductor of electricity. A small quantity is used in the ceramic industry.

Tests for Identity.—Identification tests for both *Selenites* and *Selenates* are based upon their easy reduction.

1. *Selenites* in solution yield a red precipitate of selenium with sodium bisulfite T.S. (1) as well as with other reducing agents.

(1) $H_2SeO_3 + 2NaHSO_3 \rightarrow Se \downarrow + 2NaHSO_4 + H_2O$

2. *Selenates* in solution yield a red precipitate with stannous chloride T.S. (2), the precipitate being soluble upon boiling the solution.

(2) $H_2SeO_4 + 3SnCl_2 + 6HCl \rightarrow Se \downarrow + 3SnCl_4 + 4H_2O$

Similar tests may be used for tellurium compounds.

Pharmacological Actions of Selenium and Tellurium Ions.—Perhaps the most interesting development with respect to selenium has been the identification of selenium as the so-called Factor 3 in preventing liver necrosis in rats. Since this discovery, it has been found that selenium compounds may be of great importance in microgram quantities in the prevention of a number of diseases that occur among farm animals. In spite of the known toxicity of selenium in relatively large amounts the fact that it appears to be an essential nutrient in minute quantities will insure investigations to assess its role. At present it has been suggested, in a preliminary report, that small quantities of selenium may be of therapeutic value in the treatment of kwashiorkor, a nutritional deficiency disorder affecting millions of children and infants in South America, Africa and Asia.

The actions of selenium, selenate, and selenite ions closely resemble those of arsenic and tellurium. The oral administration of large doses of selenium salts produces intestinal irritation and paralysis of the small blood vessels and blood-forming organs. Selenium compounds were suggested by Wassermann as being specific for tumors and cancers. It has been shown that non-toxic doses will not destroy cancer cells.

Slinger and Hubbard,[1] in 1951, suggested that, on the basis of Periodic Table relationships, selenium might be useful in the treatment of certain dermatoses inasmuch as sulfur had long enjoyed a reputation in this field. They recognized the possibility of toxic manifestations and the fact that some organic and inorganic selenium compounds can be absorbed through the intact skin. However, little was known at that time of the absorption of the more stable insoluble selenium compounds. Selecting selenium disulfide as the test chemical they were able to show that, in the form of a shampoo (2.5%), it was not absorbed significantly, was nonirritant and was effective in treating seborrheic dermatitis of the scalp (common dandruff) in 85 to 95 per cent of the cases treated. More recently, Cohen[2] has demonstrated the effectiveness of an 0.6 per cent ointment in the treatment of blepharitis marginalis. Commercial preparations of selenium disulfide are available as an 0.5 per cent cream (Selsun Cream) and a 2.5 per cent shampoo (Selsun Suspension). Patients using these preparations are cautioned against permitting the product to enter the conjunctival sac because stinging and irritation will ensue with possible resultant keratitis.

Tellurium, like selenium, resembles arsenic in its action. Because of the ease and rapidity with which tellurium compounds are reduced to the metallic state, they are relatively non-toxic.

Toxic doses produce paralysis of the blood vessels and also marked changes in the blood-forming organs. Tellurium salts act as antidiaphoretics and sodium tellurate has been used to suppress the night-sweats of phthisis. The oral administration of tellurium salts is followed by the deposition of the metal in all parts of the body. All living cells effect the reduction of tellurium salts to an ultramicroscopic form of the metal, which is slowly but continuously converted into methyl telluride [$(CH_3)_2Te$]. This alliaceous smelling substance is excreted in the breath, perspiration, urine, and feces. When taken orally, the larger part of a tellurium salt is reduced to the metal which is excreted in the feces.

[1] Slinger, W. N., and Hubbard, D. M.: Arch. Dermat. and Syph., 64, 41 (1951). This paper also contains leading references to the toxicology of selenium.

[2] Cohen, L. B.: Amer. J. Ophth., 38, 560 (1954).

SELENIUM SULFIDE

Selenium Sulfide, U.S.P. XVII

Formula, SeS_2 Molecular Weight, 143.09

Physical Properties.—Selenium sulfide occurs as a bright-orange powder having not more than a faint odor. It is practically tasteless and is virtually insoluble in water and in organic solvents.

Chemical Properties.—The insolubility of selenium sulfide in water precludes most incompatibilities of the usual type where precipitation reactions are a factor. It is soluble in nitric acid, however, in which case it is oxidized to a mixture of sulfuric and selenous acids (1). The selenous acid acts as an oxidizing agent when potassium

$$(1) \quad SeS_2 + 16HNO_3 \rightarrow H_2SeO_3 + 2H_2SO_4 + 16NO_2 \uparrow + 5H_2O$$

iodide is introduced into the solution (2). However, the excess nitric acid must be inactivated and any nitrous acid destroyed by the use of an excess of urea (3) before this reaction is carried out.

$$(2) \quad 4KI + H_2SeO_3 + 4HNO_3 \rightarrow 2I_2 \downarrow + Se \uparrow + 3H_2O + 4KNO_3$$

$$(3) \quad CO(NH_2)_2 + 2HNO_2 \rightarrow CO_2 \uparrow + 2N_2 \uparrow + 3H_2O.$$

The assay for Selenium Sulfide involves the same reactions as those given for the identification of the compound (1,2,3) except that the liberated iodine is titrated with standard thiosulfate solution.

Official Tests for Identity.—Selenium sulfide (50 mg.) is digested by gentle heating with 5 ml. of nitric acid for 30 minutes (1). Water is added to make about 50 ml., the mixture filtered and to 5 ml. of the filtrate is added 10 ml. of water and 5 Gm. of urea. This is heated to boiling during which time the urea forms the nitrate with nitric acid and decomposes nitrous acid (3). The cooled solution is then treated with 2 ml. of potassium iodide solution (1 in 10) to liberate free iodine as well as selenium (2). The iodine and selenium give a yellowish-orange to orange color that rapidly darkens and is a positive test for selenium. The mixture is allowed to stand for 10 minutes, is filtered, and the filtrate treated with barium chloride T.S. The formation of a white precipitate indicates the presence of sulfate and is a positive test for sulfur in the original compound.

Commercial Manufacture.—The preparation of selenium disulfide may be carried out by passing hydrogen sulfide into a solution of selenous acid to form a yellow precipitate of selenium disulfide (4).[1]

$$(4) \quad H_2SeO_3 + 2H_2S \rightarrow SeS_2 \downarrow + 3H_2O$$

[1] Encyclopedia of Chemical Reactions, Vol. VI, by C. A. Jacobson, ed. by C. A. Hampel, New York, Reinhold Pub. Corp., 1956, p. 76.

It can also be prepared by passing hydrogen sulfide into a solution of potassium selenite (5) although excess hydrogen sulfide results in formation of metallic selenium (6).

(5) $K_2SeO_3 + 3H_2S \rightarrow SeS_2 \downarrow + K_2S + 3H_2O$

(6) $SeS_2 + 2KOH + H_2S \rightarrow Se \downarrow + K_2S + 2S + 2H_2O$

The shampoo preparation contains SeS_2 together with bentonite, a detergent (*i.e.*, an alkylaryl sulfonate) and an acidic material to bring the pH to between 3.6 to 4.5.

Uses.—*Selenium Sulfide*, U.S.P. XVII, (Selenium Disulfide) contains not less than 52 per cent and not more than 55.5 per cent of Se. It is used in the form of a 2.5 per cent suspension, officially recognized as *Selenium Sulfide Detergent Suspension*, containing a suitable dispersing agent, buffer, and detergent. The application is topically to the scalp by applying 5 to 10 ml. for 5 minutes and then washing off thoroughly. (See also p. 577.)

43

Chromium and Chromium Compounds

CHROMIUM

Symbol, Cr.   Valences, 2, 3, 6.   Atomic Weight, 51.996;
Atomic Number, 24

History and Occurrence.—In 1762, Lehman discovered a red mineral in Siberia which he named crocoite. About 1797, Vauquelin and Klaproth, working independently, found this mineral to be a compound of lead in combination with an acid which they found to be an oxide of a new element. The name *chromium* (Greek, χρῶμα, color) was assigned to the latter because all of its compounds were found to be highly colored.

Chromium always occurs in combination in Nature. Its principal ore is *chromite* or *chrome iron ore* ($FeO.Cr_2O_3$), of which the largest deposits are found in southern Rhodesia, Turkey, New Caledonia, India, and Greece. Chromite is widely distributed in and around serpentine and other basic rock areas in the United States. Such rocks are found in Pennsylvania, Maryland, North Carolina, western and central California, etc. Native lead chromate, *crocoite* ($PbCrO_4$) is found chiefly in Siberia.

Physical Properties.—Chromium is a very hard, crystalline, silvery gray metal having a density of 7.14. It melts at about 1900° C. and boils at 2480° C. It is non-magnetic and its ductility and malleability are very low.

Chemical Properties.—The chemical properties of chromium will be considered as (1) metallic chromium, (2) divalent chromium, (3) trivalent chromium, and (4) hexavalent chromium.

1. *Metallic chromium* does not oxidize (tarnish) in air, but when heated, it burns with a bright light in oxygen or in the oxyhydrogen flame and gives the sesquioxide (Cr_2O_3). Chromium metal exists in an *active* and a *passive* form. The former is easily soluble in dilute acids with the evolution of hydrogen and the formation of blue chromous salts which are rapidly changed by the oxygen of the air to green chromic salts. However, if the metal is allowed to stand exposed to air, or is treated with chromic acid or concentrated nitric acid, it is changed to the *passive* form and as such is not acted upon by dilute acids.

(581)

38

2. *Chromous* ion is a divalent ion (Cr^{++}) possessing a blue color. It is quite unstable, being readily converted to the chromic form. It is, therefore, a strong reducing agent. There are relatively few stable compounds containing the divalent form of chromium, the principal ones being the halogen salts and the acetate. This form of chromium is rarely encountered and is of little importance.

3. Chromium exists more commonly in the trivalent form. The *chromic* salts are usually obtained by reducing dichromates in acid solution (1).

$$(1)\ Cr_2O_7^= + 6I^- + 14H_3O^+ \rightarrow 2Cr^{+++} + 3I_2 + 21H_2O$$

When chromic salts are treated with alkali hydroxides they yield chromic hydroxide (2). This hydroxide when treated with acids yields chromic salts (3) and when treated with alkali yields chromites (4).

$$(2)\ Cr^{+++} + 3OH^- \rightarrow Cr(OH)_3 \downarrow$$
$$(3)\ Cr(OH)_3 + 3H_3O^+ \rightarrow Cr^{+++} + 6H_2O$$
$$(4)\ Cr(OH)_3 + OH^- \rightarrow CrO_2^- + 2H_2O$$

4. *Hexavalent chromium* is the form in which it occurs in most salts, and as such it exhibits an entirely non-metallic character. In the hexavalent form it exists with few exceptions either as chromate or dichromate.

Some of the characteristic reactions of chromates and dichromates are as follows:

(*a*) *Chromates.*—1. When a neutral or alkaline solution of a chromate is treated with hydrogen sulfide or ammonium sulfide, chromium hydroxide and sulfur are precipitated (5).

$$(5)\ 2Na_2CrO_4 + 7(NH_4)_2S \rightarrow 2Cr(OH)_3 \downarrow\ + 4NaSH + 3S \downarrow$$
$$+ 2H_2O + 14NH_3 \uparrow$$

2. Lead ion precipitates soluble chromates (6) or dichromates (7), free from mineral acids, as yellow lead chromate. The precipitate is soluble in hydrochloric acid and in fixed alkalies.

$$(6)\ CrO_4^= + Pb^{++} \rightarrow PbCrO_4 \downarrow$$
$$(7)\ Cr_2O_7^= + 2Pb(CH_3COO)_2 + H_2O \rightarrow 2CH_3COOH + 2CH_3-$$
$$COO^- + 2PbCrO_4 \downarrow$$

3. When a solution of a chromate is boiled with hydrochloric acid, the chromate is reduced to the chloride and chlorine is evolved (8).

$$(8)\ 2CrO_4^= + 6Cl^- + 16H_3O^+ \rightarrow 2Cr^{+++} + 3Cl_2 \uparrow + 24H_2O$$

4. In the presence of NaOH, $Cr(OH)_3$ or CrO_2^- are readily oxidized by H_2O_2 or the halogens to $CrO_4^=$ which may be identified as yellow $PbCrO_4$ or as red Ag_2CrO_4.

(b) *Dichromates.*—1. Hydrogen sulfide reduces a dichromate in acid solution to a chromic salt and sulfur is precipitated (9).

(9) $Cr_2O_7^= + 3H_2S + 8H_3O^+ \rightarrow 2Cr^{+++} + 3S \downarrow + 15H_2O$

2. When an acidulated solution of a dichromate is treated with hydrobromic or hydriodic acids, the respective halogen is set free (10).

(10) $Cr_2O_7^= + 6I^- + 14H_3O^+ \rightarrow 2Cr^{+++} + 3I_2 + 21H_2O$

Tests for Identity.—The official compendia do not give identification tests for any form of chromium.

However, *Chromate* and *Dichromate* when free of mineral acids respond to the following tests:

(a) They yield with lead acetate T.S. a yellow precipitate of lead chromate (6) (7), which is insoluble in acetic acid.

(b) When acidified with diluted sulfuric acid and treated with solution of hydrogen peroxide, a transient blue color is produced. Upon shaking the solution immediately with ether, the blue color passes into the ether layer. (For further discussion see Hydrogen Peroxide, p. 53.)

Commercial Manufacture.—1. When the mineral, chromite, is fused with sodium carbonate, sodium chromate (Na_2CrO_4) is produced. This is leached out, converted to the dichromate, and electrolyzed to produce the metal.

2. The commercial production of aluminum made it practical to use this metal in the reduction of the oxides of those metals that are not only difficult to reduce with carbon but also have a tendency to form carbides with the same. The application of *aluminothermy* (Goldschmidt method, *q.v.*) to the reduction of chromium oxide has made it possible to obtain a very high grade of chromium metal (11).

(11) $Cr_2O_3 + 2Al \rightarrow 2Cr + Al_2O_3 + 112,000$ calories

3. A method first employed by Moissan in 1894, yields an impure product which is unfit for use in hardening steel. The oxide (Cr_2O_3) is reduced with carbon in an electric furnace (12) and the crude metal is freed from most of its carbide by heating with oxide.

(12) $Cr_2O_3 + 3C \overset{\triangle}{\rightarrow} 2Cr + 3CO \uparrow$

4. When chrome iron ore or chromium oxide is reduced with carbon or silicon (13) in an electric furnace, an alloy of iron and chromium, known as *ferrochrome*, is produced (14).

(13) $2Cr_2O_3 + 3Si \overset{\triangle}{\rightarrow} 4Cr + 3SiO_2$

(14) $FeO.Cr_2O_3 + 4C \overset{\triangle}{\rightarrow} (Fe + 2Cr) + 4CO \uparrow$

Pharmacological Action of Chromium Ion.—The pharmacodynamic actions of chromium salts, chromates, and dichromates are very similar. They are destructive to tissue, regardless of whether applied topically or administered orally. When taken internally, they produce a characteristic nephritis and glycosuria. Persons exposed to "chromate dust" develop deep ulcers of the skin and nasal mucosa that heal very slowly.

Chromium trioxide (CrO_3) is a powerful oxidizing agent. It is used as a caustic. One to 3 per cent solutions are used as local astringents, whereas dilute solutions are employed for urethral injections. The dichromates, especially potassium dichromate, have been used in the treatment of cancer.

Uses.—Chromium *as such* is never used in medicine. Chromium trioxide (CrO_3) is sometimes employed as a caustic; in 2 to 3 per cent solution as an astringent; in 5 per cent solution for perspiring feet; and in 0.05 to 0.025 per cent solution for urethral injections. Potassium dichromate has been used ($\frac{1}{10}$ to $\frac{1}{6}$ grain) internally against gastric ulcer.

Non-Official Chromium Compound

Chromium Trioxide, N.F. X, CrO_3, (Chromic Anhydride) occurs in long, needle-shaped crystals, in rhombic prisms having a metallic luster or in flakes. The color of the crystals ranges from a scarlet to a dark purplish-red. It is deliquescent in moist air. This oxide is a vigorous oxidizing agent, destroying both animal and vegetable tissues and, therefore, should not be brought in intimate contact with organic substances (sugar, charcoal, powdered vegetable drugs, etc.) as an explosion may occur.

One Gm. of chromium trioxide dissolves in 0.6 ml. of water at 25° C., giving a solution that apparently contains *dichromic acid*, a substance unknown in the pure state. One Gm. is soluble in 0.5 ml. of boiling water. When the hot saturated solution is cooled, rose-red crystals of *chromic acid* (H_2CrO_4) separate out. Chromium trioxide oxidizes organic solvents, *e.g.*, alcohol to acetaldehyde, so rapidly that the reaction may become dangerously violent. When warmed with hydrochloric acid, chlorine is evolved.

Chromium trioxide darkens when heated and at about 196° C. fuses to a reddish-brown liquid. At 250° C., it loses oxygen and is converted into chromic chromate ($CrO_3.Cr_2O_3$) (1). At higher temperatures it loses more oxygen, until a residue of green chromic oxide (Cr_2O_3) remains (2).

(1) $6CrO_3 \xrightarrow{\triangle} 2CrO_3.Cr_2O_3 + 3O_2 \uparrow$

(2) $4CrO_3.Cr_2O_3 \xrightarrow{\triangle} 6Cr_2O_3 + 3O_2 \uparrow$

Chromic anhydride (CrO_3) is analogous to sulfuric anhydride (SO_3) and forms one series of salts (chromates, M_2CrO_4) analogous to sulfates, and another series (dichromates, $M_2Cr_2O_7$) which corresponds to the pyrosulfates.

When chromium trioxide is warmed with hydrochloric acid, chlorine is evolved (3).

$$(3) \ 2CrO_3 + 6HCl \overset{\triangle}{\rightarrow} Cr_2O_3 + 3H_2O + 3Cl_2 \uparrow$$

Ammonia gas reduces chromium trioxide to chromic oxide (Cr_2O_3), nitrogen and water (4).

$$(4) \ 2CrO_3 + 2NH_3 \rightarrow Cr_2O_3 + 3H_2O + N_2 \uparrow$$

Chromium Trioxide should not be brought into intimate contact with organic substances or other reducing substances, as serious explosions are likely to result.

2. Chromium trioxide is prepared by adding concentrated sulfuric acid to a cold saturated solution of potassium chromate (5). The long needle-shaped red crystals are separated from the mother liquor and washed with concentrated nitric acid. The excess nitric acid is removed by means of a current of dry air.

The use has been discussed under Pharmacological Action of Chromium Ion.

44

Molybdenum, Tungsten and Uranium and Their Compounds

MOLYBDENUM

Symbol, Mo.   Valences, 2 to 6.   Atomic Weight, 95.94;
Atomic Number, 42

History and Occurrence.—For many years, graphite, molybdenum sulfide, and other substances similar in appearance to lead were designated by the Greek word μόλυβδος (lead).   Cronstedt differentiated between graphite and molybdenum sulfide and, in 1778, Scheele obtained molybdic acid from the sulfide.   The pure metal was first obtained by Hjelm in 1780.

The native sulfide, *molybdenite* (MoS_2), is the principal ore of molybdenum.   It occurs widely distributed in Nature but in rather small quantities.   In the United States it is found in Maine, Utah, Arizona, etc.   There is also an apparently inexhaustible source of molybdenum ores in the mountains of Colorado.   Other minerals containing molybdenum are *wulfenite* ($PbMoO_4$), *molybdite* (MoO_3) and a hydrated ferric *molybdate ocher*.   Molybdenum is present in many iron ores.

Physical and Chemical Properties.—Molybdenum is a malleable, silvery white metal.   It is permanent in air.   It crystallizes in the regular system, has a density of 10.2, melts at 2622° C. and boils at 4510° C.   It is not as hard as glass but is harder than topaz.

When heated above 600° C. in air, molybdenum is converted into the trioxide.   It forms many compounds in which it exercises valences from 2 to 6.   Like the other members of this family, it forms oxychlorides (MoO_2Cl_2).   The group tendency to form poly-salts containing a large excess of acidic anhydride [$(NH_4)_3PO_4.-12MoO_3$] is very pronounced in molybdenum.   The metal is soluble in nitric or nitrohydrochloric acids.   It forms a blue solution when dissolved in concentrated sulfuric acid.   When this solution is heated it becomes colorless, evolves sulfur dioxide and precipitates molybdenum trioxide.   The metal is insoluble in hydrochloric, hydrofluoric, and dilute sulfuric acids.

(586)

Tests for Identity.—1. When a dry molybdenum compound is heated on a platinum foil with concentrated sulfuric acid until nearly all of the acid is driven off, a blue residue remains.

2. Sodium phosphate precipitates yellow ammonium phosphomolybdate from warmed solutions of molybdates acidified with nitric acid (1). The precipitate is soluble in ammonia T.S. The composition of this precipitate varies with the conditions under which it is formed. When dried at 130° C., it has the formula $(NH_4)_3PO_4.12MoO_3$. Arsenates, silicates, and tungstates interfere with this test as they give analogous precipitates.

$$(1)\quad 12(NH_4)_2MoO_4 + H_3PO_4 + 21HNO_3 \rightarrow (NH_4)_3PO_4.12MoO_3\downarrow + 21NH_4NO_3 + 12H_2O$$

3. When a solution of a molybdate is treated with zinc and sulfuric acid, a blue coloration is produced. The blue color of the solution gradually turns a greenish-gray and finally brown.

Commercial Manufacture.—Metallic molybdenum is made by first roasting the disulfide and leaching the resulting trioxide with ammonia water to form ammonium molybdate $[(NH_4)_2MoO_4]$ which, in turn, is ignited to MoO_2. This is reduced to the metal with carbon in an electric furnace or by the Goldschmidt process (q.v.). When prepared in this manner, molybdenum metal is a gray powder which, at a very high temperature (about 2620° C.), fuses into a silvery white mass.

Uses.—Molybdenum metal is never used in medicine. Its principal industrial use is in the manufacture of special grades of very tough and hard steel. Molybdenum oxide (3 mg.) together with ferrous sulfate (195 mg.) in a specially co-precipitated complex is marketed in the form of tablets as a hematinic preparation (Mol-Iron). It is said to potentiate the uptake of iron by the body.

TUNGSTEN (WOLFRAM)

Symbol, W.   Valences, 2 to 6.   Atomic Weight, 183.85;
Atomic Number, 74

History.—In 1781, Scheele and Bergman detected this element in scheelite, and in 1783, Juan and José d'Elhujar found it in wolfram ocher.

Occurrence.—Wolfram is found in Nature as *wolframite*, a ferrous manganese tungstate $(FeWO_4.MnWO_4)$, as *wolfram ocher* or tungsten trioxide (WO_3), as *scheelite* or calcium tungstate $(CaO.WO_3)$ and as metallic tungstates, such as *lead tungstate* $(PbO.WO_3)$, *barium tungstate* $(BaO.4WO_3.9H_2O)$, *copper tungstate* $(CuO.WO_3)$, etc.

Properties.—Tungsten is a very hard, brittle, silver-white to steel-gray, lustrous metal. It has a density of 19.35, melts at about 3410° C., which is the highest melting-point of any metal. It boils at 5900° C. By proper treatment, the metal becomes very ductile and then may be drawn into fine wires. The metal resists attack by most chemical agents. It is readily attacked by a mixture of hydrofluoric and nitric acids. By fusion with sodium carbonate or a mixture of sodium nitrate and sodium hydroxide it is converted into the soluble sodium tungstate ($Na_2WO_4 . 2H_2O$).

Tests for Identity.—Soluble tungstates or phosphotungstates are reduced by stannous chloride to insoluble yellow tungsten trioxide. When this precipitate is heated with hydrochloric acid, it changes to a blue color (1).

$$(1)\ 3WO_4^= + Sn^{++} + 8H_3O^+ \rightarrow (WO_2)_2WO_4 + Sn^{++++} + 12H_2O$$

Solutions of tungstates, when evaporated to dryness with hydrochloric acid, leave a yellow residue which is soluble in ammonia test solutions.

Metallurgy.—Tungsten is obtained by fusing its ores with sodium carbonate and leaching out the sodium tungstate so produced with water. This solution is treated with an acid which precipitates tungstic acid ($H_2WO_4 . H_2O$). The tungstic acid is either ignited to the oxides which are subsequently reduced by hydrogen in an electric furnace or it is reduced to the metal by the Goldschmidt process (*q.v.*). The gray powder which results is compressed into bars and heated to a very high temperature in an electric furnace. These heated bars of metal are swaged and worked into slender rods which are sufficiently ductile to be drawn out into very fine wires.

Uses.—The high melting-point of this metal, together with its low volatility (less than carbon), makes it admirably suited for filaments in electric light bulbs. Tungsten imparts great hardness to steel. These steels retain their temper even at red heat and are used in high-speed cutting tools.

Tungsten compounds are not used in medicine.

COMPOUNDS OF TUNGSTEN

The principal compound of tungsten is the trioxide (WO_3). It is prepared either by decomposing hot solutions of tungstates with nitric acid or by igniting tungstic acid. It is insoluble in acids, but dissolves in alkalies to form a series of normal tungstates and also a series of polytungstates, which are the salts of simple tungstic acid and complex tungstic acid, respectively.

Tungstic acid, like the corresponding acids of molybdenum and uranium, forms complex compounds with phosphoric, arsenic, antimonic, boric, and vanadic acids. The U.S. Pharmacopoeia XVII recognizes *phosphotungstic acid* as a reagent. On account of the insolubility of its alkaloidal salts, this acid is used as a qualitative reagent for alkaloids. This complex acid occurs as white or yellowish-green crystals or as a crystalline powder. The approximate formula $P_2O_5.24WO_3.(H_2O)_n$ has been assigned to it. It dissolves in water and in alcohol but it is only slightly soluble in ether.

URANIUM

Symbol, U.   Valences, 4, 6.   Atomic Weight, 238.03;
Atomic Number, 92

History.—In 1789, Klaproth obtained from pitchblende a yellow oxide which he considered to be the oxide of a new metal. He named the element *uranium* after the planet, Uranus, which Herschel only recently had discovered. In 1823, Berzelius prepared some of the uranyl salts. He thought that the radical, uranyl (UO_2), was the true metal. This misconception was proven by Péligot in 1840.

Properties.—Metallic uranium is a white metal resembling nickel in appearance but is a black powder when obtained by reduction. It has a density of 19.05 and a melting-point of 1150° C. Uranium acts as a true metal by displacing the hydrogen of acids. The element and also its compounds are radioactive.

Metallurgy.—A large quantity of uranium is obtained from pitchblende by first roasting the ore to drive off any sulfur and arsenic and then converting the metals into sulfates by treating the purified ore with hot concentrated nitric acid followed by evaporation with sulfuric acid. The residue of mixed sulfates is lixiviated with water which dissolves out the soluble uranium and other sulfates but leaves the silica, insoluble lead sulfate, etc. After filtration, hydrogen sulfide is passed through the solution. This precipitates any arsenic, iron, copper, etc., present in the liquid. The filtrate is boiled with nitric acid and the uranium, iron, and aluminum are precipitated by the addition of an excess of ammonium hydroxide. The well-washed precipitate is then digested with a warm concentrated solution of ammonium carbonate. This effects the solution of the uranium as ammonium uranate and leaves behind the hydrated oxides of iron, aluminum, etc., which are filtered off. When the liquid is concentrated and cooled, crystals of ammonium uranate separate out. These crystals yield a mixed oxide when ignited in a platinum crucible. These oxides are usually purified by dissolving them in nitric acid and then precipitating the uranium as the oxalate with oxalic acid. When uranyl oxalate ($UO_2.C_2O_4$) is ignited, it yields a much purer mixture of oxides, U_3O_8 or $UO_2.2UO_3$. When the oxide is heated with coke in an electric furnace, a uranium metal of about 98 per cent purity is obtained.

A very pure metal may be obtained also by the **reduction of** uranous chloride (UCl_4) with metallic sodium.

COMPOUNDS OF URANIUM

Uranium forms two principal oxides, *viz.*, uranous oxide or uranyl (UO_2) and uranic oxide (UO_3). The former is basic in character, whereas the latter is both acid- and base-forming (amphoteric). These two oxides are the sources of several series of salts. When the basic oxide is dissolved in acids, it forms normal *uranous* salts, *e.g.*, UCl_4, $U(SO_4)_2$, UI_4, etc. The uranous salts are quite unstable. They are active reducing agents. Uranic oxide (UO_3) dissolves in acids to form the basic *uranyl* salts in which the UO_2 radical acts as a metal (1).

$$(1) \quad UO_3 + H_2SO_4 \rightarrow UO_2(SO_4) + H_2O$$

Uranyl nitrate $(UO_2[NO_3]_2 . 6H_2O)$ was official as *Uranii Nitras* in the ninth revision of the U. S. Pharmacopœia. This efflorescent, radioactive salt occurs in light yellow prisms which are odorless but have a bitter astringent taste. It is soluble in 1.2 parts of water at 25° C. and freely soluble in alcohol and in ether. Because of its slight radioactivity, this salt was given in 10-mg. ($\frac{1}{6}$-grain) doses in the treatment of spreading sluggish ulcers. It was directed to be used with caution.

Uranyl nitrate is used in the volumetric determination of phosphoric acid (2). Glass, made by adding uranium nitrate or any other uranium salt to the melt, has a greenish-yellow fluorescence.

$$(2) \quad Na_2HPO_4 + UO_2(NO_3)_2 \rightarrow UO_2HPO_4 \downarrow + 2NaNO_3$$

Uranic oxide dissolves in alkalies to form *uranates* (3) and *diuranates* (4), which correspond to the chromates and dichromates.

$$(3) \quad UO_3 + 2NaOH \rightarrow Na_2UO_4 + H_2O$$

$$(4) \quad 2UO_3 + 2NaOH \rightarrow Na_2U_2O_7 + H_2O$$

In the presence of ammonium chloride, ammonium hydroxide precipitates ammonium diuranate from a solution of a uranyl salt (5).

$$(5) \quad 2UO_2(NO_3)_2 + 6NH_4OH \rightarrow (NH_4)_2U_2O_7 \downarrow + 4NH_4NO_3 + 3H_2O$$

Ammonium sulfide precipitates an unstable, brown uranyl sulfide (UO_2S) from solutions of a uranyl salt (6).

$$(6) \quad UO_2(NO_3)_2 + (NH_4)_2S \rightarrow UO_2S \downarrow + 2NH_4NO_3$$

SUBGROUP VIIA

Introduction.—The only metal of pharmaceutical importance in this subgroup is manganese. Technitium is a product of radioactive change, not occurring naturally, and little is known of its properties. Rhenium is extremely rare although a fair amount of knowledge is available concerning its properties.

In the oxidation state of +7, manganese and rhenium form MnO_4^- and ReO_4^- ions, respectively. It is only in this oxidation state that there are any real resemblances to other Group VII elements. The higher valence states of rhenium are more stable than those of manganese whereas the opposite is true of the lower valence states. In common with most transition metals possessing an incomplete inner subshell these elements form colored ions.

PROPERTIES OF SUBGROUP VIIA

Properties	Manganese	Technitium	Rhenium
Atomic Number	25	43	75
Atomic Weight	54.9380	99	186.2
Isotopes	55	99	185, 187
Electrons	2-8-(8 + 5)-2	2-8-18-(8 + 6)-1	2-8-18-32-(8 + 5)-2
Density	7.23	——	20.5
M.P.	1247°	——	3180°
B.P.	2032°	——	5900°
Common Oxidation States	0, +2, +3, +4, +6, +7	——	+3, +4, +5, +6, +7
Ionization Potential, first, volts	7.43	7.23	7.87
Radius (cov.), Å	1.17	——	1.36
Radius (ion), Å	0.80 (+2)	——	——

45

Manganese and Manganese Compounds

MANGANESE

Symbol, Mn.   Valences, 2, 3, 4, 6, 7.   Atomic Weight, 54.9380;
Atomic Number, 25

History.—Pyrolusite, a naturally occurring manganese dioxide, has been known from early times. This substance was thought to be a magnetic oxide of iron or magnetite until in 1740, J. H. Pott showed that this ore did not contain iron and that a definite series of salts could be obtained from it. In 1774, C. Scheele showed it to be an oxide of a new element and in the same year, J. G. Gahn isolated the metal.

Occurrence.—Manganese is chemically and geologically related to iron and hence is frequently found in Nature associated with it. Average igneous rocks contain about 0.078 per cent of manganese. *Pyrolusite*, native MnO_2, is the principal manganese ore. It occurs widely distributed. Manganese is the chief constituent of the following minerals: *Pyrochroite* ($MnO.H_2O$), *wad* (impure oxides), *manganite* ($Mn_2O_3.H_2O$), *polianite* (MnO_2), *hausmannite* (Mn_3O_4) and *psilomelane* ($Mn_2O_3 + H_2O$). Manganese occurs as the sulfate in *mallardite* ($MnSO_4.7H_2O$), as the sulfide in *alabandite* ($MnS)_3$, as the carbonate in *rhodochrosite* ($MnCO_3$), and as the silicate in *rhodonite* ($MnSiO_2$).

Traces of manganese occur in almost all organs of both man and animals. The smaller part of this manganese is derived from vegetable foods, whereas the larger amount comes from animal sources.

Physical Properties.—Manganese is a very hard, brittle, lustrous, gray-white metal resembling cast-iron in appearance. It has a density of 7.23. It melts at 1247° C. and boils at 2032° C.

Chemical Properties.—The pure metal oxidizes readily in moist air, but its alloys containing iron resist oxidation. Manganese decomposes steam, whereas water at 23° C. is decomposed by the finely divided metal. It reacts with dilute acids and liberates hydrogen and forms manganous salts (1).

$$(1)\ Mn + 2H_3O^+ \rightarrow Mn^{++} + H_2 \uparrow + 2H_2O$$

(592)

The element manganese due to the arrangement of the electrons in two outer orbits of the atom can exhibit several valence forms. See the following table.

Name	Valence	Example
Manganous	2	$Mn(PH_2O_2)_2$
Manganic	3	$Mn_2(SO_4)_3$
Manganite	4	Na_2MnO_3
Manganate	6	Na_2MnO_4
Permanganate	7	$KMnO_4$

The valence forms used in pharmacy are the manganous and permanganate.

When an element can exist in several oxidation states the lower oxides formed tend to form bases (MnO), the intermediate oxides are amphoteric (Mn_2O_3 and MnO_2), while the higher oxides are only acid-forming (MnO_3 and Mn_2O_7). This same observation may also be made with chromium.

Manganese in its lower states of oxidation is a reducing agent and is very readily oxidized. The intermediate oxidation states as in the compounds Na_2MnO_3 and Na_2MnO_4 are reduced by hydrogen sulfide to MnS and may be oxidized by strong oxidizing agents such as lead tetraoxide (PbO_4) or sodium bismuthate ($NaBiO_3$) to permanganate.

Manganous ions are solubilized by sequestering agents such as citrates. A complex ion with sodium citrate was used in Manganous Citrate N.F. X. The solid product was noncrystalline but occurred as granules.

Solutions of manganous salts exhibit the following reactions:

1. When a fixed alkali is added to a solution of a manganous salt, a white precipitate of manganous hydroxide is produced (2). The precipitate soon darkens by absorption of oxygen from the air and is converted into hydrated manganic hydroxide [$MnO(OH)_2$ or H_2-$MnO(OH)_2$]. Manganous hydroxide is soluble in an excess of ammonium salts (3).

(2) $Mn^{++} + 2OH^- \rightarrow Mn(OH)_2 \downarrow$

(3) $Mn(OH)_2 + 4NH_4Cl \rightarrow MnCl_2 . 2NH_4Cl + 2NH_4OH$

2. Alkali carbonates precipitate white manganous carbonate from solutions of manganous salts (4). The precipitate turns brown on exposure to air, due to the formation of hydrated manganic hydroxide (5).

(4) $Mn^{++} + CO_3^= \rightarrow MnCO_3 \downarrow$

(5) $2MnCO_3 + O_2 + 2H_2O \rightarrow 2H_2MnO_3$ [or $2MnO(OH)_2$] + $2CO_2 \uparrow$

Oxidation may be more evident by the addition of a small quantity of hydrogen peroxide T.S. (6).

(6) $2H_2O_2 \rightarrow 2H_2O + O_2$
$MnCO_3 \rightleftharpoons Mn^{++} + CO_3^=$
$2Mn^{++} + 2H_2O + 2O_2 \rightarrow 2H_2MnO_3$ or $[2MnO(OH)_2]$
(brown)
$CO_3^= + H_2O \rightarrow H_2CO_3 \rightarrow H_2O + CO_2 \uparrow$

If an excess of sodium hydroxide is added to the brown precipitate it will be noted that it is amphoteric.

3. Ammonium sulfide precipitates salmon colored manganous sulfide from neutral solutions of manganous salts and turns freshly precipitated manganous hydroxide into sulfide (7). The precipitate is soluble in acetic and in diluted mineral acids.

(7) $Mn^{++} + S^= \rightarrow MnS \downarrow$

4. When a small quantity of a manganese compound (not the dioxide) is heated to boiling with diluted nitric acid and a little brown oxide of lead, the supernatant liquid will have a reddish-purple color, due to permanganic acid (8).

(8) $2Mn^{++} + 5PbO_2 + 4H_3O^+ \rightarrow 2MnO_4^- + 5Pb^{++} + 6H_2O$

5. When a manganese compound is fused on a porcelain crucible cover with a little potassium chlorate and potassium hydroxide, the melt becomes dark green (9). When the mass is lixiviated with water and the solution acidified, the color changes to a reddish-purple (10).

(9) $2MnO_2 + 4KOH + O_2 \overset{\triangle}{\rightarrow} 2K_2MnO_4 + 2H_2O$
(10) $3MnO_4^= + 2H_2O \rightarrow 2MnO_4^- + 4OH^- + MnO_2 \downarrow$

6. Sodium bismuthate (approx. $NaBiO_3$) in nitric acid solution will oxidize Mn^{++} to purple MnO_4^- ion (11). Provided nothing is present to react with the permanganate ion, this is a very delicate test for manganese.

(11) $2Mn^{++} + 5NaBiO_3 + 16H_3O^+ \rightarrow 5Na^+ + 5Bi^{+++} + 23H_2O$
$+ 2HMnO_4$

7. Manganese compounds impart an amethyst color to a borax bead.

Official Test for Identity.—Solutions of manganous salts yield a salmon-colored precipitate with ammonium sulfide T.S. (7), soluble in acetic acid.

Commercial Manufacture.—The various oxides of manganese are difficult to reduce even at high temperatures with hydrogen. A very crude metal may be obtained by reducing the oxide with carbon in an electric furnace. Various processes have been recommended for the reduction of manganese oxides (Brunner, Glatzel, Moissan, etc.), but the one most generally used is the "thermite" method of H. Goldschmidt (*q.v.*).

Because most of the manganese ores available in the U. S. have a low concentration of manganese (usually about 20 per cent), 90 per cent of the manganese requirement is obtained from imported ores (at least 50 per cent Mn). This situation obviously has its drawbacks and it is desirable to have a process to handle the low grade domestic ores, thus giving this country an independence from imported raw materials. To this end, a new process (Nossen process) has been devised. In this process the manganese ore is treated with nitric acid to give a nitrate solution which is then decomposed on a revolving heated drum. The nitric acid is recovered and the dried manganese dioxide is continually removed by a scraper. Actually, the process is in its infancy but if it lives up to its promises it will make the U. S. self-sufficient in manganese for at least 100 years.

Commercial alloys of manganese and iron are made by reducing the respective ores in a blast furnace. *Ferromanganese* (25 to 85 per cent of Mn) and *spiegeleisen* (12 to 33 per cent of Mn) are examples of manganese alloys.

Pharmacological Action of Manganese Ions.—When orally administered, manganese salts (not permanganates) produce no noticeable effects. A small quantity of the manganese is absorbed from the alimentary tract and is deposited principally in the kidneys and liver. It is excreted as sulfide in the feces. It has never been conclusively shown that manganese exercises any hematinic action. It is sometimes prescribed with iron because of its possible synergistic action.

The permanganates are powerful oxidizing agents. Solutions containing from 0.02 to 0.1 per cent are used for urethral injections. Large doses of permanganates produce very severe gastro-enteritis.

Uses.—Manganese is used in the preparation of its salts. Manganese alloys containing less than 7 per cent of this metal are soft and ductile but, as the per cent of manganese increases, they become hard and brittle. Manganese steel, containing from 7 to 20 per cent of manganese, is very hard and hence is used in making burglar-proof safes, armor plate, and crushing and grinding machinery. Various alloys of manganese containing copper, zinc, nickel, etc., are of industrial importance.

Manganese compounds are used in the manufacture of glass, colored bricks, dryer in paints and varnishes, dry cells, chemicals, etc.

Non-Official Manganese Compounds

Soluble Manganese Citrate N.F. X, $Mn_3(C_6H_5O_7)_2$, occurs as a pale orange or pinkish-white powder, as granules, or as translucent scales, and is permanent in the air. It is odorless, and has a slightly bitter, astringent taste. Normal manganese citrate is only slightly soluble in water. However, Soluble Manganese Citrate includes sodium citrate and is soluble in about four times its weight of water at 25° C. It is almost insoluble in alcohol but is soluble in boiling water.

The chemical properties of a solution of Soluble Manganese Citrate are characteristic of the manganous ion (*q.v.*) and the citrate ion (*q.v.*). Ammonium hydroxide readily precipitates manganous hydroxide (1) which is oxidized to manganic hydroxide with hydrogen peroxide (2).

(1) $Mn_3(C_6H_5O_7)_2 + 6NH_4OH \rightarrow 3Mn(OH)_2\downarrow + 2(NH_4)_3\text{-}C_6H_5O_7$

(2) $4Mn(OH)_2 + 2H_2O_2 \rightarrow 4Mn(OH)_3$

Upon igniting the $Mn(OH)_3$, manganous-manganic oxide is formed (3).

(3) $6Mn(OH)_3 \overset{\triangle}{\rightarrow} 2Mn_3O_4 + 9H_2O + (O)$

It is prepared by the interaction of manganous hydroxide and citric acid. The excess citric acid is neutralized with sodium carbonate and the solution evaporated. Manganous citrate itself is not soluble, but by sequestering the manganous ion with sodium citrate it is solubilized. The salt as formerly recognized officially contained not less than 48 and not more than 52 per cent of $Mn_3(C_6H_5O_7)_2$.

Because a trace of manganese is essential to health, it has been used for many years as a tonic. The role of manganese in the animal body is unknown. There has been some evidence that manganese is beneficial in certain types of anemia but it is considered by most physicians to have little real value in the treatment of disease. Usual dose—0.2 Gm.

Manganese Glycerophosphate, N.F. X, $MnC_3H_5(OH)_2PO_4$, is a white or pinkish powder, having no odor and almost no taste. In the presence of citric acid (1 in 4), normal manganese glycerophosphate is soluble in about five times its weight of water at 25° C. It is insoluble in alcohol and slightly soluble in water.

Manganese glycerophosphate is obtained from manganese carbonate and glycerophosphoric acid (2). This acid is prepared by heating together glycerin and metaphosphoric acid (1).

(1) $C_3H_5(OH)_3 + HPO_3 \overset{\triangle}{\rightarrow} H_2C_3H_5(OH)_2PO_4$

(2) $H_2C_3H_5(OH)_2PO_4 + MnCO_3 \overset{\triangle}{\rightarrow} MnC_3H_5(OH)_2PO_4 + CO_2\uparrow + H_2O$

Because of the therapeutic reputation (doubtful) of manganese and glycerophosphate, these two appeared to be a logical tie-up for use as a tonic. The product is considered of little value, however, and finds practically no medical use except in proprietaries. Usual dose—0.2 Gm.

Manganese Hypophosphite, N.F. X, $Mn(PH_2O_2)_2.H_2O$, is an odorless and nearly tasteless, granular or crystalline, pink powder. It is stable in air, dissolves in about 6.5 ml. of water at 25° C., or in about 6 ml. of boiling water. It is insoluble in alcohol.

A water solution of manganous hypophosphite exhibits the chemical properties of the manganous ion (*q.v.*) and the hypophosphite ion.

It is made by mixing a solution of calcium hypophosphite with a solution of manganous sulfate (1). The mixture is allowed to stand in a warm place to permit the calcium sulfate to crystallize out, filtered, and either evaporated to crystallization or granulated.

$$(1)\ MnSO_4 + Ca(PH_2O_2)_2 + H_2O \rightarrow Mn(PH_2O_2)_2.H_2O + CaSO_4 \downarrow$$

Caution should be observed in compounding this salt with oxidizing agents such as nitrates and chlorates, as explosions may occur if it is triturated or heated.

Hypophosphites, like the glycerophosphates, have enjoyed considerable unwarranted medicinal popularity. The compound is used for the supposed tonic benefits of manganese and hypophosphite. Usual dose—0.2 Gm.

GROUP VIII

Introduction.—This is a rather unusual group of metals and is composed of nine elements which are arranged as groups of three in periods 4, 5 and 6 following Group VIIA and preceding Group IB. Mendéleeff originally termed these triads the "transition metals" because they enabled the bridging necessary for his "short form" of the Periodic Table. Since then the concept of transition metals has been expanded concomitant with the increased knowledge of electron arrangement. Quite generally these elements are considered as horizontal triads rather than as vertical groups although there is probably as much reason to consider them vertically as horizontally. Nevertheless, convention dictates the consideration of iron, cobalt and nickel as a triad. The rest of the metals are termed the "platinum metals" with ruthenium, rhodium and palladium being the "light" platinum metals and osmium, iridium and platinum the "heavy" platinum metals.

The electronic configurations of the iron triad show two $4s$ electrons in the outermost shell together with a partially filled $3d$ subgroup in the next outermost shell. It is the $4s$ electrons that are utilized in the formation of divalent ions, whereas a $3d$ electron must be used to form the trivalent ion. Observation of the relative stabilities of the divalent and trivalent states of the three elements leads to the conclusion that the higher valence state becomes less stable as the atomic number increases. This is tantamount to saying that the $3d$ electron becomes more difficult to utilize in bonding as the $3d$ shell becomes more saturated. For all practical purposes, the higher valence states of the iron triad are very unstable. Much

PROPERTIES OF GROUP VIII

IRON TRIAD

Properties	Iron	Cobalt	Nickel
Atomic Number	26	27	28
Atomic Weight	55.847	58.9332	58.71
Isotopes	54, 56–8	59	58, 60–2, 64
Electrons	2–8–(8 + 6)–2	2–8–(8 + 7)–2	2–8–(8 + 8)–2
Common Oxidation States	0, +2, +3, +4, +6	0, +2, +3, +4	0, +2, +3, +4
Density	7.86	8.92	8.9
M.P.	1535°	1493°	1455°
B.P.	3000°	3550°	3075°
Ionization Potential first, volts	7.83	ca. 8.5	7.6
Oxidation Potential, volts. $M \rightarrow M^{++}$	+0.44	+0.277	+0.250

(599)

PROPERTIES OF GROUP VIII—(*Continued*)

LIGHT PLATINUM METALS

Properties	Ruthenium	Rhodium	Palladium
Atomic Number	44	45	46
Atomic Weight	101.07	102.905	106.4
Isotopes	96, 98–102, 104	103	102, 104–6, 108, 110
Electrons	2–8–18–(8 + 7)–1	2–8–18–(8 + 8)–1	2–8–18–(8 + 9)–1
Common Oxidation States	0, 2, 3, 4, 5, 6, 7, 8	0, 2, 3, 4, 6	0, 2, 3, **4**, 6
Density	12.2	12.42	12.0
M.P.	2450°	1966°	1555°
B.P.	4150°	4500°	3980°
Ionization Potential, first, volts.	7.37	7.7	8.3
Oxidation Potential, volts. $M \rightarrow M^{++}$	−0.45	ca. −0.6	−0.98

HEAVY PLATINUM METALS

Properties	Osmium	Iridium	Platinum
Atomic Number	76	77	78
Atomic Weight	190.2	192.2	195.09
Isotopes	184, 186–90, 192	191, 193	192, 194–6, 198
Electrons	2–8–18–32–(8 + 6)–2	2–8–18–32–(8 + 7)–2	2–8–18–32–(8 + 8)–2
Common Oxidaton States	0, 2, 3, 4, 6, 8	0, 2, 3, 4, 6	0, 2, 3, **4**, 6
Density	22.5	22.4	21.45
M.P.	2700°	2450°	1773°
B.P.	5500°	5300°	4530°
Ionization Potential, first, volts.	8.7	9.2	8.96
Oxidation Potential, volts, $M \rightarrow M^{++}$	−0.7	< −1.0	ca. −1.2

of the chemistry of these elements is concerned with complexes which will not be considered here.[1]

One of the principal differences between the iron triad and the platinum metals is the marked tendency of the former group to form simple cations in contrast to the definite reluctance to do so by the latter. The platinum metals seem to prefer the higher oxidation states. Whereas there is an increase in atom size when comparing the iron triad with the platinum metals, the latter do not differ greatly in size. This accounts for the much greater density of the heavy platinum metals in comparison to the light. Indeed, osmium is the heaviest known substance.

All of the Group VIII elements are grayish-white metals with high melting and boiling points. They all have some absorptive ability for hydrogen with palladium exhibiting unusual activity in this regard. Reactivity with oxygen is noted in the iron triad, particularly, with the affinity dropping off rapidly as the atomic number

[1] For a discussion of these see E. S. Gould, "Inorganic Reactions and Structure," page 358, publ. by Henry Holt & Co., Inc. New York, 1955.

increases. This same trend of high oxygen affinity in the left hand member of the series is noted in each succeeding triad of the platinum metals as well. The platinum metals are classed as "noble" metals because they show low oxidation potentials and low reactivity. Because of this lack of reactivity they are not easily tarnished. However, the light platinum metals are more susceptible to oxidizing agents than are the heavier metals.

The magnetic properties of the iron triad are unique in that these are the only elements possessing this property at room temperature. This property is thought to be due in some way to the incomplete d subgroup.

Most of these metals in Group VIII have a unique property in forming "carbonyls" with carbon monoxide. These are low melting liquids which decompose rather readily to the metal and carbon monoxide on heating.

46

Iron and Iron Compounds

IRON

Symbol, Fe.   Valences, 2, 3.   Atomic Weight, 55.847;
Atomic Number, 26

History.—Iron tools, vessels and ornaments, fashioned by prehistoric man have been found in Egypt. The discovery of iron ore
and the development of methods for recovering the metal therefrom
exercised a very marked influence on the civilization of a certain
early period known as the *Iron Age*. Ancient Persian and Assyrian
cuneiform inscriptions show that iron was used by these people. A
teacher (Tubal-cain) of workers in iron and copper is mentioned in
the Old Testament. The earliest source of iron ores was in India
and undoubtedly the Hindus were the first to develop processes for
making malleable and wrought iron. Steel was manufactured by
the Greeks, and the Chalybes, a people living on the south coast
of the Black Sea, were noted for producing high-grade steels. The
Romans obtained their iron ore from the Chalybeans and also from
Spain, Elba, etc. It is said that the first blast furnace was operated
in Germany about 1350 A.D. The symbol Fe is derived from the
Latin, *Ferrum*. The name *"iron"* is derived from the Anglo-Saxon,
isen.

Occurrence.—Metallic iron is found in Nature only in meteorites
that have fallen upon the earth. The metal found in meteorites is
associated with from 3 to 9 per cent of nickel. With the exception
of aluminum, iron in combination occurs more widely distributed
and in larger quantities than any other metallic element. It occurs
in soil and in small quantities in natural waters and plants. Iron
is a necessary constituent of the blood (hemoglobin) and of the
oxidases. It is found in all chromatin and, therefore, should be
found in all cells.

The principal ores of iron consist of the oxides and carbonate.
These ores may be reduced by smelting with carbon and yield a
metal that invariably contains either free or combined carbon or
both, and whose properties are dependent upon the amount of such
carbon present. In the United States (Minnesota) the most impor-

tant source of iron is the red oxide, *hematite* (Fe_2O_3). A comparatively small amount of black magnetic oxide of iron, *magnetite* (Fe_3O_4), is mined in some of the eastern states, but in Norway and Sweden this is the principal iron ore. Germany and France are dependent upon a brown hydrated oxide known as *limonite* ($2Fe_2O_3$.-$3H_2O$). An admixture of native ferrous carbonate (*siderite*), clay and shale, known as *iron stone* ($FeCO_3$) is the chief iron ore of Great Britain. *Iron pyrites*, native iron sulfide and sometimes called "fools' gold," is widely distributed in shining golden yellow crystals. The oxidized residues obtained by roasting this sulfide are not easily reduced and consequently this ore is never worked for iron. It can be used as a source of sulfur dioxide for sulfuric acid manufacture.

Physical Properties.—Pure iron is a silvery-white metal having a density of 7.86 and a melting-point of 1535° C. It boils at 3000° C. It is attracted by a magnet and may be temporarily magnetized. Pure iron is very soft and is not much stronger than lead.

The physical properties of the formerly official forms of metallic iron, *i.e.*, *Iron* and *Reduced Iron* are as follows:

1. *Iron.*—It was described as elementary iron (Fe) in the form of fine, bright wire, filings or powder. It was almost chemically pure metallic iron and its description was essentially that given above for iron.

2. *Reduced Iron.*—This was an odorless, grayish-black powder, all of which was required to pass through a No. 100 sieve. It had no luster or not more than a slight luster. If it was examined under a microscope capable of magnifying 100 diameters, it appeared as an amorphous powder, free from particles having a crystalline structure. It was stable in dry air.

Chemical Properties.—The chemical properties of iron will be considered as (1) metallic iron, (2) ferrous ion, and (3) ferric ion.

1. The *pure metal* is very active chemically. It burns brilliantly in an atmosphere of oxygen, although *pure* iron is quite resistant to atmospheric oxidation. Rusting of iron is probably due to the presence of impurities in the iron. Carbon dioxide greatly stimulates the formation of hydrated ferric oxide (ferric hydroxide or rust).

Iron combines directly with sulfur to form ferrous sulfide (1).

(1) $Fe + S \xrightarrow{\Delta} FeS$

It also reacts more or less readily with the halogens to form first the ferrous halide and then the ferric halide.

Since iron is above hydrogen in the electromotive series it will react with dilute acids to liberate hydrogen and form the corresponding ferrous salt. Hydrochloric acid, for example, reacts with metallic iron to form soluble ferrous chloride and hydrogen (2).

(2) $Fe + 2HCl \rightarrow FeCl_2 + H_2 \uparrow$

The reaction of nitric acid with iron is dependent upon the concentration of the nitric acid. Dilute nitric acid reacts with iron to form soluble ferrous nitrate (3), but at the same time the nitrogen of the nitric acid is reduced to ammonia.

$$(3) \quad 4Fe + 10HNO_3 \rightarrow 4Fe(NO_3)_2 + NH_4NO_3 + 3H_2O$$

More concentrated acid causes the formation of ferric nitrate (4).

$$(4) \quad Fe + 4HNO_3 \rightarrow Fe(NO_3)_3 + 2H_2O + NO \uparrow$$

Iron forms two series of salts, the ferrous (Fe^{++}) and the ferric (Fe^{+++}). It forms, however, three oxides, FeO, Fe_2O_3 and Fe_3O_4.

The last oxide, *magnetite*, is probably ferrous ferrite, $Fe\begin{smallmatrix} O-Fe=O \\ O-Fe=O \end{smallmatrix}$ rather than a mixture of Fe_2O_3 and FeO.

2. *Ferrous salts* are colorless when anhydrous, but when they have water of crystallization they are green in color.

When in the solid state, the ferrous salts are only slowly oxidized by atmospheric oxygen, but when in solution the transformation to the corresponding basic ferric salts (5) is much more rapid.

$$(5) \quad 4FeSO_4 + 2H_2O + O_2 \rightarrow 4Fe(OH)SO_4 \downarrow$$

These basic salts are insoluble and usually are brown in color. This accounts for the brown precipitate and scum which slowly form in ferrous sulfate solutions.

Ferrous compounds have a strong tendency to be oxidized to ferric compounds. For this reason they are effective reducing agents. Ferrous sulfate, for example, is readily converted to ferric sulfate by means of nitric acid together with some sulfuric acid to supply sulfate ion (6).

$$(6) \quad 6FeSO_4 + 3H_2SO_4 + 2HNO_3 \rightarrow 3Fe_2(SO_4)_3 + 2NO \uparrow + 4H_2O$$

Ferrous ion is readily precipitated from solution by alkali carbonates to form white ferrous carbonate (7), which on contact with air turns green and on further oxidation turns brown due to loss of CO_2 and consequent formation of ferric hydroxide (8).

$$(7) \quad Fe^{++} + CO_3^{=} \rightarrow FeCO_3 \downarrow$$
$$(8) \quad 4FeCO_3 + 6H_2O + O_2 \rightarrow 4Fe(OH)_3 + 4CO_2 \uparrow$$

Ferrous ion is also precipitated more or less completely by alkali hydroxides as greenish-white ferrous hydroxide (9). Contact with the air, however, converts this rather quickly to brown ferric hydroxide.

$$(9) \quad Fe^{++} + 2OH^- \rightarrow Fe(OH)_2 \downarrow$$

Potassium cyanide precipitates ferrous ion as ferrous cyanide (10), the precipitate being soluble in excess potassium cyanide to form potassium ferrocyanide (11). Potassium ferrocyanide is sometimes known as *yellow prussiate of potash* which distinguishes it from *red prussiate of potash* (potassium ferricyanide). Potassium ferricyanide reacts with ferrous ion to form a dark blue precipitate known as Turnbull's blue (12). This reaction is utilized as a sensitive test for ferrous ion, since ferric ion does not react with ferricyanide ion.

(10) $Fe^{++} + 2CN^- \rightarrow Fe(CN)_2 \downarrow$

(11) $Fe(CN)_2 + 4CN^- \rightarrow [Fe(CN)_6]^{= =}$

(12) $3Fe^{++} + 2[Fe(CN)_6]^{\equiv} \rightarrow Fe_3[Fe(CN)_6]_2 \downarrow$

3. *Ferric salts* are usually brown or yellow in color with few exceptions. As a rule, they react acidic in solution because of hydrolysis, the hydrolysis being increased with dilution and heating. It follows that dilution and heating are apt to cause a deposition of basic ferric salts from aqueous solutions (13).

(13) $Fe_2(SO_4)_3 + H_2O \rightarrow Fe_2O(SO_4)_2 \downarrow + H_2SO_4$

Ammonia and alkali hydroxides precipitate ferric ion as a brown, gelatinous ferric hydroxide (14).

(14) $Fe^{+++} + 3OH^- \rightarrow Fe(OH)_3 \downarrow$

The reaction of ferric ion with thiocyanate ion has been previously discussed (see p. 267).

Ferric ion is precipitated as an intense blue precipitate by potassium ferrocyanide (15). This precipitate is known as Prussian blue and is used as a sensitive test for ferric ion.

(15) $4Fe^{+++} + 3[Fe(CN)_6]^{= =} \rightarrow Fe_4[Fe(CN)_6]_3 \downarrow$

Sodium phosphate precipitates ferric ion as ferric phosphate especially when sodium acetate is added (16).

(16) $Fe^{+++} + HPO_4^{=} + CH_3COO^- \rightarrow FePO_4 \downarrow + CH_3COOH$

In the presence of sodium thiosulfate, ferric ion in neutral solution is reduced to ferrous ion (17), forming sodium tetrathionate simultaneously.

(17) $2Fe^{+++} + 2S_2O_3^{=} \rightarrow 2Fe^{++} + S_4O_6^{=}$

Ferric salts give dark-colored precipitates with tannins.

The assay of iron (Reduced Iron) is carried out by first dissolving the iron in diluted sulfuric acid (18) taking precautions to prevent any oxidation of the ferrous sulfate to ferric sulfate. The ferrous sulfate is then titrated with standard ceric sulfate (19) solution which oxidizes the ferrous iron to the ferric form quantitatively. The indicator for the end point is *ortho*-phenanthroline T.S. which is oxidized to a blue color by the first extra drop of ceric sulfate solution.

(18) $Fe + H_2SO_4 \rightarrow FeSO_4 + H_2 \uparrow$

(19) $2Ce(SO_4)_2 + 2FeSO_4 \rightarrow Fe_2(SO_4)_3 + Ce_2(SO_4)_3$

Official Tests for Identity.—Both ferrous and ferric salts yield a black precipitate with ammonium sulfide T.S. (20). This precipitate dissolves completely in cold diluted hydrochloric acid with the evolution of hydrogen sulfide (21).

(20) $Fe^{++} + (NH_4)_2S \rightarrow FeS \downarrow + 2NH_4^+$

and

$2Fe^{+++} + 3(NH_4)_2S \rightarrow Fe_2S_3 \downarrow + 6NH_4^+$

(21) $FeS + 2HCl \rightarrow FeCl_2 + H_2S \uparrow$

and

$Fe_2S_3 + 6HCl \rightarrow 2FeCl_3 + 3H_2S \uparrow$

The official compendia further supplement the sulfide test with specific tests for the two kinds of Fe ions.

(a) *Ferric Salts.*—1) Acid ferric salt solutions give a dark blue precipitate with potassium *ferro*cyanide T.S. (15).

2) Excess sodium hydroxide T.S. produces a reddish-brown precipitate of ferric hydroxide (14).

3) With ammonium thiocyanate T.S. a deep red color (not destroyed by mineral acids) is formed.

(b) *Ferrous Salts.*—1) Solutions of ferrous salts give a dark blue precipitate with potassium *ferri*cyanide T.S. (12). The precipitate is insoluble in diluted hydrochloric acid but is decomposed by sodium hydroxide T.S. (22).

(22) $Fe_3[Fe(CN)_6]_2 + 8NaOH \rightarrow 2Na_4[Fe(CN)_6] + 2Fe(OH)_3 \downarrow$
$+Fe(OH)_2 \downarrow$

2) With ferrous salts sodium hydroxide T.S. forms a greenish-white precipitate (9). The color of this precipitate changes rapidly on shaking to green and then to brown.

Commercial Manufacture.[1]—Practically all iron is made from *hematite, limonite,* or *magnetite* ores by a process of reduction. This is accomplished by heating the iron ore together with coke and limestone in a blast furnace. The function of the blast furnace is to (a) reduce the iron oxide to metallic iron, and (b) to remove small quantities of foreign elements (gangue) as slag. The coke indirectly accomplishes the first objective, whereas the limestone does the second.

[1] For a more extended discussion of the metallurgy of iron, see the 3rd edition of this textbook.

The crude metal that is obtained from the blast furnace is called *cast iron* or *pig iron*. It contains from 92 to 94 per cent of iron together with varying quantities of carbon (2.5 per cent), silicon (1 to 3 per cent), manganese (0.7 to 0.9 per cent), phosphorus (0.7 per cent) and sulfur (0.02 to 0.05 per cent), depending upon the character of the ore and coke and also upon the method of operating the furnace. The proportionate amounts of these impurities, together with the rate at which the molten metal is cooled, largely determine the physical properties of iron.

When molten iron is rapidly cooled, the product is a solid solution of hard, brittle iron carbide (Fe_3C) called *cementite*. This variety is very hard and brittle and is known as *white cast iron*. When the liquid iron is run into sand molds and allowed to cool slowly, it contains most of its carbon in the form of *graphite scales*. Such a variety is called *gray cast iron* and is much softer and less brittle than the white variety.

Cast iron has a density of about 7.76 and melts between 1000° C. and 1300° C. It is not attacked by alkalies and only slightly by concentrated acids. Weak acids dissolve it.

Wrought Iron.—Wrought iron is a product obtained by removing most of the impurities from cast iron. It contains from 99.8 to 99.9 per cent of pure iron. It averages about 0.15 per cent of carbon and contains only minute traces of other elements. The microstructure of wrought iron shows slag fibers and plates and a distinct laminated structure. For this reason, it can be forged when hot, with the slag acting more or less like a lubricant. Wrought iron is very malleable and ductile and can be rolled into sheets or drawn into wire. In these forms the metal is very tough and possesses a high tensile strength. Wrought iron begins to soften at about 1000° C., and hence can be forged and welded. It melts at 1500° C. and has a density of 7.25 to 7.78. It rusts more rapidly than cast iron and cannot be tempered. At high temperatures it is readily attacked by acids and alkalies.

Because of its purity, wrought iron is used to make *crucible steel*. Its properties make it suitable for manufacturing chains, anchors, wire, nails, etc. Because of the purity of this commercial variety of iron, it was recognized under the title *Iron* in the N.F. XI.

Reduced Iron.—Although no longer official, Reduced Iron and its methods of preparation can be considered profitably. For many years the N.F. required that it be made by the action of hydrogen on ferric oxide. This had forestalled the recognition of even purer forms of iron than Reduced Iron because they did not meet the manufacturing requirement. The N.F. IX finally recognized two other methods of manufacture.[1] The commercial manufacture of Reduced Iron may be considered under the three categories: (*a*) the

[1] Shelanski, H. A.: Bull. of Nat. Formulary Committee, **18**, 81 (1950).

classical reduction of iron oxide, (b) the preparation of electrolytic iron, (c) the preparation of finely divided iron from iron penta-carbonyl.

(a) Reduction of iron oxide is carried out by placing dried pure ferric oxide in an iron reduction tube which is so arranged that it may be heated to dull redness during the passage through it of washed (with dilute potassium permanganate) and dried (with concentrated sulfuric acid) hydrogen gas. Between 280° and 300° C., the ferric oxide is changed to the ferroso-ferric oxide (Fe_3O_4) (23), which at a temperature of 400° C. or above is reduced to metallic iron (24). A bright red heat during the reduction results in a compact, dense product which is undesirable.

$$(23) \quad 3Fe_2O_3 + H_2 \overset{\triangle}{\rightleftarrows} 2Fe_3O_4 + H_2O$$

$$(24) \quad Fe_3O_4 + 4H_2 \overset{\triangle}{\rightleftarrows} 3Fe + 4H_2O$$

As soon as the cessation of water vapor from the tube indicates that reduction is complete, the contents are allowed to cool slowly. A slow current of hydrogen is continued during the cooling in order to prevent the re-oxidation of the iron, which at the high temperature would take place very rapidly in the air. At room temperature, reduced iron is stable.

(b) As the name implies, electrolytic iron is prepared by electro-deposition. This has been on the market in the form of *Plast-Iron* for some time. It is produced from a ferrous sulfate electrolyte using Armco Iron anodes and stainless steel cathodes. The electrolytic process leaves the iron on the cathode in 1/16 inch to 1/8 inch thick brittle sheets. These are stripped from the cathode, washed thoroughly, and pulverized to an extremely fine powder (passes through 325 mesh screen). This powder exceeded the N.F. requirements for Reduced Iron and was found to be just as acceptable for use in therapy.[1] Indeed, the powder had been used for years to enrich flour with no untoward results.

(c) The process for making iron by the decomposition of iron pentacarbonyl has been known for years, and a product answering all requirements for N.F. X Reduced Iron except for method of manufacture had been on the market as *GA and F Carbonyl Iron Powder*.[2] Impure iron is reacted with carbon monoxide gas to form liquid iron pentacarbonyl (25), leaving behind the impurities originally present in the iron. When the liquid pentacarbonyl is vaporized and heated above 200° C. it decomposes into iron and carbon monoxide (26). The particle size of the resulting iron is controlled by the conditions of temperature, pressure, etc., during the decomposition, the particles being almost perfectly spherical. Toxicity studies, etc. on this iron powder have shown it to be the equivalent of Reduced Iron in all respects.

[1] Shelanski, H. A.: Bull. of Nat. Formulary Committee, **18**, 81 (1950).
[2] Shelanski, H. A.: Bull. of Nat. Formulary Committee, **18**, 87 (1950).

(25) $Fe + 5CO \rightarrow Fe(CO)_5$

(26) $Fe(CO)_5 \overset{\triangle}{\rightarrow} Fe + 5CO \uparrow$

Steel.—This commercial variety of iron may be characterized as one that contains carbon in definitely known amounts with almost no silicon, phosphorus or sulfur. There are many kinds of steel, each one of which possesses definite and known properties that have been imparted to it through the several processes of manufacture, by special operations or by added constituents.

Pharmacological Action of Iron and Its Salts.[1]—The role of iron in the body economy has been the subject of much and varied research. It is, of course, well established that iron forms an essential part of the hemoglobin in the blood. Also, much evidence has been accumulated to show that traces of iron in the blood and tissues play a significant part in the oxidation-reduction reactions constantly taking place in normal metabolism.

Viewed from a medicinal standpoint, iron and its preparations fall into two classifications, (1) those used *externally,* and (2) those used *internally.*

1. *External* iron preparations are almost exclusively of the ferric type, and depend for their action principally on their ability to precipitate protein. This ability to precipitate protein is directly reflected in the fact that ferric salts when used externally are astringents. The astringent action is of value in stopping the bleeding of small cuts, in gargles, etc. One of the disadvantages of iron salts is that they are colored, whereas lead salts, for example, are colorless.

The use of ferric chloride solution as an application to the skin in cases of poison ivy poisoning is based largely on the ability of ferric salts to precipitate phenols, vesicant phenols being the causative agent in poison ivy poisoning. This phenol-precipitating power combined with the potential oxidizing properties of the ferric ion on the sensitive phenols was probably the rationale for the introduction of iron into poison ivy therapy. It has been established, however, that the iron-phenol precipitate is still an exceedingly active irritant to the skin. This tends to prove that the use of ferric chloride (the ferric salt most commonly used) in poison ivy treatment is without sound scientific background.

2. *Internal* iron preparations are used to supplement the iron present in the body which is so essential to the formation of hemoglobin. Normally, an adult requires from 3 to 15 mg. of iron per day, children under 12 need 7 to 12 mg. and adolescents from 14 to 20 need 15 mg. The second half of pregnancy requires 15 mg. daily as well. For this purpose iron can be used therapeutically in one or all of three forms: (*a*) metallic iron, (*b*) ferric salts, (*c*) ferrous salts.

[1] Excellent articles for additional reading are: (*a*) Demulder, R., A.M.A. Arch. Int. Med., **102**, 254 (1958); (*b*) Erlandson, M. E., Ped. Clin. No. Am., **9**, 673 (1962); (*c*) Brise, H. and Hallberg, L., Acta Med. Scand., **171**, Suppl. 376 (1962).

Each of these basic forms of iron has been used in the regeneration of hemoglobin with some success. However, it is well to note that the actual per cent of iron in a preparation or salt has no bearing on the amount which will be absorbed and ultimately be effective. For example, metallic iron has by far the greatest content of iron on a percentage basis but weight for weight is inferior in hematinic activity to ferrous sulfate with much less iron. The effectiveness of iron preparations is thought to be a function of the extent to which ferrous iron is liberated and absorbed as a result of gastric and intestinal secretions. The preceding statement is borne out by much research and clinical observation, all of which show that the administration of ferrous salts results in greater hemoglobin response than that obtained with any other form of iron. However, metallic iron in the absence of achlorhydria is a fairly good source of ferrous iron. The low order of activity associated with ferric iron is at least partly due to its tendency to form insoluble compounds with phosphates, carbonates and proteins; this even in the normally acid medium of the stomach. Ferrous salts do not ordinarily precipitate in this manner unless in an alkaline medium. Since the normal stomach reaction is acid there is little possibility of inactivating ferrous iron.

It is well known that the most active site for iron absorption is in the acidic duodenal section of the gastrointestinal tract with lesser absorption occurring in the more alkaline intestinal tract. Since there is no bodily mechanism for excretion of iron other than sloughing off of cells, hemorrhage, menstruation, etc. (loss is about 1 mg. daily) the control of bodily iron levels is exerted in the absorption phase. The mechanism of iron absorption has been the object of much research and, as a result, at least three hypotheses have been promulgated to account for the regulation and control of intestinal iron absorption into the blood. It should, however, be emphasized that much of the iron needed for heme synthesis daily is obtained from worn-out cells, the spleen being largely responsible for the reclamation of this iron. An interesting observation is that there is approximately 250 mg. of iron in the body of a normal infant, whereas the body of a normal male adult contains about 4.5 Gm. Thus, from birth to adulthood the gain is 4.25 Gm. of iron together with small amounts needed to compensate for the approximately 1 mg. per day loss by various means. Naturally, the amount is larger in the case of bleeding or donation of iron to fetus from the mother.

Possibly the best known of the three hypotheses for iron absorption is the "mucosal block" postulation suggested by Hahn[1] and further developed by Granick[2] (see Fig. 7). It suggests that dietary

[1] Hahn, P. F. et al.: J. Exptl. Med., **78**, 169 (1943).
[2] Granick, S.: Bull. New York Acad. Med., **30**, 81 (1954).

or administered iron is reduced to the ferrous form which diffuses into the mucosal cell where it is reoxidized and then combined with apoferritin (continually forming and being destroyed) to form stable ferritin, the iron-carrying protein. As ferritin it crosses the cell and is released to be again reduced to Fe^{++} for diffusion across the serosal cell membrane and eventual oxidation to Fe^{+++} and combination with latent iron-binding protein to form transferrin (also known as siderophilin). In this form it is transferred to liver for storage (as ferritin) or to the bone marrow for use in heme synthesis for erythrocyte production. The key to the mucosal block is the assertion that only small amounts of ferritin can be formed in any one cell. Once the full complement of ferritin is obtained for a cell it can no longer pick up iron no matter what the concentration in the lumen of the intestine. Further absorption occurs only in cells that do not have their full amount of ferritin or if the ferritin unloads its iron through the serosal membrane to regenerate apoferritin. There are numerous arguments against this hypothesis among which are the fact that no maximum limit of absorption has been demonstrated, that increased amounts (although smaller percentages) of iron are absorbed from larger doses and that unphysiologic amounts of iron are required to show the blocking effect.

The second hypothesis, suggested by Crosby et al.[1] and Schachter et al.,[2] may be termed the "active transport" mechanism (see Fig. 8). As in the mucosal block mechanism Fe^{++} enters the mucosal cell by diffusion where it combines with endogenous low molecular weight ligands or is stored as ferritin. To cross the serosal membrane into the blood a specific transport system intimately linked to metabolic energy (ATP)[3] is suggested. The control of iron entry into the blood is by this active transporting system. Once past the serosal membrane the events are the same as with the mucosal block hypothesis. Although attractive, this hypothesis fails in that there has been no demonstration that iron movement across the serosal membrane is dependent on metabolic energy. Indeed, Saltman et al.[4] have demonstrated that passive diffusion of the chelated form is the most likely process. Perhaps one of the most telling arguments against this hypothesis is the fact that iron movement is not affected by an anaerobic condition whereas other known active transport processes (e.g., Na^+) are vitally affected.

The third mechanism has been postulated by Saltman and his group[6] (see Fig. 9). They propose that primary control is exerted by exogenous or endogenous ligands or chelating agents which can bind either oxidation state of iron forming low molecular weight.

[1] Wheby, M. S., Jones, L. G., and Crosby, W. H.: J. Clin. Invest., **43**, 1433 (1954)
[2] Dowdle, G. B., Schachter, D., and Schenker, H.: Am. J. Physiol., **198**, 609 (1960).
[3] Adenosine triphosphate.
[4] Saltman, P. J.: Chem. Educ., **42**, 682 (1965).

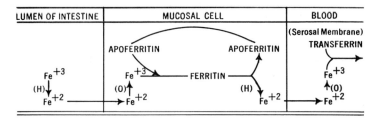

FIG. 7.—*The Mucosal Block Hypothesis;* Iron absorption regulated and controlled by availability of apoferritin.

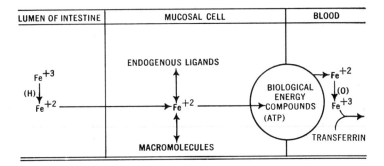

FIG. 8.—*The Active Transport Hypothesis;* Regulation and control of iron absorption by regulating the amount of cellular energy available for active transport.

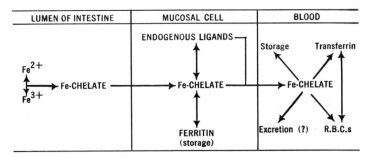

FIG. 9.—*The Iron-Chelate Hypothesis;* Primary control of iron absorption resides in the presence of endogenous or exogenous chelating agents which are able to bind either Fe^{2+} or Fe^{3+} to form soluble low molecular weight complexes. (Figures 7 to 8 from the paper by P. Saltman, J. Chem. Educ., *42*, 683, 1965—with some modification.)

complexes capable of passively diffusing through the mucosal cell membrane from the intestine. No prior reduction to Fe^{++} is postulated. Within the cell the iron can be transferred to other endogenous ligands or stored as ferritin. Diffusion across the serosal membrane is viewed as occurring with either the original chelating material or with some endogenous ligand. Once across the membrane the iron is transported in the chelated form to depot cells where it is transferred to transferrin. The sequence following this is as in the other hypotheses. The major attributes of this hypothesis are that no redox reactions or metabolic energy are directly involved. The hypothesis is rather new and further experimentation will determine whether it has substance. The suggestion that both ferrous and ferric ions are equally complexed for diffusion into the mucosal cell is a concept difficult to understand in face of the large body of empirical fact indicating the superior absorption of ferrous iron over ferric.

Assuming that ferrous salts are the most advantageous form in which to administer iron, it only remains to determine the most suitable anion to accompany it. Experience has indicated that the sulfate is fairly stable and that in most cases it does not cause any marked gastric upset. However, there is a small percentage of patients who do get a gastroenteritis from the use of ferrous sulfate. This may be avoided in some cases by the administration of the ferrous sulfate in an enteric coated tablet, whereas others require changing the salt. In the case of the latter, the use of organic ferrous salts has met with some success the most impressive to date being *Ferrous Fumarate*, U.S.P. By and large, however, ferrous sulfate is probably the most economical and most satisfactory form of ferrous iron on the market today. Its toxic nature should be recognized, however, and preparations of it as well as other iron salts should be kept out of the reach of small children. Accidental ingestion of large amounts of iron can produce serious and even fatal toxicity.[1]

Parenteral forms of iron have not been well received, partly because they often cause marked local and systemic reactions and also because transfusions in most cases will serve just as well. However, *Iron Dextran Injection* U.S.P., a sterile, colloidal solution of ferric hydroxide in complex with partially hydrolyzed dextran of low molecular weight, in water for injection has been used successfully by the intramuscular route for the treatment of iron-deficiency anemias.

The chief indication for the use of iron salts is in the treatment of so-called "secondary anemias." The derivation of the terminol-

[1] Smith, N. J.: J. of Pediatrics, **53**, 37 (1958).

ogy "secondary" is due to the fact that these iron-deficiency diseases are secondary to some other disease, that is, they are a result of another disease. Any and all disease conditions which can affect the body may, and most of them do, ultimately lead to a secondary anemia, which is characterized by a hemoglobin which is low in proportion to the decrease in the number of red blood cells. These secondary anemias are also classified as "hypochromic microcytic anemias" indicating a low hemoglobin content and small size cells. Still another classification is as "dyshemopoietic anemias" implying that they are the result of inefficient production of blood cells (with iron deficiency being one of several causative factors). Some of the disease conditions which cause this type of anemia are bleeding peptic ulcer, ulcerative colitis, tuberculosis, etc. Iron is indicated in all of these secondary anemias, although sometimes liver in one form or another is administered simultaneously.

In contrast to the secondary anemias are the so-called "primary anemias" which are typified by pernicious anemia. They are also called "macrocytic anemias" to indicate that the blood cells are larger than normal. The blood picture in the primary anemia group shows that the cells are normally colored but are of a larger size than normal. These anemias are not secondary to some other disease but are due to a diseased condition of the blood-making portions of the body. They are treated with vitamin B_{12} or other similar preparations. Iron is of little value in this type of anemia.

Uses.—*Iron* (Ferrum), N.F. XI, was "Elementary Iron (Fe) in the form of fine, bright wire, filings or powder." This form of iron was used mostly for preparing certain iron salts, *e.g.*, ferrous iodide, ferrous chloride, etc. Its official recognition was based on its use in the preparation of *Ferrous Iodide Syrup* where it reacted with iodine (27) to form ferrous iodide.

$$(27) \; Fe + I_2 \rightarrow FeI_2$$

This preparation is often made in the pharmacy from commercial ampuls which contain an amount of an aqueous solution of ferrous iodide sufficient to make a designated quantity of the syrup. The contents of an ampul are added to syrup at any desired time to give a freshly made syrup. Syrup of Ferrous Iodide is a hematinic preparation. Usual dose—1 ml. which contains about 70 mg. of FeI_2.

Reduced Iron (Ferrum Reductum), N.F. X.—Before the N.F. IX permitted Reduced Iron to be made by other methods than by hydrogen reduction this form was also known as Iron by Hydrogen or Quevenne's Iron. This form of iron was used for internal administration to obtain the hematinic effects of iron. It is probably converted in part to ferrous chloride in the acid stomach juices and as such exerts its effect. Usual dose—0.5 Gm.

OFFICIAL IRON COMPOUNDS

FERROUS FUMARATE

Ferrous Fumarate, U.S.P. XII

Formula, $C_4H_2FeO_4$;

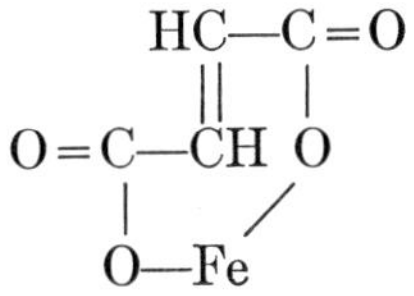

$$\begin{array}{c} HC\!-\!C\!=\!O \\ ||| \\ O\!=\!C\!-\!CHO \\ |/ \\ O\!-\!Fe \end{array}$$

Molecular Weight, 169.91

Physical Properties.—Ferrous Fumarate is a reddish orange to red-brown, odorless and virtually tasteless powder. It may contain soft lumps that produce a yellow streak when crushed. It is soluble to the extent of 0.14 Gm. in each 100 ml. of water but it is only very slightly soluble in alcohol. It dissolves in $1N$ hydrochloric acid (0.45 Gm./100 ml.) and in $0.1N$ hydrochloric acid (0.6 Gm./100 ml.) but the solubility is limited by the separation of free, insoluble fumaric acid (1).

(1) $FeC_4H_2O_4 + 2HCl \rightarrow FeCl_2 + H_2C_4H_2O_4 \downarrow$

Chemical Properties.—Since the solubility of Ferrous Fumarate is rather low in water it is not used in solution and, therefore, it has few incompatibilities. However, the reaction (1) with hydrochloric acid represents a decomposition which goes to completion because of the insolubility of the fumaric acid.

One of the useful attributes of this salt is its resistance to oxidation on exposure to air. In this respect it is superior to either ferrous sulfate or ferrous gluconate. Even on exposure to a hot humid atmosphere over an extended period of time there is little conversion to the ferric form.

The assay of Ferrous Fumarate is carried out by dissolving the sample in dilute hydrochloric acid and then reducing it completely to the ferrous form (colorless) with stannous chloride. After cooling and treatment with mercuric chloride to remove excess stannous chloride the sample is acidified with sulfuric acid and phosphoric acid (to complex with any possible Fe^{+++}). This solution is then titrated with standard ceric sulfate solution using orthophenanthroline T.S. as the indicator for the conversion of the ferrous form to the ferric form.

Official Tests for Identity.—Two tests are provided in order to identify both the fumarate and the ferrous portion of the salt.

A. To test for the fumarate ion 1.5 Gm. of the salt is treated with 25 ml. of dilute hydrochloric acid (1 in 2), diluted to 50 ml., and heated to effect solution. On cooling, the separated fumaric acid is filtered off and washed with dilute hydrochloric acid (3 in 100). The filtrate is saved for the test for *Iron* (see below). The dried fumaric acid (400 mg.) is treated with 3 ml. of water and 7 ml. of 1*N* sodium hydroxide and stirred until completely in solution. It is converted to the *p*-nitrobenzyl ester by refluxing for 2 hours with 1 Gm. of *p*-nitrobenzyl bromide which is added together with alcohol (10 ml.) to the above solution after slight acidification with diluted hydrochloric acid. If the precipitate after washing, drying and recrystallization has a melting point of about 152° this identifies it as *p*-nitrobenzyl fumarate.

B. A portion of the filtrate from the above procedure (*q.v.*) responds to the usual tests for *Iron* (*q.v.*).

Commercial Manufacture.—Ferrous Fumarate is made by the interaction of hot, aqueous solutions of ferrous sulfate and sodium fumarate (2), preferably by adding the sodium fumarate to the

$$(2) \quad FeSO_4 + Na_2C_4H_2O_4 \rightarrow FeC_4H_2O_4 \downarrow + Na_2SO_4$$

ferrous sulfate. The precipitate of ferrous fumarate is removed by filtration, washed, dried and reduced to a 100 mesh powder.

Uses.—*Ferrous Fumarate*, U.S.P. XII, contains not less than 96.5 per cent and not more than 101.0 per cent of $C_4H_2FeO_4$. It was introduced in 1957 under the trade name of Toleron and has since been also marketed as Ircon. Since its introduction it has had a rapid rise in popularity and is present in many of the leading hematinics on the market. In equivalent doses it provides at least as good a hematologic response in iron deficiences as any other available preparation. In addition, there is some evidence to show that it is less irritating to the gastrointestinal tract than other commonly used ferrous salts although it is evident from scattered reports that such irritation is not completely absent. In addition, while it is well to exercise all precautions possible to prevent ingestion of excessive amounts of any iron salt, it is probable that Ferrous Fumarate possesses a toxicity potential that compares very favorably with all other widely used hematinic salts. The official dosage form is *Ferrous Fumarate Tablets* which usually are provided in 200 or 300 mg. sizes. Usual dose: 200 mg. (equivalent to 66 mg. Fe) three times a day. The dosage range is 200 to 400 mg. three times a day.

FERROUS GLUCONATE

Ferrous Gluconate, N.F. XII

Molecular Weight, 482.18

Formula, $C_{12}H_{22}FeO_{14} \cdot 2H_2O$;

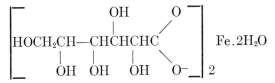

Physical Properties.—This salt occurs as a fine, yellowish-gray or pale greenish-yellow powder or granules. It has an odor suggesting burned sugar.

One Gm. is soluble in 10 ml. of water. It is nearly insoluble in alcohol.

Chemical Properties.—Its aqueous solutions are acid in reaction. The reactions of this salt in aqueous solution are essentially those of the ferrous salts (*q.v.*) and of the gluconate ion (*q.v.*). Aqueous solutions are stabilized by the use of glucose.

This salt is assayed in essentially the same manner as is Reduced Iron (*q.v.*), *i.e.*, by titration with ceric sulfate solution. However, the pretreatment of the sample involves the dissolving of the sample in a dilute sulfuric acid solution followed by treatment with zinc dust to insure reduction of all iron to the ferrous form.

Official Tests for Identity.—1. Five ml. of a warmed 1 in 10 aqueous solution of the salt is treated with 0.65 ml. of glacial acetic acid and 1 ml. of freshly distilled phenylhydrazine and then warmed on a steam bath for thirty minutes. When allowed to cool it will deposit crystals of gluconic acid phenylhydrazide either spontaneously or with scratching of the test-tube walls. (For reactions, see Calcium Gluconate.)

2. A 1 in 20 solution responds to all tests for *Ferrous Salts* (*q.v.*).

Commercial Manufacture.—To produce ferrous gluconate the first step is the production of gluconic acid by the fermentative oxidation of glucose (1). The solution of gluconic acid so obtained is then treated with ferrous carbonate to form soluble ferrous gluconate (2). From the resulting solution the ferrous gluconate is crystallized. The salt contains 2 molecules of water of crystallization. This is then dried and packaged.

(1) $C_6H_{12}O_6 + (O) \rightarrow HC_6H_{11}O_7$

(2) $2HC_6H_{11}O_7 + FeCO_3 + H_2O \rightarrow Fe(C_6H_{11}O_7)_2 \cdot 2H_2O + CO_2 \uparrow$

It can also be made by the interaction of ferrous sulfate and calcium gluconate (3), although this method is not used commercially.

(3) $Ca(C_6H_{11}O_7)_2 + FeSO_4 \rightarrow Fe(C_6H_{11}O_7)_2 + CaSO_4 \downarrow$

Uses.—*Ferrous Gluconate*, N.F. XII, contains not less than 95 per cent of $C_{12}H_{22}FeO_{14}$, calculated on the anhydrous basis. This preparation is one of the more useful ferrous compounds to appear on the market. It was introduced into therapy in 1937. As previously pointed out, it has the advantage of causing less gastric irritation than most of the other commonly used completely inorganic ferrous salts, *e.g.*, ferrous sulfate. It is obtainable commercially as tablets and elixir under the trade name "Fergon," and as capsules and elixir under its own name. It is also utilized for intramuscular injection and from the standpoint of irritation and pain is said to be one of the less objectionable iron salts. Usual dose—0.3 Gm. three times a day with a range of 0.2 Gm. to 0.6 Gm.

FERROUS SULFATE

Ferrous Sulfate, U.S.P. XVII

Formula, $FeSO_4 . 7H_2O$.   Molecular Weight, 278.02

Physical Properties.—The official salt occurs in the form of large pale bluish-green, monoclinic prisms having a density of 1.8987. It is odorless, and has a saline, styptic taste. In dry air the salt effloresces and becomes coated with a grayish-white powder of the anhydrous salt. In moist air the crystals rapidly oxidize to a brownish-yellow, basic ferric sulfate, which makes the salt unfit for use in medicinal preparations. When the crystals are slowly heated to 115° C., they disintegrate and lose most of their water of hydration.

Ferrous sulfate dissolves in 1.5 times its weight of water at 25° C., and in less than one-half its weight of boiling water to form solutions that are acid to litmus paper. A 1 in 10 solution has a pH of about 3.7.

Chemical Properties.—In general, it may be said that the reactions of ferrous sulfate are those of the ferrous ion and of the sulfate ion.

Ferrous sulfate combines with the alkali sulfates to form double salts. The most important one of these compounds is *ferrous ammonium sulfate* $FeSO_4 . (NH_4)_2SO_4 . 6H_2O$ This very stable salt is prepared by dissolving equimolecular weights of the two salts in water and crystallizing. It is known as Mohr's Salt and is used in analytical chemistry.

Ferrous Sulfate is assayed officially by dissolving it in dilute sulfuric acid and titrating with standard potassium permanganate solution which quantitatively oxidizes ferrous sulfate to ferric sulfate (1).

(1) $10FeSO_4 + 2KMnO_4 + 8H_2SO_4 \rightarrow 5Fe_2(SO_4)_3 + 2MnSO_4 + K_2SO_4 + 8H_2O$

Official Tests for Identity.—This salt responds to the tests for *Ferrous Salts (q.v.)* and *Sulfate (q.v.)*.

Commercial Manufacture.—1. The best grade of ferrous sulfate is obtained by dissolving iron in diluted sulfuric acid and concentrating to crystallization.

2. The commercial grades of this salt are made by piling iron pyrites in heaps and exposing it to atmospheric oxidation (2). The mass is leached with water and the dilute solution of ferrous sulfate is run into large vats. Scrap iron is added to take care of any free sulfuric acid and to precipitate any copper ion present in the solution. The liquid is concentrated to crystallization.

(2) $2FeS_2 + 7O_2 + 2H_2O \rightarrow 2FeSO_4 + 2H_2SO_4$

3. Appreciable quantities of ferrous sulfate are obtained by concentrating the vat liquor obtained in the "pickling" of steel (q.v.).

Uses.—*Ferrous Sulfate* (Iron Sulfate), U.S.P. XVII, "contains an amount of $FeSO_4$ equivalent to not less than 99.5 per cent and not more than 104.5 per cent of $FeSO_4.7H_2O$." *Note—Ferrous Sulfate oxidizes readily on exposure to moist air and the crystals become coated with brownish yellow basic ferric sulfate. Do not use Ferrous Sulfate so deteriorated.* This salt is the most popular of the ferrous salts as well as the most economical. It is an efficient hematinic. The salt also occurs in the form of *Ferrous Sulfate Syrup*. Usual dose—0.3 Gm. three times a day with a range of from 0.2 Gm. to 0.6 Gm.

Dried Ferrous Sulfate (Exsiccated Ferrous Sulfate), U.S.P. XVII, "contains not less than 80 per cent of anhydrous ferrous sulfate $(FeSO_4)$." Of the forms in which ferrous sulfate exists, the exsiccated form is probably the most used, principally because it can be given in smaller doses than the form containing water of crystallization, and because it does not effloresce. It is made by allowing the hydrated salt to effloresce at a temperature of about 40° C. in dry air and then heating it with constant stirring on a water-bath until it is reduced to between 64 and 65 per cent of its original weight. The resulting material is reduced to a fine powder and immediately placed in dry, tightly stoppered bottles. It is required to contain not less than 80 per cent of anhydrous ferrous sulfate $(FeSO_4)$. Usual dose—0.2 Gm.

Ferrous Sulfate Tablets, U.S.P. XVII, are a convenient form for administering either hydrated or dried ferrous sulfate. In general, the tablets containing the exsiccated form predominate, a typical example being "Feosol" tablets. The smaller size tablet as compared to tablets of the hydrated form is of advantage for oral use. A few firms market an enteric coated tablet which is claimed to eliminate the gastric discomfort occasionally encountered when ferrous sulfate is used. Despite claims that the enteric coated tablet cannot be absorbed very well since it is not exposed to the acid gastric juices but only to the alkaline intestinal juices, many physicians find that satisfactory hematinic responses are obtained.

Ferric Subsulfate Solution (Monsel's Solution), N.F. XI, was a water solution containing, in each 100 ml., basic ferric sulfate equivalent to not less than 20 Gm. and not more than 22 Gm. of Fe. Coarsely powdered ferrous sulfate was added in four approximately equal portions to a mixture of sulfuric and nitric acids which had previously been heated to nearly 100° C. Nitric acid was added, drop by drop, to the constantly stirred hot solution until red fumes ceased to be evolved and the liquid had assumed a dark, reddish brown color. The solution was then boiled to free it of nitric acid, maintaining the volume at about 1000 ml. by the addition of distilled water as needed and, when cool, diluted with distilled water to the required volume. The product was filtered, if necessary, until clear.

The product was a dark, reddish-brown liquid, odorless or nearly so, with a sour, strongly astringent taste. At 25° C. it had a specific gravity of about 1.548, and was miscible with both water and alcohol.

Solution of subsulfate of iron sometimes congeals to a semi-solid mass when cooled or upon long standing. The application of gentle heat will restore it to the liquid state.

Ferric subsulfate is of variable composition and therefore the reaction cannot be definitely expressed in the form of an equation. The following equation has been suggested as being representative (3).

(3) $12FeSO_4 + 3H_2SO_4 + 4HNO_3 \rightarrow 3Fe_4O(SO_4)_5 + 4NO \uparrow + 5H_2O$

It is a highly astringent preparation used to check bleeding from small cuts, etc. As a styptic it is used undiluted.

IRON DEXTRAN

Iron Dextran Injection, U.S.P. XVII

Formula, $Fe(OH)_3$(colloid) + Dextran

Physical Properties.—Iron Dextran Injection is a dark brown, slightly viscous liquid miscible with water. It is sterile and the pH of the Injection is between 5.2 and 6.0.

Chemical Properties.—This Injection contains iron as colloidal ferric hydroxide in a complexed form and the iron present does not exhibit the usual reactions of this ion. For example, addition of stronger ammonia water does not precipitate iron hydroxide since it is already in the hydroxide form and there is no free ferric ion. If, however, hydrochloric acid is added to the solution to convert the ferric hydroxide to ferric chloride (1) and stronger ammonia water then added, the normal precipitation of non-colloidal ferric hydroxide occurs (2).

(1) $Fe(OH)_3 + 3HCl \rightarrow FeCl_3 + 3H_2O$

(2) $FeCl_3 + 3NH_4OH \rightarrow Fe(OH)_3 \downarrow + 3NH_4Cl$

The assay of this preparation is carried out by conducting a Kjeldahl digestion of a measured sample with sulfuric and nitric acids to destroy organic matter, a standard solution of ferrous ammonium sulfate being treated in the same way. After suitable dilution and reduction to ferrous ion with ascorbic acid, accurately measured samples of standard and assay preparation are then treated with 2,2′-bipyridine to develop the characteristic red color of the bi-pyridine-ferrous ion complex. Spectrophotometric measurement of absorbance at 510 mμ, *i.e.*, the wavelength of maximum absorbance, provides a measure of the amount of iron in the original sample when compared to the standard.

Official Tests for Identity.—To 1 ml. of the Injection on a watch glass add 2 drops of stronger ammonia water; no precipitate is formed. Add 2 ml. of hydrochloric acid (1), mix, and add 2 ml. of stronger ammonia water: a brown precipitate is formed (2).

Commercial Manufacture.—Although no specific procedure seems to be published, the probable procedure[1] is the slow addition of a calculated amount of ferric chloride or ferric sulfate dissolved in a solution of the appropriate dextran to a solution of the calculated amount of sodium hydroxide in a heated vessel under suitable pH control. Boiling of the solution followed by adjustment of pH and removal of the electrolytes by dialysis together with concentration by evaporation to the desired concentration and sterilization completes the procedure. The concentration is 50 mg. iron per ml. in varying size ampuls.

Uses.—*Iron Dextran Injection*, U.S.P. XVII, "is a sterile, colloidal solution of ferric hydroxide in complex with partially hydrolyzed dextran of low molecular weight, in Water for Injection. It contains not less than 95 per cent and not more than 105 per cent of the labeled amount of iron. It may contain not more than 0.5 per cent of phenol as preservative." This preparation is represented commercially by the product Imferon and was introduced in 1955. It should be noted that the low molecular weight dextran is quite dif-

---

[1] Czech. pat. 97, 467, Nov. 15, 1960.

ferent from the high molecular weight one which has been used as plasma expander or substitute. Iron Dextran Injection is intended only for intramuscular use and, further, should be reserved for use only where oral therapy is contraindicated or ineffective and where a severe iron deficiency anemia is present. It should not be used in a prophylactic manner. In the dosage schedule it will be noted that a small test dose is given initially, followed by the desired dose. This is to help detect sensitivity since severe anaphylactic reactions can occur and some fatalities have been reported. Reports of carcinogenicity in animal studies do not appear to extend to humans and the possibility is considered unlikely. Prior to initiation of therapy the total iron requirement of the patient should be ascertained and the required amount of dosage calculated. Dosage schedules for infants, children and adults are provided by the manufacturer and should be adhered to faithfully. For use as a hematinic in iron-deficiency anemia the intramuscular dose is 1 ml. initially (equivalent to 50 mg. elemental iron), then up to 5 ml. daily. One of the important advantages of this preparation over other parenteral forms of iron is the experience that has been accumulated making it possible to evaluate untoward effects with greater accuracy.

NON-OFFICIAL COMPOUNDS OF IRON

Dextriferron (Astrafer), N.D.—This product, introduced in 1958, is a colloidal aqueous solution of ferric hydroxide which has been complexed with partially hydrolyzed dextrin, ampulled and sterilized. The 5 ml. ampuls contain 20 mg. of elemental Fe per ml. and it is only to be used intravenously. Its use, in common with other parenteral forms of iron, is contraindicated if the patient can accept oral medication since there is a much greater danger of toxic reaction from parenterals than from oral dosage forms. It is only to be used for severe iron deficiency anemia. In all cases, the total amount of iron required should be determined prior to administration and the usual dosage regimen for adults is 1.5 ml. the first day with an increase of this dose by increments of 1 or 1.5 ml. each day until the total amount of iron is given. The rate of administration should be no greater than 5 ml./10 min. Too rapid injection results in nausea, vomiting, hypotension, flushing of the face, collapse, etc. Anaphylactoid reactions can also occur requiring epinephrine or corticosteroids.

Ferric Ammonium Citrate, N.F. XI, occurs in thin, transparent scales which are garnet-red in color and odorless. It also occurs as granules or as a brownish powder. It deliquesces in air and is affected by light.

It is very soluble in water, the solutions having a saline, mildly ferruginous taste. Aqueous solutions are neutral or only faintly acid or alkaline in reaction. It is insoluble in alcohol.

Although this preparation contains the ferric form of iron, it does not exhibit the normal reactions of that ion when in solution. For example, it does not precipitate with ammonium hydroxide, it fails to precipitate protein and it does not react with potassium ferrocyanide. It is only after acidification with hydrochloric acid that it is possible to get the normal reactions of ferric ion. This preparation is made by adding ammonium hydroxide in slight excess to a solution of ferric citrate, which previously has been made by dissolving freshly precipitated ferric hydroxide in a solution of citric acid (1).

(1) $Fe(OH)_3 + H_3C_6H_5O_7 \rightarrow FeC_6H_5O_7 + 3H_2O$

Addition of ammonium hydroxide to the ferric citrate then gives a solution which is evaporated to a syrup, spread on glass plates, and "scaled." Scaling is a pharmaceutical process whereby a syrup which is thinly spread on glass plates loses water by evaporation. When sufficient water has evaporated the residue begins to break away from the glass plate in the form of scales. These scales are not crystalline, although sometimes they may appear to be.

The product contains not less than 16.5 per cent and not more than 18.5 per cent of Fe. This scale salt of iron has been used as a convenient source of iron for hematinic purposes. Because of its solubility, it lends itself very nicely to incorporation into syrups, elixirs, etc. Its chief disadvantage lies in the fact that it requires quite large doses to produce the hematinic action. As a comparison, it is only one-eighth as effective as an equal weight of Dried Ferrous Sulfate.

Green Ferric Ammonium Citrate, N.F. XI, occurs in the form of thin, transparent scales, granules, or as a powder. It is green in color. It deliquesces in air and is affected by light. It dissolves very readily in water to give solutions which are acid to litmus. The preparation is odorless and has a saline, mildly ferruginous taste. It is insoluble in alcohol.

The properties of this preparation are very similar to those of the closely related Ferric Ammonium Citrate. The principal difference is that this preparation contains slightly less iron on a per cent basis. It is made in exactly the same manner as Ferric Ammonium Citrate. However, it does contain more ammonium citrate (approximately 8 per cent) and contains not less than 14.5 per cent and not more than 16 per cent of Fe. This preparation has an advantage over Ferric Ammonium Citrate in that it may be injected intramuscularly without as much irritation. Although injections of this preparation are quite painful, it was at one time the iron preparation of choice for parenteral use. Usual dose—intramuscular, 0.1 Gm.

Ferric Cacodylate, N.F. X, $Fe[(CH_3)_2AsO_2]_3$, occurs as a yellowish, amorphous powder. One Gm. is soluble in about 30 ml. of water at 25° C. It is only slightly soluble in alcohol.

The chemical properties of this compound are essentially those of the ferric and cacodylate ions (*q.v.*).

Details of the manufacture of this compound are difficult to obtain. However, the probable method of manufacture is by reacting cacodylic acid, which is made from arsenic trioxide, with ferric hydroxide (1).

$$(1) \quad 3(CH_3)_2AsOOH + Fe(OH)_3 \rightarrow Fe[(CH_3)_2AsOO]_3 + 3H_2O$$

This salt has been used in the treatment of leukemias as well as a source of iron in anemias. Usual dose—60 mg.

Ferric Chloride, $FeCl_3.6H_2O$, occurs as very deliquescent, crystalline lumps having a brownish-yellow to orange color. Ordinarily, they have an odor of hydrochloric acid. It is affected by light.

One Gm. dissolves in 0.25 ml. of water, and in 1.2 ml. of alcohol. It is freely soluble in acetone. It is also soluble in ether or glycerin.

This salt gives an acid reaction in aqueous solution because of hydrolysis, a characteristic of ferric salts.

Ferric chloride may be prepared either by heating iron in a current of chlorine (1) or by oxidizing a solution of ferrous chloride (obtained by reacting iron with hydrochloric acid) (2) with nitric acid (3).

$$(1) \quad 2Fe + 3Cl_2 \rightarrow 2FeCl_3$$

$$(2) \quad Fe + 2HCl \rightarrow FeCl_2 + H_2 \uparrow$$

$$(3) \quad 3FeCl_2 + 3HCl + HNO_3 \rightarrow 3FeCl_3 + NO \uparrow + 2H_2O$$

Reaction (1) produces an anhydrous form of ferric chloride which exists as dark green crystals having a metallic luster. This form is quite volatile. Once it is dissolved in water, or if the ferric chloride is made by reactions (2) and (3) it is no longer possible to get back the anhydrous form. When an aqueous solution of ferric chloride is evaporated, several different hydrates may be formed. Usually the hexahydrate is the one that is isolated. If one attempts to drive off all of the water, the concentrated material evolves hydrogen chloride fumes and eventually leaves behind a residue of ferric oxide.

Ferric Chloride Solution (Iron Perchloride Solution), N.F. XI, was a water solution containing, in each 100 ml., not less than 37.2 Gm. and not more than 42.7 Gm. of $FeCl_3$, and not less than 3.85 Gm. and not more than 6.6 Gm. of HCl. It was a yellowish-orange liquid having a faint odor of hydrochloric acid and an acid reaction to litmus. This solution was used principally for making *Ferric Chloride Tincture*, N.F. XI and *Ferric Citrochloride Tincture*, N.F. X. However, it was also used externally for the astringent and styptic effect of the ferric ion. In a diluted form or in one of the above tinctures, it has been used as a hematinic, although there are other preparations much more satisfactory. Usual dose—0.1 ml.

Ferric Chloride Tincture (Iron Tincture), N.F. XI, was a hydro-alcoholic solution containing, in each 100 ml., not less than 13 Gm. and not more than 15 Gm. of $FeCl_3$. It was prepared by mixing 350 ml. of Ferric Chloride Solution with enough alcohol to make 1000 ml. of finished product. It has been used externally as a styptic and astringent, and internally as a hematinic and tonic. Usual dose —0.6 ml.

This tincture has also been used to prepare another hematinic preparation, *Iron and Ammonium Acetate Solution* N.F. X (Basham's Mixture).

Ferric Citrochloride Tincture, N.F. XI, was a hydro-alcoholic solution containing, in each 100 ml., ferric citrochloride equivalent to not less than 4.48 Gm. of Fe. It was prepared by mixing 350 ml. of Ferric Chloride Solution with 150 ml. of water and dissolving 450 Gm. of sodium citrate in this mixture with the aid of gentle heat. Alcohol (150 ml.) was then added when cool. The mixture was then made up to 1000 ml. with water and allowed to stand in a cold place for a few days to let excess saline matter (NaCl, which is insoluble in alcohol) settle out. It was then filtered.

The reaction taking place in this preparation has been considered to be one of sequestration. The brown color of Ferric Chloride Solution changes to a green color. Accompanying this color change is a change in the chemical reactivity of the iron which apparently is bound up (sequestered) in an undissociated form because it no longer gives the reactions of ferric ion, and has lost its astringent and styptic properties. This tincture is, therefore, unsuited for astringent use, but has been used internally as a hematinic, since it lacks many of the objectionable qualities associated with Ferric Chloride Tincture. In addition, it has been of service in avoiding many of the incompatibilities associated with Tincture of Ferric Chloride, such as the dark colored precipitate which iron in an ionized form gives with tannins, etc. Usual dose—0.5 ml.

Ferric Citrochloride Tincture has also been employed in the preparation of *Iron, Quinine and Strychnine Elixir*, a tonic preparation with some hematinic properties imparted by the iron content.

Ferric Glycerophosphate, N.F. X, $Fe_2[C_3H_5(OH)_2PO_4]_3$, occurs as orange- to greenish-yellow, transparent, amorphous scales, or powder. It is odorless and nearly tasteless. It is affected by light.

One Gm. dissolves slowly in about 2 ml. of water at 25° C. but it is insoluble in alcohol.

Due to hydrolysis, aqueous solutions of the salt are acidic in reaction.

It is made by dissolving freshly precipitated ferric hydroxide in glycerophosphoric acid (1) and concentrating the liquid to a syrupy consistency in a vacuum. It is then spread on glass plates, dried and scaled.

(1) $2Fe(OH)_3 + 3C_3H_5(OH)_2PO_4H_2 \rightarrow Fe_2[C_3H_5(OH)_2PO_4]_3 + 6HO_2$

This salt has been used for iron deficiency anemias in a usual dose of 0.2 Gm.

Ferric Hydroxide [$Fe(OH)_3$].—Ferric hydroxide is formed as a brown gelatinous precipitate when an alkali hydroxide is added to a solution of a ferric salt. The precipitate is insoluble in an excess of the precipitant but readily dissolves in hydrochloric acid. When the freshly precipitated ferric hydroxide is boiled in or allowed to stand in contact with water, it is gradually converted first into the basic hydroxide [$Fe_2O(OH)_4$ or $Fe_2O_3.2H_2O$] and then into a bright red, amorphous powder having the composition $Fe_2O_2(OH)_2$ or $Fe_2O_3.H_2O$. Ferric hydroxide strongly tends toward forming colloidal solutions. Thomas Graham obtained a colloidal solution by dissolving freshly precipitated ferric hydroxide in a solution of ferric chloride and then dialyzing the solution. Such solutions are known as *"dialyzed iron,"* and are said to contain about 98.5 per cent of colloidal ferric hydroxide and about 1.5 per cent of ferric chloride. Ferric hydroxide is very feebly basic and dissolves in very strong bases to form ferrites (1). This amphoteric property, however, in comparison to aluminum hydroxide is almost negligible. Freshly precipitated ferric hydroxide reacts very quickly with soluble arsenic compounds to form insoluble ferric salts (2). Therefore, when mixed with MgO in a magma, it was at one time known as the official Arsenic Antidote. It is held in less esteem in present-day medicine because it is only effective if used as a gastric lavage immediately following arsenic poisoning. If used, it should be freshly made because it loses its activity upon standing.

(1) $Fe(OH)_3 + NaOH \rightarrow NaFeO_2 + 2H_2O$

(2) $Fe(OH)_3 + 3KAsO_2 \rightarrow Fe(AsO_2)_3 \downarrow + 3KOH$

Ferric Hypophosphite, N.F. X, $Fe(PH_2O_2)_3.xH_2O$, is a white or grayish-white powder. It is odorless and nearly tasteless. It is stable in air.

One Gm. of the salt is soluble in about 2300 ml. of water at 25° C. and in about 1200 ml. of boiling water. Hypophosphorous acid increases its solubility. It dissolves readily in a warm, concentrated solution of an alkali citrate to form a green solution. It is soluble in hydrochloric acid.

When strongly heated, ferric hypophosphite decomposes into poisonous phosphine and ferric pyrophosphate (1).

(1) $4Fe(PH_2O_2)_3 \rightarrow 6PH_3 \uparrow + Fe_4(P_2O_7)_3 + 3H_2O$

The solubility of the salt in acids such as acetic and hydrochloric is probably due to the formation of the corresponding ferric salt (2) together with hypophosphorous acid. When thus solubilized it gives the reactions of the ferric ion and also of the hypophosphite ion.

(2) $Fe(PH_2O_2)_3 + 3HCl \rightarrow FeCl_3 + 3HPH_2O_2$

This salt can be prepared by gradually adding a solution of ferric chloride to a solution of calcium hypophosphite (3).

$$(3)\ 3Ca(PH_2O_2)_2 + 2FeCl_3 \rightarrow 2Fe(PH_2O_2)_3 \downarrow + 3CaCl_2$$

It also may be prepared by dissolving ferric hydroxide in hypophosphorous acid, concentrating the solution and "scaling."

Ferric Hypophosphite is used as a source of iron in iron deficiency anemias in a usual dose of 0.2 Gm.

Caution should be observed in compounding this salt with other substances, as an explosion may occur if it is triturated or heated with nitrates, chlorates or other oxidizing agents.

Iron Sorbitex (Jectofer), N.D.—This product, introduced in 1965, is a chemical complex of iron, sorbitol, and citric acid with dextrin as a stabilizer. The molecular weight of the complex is about 5,000 and is considerably less than that in Iron Dextran Injection and Dextriferron. As a consequence, it is absorbed directly into the blood stream as well as into the lymphatics as the others are. This parenteral product is only used intramuscularly (*never* intravenously) and reaches a peak serum level in 2 hours but is rapidly cleared from the blood with 30 per cent being excreted via the kidney within 24 hours. As with other parenteral iron preparations this product should not be used if it is at all possible to use the oral mode of administration. Some side effects have been noted with its use such as sweating, headache, dizziness, nausea, vomiting, hypotension and collapse. Parenteral use of Iron Sorbitex should never accompany oral iron therapy since oral iron tends to saturate the transferrin and the injected iron then has no protein with which to bind. It is believed that it is this unbound iron that is responsible for the acute toxic symptoms. As with all parenteral iron therapy, the amount of iron required should be determined keeping in mind the 30 per cent urinary loss per 24 hours. The single daily dose is 1.5 mg. Fe/Kg. body weight. The usual total daily dose for an average individual is about 100 mg. Fe but no more than 207 mg. should be given in a 24-hour period. A small test dose, usually one-half the initial dose, is given initially to determine whether hypersensitivity exists.

Saccharated Ferric Oxide (Soluble Ferric Oxide, Eisenzucker), N.F. VII, contains, in each 100 Gm., the equivalent of not less than 2.8 Gm. and not more than 3.2 Gm. of Fe. This preparation consists of a mixture of sugar and ferric saccharate, $C_{12}H_{22}O_{11}(Fe_2O_3)_2$ + $C_{12}H_{22}O_{11}Na_2O$. It is prepared by adding a solution of ferric chloride to a solution of monohydrated sodium carbonate (1).

$$(1)\ 2FeCl_3 + 3Na_2CO_3 . H_2O \rightarrow 2Fe(OH)_3 \downarrow + 6NaCl + 3CO_2 \uparrow$$

The liquid is decanted and the ferric hydroxide washed with distilled water until a portion of the washings, when diluted with 5 volumes of distilled water, gives only a slight opalescence with

AgNO$_3$ T.S. The precipitate is transferred to a porcelain dish, sugar together with a sufficient quantity of a 15 per cent solution of sodium hydroxide to produce a clear solution, is added. The mixture is then evaporated to dryness on a water-bath. Usual dose— 2 Gm.

A commercial preparation named "Proferrin" is on the market and offers saccharated ferric oxide in a sterile solution form for intravenous iron therapy. Its suggested dosage is 1000 mg. spread over a seven-day period.

Soluble Ferric Phosphate, N.F. XI (FePO$_4$ + Na$_3$C$_6$H$_5$O$_7$), occurs in the form of thin, bright green, transparent scales. It also occurs as granules. It is odorless and has an acidulous, slightly saline taste. Because it is discolored in the presence of moisture and light, it should be kept in well-closed containers protected from light.

This scale salt is freely soluble in water, but is insoluble in alcohol.

Most of the iron in this preparation is bound (sequestered) in a non-ionized form. This is evidenced by the fact that it does not give a precipitate with ammonium hydroxide. It is, however, decomposed by alkali hydroxides to give a precipitate of ferric hydroxide.

This product of undetermined composition is made by dissolving ferric citrate in distilled water with the aid of heat and then dissolving secondary sodium phosphate in the solution. The clear solution is evaporated to a thick syrup on a water-bath at a temperature not exceeding 60° C., and then spread on glass plates and dried. By scraping off the salt, it is obtained in the form of thin, bright green, transparent scales.

It was officially described as ferric phosphate rendered soluble by the presence of sodium citrate, and yielded not less than 12 per cent and not more than 15 per cent of Fe. This salt was quite suitable for making liquid preparations of iron. It is non-irritating to the gastric system, and has a good hematinic action. This action has been utilized in *Iron, Quinine and Strychnine Phosphates Elixir.* Usual dose—0.25 Gm.

Ferric Pyrophosphate [Fe$_4$(P$_2$O$_7$)$_3$.9H$_2$O]. —This salt is formed as a yellowish-white precipitate when a solution of sodium pyrophosphate is treated with ferric sulfate. Although insoluble in water, it readily dissolves in solutions of the alkali citrates to form green solutions.

Ferric pyrophosphate was recognized under the title, *Ferri Pyrophosphas Solubilis* in the seventh edition of the *National Formulary.* It was described as "ferric pyrophosphate rendered soluble by the presence of sodium citrate, and yields not less than 10.5 per cent and not more than 12.5 per cent of Fe." This compound is made by dissolving uneffloresced sodium pyrophosphate in an aqueous solution of ferric citrate. The solution is concentrated to a syrupy consistency on a water-bath at a temperature not exceeding 60° C. and then spread on glass plates and dried. When scraped from the plates, the salt occurs in thin, transparent, odorless, apple-green scales. It also occurs in pearls or granules. The "scale salt" is readily soluble with a slightly acid reaction in water. It is insoluble in alcohol. Moist air and light decompose it. Usual dose—0.25 Gm.

Ferrocholinate (Chel-Iron, Ferrolip), N.D.—This hematinic product, introduced in 1958, is an iron choline citrate chelate with the following probable formula:

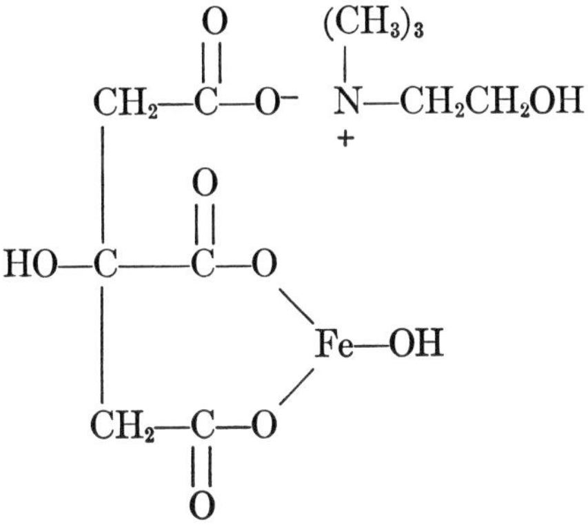

This product is claimed to be better absorbed into the circulation due to its being a chelated form of iron, although the fact that the iron is in the ferric form brings about a poorer absorption than with the ferrous salts. Nevertheless, when comparable amounts of iron are administered in this form, the hematinic results can be expected to be approximately comparable to those obtained with other forms of iron (*e.g.*, ferrous sulfate, ferrous fumarate, etc.). Mild gastrointestinal upset occurs on occasion but rarely requires discontinuation of therapy. It is only effective in iron deficiency anemia and is used orally in a dosage of 330 to 660 mg. 3 times a day which supplies a total of 120 to 240 mg. Fe daily. For infants a safe dosage schedule is 1 to 1.5 mg. Fe/Kg. body weight per day. An adequate dose for older children is 1.5 to 2 mg. Fe/Kg. body weight 3 times daily.

Ferrous Carbonate, $FeCO_3$, when freshly precipitated is white in color. However, when in contact with air it quickly becomes green, and finally changes to brown. These color changes are due to oxidative changes caused by atmospheric oxygen. Usually, the decomposition is attended by loss of CO_2 and the formation of ferric hydroxide (1). When treated with acids, ferrous carbonate effervesces due to liberation of carbon dioxide (2), this reaction probably being the fate of ferrous carbonate when administered orally. On this basis, ferrous chloride has been advocated as the most desirable form of ferrous salt to use since it eventuates in that form in the stomach.

(1) $4FeCO_3 + 6H_2O + O_2 \rightarrow 4Fe(OH)_3 \downarrow\ + 4CO_2 \uparrow$

(2) $FeCO_3 + 2HCl \rightarrow FeCl_2 + H_2O + CO_2 \uparrow$

41

Ferrous carbonate occurs naturally as the mineral *siderite* ($FeCO_3 . H_2O$) or *spathic iron ore*. However, the commercial supplies for medicinal uses have been made by adding sodium carbonate (3), potassium carbonate (4), or sodium bicarbonate (5) to solutions of ferrous sulfate.

(3) $FeSO_4 . 7H_2O + Na_2CO_3 . H_2O \rightarrow Na_2SO_4 + FeCO_3 \downarrow + 8H_2O$

(4) $FeSO_4 . 7H_2O + K_2CO_3 \rightarrow K_2SO_4 + FeCO_3 \downarrow + 7H_2O$

(5) $FeSO_4 . 7H_2O + 2NaHCO_3 \rightarrow FeCO_3 \downarrow + Na_2SO_4 + 8H_2O + CO_2 \uparrow$

Reaction (3) was used in the preparation of *Ferrous Carbonate Mass,* N.F. X. Reaction (4) was used in the preparation of *Ferrous Carbonate Pills*, N.F. XI, and reaction (5) was used in the preparation of *Saccharated Ferrous Carbonate*, N.F. X. Reaction (5) is said to be an especially desirable way of making ferrous carbonate because it is attended with the formation of CO_2 which helps to prevent oxidation of the ferrous carbonate which forms.

Ferrous carbonate was last official only in the form of *Ferrous Carbonate Pills*, N.F. XI, also known as Chalybeate Pills, Blaud's Pills, and Ferruginous Pills. Each pill contained not less than 60 mg. of $FeCO_3$.[1] The usual dose was 5 pills.

Ferrous Chloride ($FeCl_2$).—Native ferrous chloride is known as *Lawrencite*. White, shining crystals of anhydrous ferrous chloride may be obtained by passing hydrogen chloride over red hot iron or by reducing ferric chloride in a current of hydrogen. Greenish-blue, monoclinic crystals of the tetrahydrate ($FeCl_2 . 4H_2O$) are obtained by evaporating *in vacuo* a solution of iron or iron carbonate in hydrochloric acid. The salt is very unstable as it deliquesces in air and effloresces in a desiccator. It is readily soluble in water and in alcohol. When heated in air, it decomposes into ferric oxide and ferric chloride but when heated in steam it forms the ferroso-ferric oxide, hydrochloric acid, and hydrogen. It unites directly with ammonia to form an addition product, $FeCl_2 . 3NH_3$, which loses ammonia when heated.

Ferrous chloride is used medicinally in the form of an elixir for its hematinic properties.

Ferrous Lactate [$Fe(C_3H_5O_3)_2 . 3H_2O$].—It occurs as a greenish-white crystalline powder, or in crystalline crusts. It is slowly soluble in about 40 parts of water at 25° C., and in 12 parts of boiling water, giving solutions that are slightly acid to litmus. Alkali citrates form green solutions of the salt. It is nearly insoluble in alcohol.

It can be made by digesting iron with lactic acid. When the reaction has ceased, the solution is filtered, concentrated, and crys-

[1] For an interesting history of Blaud's Pills see Neuroth, M. L. and Lee, C. O., J. Am. Pharm. Assoc., Sc. Ed., **30**, 60 (1941).

tallized. It may be obtained also by dissolving crystallized calcium lactate in water and then agitating the solution with ferrous sulfate. Alcohol is then added to facilitate the separation of calcium sulfate, the mixture is filtered, and the filtrate evaporated to crystallization.

It has been used in the treatment of iron deficiency anemia in a dose of 200 to 400 mg. orally.

47

Cobalt and Cobalt Compounds

COBALT

Symbol, Co.   Valences, 2, 3.   Atomic Weight, 58.9332;
Atomic Number, 27

History and Occurrence.—At one time, the name "cobalt" was given to a certain mineral which was used to produce a blue color in glass.   In 1735, G. Brandt succeeded in preparing an impure cobalt which he called *Kobalt-rex*.   It is said that the element obtained its name from the German word *der Kobold* ("a goblin or gnome"). This name was used to designate iron ores from which it was thought to be impossible to obtain metallic iron because of the interference of evil spirits.

This metallic element is usually found in Nature associated with nickel, iron, copper, and silver minerals in the form of arsenides and sulfarsenides [*smaltite*, $CoAs_2$, *speiss-cobalt* (Co, Ni, Fe)As_2, *cobalt glance* $(CoFeAs)S_2$, *cobaltite*, CoAsS].   It occurs also as the sulfides (*linnæite*, Co_3S_4, *syepoorite*, CoS), arsenate (*erythrite* [cobalt bloom], $Co_3As_2O_7 . 8H_2O$), and as mixed oxides of cobalt and manganese (*asbolite*, *wad*, $CoMnO . 2MnO_2 . 4H_2O$).   Nearly all of the cobalt used in the United States is imported from Europe, where most of it is recovered as a by-product from the smelting of copper ores obtained from Belgian Congo.   The silver ore deposits near Cobalt, Ontario, are rich in cobalt, however, and now supply the United States with large quantities.

Properties.—Pure cobalt is a pinkish-white metal having a density of 8.92.   It is harder than iron, possesses magnetic properties, and melts at 1493° C.   It boils at 3550° C.   It crystallizes in the hexagonal or cubic system.

Cobaltous salts are pink in color when hydrated but blue when anhydrous.   The simple cobaltic ion is not stable as such but is stabilized through formation of various complex compounds, *e.g.*, the several ammine cobaltichlorides.

Chemical Properties.—It dissolves slowly in dilute acids and, like iron, exhibits the phenomenon of passivity (*q.v.*).   Cobalt forms two series of salts, *cobaltous* (Co^{2+}) and *cobaltic* (Co^{3+}).   Cobalt reacts with carbon monoxide to form carbonyls.   The following equations represent some of the reactions of cobalt in solution.

1. Alkali sulfides precipitate black, cobaltous sulfide from solutions of cobaltous salts (1).

(1) $Co^{++} + S^= \rightarrow CoS \downarrow$

2. Fixed alkali hydroxides precipitate blue basic salts, which rapidly change to an olive green color (2). If boiled soon after its precipitation, the color changes from blue to pink, due to the formation of cobaltous hydroxide $[Co(OH)_2]$ (3).

(2) $Co^{++} + Cl^- + OH^- \rightarrow Co(OH)Cl \downarrow$

(3) $Co(OH)Cl + OH^- \rightarrow Co(OH)_2 + Cl^-$

3. Ammonium hydroxide precipitates blue basic salts from solutions of cobaltous salts. The precipitates are soluble in an excess of the reagent and form bright colored solutions of complex ammino-cobaltous hydroxide $[Co(NH_3)_6(OH)_2]$ which rapidly oxidize to ammino-cobaltic hydroxide $[Co(NH_3)_6(OH)_3]$.

4. Alkali carbonates precipitate reddish, basic cobaltous carbonate $[Co_8O_5(CO_3)_3]$, which turns violet to blue when boiled.

5. When a solution of a cobaltous compound is warmed with potassium chloride, potassium nitrite, and acetic acid, a yellow precipitate of potassium cobaltinitrite is formed (4).

(4) $CoCl_2 + 6KNO_2 + HNO_2 + CH_3COOH \rightarrow Co(NO_2)_3.-$
$3KNO_2 \downarrow + 2KCl + CH_3COOK + H_2O + NO \uparrow$

6. When cobalt compounds are fused into a borax bead, a blue color (due to cobalt metaborate, $[Co(BO_2)_2]$ is produced.

7. When a fused aluminum compound is moistened with a solution of cobalt nitrate, a blue color (due to cobalt aluminate, $Co[AlO_2]_2$) is produced.

8. Vogel's reaction: When a concentrated solution of ammonium thiocyanate is added to a cobaltous solution, ammonium cobalto-thiocyanate (beautiful blue) is formed (5). Ferric ion interferes with this test but may be removed by the addition of stannous chloride.

(5) $Co^{++} + 2NH_4^+ + 4CNS^- \rightarrow (NH_4)_2(Co(CNS)_4)$

Commercial Manufacture.—Cobalt can be obtained (1) by the reduction of the monoxide or chloride with hydrogen or carbon monoxide, (2) by the Goldschmidt process, (3) by heating the oxalate under a layer of powdered glass, (4) by the electrolysis of the chloride, and (5) by chemical solution and precipitation.

Pharmacological Action of the Cobalt Ion.—Cobalt salts administered by parenteral injection cause marked circulatory effects such as a fall in blood pressure and general capillary damage. The blood pressure is lowered, probably by injuring the blood vessels. There are convulsive movements which indicate central nervous system stimulation followed by tremors and chorea-like movements, later by tetanus, and finally paralysis.

When taken orally cobalt salts may induce vomiting and diarrhea. They are not especially irritating to mucous membrane. The salts are rapidly absorbed from the intestinal tract and are excreted largely in the urine. Nephritis may result from kidney damage.

Cobalt has been found to stimulate the hematopoietic system when ingested in extremely small quantities over a period of time. This element is essential in the development of erythrocytes and hemoglobin. It is believed to stimulate the bone marrow. As far as is known cobalt does not affect leukocyte formation. Since only traces of cobalt are necessary for the body and this amount is in the daily diet, there is little occasion to administer it.

Cobalt is known to be present as a part of the molecule of vitamin B_{12}, a vitamin which seems to have as at least one of its functions, the catalysis of "transmethylation" reactions. The administration of small amounts of cobalt salts to rats has resulted in a marked increase in the vitamin B_{12} activity of these animals. It has also been observed that sheep, cattle, and hogs when fed tiny amounts of cobalt put on weight much faster than control animals. The mechanism whereby these effects take place is not known but the implication is that intestinal bacteria may possibly utilize the cobalt to synthesize vitamin B_{12}, which in turn boosts the growth processes.

Uses.—The principal use of cobalt metal is in the manufacture of special steels and alloys. Cobalt alloys are very hard, resist oxidation, take a high polish, and maintain their temper even at high temperatures.

The compounds of cobalt have not found much use in therapy although the cobalt-cobaltic oxide (Co_3O_4) has been used as an astringent and cobalt nitrate [$Co(NO_3)_2 . 6H_2O$] has been suggested as an antidote for cyanide poisoning because it forms an insoluble compound with cyanides. Because of the speed of cyanide poisoning, however, no antidote has been very successful.

48

Nickel and Nickel Compounds

NICKEL

Symbol, Ni.   Valences, 2, 3.   Atomic Weight, 58.71;
Atomic Number, 28

History and Occurrence.—This metallic element has been known from earliest times.   Many centuries before Christ, the Chinese smelted ores containing nickel and copper with those of zinc and tin to make an alloy called *pakfong*.   This they used in making coins, ornaments, etc.   An ore composed of nickel arsenide (NiAs) was known in 1694.   This natural product closely resembled ores rich in copper.   However, when it failed to yield any copper upon smelting, it was called "Old Nick's copper" or *Kupfernickel*, the word from which this element gets its name.   In 1754, A. F. Cronstedt obtained the metal in an impure state from *niccolite* and the results of his work were corroborated in 1775 by T. O. Bergman.

Nickel occurs free and also alloyed with iron in meteorites.   The principal ore deposits are around Sudbury, Ontario, and in the French Colony of New Caledonia in the South Pacific.   The ores of the Sudbury district consist of copper-nickel-iron sulfides (*pyrrhotite, chalcopyrite* and *pentlandite*) associated with more or less cobalt, whereas, those of New Caledonia, known as *garnierite* from their discoverer, J. Garnier (1865), are hydrated silicates of nickel and magnesium, approximating the formula $H_2(Ni.Mg)SiO_4.(H_2O)_n$.

Physical Properties.—Nickel is a lustrous, white metal having a density of 8.9.   Sometimes it has a slightly grayish or yellowish tinge.   It is malleable and ductile, takes a high polish, is very hard, and possesses magnetic properties when exposed to moist air. It melts at 1455° C. and boils at 3075° C.

A special form of nickel is known as *Raney nickel*.   This form is supplied commercially as a nickel-aluminum alloy, which is boiled with strong caustic soda to remove the aluminum.   This leaves a finely divided black pyrophoric residue of nickel.   This form of nickel is important as a catalyst for hydrogenations, *e.g.*, of unsaturated vegetable oils.

Chemical Properties.—The metal slowly becomes covered with a superficial film of oxide.   Dilute acids slowly act upon nickel and liberate hydrogen.   It is readily attacked by dilute nitric acid. The metal resists the corrosive action of alkalies.

Solutions of nickel salts respond to the following chemical reactions: 1. Alkali sulfides precipitate black nickel sulfide from solutions of nickel salts (1).

(1) $Ni^{++} + S^{=} \rightarrow NiS \downarrow$

2. From solutions of nickel salts, fixed alkali hydroxides precipitate pale-green nickel hydroxide [$Ni(OH)_2$] which is insoluble in excess of alkalies, but dissolves in ammonium hydroxide or ammonium salts to form blue solutions containing the complex, $Ni(NH_3)_6$-$(OH)_2$.

3. Alkali carbonates precipitate a green, basic nickelous carbonate of variable composition [$Ni_5(OH)_6(CO_3)_2$]. The precipitate dissolves in ammonium hydroxide or ammonium salts to form blue solutions.

4. Potassium cyanide precipitates yellowish-green nickel cyanide from solutions of nickel salts (2). The precipitate dissolves in an excess of the precipitant to form double cyanides (3).

(2) $Ni^{++} + 2CN^{-} \rightarrow Ni(CN)_2 \downarrow$

(3) $Ni(CN)_2 + 4CN^{-} \rightarrow [Ni(CN_6)]^{==}$

5. Potassium ferrocyanide precipitates greenish-white nickel ferrocyanide from solutions of nickel salts (4).

(4) $2Ni^{++} + Fe(CN)_6^{==} \rightarrow Ni_2Fe(CN)_6 \downarrow$

Potassium ferricyanide precipitates greenish-yellow nickel ferricyanide from solutions of nickel salts (5).

(5) $3Ni^{++} + 2Fe(CN)_6^{\equiv} \rightarrow Ni_3[Fe(CN)_6]_2 \downarrow$

6. If dimethylglyoxime is added to an ammoniacal solution of a nickel salt, a bright red, insoluble, crystalline precipitate is obtained. Cobalt does not react with this reagent.

(6) 2
$$\begin{array}{l} CH_3-C=NOH \\ \qquad | \\ CH_3-C=NOH \end{array} + Ni^{++} + 2NH_3 \rightarrow 2NH_4^{+} + (C_4H_7N_2O_2)_2Ni$$

7. Nickel colors the borax bead brown in the oxidizing flame. The color is masked by a small amount of cobalt. In the reducing flame, metallic nickel "clouds" the bead.

Commercial Manufacture.—The ore containing sulfides of copper, nickel, and iron (*pentlandite*) is roasted to convert the sulfur and iron to oxides and then smelted in a blast furnace. This blasting usually removes all but a very small amount (less than 1 per cent) of iron and a *matte* is obtained which consists of about 40 per cent of copper-nickel alloy and 60 per cent of sulfur. The larger part of the sulfur is burned off in a Bessemer converter and a product containing about 80 per cent of the copper-nickel alloy is obtained. This alloy

(*Monel metal*) is more resistant to corrosion than steel and is used for wire, screens, sheet-metal, etc.

Pure nickel may be made from this copper-nickel alloy either by the Browne electrolytic process or by the Mond process.

In the Browne electrolytic process, the Bessemerized matte is crushed, roasted and reduced in a reverberatory furnace to metal, which is cast into anode plates. When these are electrolyzed, the nickel goes into solution, any copper remaining therein is precipitated as sulfide and the iron is removed as hydroxide with caustic soda. The solution is then concentrated, the precipitated sodium chloride filtered off, and the hot solution of nickel chloride again electrolyzed.

In the Mond process, the copper-nickel matte is crushed, treated with warm, dilute sulfuric acid to remove the copper and the residue reduced with cold water-gas in a tower to a yellow, volatile nickel tetracarbonyl (Ni[CO]$_4$). This liquid carbonyl boils at 43° C., and decomposes at 200° C. into pure nickel and carbon monoxide. It will be noted that cobalt does not form a carbonyl under the above conditions.

Pharmacological Action of Nickel Ion.—There is nothing characteristic about the action of nickel. When hypodermically injected it causes marked circulatory effects. The blood pressure is lowered, probably by injuring the blood vessels. Its elimination by the kidneys causes nephritis. These effects are common to all of the metallic salts.

Although the salts of nickel have from time to time been suggested for use in medicine they have not met with any success. For example, nickel bromide has been suggested for epilepsy; the carbonate and sulfate for use as tonics and hematinics; and a 1 or 2 per cent solution of nickel sulfate has been used for certain parasitic skin diseases.

Perhaps the only nickel preparation in use today that seems to have some effectiveness is nickel pectinate (Tomectin), a preparation utilized for the treatment of diarrheas. It has been demonstrated rather conclusively that, whereas pectin itself is of no value in diarrheas and indeed may aggravate the condition, nickel pectinate may cause the abatement of symptoms. Pectin is a colloidal acid and when treated with metallic salts will form the metallic pectinate, *e.g.*, nickel pectinate which is quite stable in an acid medium. The metal ion is not ionized from pectinates in sufficient quantities to cause toxic manifestations, and they are, therefore, safe for internal use. The mechanism of action is unknown although some hypotheses have been advanced. For example, it has been known for a long time that nickel ions are toxic to bacteria, and no doubt some of the bacterial inhibition is due to this action. It has also been suggested that nickel ion may play a catalytic role in the production of antitoxin and agglutinin.

Uses.—Nickel is used extensively in the form of its alloys for making domestic utensils, coins, surgical instruments, automobile parts, chemical apparatus, etc. A nickel, zinc and copper alloy forms the well-known German silver. Finely divided nickle is a very active catalyst and is extensively used in the hydrogenation of cottonseed and linseed oils and other unsaturated organic compounds.

Aside from nickel pectinate that has already been discussed under the "Pharmacological Action of Nickel Ion" the only other salt that has been used is nickelous sulfate ($NiSO_4.6H_2O$) which has been employed as a parasiticide in certain skin diseases in a 1 or 2 per cent solution.

49

The Platinum Metals and Their Compounds[1]

RUTHENIUM

Symbol, Ru. Valences, 1, 2, 3, 4, 7, and 8
Atomic Weight, 101.07; Atomic Number, 44

Ruthenium was discovered by Claus in 1845. It is named after *ruthen*, for Russia. This element is a dark gray or black metal. It is very hard and brittle. It has a density of 12.2 and melts at about 2450° C. When finely divided and heated to 600° C., the dioxide (RuO_2) is formed. When sublimed, it forms green iridescent crystals. Its other oxides are Ru_2O_3 and RuO_4 (yellow volatile peroxide). Ruthenium forms several chlorides, *e.g.*, $RuCl_2$, $RuCl_3$ and $RuCl_4$. The addition of an alkali hydroxide to a solution of $RuCl_3$ produces the hydroxide $Ru(OH)_3$. Potassium chlororuthenate (K_2RuCl_6) is formed by igniting a mixture of the metal and potassium chloride in a current of chlorine. Ruthenium is converted into potassium ruthenate (K_2RuO_4) by fusion with potassium nitrate and potassium hydroxide. This salt separates as black crystals from the yellow aqueous solution obtained by lixiviating the "melt." By passing chlorine or steam through the mother liquor, the volatile RuO_4 (1) is obtained as yellow crystals which melt at about 45.5° C. and boil at about 100.8° C. Dilute acid acts upon potassium ruthenate to form potassium peruthenate ($KRuO_4$). This reaction recalls the behavior of manganese compounds. This oxygen compound forms deep green aqueous solutions. Ruthenium dissolves slowly in aqua regia.

(1) $K_2RuO_4 + Cl_2 \rightarrow 2KCl + RuO_4 \uparrow$

Neither the metal nor any of its compounds has any uses.

RHODIUM

Symbol, Rh. Valences, 2, 3, 4, 6. Atomic Weight, 102.905;
Atomic Number, 45

Rhodium was discovered by Wollaston in 1803. It is named after the Greek *rodon*, a rose, in allusion to the color of many of its salts.

---

[1] See Cochrane, J., "The Platinum-Group Metals," J. Chem. Educ., **31**, 407, 1954.

In appearance it resembles aluminum. It has a density of 12.42 and melts at 1966° C. When heated strongly in oxygen, it forms the sesquioxide (Rh_2O_3). The sesquioxide is basic and gives derivatives such as $Rh_2(SO_4)_3.12H_2O$ and $Rh(NO_3)_3$. The other oxides are Rh_3O_4, RhO_2, Rh_2O_5 and RhO_3. Free chlorine attacks it and forms $RhCl_2$ and $RhCl_3$ (dark red). The latter forms K_2RhCl_5 with potassium chloride. Ammino-complexes of the type formed by cobalt are known. Example: $Rh(NH_3)_6Cl_3$. The pure metal in massive form is insoluble in acids and almost insoluble in aqua regia. When in a fine state of division, the metal slowly dissolves in aqua regia, in concentrated sulfuric acid, or in fused potassium hydrogen sulfate. Rhodium sulfate forms alums (*q.v.*) with alkali sulfates. The volatility of platinum is reduced by the addition of from 3 to 5 per cent of rhodium. Such an alloy, being harder and more durable than platinum, is especially adapted for making "platinum" crucibles.

PALLADIUM

Symbol, Pd.   Valences, 2, 3, 4, 6.   Atomic Weight, 106.4;
Atomic Number, 46

With the exception of platinum, palladium occurs in larger amounts than any other member of the family. It was discovered in 1803 by Wollaston and named by him in honor of the asteroid, Pallas, which in turn was named after a Greek goddess. It is found associated with platinum in the Urals and in Brazil. It is also found in the nickel ores of Sudbury, Ontario. It has a silvery appearance, is softer than platinum, has a density of about 12.0 and a melting-point of about 1555° C. which is the lowest melting-point of any of the platinum metals. The metal may be precipitated from solution in the form of a black powder.

Palladium usually exhibits a valence of 2 or 4. It unites with oxygen to form PdO, Pd_2O_3 and PdO_2. When heated, it combines directly with sulfur to form PdS. The halogens attack palladium and form the respective halides ($PdCl_2$, $PdBr_2$, etc.). Strong concentrated acids, *e.g.*, hydrochloric acid, hot sulfuric acid, nitric acid, act upon the metal and form the chloride ($PdCl_2$), the sulfate ($PdSO_4$), and the nitrate ($Pd[NO_3]_2$), respectively. From these reactions, we find that palladium is the most basic element of the family. Aqua regia acts vigorously upon it to form chloropalladic acid (H_2PdCl_6).[1]

Solutions of palladous salts yield with ammonia T.S., a salmon-colored precipitate which is soluble in an excess of the reagent.

---

[1] From this compound, potassium iodide precipitates black palladous iodide (PdI_2) which is soluble in an excess of the reagent. This reaction is used as a test for palladium, but it is not as good as the formation of a reddish-brown precipitate by adding α-nitroso-β-naphthol to a solution of palladous chloride.

Hydrochloric acid added to this solution produces a yellow precipitate of dichlorodiamminepalladium [Pd(NH₃)₂Cl₂]. Solutions of palladous salts yield with potassium iodide T.S. a black precipitate of PdI_2 which is visible in 1 to 500,000 parts of solution.

Finely divided palladium possesses to a greater degree than any other element the property of "occluding" or adsorbing large quantities of hydrogen. The finely divided metal ("palladium sponge") will adsorb at room temperature over seven hundred times its own volume of the gas. The action of hydrogen, which is inactive at ordinary temperatures, is catalyzed by palladium. For example, it replaces copper from its salts (1), reduces ferric to ferrous salts (2) and converts chlorine into hydrogen chloride. Also, when a mixture of air and hydrogen is led over the powdered metal, the hydrogen is burned to water.

(1) $CuSO_4 + H_2 \rightarrow H_2SO_4 + Cu$

(2) $2FeCl_3 + H_2 \rightarrow 2FeCl_2 + 2HCl$

Palladium is used as an adsorbent for hydrogen in gas analysis. Its alloys with gold ("palau"), etc., resist corrosion and, therefore, are used for making jewelry, in dental practice, for coating reflectors, etc. The salts of the metal are sometimes used in photography. Also, metals are frequently coated with palladium.

OSMIUM

Symbol, Os. Valences, 2, 3, 4, 6, and 8. Atomic Weight, 190.2; Atomic Number, 76

Osmium was discovered by Tennant in 1803. It was named from the Greek *osme*, a smell, in reference to the pungent odor of its tetroxide. This element has a density of 22.5 and is the heaviest known substance. It closely resembles zinc in color and luster and melts at 2700° C. Osmium occurs in platinum ores and in the form of an iridium alloy known as *osmiridium*.

Osmium forms several oxides, *viz.*, OsO, Os_2O_3, OsO_2, and OsO_4. Osmium tetroxide (OsO_4) is analogous to ruthenium tetroxide (RuO_4) and is by far the most important compound of the element. It is formed by heating powdered osmium in air or oxygen, or by treating the finely divided metal with aqua regia or nitric acid (either fuming or concentrated). It is volatile in steam; melts at 41° C.; and boils when heated to 134° C. The vapors are colorless, possess a disagreeable chlorine-like odor, and are very toxic and irritating to mucous membrane. Perhaps its greatest danger is its action on the eyes. Osmium tetroxide is sometimes called *osmic acid*. This is erroneous because the oxide does not form salts and its aqueous solutions are neutral in reaction. Aqueous solutions of osmium tetroxide are used for hardening and coloring (black) histological specimens from which microscopic sections are to be made.

In the massive condition, osmium is not attacked even by aqua regia. However, when finely divided, it is acted upon by concentrated inorganic acids. Osmium conforms to the group tendency to form double and complex salts with ammonia [$(NH_4)_2OsCl_6$] and the halogens (K_2OsCl_6).

IRIDIUM

Symbol, Ir. Valences, 2, 3, 4, and 6. Atomic Weight, 192.2; Atomic Number, 77

In 1802, Tennant discovered iridium. It was named from the Greek *iris*, a rainbow, owing to the wide range of colors of its salts. It is a white, hard, brittle metal having a density of 22.4. It is malleable at red heat and melts at 2450° C. In the massive state, it is nearly insoluble in aqua regia, but when finely divided, it dissolves slowly in this reagent. It also combines at red heat with oxygen, sulfur and phosphorus. When heated in the presence of sodium chloride, it reacts with chlorine to form the chloroiridate (Na_2IrCl_6). It is oxidized by strongly heating it with sodium hydroxide and potassium nitrate. If the fused mass is treated with aqua regia, a dark red solution of Na_2IrCl_6 is obtained. Finely powdered iridium is a very powerful catalytic agent. Iridium imparts to its alloys its inherent property of resisting attack by powerful chemical reagents, *e.g.*, fluorine. Therefore, it is alloyed with 90 per cent of platinum and used for making crucibles, thermocouples, standard weights and measures, and other chemical apparatus. Alloys of iridium with either platinum or osmium are used to tip gold pens. Its salts are sometimes used in photography and its oxides for coloring china.

Iridium and its compounds closely resemble those of rhodium and nickel (*q.v.*). Three oxides of iridium are known, *viz.*, IrO, Ir_2O_3 and IrO_2. Ir_2O_3 forms salts. Iridium forms four chlorides, *viz.*, IrCl, $IrCl_2$, $IrCl_3$ and $IrCl_4$. This element is more basic than acidic and possesses the group tendency to form double salts and complex compounds with the halogens and ammonia, $Ir(NH_3)_2Cl_2$, $Ir(NH_3)_4Cl_2$.

PLATINUM

Symbol, Pt. Valences, 2, 3, 4, 6. Atomic Weight, 195.09; Atomic Number, 78

History and Occurrence.—The name of this element is derived from the Spanish *platina*, the diminutive of *plata*, meaning silver.

Native platinum was first discovered as early as the 16th century in Colombia by Spanish travelers. It was named Platina de Pinto in reference to small silver-like particles found in the auriferous placers of the River Pinto. This metal was first described by Watson (1750) and later studied by Marggraf and Bergman. Like gold, platinum occurs widely distributed in Nature, but in exceedingly small amounts. It is found alloyed with other metals, *e.g.*, ruthenium, rhodium, palladium, iridium, osmium, gold, silver, copper, iron, and in alluvial sands and gravels. The principal deposits are found in Canada, the U.S.S.R. and the Union of South Africa. The world production of platinum in 1946 is estimated to have been 576,000 troy ounces. The United States is the largest user of this metal.

Physical Properties.—Platinum is a grayish-white, lustrous metal. It can be welded at red heat and easily fused in the oxyhydrogen flame (melting-point, 1773° C.). It boils at 4530° C. Its ductility approaches that of gold and silver. Its usual malleability is markedly lessened by the presence of other metals, such as iridium, osmium, etc. It has a density of 21.45 and is fairly hard and tough. It is a good conductor of electricity and it has the lowest coefficient of expansion of all the metals. It may be sealed into glass. Molten platinum, like silver, adsorbs a large volume of oxygen. As the metal cools, oxygen is spasmodically liberated and gives rise to the phenomenon known as "spitting." When finely divided, platinum also adsorbs large quantities of gases, especially oxygen and hydrogen. These gases become so "activated" that they explosively combine with one another. Finely divided platinum often acts as an efficient catalyst. Its use in the form of platinized asbestos has been mentioned in connection with the contact process for making sulfuric acid. Since hydrogen diffuses through red hot platinum, it is unsafe to heat easily reducible substances in platinum vessels.

Chemical Properties.—Platinum forms two series of compounds, the *platinous* and the *platinic*, in which the metal exhibits valences of 2 and 4, respectively. It forms complex salts with ammonia.

Platinum is permanent in air and is not affected by hot or cold oxygen. It is not acted upon ordinarily by the common acids or by fused alkali carbonates. It is not attacked by dilute sulfuric acid, but the hot concentrated acid slowly acts on the metal and forms $Pt(OH).(HSO_4)_2$. Neither hydrochloric nor nitric acid acts upon pure platinum, but aqua regia converts it into chloroplatinic acid (H_2PtCl_6) (1). The addition of zinc to chloroplatinic acid reduces the latter to an extremely fine, hard, black powder known as *platinum black*. This substance will adsorb and activate large quantities of gases, such as hydrogen, oxygen, carbon monoxide, etc. Therefore, it is a powerful catalytic agent. Platinum is attacked by the halogens, sulfur, phosphorus, arsenic and carbon (smoky flame of burner). Fused sulfates and nitrates have some action upon it and fused hydroxides and peroxides have a more pronounced action.

Platinum will form alloys with low melting-point metals, such as lead. The chlorides of magnesium and lithium will materially injure platinum.

$$(1) \quad 3Pt + 18HCl + 4HNO_3 \rightarrow 3H_2PtCl_6 + 4NO\uparrow + 8H_2O$$

Commercial Manufacture.—Much of the platinum is obtained as a secondary metal during the refining of Cu, Pb, Ni, etc. The platinum-bearing sands and gravels are levigated to obtain a residue containing from 60 to 80 per cent of platinum and associated metals. This is digested with aqua regia, which slowly dissolves the platinum and allied metals, filtered, and the filtrate made almost neutral with a solution of calcium hydroxide. This precipitates most of the iron, copper, rhodium, and iridium and some of the palladium which are filtered off and the solution evaporated to dryness. The dried material is heated to about 125° C. and extracted with water and hydrochloric acid. Ammonium chloride is added to the solution to precipitate the difficultly soluble ammonium chloroplatinate $[(NH_4)_2PtCl_6]$. The precipitate is dried and heated to redness to decompose the salt into a porous, metallic mass called *spongy platinum*. The massive or compact form of the metal is obtained by hammering the spongy metal at red heat or by melting it in a refractory crucible which is heated by the oxyhydrogen flame. The melted platinum is then cast into bars weighing from 2 to 5 kilos.

Uses.—The physical properties of platinum, *viz.*, malleability, ductility and high melting-point, together with its chemical inactivity, *viz.*, resistance to acids and fused alkali carbonates, make it especially suited for making crucibles, dishes, wire, foil and other physical and chemical apparatus. It is used for plating other metals and for making jewelry. In a finely divided form, platinum is used extensively as a catalyst.

50

The Inert Gases

DURING the years 1893–1895, Lord Rayleigh made a series of very accurate determinations of the densities of gases. He noticed that nitrogen isolated from the atmosphere was always heavier than the nitrogen he prepared from compounds, such as ammonium nitrite, urea and the oxides of nitrogen. A constant difference in density of 0.065 (H = 1) was too great to be considered as an experimental error by such a careful investigator as Rayleigh, so he was led to suspect the presence of some new gas in the atmosphere. In 1785, Cavendish came to the same conclusion after eliminating the ordinary components of air and finding a small, inactive gaseous residue that would not unite with oxygen on sparking over a concentrated solution of potassium hydroxide. Cavendish did not pursue the subject further, but Rayleigh repeated the experiment in conjunction with Sir William Ramsay and, on removal of the last traces of nitrogen with red hot magnesium, found that the residual gas gave a spectrum different from that of any known element. Ramsay named the new element *argon* (Greek, meaning *lazy*) because of its complete chemical inertness. Ramsay and Travers then fractionated large quantities of liquid air and discovered neon, krypton and xenon. Ramsay also found helium in crude liquid argon, but a further search of 120 tons of liquid air failed to reveal the presence of any other new gases.

HELIUM

Helium, U.S.P. XVII

Symbol, He. Atomic Number, 2. Atomic Weight, 4.003

Physical Properties.—Helium is a colorless, tasteless, odorless gas with a density of 0.1368 (air = 1). Helium is the lightest of all gases with the exception of hydrogen, and has a buoyancy of 92.6 per cent of the latter gas. A liter of the gas at standard temperature and pressure weighs not less than 177 mg. and not more than 220 mg. Helium is practically insoluble in water. Experiments recently carried out show that it is also insoluble in blood (nitrogen, however, is much more soluble).

(645)

Chemical Properties.—Helium is chemically inert. It does not support combustion and will prevent hydrogen from burning when mixed with it.

Official Tests for Identity.—A burning splinter of wood is extinguished in an atmosphere of Helium. Mixtures of hydrogen and Helium are neither inflammable nor explosive when oxygen is excluded.

Commercial Manufacture.—In 1895, helium was shown to be present in the air. Ramsay found the amount to be 0.0004 per cent by volume, or 0.000056 per cent (1 part in 1,800,000 parts) by weight. The gas is found in small percentages dissolved in many spring waters and mixed with the gases issuing from these springs. Helium has been detected in volcanic gases, in natural gases and occluded in all radioactive minerals. Natural gases have been found with a helium content of 2 per cent; the average content of the wells in a zone comprising Texas, Oklahoma, Kansas, Illinois, Ohio, Pennsylvania and New York is only 0.5 per cent. Natural gas wells all over the rest of the world contain very small percentages of helium. The wells richest in helium are those in Texas, Oklahoma and Kansas. These wells give the United States a monopoly as far as production on a commercial scale is concerned. The separation of helium from the other gases with which it is associated in natural gas is accomplished in a modified form of liquid air machine. Helium approaching a purity of 100 per cent can be obtained in the final stage by adsorbing the remaining quantities of contaminating gases in coconut charcoal at the temperature of liquid air.

Helium resisted all attempts at liquefaction until 1908, when the efforts of H. K. Onnes were successful. Expansion of compressed helium at the temperature of liquid hydrogen resulted in liquefaction. Onnes found liquid helium to be colorless and very mobile; the liquid boils at $-268.9°$ C. and has a density of 0.147 at $-270.8°$ C. The critical temperature of helium is given as $-267.9°$ C.; the critical pressure is 2.26 A. It is interesting to note that at the temperature of liquid helium, the electrical resistance of metals drops practically to zero; the metals become "superconductors."

Uses.—*Helium*, U.S.P. XVII, contains not less than 95 per cent by volume of He, the remainder consisting mainly of nitrogen.

Helium was introduced into therapy by A. L. Barach[1] in 1934. Although physiologically inert, its use as a therapeutic gas depends upon the fact that helium is the lightest gas with the exception of hydrogen, and that it has a specific gravity one-seventh that of nitrogen. When mixed with oxygen in the proportions of 20 per cent oxygen and 80 per cent helium, a respirable gas is obtained that has a specific gravity only one-third that of air or oxygen. Because of the lighter weight of the oxygen-helium mixture it can be breathed

---

[1] A. L. Barach, J.A.M.A., **107**, 1273 (1936); see also U. H. Eversole, J.A.M.A. **110**, 878 (1938).

with much less effort than air. By decreasing the effort required in breathing, the dyspnea of patients with severe asthma or obstructive lesions in the larynx and trachea is also decreased. For this reason, and as a diluent for medicinal gases, the U.S.P. recognizes this gas. It is also used for the prevention of "bends" and to avoid the narcotic effect of nitrogen under pressure in underwater workers.

Other suggested uses for helium include the cooling of electrical equipment, the preservation of food, and the formation of an inert atmosphere for carrying out chemical reactions which are sensitive to air.

NEON

Symbol, Ne.   Atomic Number, 10.   Atomic Weight, 20.183.

Ramsay and Travers first obtained neon (Greek, meaning *new*) by fractional distillation of liquid air. The gas is colorless, odorless and chemically inert like the other members of this group. The density is 0.6962 (air = 1). Neon can be condensed to a liquid which has a specific gravity of 1.204 at its boiling-point of $-245.9°$ C. The critical temperature of the gas is $-228.7°$ C., and the critical pressure is 25.9 A.

The element is readily identified by a characteristic spectrum showing many bright lines in the red and in the orange portions. When an electrical discharge is sent through neon under diminished pressure, a brilliant orange-red glow results. Extensive use of this property is made for advertising purposes. Neon-filled glass tubes bent in the shape of letters and various designs make attractive signs and create unique decorative effects. The light has considerable penetrating power for fogs, so neon lamps have been installed in lighthouses, at airports and along passenger and air mail routes.

ARGON

Symbol, A.   Atomic Number, 18.   Atomic Weight, 39.944.

The discovery of argon has been discussed at the beginning of this chapter. By far the most abundant and the most widely distributed of the inert gases, argon is found in the air (0.94 per cent by volume), in natural gas, occluded in minerals and dissolved in the oceans and in all fresh waters. It has been calculated that about 800,000,000 pounds of argon are contained in the air above each square mile of the surface of the earth.

Argon is a colorless, odorless gas with a density of 1.378 (air = 1). Liquid argon boils at $-185.7°$ C. and has a specific gravity of 1.402 at its boiling-point. The critical temperature of the gas is $-122.4°$ C., the critical pressure is 48 A. Solid argon melts at $-189.2°$ C.

The abundance of the gas, and the fact that it is a by-product of several liquid air processes, insure a low cost of production. At present, it is filled into electric lights to slow up the blackening of the bulbs and to secure longer life for the filaments. Fluorescent tubes used for lighting purposes contain a mixture of mercury vapor and argon at a low pressure (3 mm.).

KRYPTON

Symbol, Kr.   Atomic Number, 36.   Atomic Weight, 83.80.

Ramsay and Travers isolated krypton (Greek, meaning *hidden*) in liquid air residues from which argon had been separated. Ramsay found 1 volume of krypton to be present in 20,000,000 volumes of air; the present value is 1 in 1,000,000. Small quantities of krypton are found in the gases issuing from thermal springs and occluded in certain minerals.

Like the other members of the family, krypton is a colorless, odorless gas with a density of 2.8675 (air = 1). The critical temperature is −63° C.; the critical pressure is 54 A. Liquid krypton has a specific gravity of 2.155 at its boiling-point of −152.9° C. Solid krypton melts at −157° C. A mixture of this gas and xenon is used in tubes to produce an intense light of short duration for high speed photography. For use of krypton as an anesthetic see xenon.

XENON

Symbol, Xe.   Atomic Number, 54.   Atomic Weight, 131.30.

The isolation of xenon by the fractionation of liquid air was accomplished by Ramsay and Travers. The name is derived from a Greek word, meaning *the stranger*. Xenon is the least abundant of the inert gases, for there is only 1 volume of the gas in 11,000,000 volumes of air. The gas has a density of 4.525 (air = 1), a critical temperature of 16.6° C., and a critical pressure of 58.2 A. Liquid xenon boils at −107.1° C.; its specific gravity is 3.06 at −109° C. Solid xenon melts at −112° C.

Since 1946 xenon and krypton have been the objects of experimental investigation directed toward their use as general anesthetics. Both gases possess fairly high oil-water solubility ratios (Xe=20; Kr=9.6) which may partially account for their effectiveness.[1]

In the case of xenon it has been shown that it has a general anesthetic potency virtually equal to that of ethylene.[2] Indeed,

[1] Cullen, S. C., and Gross, E. G.: Science. 113. 580 (1951).
[2] Cullen, S. C. and Pittenger, C. B.: Surgical Forum, 38th Clinical Congress of American College of Surgeons, 1952, Philadelphia, W. B. Saunders Co., 1953, p. 361.

it has been used successfully in surgical anesthesia in humans[1,2] although the cost of the gas is a limiting factor. On the basis of electroencephalograms during anesthesia it is apparent that the changes expected are those characteristic of other general anesthetics.[3] The anesthesia relates to the partial pressure of the gas and not to hypoxemia. It is claimed to be effective and innocuous when used with 20 per cent oxygen.

RADON

Symbol, Rn. Atomic Number, 86. Atomic Weight, 222.

In 1901, Dorn recognized the presence of a new inert gas given off by radium salts and their aqueous solutions. Rutherford and Soddy succeeded in liquefying the emanation; Ramsay and Collie demonstrated its characteristic spectrum. Ramsay called the gas *niton*, but this has since been changed to *radon*.

The gas occurs in all radium minerals and in small quantities in any waters that have come into contact with the minerals. Radon is much more soluble in certain organic solvents. Directly after the preparation of an aqueous solution of a radium salt, the rate of accumulated radon increases rapidly for a few days and then goes up more slowly, until a constant, maximum rate is reached. Radon itself undergoes radioactive disintegration but does not enter into any chemical reactions.

The density of radon is 7.525 (air = 1). The gas has a critical temperature of 104° C. and a critical pressure of 62 A. Liquid radon boils at −61.8° C. and has a specific gravity of 4.4 at its boiling-point; solid radon melts at −71° C.

Radon is used in the treatment of cancer. The emanation is collected in small glass or gold tubes, and these are applied to the area to be treated. There is an economic advantage in the use of radon instead of a radium salt. Carelessness on the part of hospital staffs or patients has sometimes resulted in the loss of radium salts and a consequent heavy financial loss. With the use of radon, the radium salt need never be removed from the room in which the gas is collected.

Radon gas is available dissolved in anhydrous lanolin by the name of Alphatron Radon Ointment (see uses under Radium).

[1] Cullen, S. C , and Gross, E. G.: Science, **113**, 580 (1951).
[2] Pittenger, C. B. *et al.*: Anesthesiology, **14**, 10 (1953).
[3] Morris, L. E. *et al.*: Anesthesiology, **16**, 312 (1955).

51

Radioactivity and the Radioactive Elements

IN 1878, Sir William Crookes discovered that when an electric discharge was passed through an evacuated tube (Crookes' tube) the rays coming from the cathode (cathode rays) produced a greenish-yellow fluorescence in the glass posteriorly to the anti-cathode. These rays were markedly different from the ordinary light rays in that they did not illuminate, could be deflected from their straight course by a magnet and caused certain chemical substances placed inside the discharge tubes to fluoresce. In 1895, while working in his laboratory with discharge tubes, Roentgen quite accidentally discovered that a fluorescent screen became luminous when placed near these tubes. He observed also that these radiations affected photographic plates and penetrated paper, flesh, wood and other substances opaque to ordinary light. Roentgen's discovery of the x-ray stimulated research in these fields and focussed attention on those phenomena which led a year later to the discovery of radioactivity.

The fluorescence of glass subjected to cathode rays led several scientists to investigate those chemical substances which were rendered fluorescent by visible light. In 1896, Prof. H. Becquerel, a noted French physicist, exposed a photographic plate to phosphorescent uranium potassium sulfate that had been wrapped in black paper, and found that the plate was fogged by rays emanating from this double salt. Furthermore, he observed that the air about the radioactive compound was conductive to electricity (ionized) as evidenced by the collapse of the leaves of a charged electroscope. Rutherford showed that this effect was due to the production of ions in the gas through which the radiations passed. Some time later, Mme. Curie conducted extensive researches to determine what elements and their compounds possessed this property of radioactivity. She found only one other element, thorium, comparable in this respect to uranium. After she had established the fact that the radioactivity of a compound was proportional to the quantity of the element (thorium or uranium) present in the compound regardless of how it was combined, she then observed that the radiations from *pitchblende* (U_3O_8) were between four and five times more intense than that of metallic uranium, of which it contained only about 50 per cent. Having faith in her hypothesis, she quite logically concluded that pitchblende contained, besides uranium, one or more radioactive substances and set about isolating them.

The Austrian government provided her with a large quantity of the residues left after the recovery of the uranium from pitchblende mined at Joachimsthal, Bohemia. These residues were found to be from three to five times as radioactive as uranium itself. From them, Mme. Curie first isolated an element that was much more radioactive than uranium, and which she named *polonium* in honor of her native country, and, in 1898, the element *radium*, which she found to be one million times more active than uranium.

The probability of natural radioactivity increases considerably for elements with atomic numbers above 80, though potassium, rubidium, samarium, and neodymium also possess this property to some degree. All radioactive compounds have the common property of emitting rays or particles which affect a photographic plate protected from visible light and also cause the discharge of electrified bodies. When an element is designated as being "radioactive," it implies that such an element is unstable and is disintegrating with the emission of energy in the form of particles and/or electromagnetic radiation. Table 12 indicates the decay process of Uranium I.

Artificial radioactive elements, which obey the same laws of disintegration, can be produced by one or several types of bombardment with nuclear particles, which may be obtained from natural and artificial radioisotopes and from combined particle emitters and accelerators. Some examples of the bombardment reactions for the production of radionuclides are given in Table 13 in the commonly accepted notation.

$^{44}_{20}$Ca (n,γ) $^{45}_{20}$Ca, meaning $^{44}_{20}$Ca $+ ^1_0$n $\rightarrow ^{45}_{20}$Ca $+$ gamma radiation.

In Chapter 1 it was pointed out that all elements are composed mainly of both positive (protons) and negative (electrons) electricity with varying numbers of neutral neutrons. By reference to the table on electron distribution the systematic building of the elements may be recognized. Each increases by one proton and one electron from the preceding element starting with hydrogen (1 proton) to uranium (92 protons). The number of protons, likewise the electrons, is called the atomic number. There are, however, nine new elements (93 to 101) prepared by means of the cyclotron and the atomic pile.

In expressing the composition of elements often the nuclear mass (mass number) is written as a superscript while the nuclear charge (atomic number) is a subscript: $^1_1$H, $^{16}_8$O, $^{23}_{11}$Na, etc. The difference between the nuclear mass and the nuclear charge is the number of electrically neutral neutrons. The nuclear mass (atomic weight) of the elements is referred to the mass of the oxygen atom which is defined as having a mass exactly equal to 16.000. The hydrogen nucleus or proton was found to have a mass of approximately 1.

TABLE 12.—URANIUM SERIES*

Radioelement	Historical Name	Symbol	Radiation Emitted	Half Life
Uranium ↓	Uranium I	$^{238}_{92}U$	α,γ	$4.51 \times 10^9 y$
Thorium ↓	Uranium X$_1$	$^{234}_{90}Th$	β,γ	24.10d
Protactinium ↓	Uranium X$_2$	$^{234}_{91}Pa$	β,γ	1.175m
Uranium ↓	Uranium II	$^{234}_{92}U$	α,γ	$2.48 \times 10^5 y$
Thorium ↓	Ionium	$^{230}_{90}Th$	α,γ	$8.0 \times 10^4 y$
Radium ↓	Radium	$^{226}_{88}Ra$	α,γ	1622y
Radon ↓	Ra Emanation	$^{222}_{86}Rn$	α,γ	3.8229d
Polonium 99.98% | 0.02%	Radium A	$^{218}_{84}Po$	α,β	3.05m
Lead	Radium B	$^{214}_{82}Pb$	β,γ	26.8m
Astatine-218	Astatine	$^{218}_{85}At$	$\alpha,\beta(0.1\%)$†	1.5–2s
Bismuth 99.96% | 0.04%	Radium C	$^{214}_{83}Bi$	α,β,γ	19.7m
Polonium	Radium C′	$^{214}_{84}Po$	α	$1.64 \times 10^{-4}s$
Thallium	Radium C″	$^{210}_{81}Tl$	β,γ	1.32m
Lead ↓	Radium D	$^{210}_{82}Pb$	β,γ	19.4y
Bismuth —100% | $5\times10^{-5}\%$	Radium E	$^{210}_{83}Bi$	α,β,γ	5.013d
Polonium	Radium F	$^{210}_{84}Po$	α,γ	138.40d
Thallium-206	Thallium	$^{206}_{81}Tl$	β	4.19m
Lead (End Product)	Radium G	$^{206}_{82}Pb$	None	Stabe 23.6% abundance

* From Radiological Health, U.S. Department of Health, Education, and Welfare Publication PB121784R, 1960.
† Branching decay from Beta Emission is not shown.

(652)

Isotopes are atoms of an element having the same number of protons but different numbers of neutrons. These atoms are identical chemically but differ from each other in mass and weight. Isotopes of the same element occupy the same position in the Periodic Table but differ in nuclear mass (atomic weight). They all have the same electron distribution. For example carbon in nature is about 99 per cent $^{12}_{6}C$ with about 1 per cent $^{13}_{6}C$. The latter has one more neutron present. There are many isotopes throughout the elements. The number for an element will vary according to the atomic number. Usually isotopes are more abundant for elements with an even atomic number. The mixture of isotopes for each element accounts in part for the fractional atomic weights of the elements. There is an isotope for practically every element, the average number being about eight. There have been over eight hundred and fifty isotopes prepared or discovered.

Isotopes are of two classes: stable isotopes and unstable (radioactive) isotopes. They differ by their ability or inability to emit radiations. The stable isotopes have no direct applications to therapeutics. Radioactive isotopes are those that undergo nuclear changes or rearrangements that result in emissions of radioactive radiations. Natural radioactive isotopes emit alpha particles, beta particles and gamma rays. Artificial radioactive isotopes emit mainly beta particles and gamma rays. A radioactive isotope emits radiations because the nuclear electrical forces become unbalanced and the cohesive forces no longer can hold the protons and neutrons together. An isotope is said to decay when radiations are given off. These are classified as follows:

1. Alpha particles.
2. Beta particles.
   (a) Negative particles or negatrons.
   (b) Positive particles or positrons.
3. Gamma rays.
4. K Capture X rays.

1. **The Alpha Particles.**—Of the four radiations, the alpha particles are the least penetrating because their range is only a few centimeters. They are stopped by a sheet of paper or a few centimeter of air. Each particle is really the nucleus of a helium atom and, therefore, has a mass of 4. It carries two positive charges, being composed of 2 protons and 2 neutrons. The element emitting this particle always changes in mass number. Alpha emission is found in elements with atomic numbers greater than 82. These particles travel with an average velocity of 18,000 miles per second and ionize the air in their paths. They are deflected by a strong magnetic field.

2. **The Beta Particles.**—These particles are of two types, electrically positive particles or positrons and electrically negative particles or

negatrons. When a nuclear proton changes to a neutron, a positron is emitted. A negatron is emitted when a neutron converts to a proton. Usually a negatron is emitted when neutrons exceed protons beyond a stable ratio that occurs mainly in elements of atomic numbers above 63. When protons exceed the stable ratio with neutrons then positrons are emitted mostly in elements with atomic numbers less than 63.

Most beta particles used are negatrons and have a greater range than alpha particles. The range in water may vary from 1 to 10 or 15 millimeters.

3. **The Gamma Rays.**—These rays are not affected by magnetic forces and appear to be of the same character as the very short electromagnetic waves called x rays. They have the speed of light. The gamma rays are often observed from those substances which emit alpha or beta particles. They are much more penetrating than either the alpha or the beta particles, and will pass through great thicknesses of metal or other material of low atomic weight without complete absorption. The production of gamma rays may be due to the vibrations of the protons and neutrons rearranging themselves after the emission of a beta or alpha particle.

4. **K Capture X Rays.**—During this type of decay the radiation is referred to as K characteristic x rays. In certain unstable nuclei where an excess of protons exist but the energy is less than 1.02 MeV (millions of electron volts) the nucleus is unable to emit positrons as radiation. To achieve stability a proton combines with an electron from the K shell to form a neutron. The rearrangement of the electrons produces the radiation.

Radioactive nuclides decay to reach a stable ground state. This process is exponential in regard to time, and its progress is expressed by the time required to reduce the radioactivity "A" by one half ($T_{\frac{1}{2}}$), when starting the timing at an arbitrary instant of time, t_o. The fraction of activity A existing at any time t can be given as

$$\frac{A_t}{A_o} = e^{-\lambda t},$$

where the decay constant $\lambda = 0.693/T_{\frac{1}{2}}$. The values of $T_{\frac{1}{2}}$ and of λ, respectively, are characteristic for each radioisotope. The activity A is generally expressed in curies, so named after Mme. Curie, who defined this unit as the activity of 0.66 mm³ of radon in equilibrium with 1 gram of radium, resulting in 3.70×10^{10} disintegrations per second. The fractional values of milli- and microcuries (mc, μc) are applied to pharmaceutical preparations.

The radiation of decay is emitted with an energy, which is also specific for each radionuclide. It is expressed in millions of electron-volts (MeV), which unit represents 1×10^6 eV, each electron-volt being equivalent to 1.60×10^{-12} ergs.

In summary, examples of the production and of the decay of pharmaceutically important radionuclides will illustrate these concepts. Table 13 exemplifies several worthy features: (a) the (n,γ) and (n,p) bombardments, (b) a fission source, (c) decay reactions to stable nuclides, some of which are the originating target materials, (d) decay radiations of β^-, β^+ and γ, and (e) a two step decay process via a meta-stable state (m).

TABLE 13.—PRODUCTION AND DECAY OF
PHARMACEUTICALLY IMPORTANT RADIONUCLIDES.

$$^{44}_{20}\text{Ca (n,}\gamma) \; ^{45}_{20}\text{Ca} \xrightarrow{\text{164 d}} \; ^{45}_{21}\text{Sc} + 0.25 \text{ MeV } \beta^-,$$

$$^{14}_{7}\text{N (n,p)} \; ^{14}_{6}\text{C} \xrightarrow{\text{5000 y}} \; ^{14}_{7}\text{N} + 0.155 \text{ MeV } \beta^-,$$

$$^{133}_{55}\text{Cs (n,}\gamma) \; ^{134\text{m}}_{55}\text{Cs} \xrightarrow{\text{3.2 h}} \; ^{134}_{55}\text{Cs} + 0.55 \text{ MeV } \beta^-, 0.127 \text{ MeV } \gamma \xrightarrow{\text{2.1 y}} \; ^{134}_{56}\text{Ba} +$$

$$0.66 \text{ MeV } \beta^-, 8\gamma \; 0.5 \text{ to } 1.4 \text{ MeV},$$

$$^{59}_{27}\text{Co (n,}\gamma) \; ^{60\text{m}}_{27}\text{Co} \xrightarrow{\text{10.5 m}} \; ^{60}_{27}\text{Co} + 1.6 \text{ MeV } \beta^-, 0.06 \text{ MeV } \gamma \xrightarrow{\text{5.2 y}} \; ^{60}_{28}\text{Ni} +$$

$$0.3 \text{ MeV } \beta^-, 2\gamma \; 1.17 + 1.33 \text{ MeV},$$

$$^{6}_{3}\text{Li (n,}\gamma) \; ^{3}_{1}\text{H} \xrightarrow{\text{12.5 y}} \; ^{3}_{2}\text{He} + 0.018 \text{ MeV } \beta^-,$$

$$^{238}_{92}\text{U, } ^{235}_{92}\text{U} \xrightarrow[\text{fission}]{4.3\%} \; ^{131}_{53}\text{I} + (\alpha,\beta^-,\gamma) \xrightarrow{\text{8 d}} \; ^{131}_{54}\text{Xe} + 0.6 \text{ MeV } \beta^-, 0.36 \text{ MeV } \gamma,$$

$$^{239}_{94}\text{Pu} \xrightarrow{3.8\%}$$

$$^{32}_{16}\text{S (n,p)} \; ^{32}_{15}\text{P} \xrightarrow{\text{14 d}} \; ^{32}_{16}\text{S} + 1.7 \text{ MeV } \beta^-,$$

$$^{64}_{30}\text{Zn (n,}\gamma) \; ^{65}_{30}\text{Zn} \xrightarrow{\text{245 d}} \; ^{65}_{29}\text{Cu} + 0.32 \text{ MeV } \beta^+, 1.11 \text{ MeV } \gamma.$$

All radiation, be it particular or electromagnetic, interacts with matter in its path. The measure of the degree of interaction with this "target" is the roentgen, named after W. C. Röntgen, the discoverer of x rays (1895). By definition 1 r equals 1 electrostatic unit (e. s. u.) of ion pairs, which are produced by any kind of ionizing radiation in 1 cm^3 of dry air. This is equivalent to 2.083×10^9 ion pairs, of which each one requires 32.5 eV of energy of formation. If the "dose" of 1 r is related to 1 Gm. of air, this definition can be expressed as corresponding to 5.2×10^7 MeV or 83 ergs of energy absorbed. More recently the unit of the "Rad" has been adopted for particle radiation, which is equal to 100 ergs of energy per gram of absorbing material; it is equal to 6.24×10^7 MeV absorbed per gram. It is thus evident that the dose of absorbed radiation is not solely a direct function of the quantity of radiation impinging on the absorbing target. Rather, the absorbed dose is principally a function of the quantity of radiation, its residual energy at the site of interaction, the density of the absorber, its nuclear proton to neutron ratio, and its configuration or "geometry."

The various processes by which ionizing radiations interact with matter are made use of in radiation detectors as well as in chemical, physical and biological radiation reactions. Seen from the pharmaceutical point of view, a short discussion of radiation sources for diagnostic and therapeutic applications is indicated, though those for radiation detectors would be beyond the intent of this book. Radiation sources are selected principally for their type and energy of radiation, which have been classified previously.

A number of radioisotopes, which are currently available for medicinal uses, decay with one or more of these radiations. They are listed in Table 14 and described on the following pages.

TABLE 14.—ISOTOPES CURRENTLY BEING USED IN MEDICINAL DIAGNOSIS, THERAPY AND RESEARCH, ARRANGED BY THEIR HALF-LIVES.

Isotope	$T_{\frac{1}{2}}$	Decay Radiation and Energy in MeV			
		β^-	β^+	γ, X	α
^{99m}Tc	6.0 h			0.140	
^{42}K	12.4 h	2.04, 3.58		1.5	
^{64}Cu	12.9 h		0.6	1.3	
^{24}Na	15.0 h	1.39		1.38, 2.75	
^{82}Br	36.0 h	0.44		0.78, 0.55, 0.62	
^{90}Y	2.6 d	2.26		1.75	
^{198}Au*	2.7 d	0.96		0.41	
^{197}Hg	2.7 d			0.07	
^{99}Mo	2.8 d	1.18		0.14	
^{131}Cs	6.7 d			0.029	
^{131}I†	8.1 d	0.61, 0.34		0.634, 0.36	
^{32}P†	14.2 d	1.71			
^{86}Rb	18.7 d	1.77		1.1	
^{51}Cr†	27.8 d			0.32	
^{59}Fe	45.0 d	0.26, 0.27		1.3, 1.1	
^{203}Hg	47.0 d	0.21		0.28	
^{125}I	59 d			0.027, 0.035	
^{85}Sr	64 d			0.51	
^{192}Ir	74 d	0.67		0.32, 0.47	
^{35}S	87 d	0.17			
^{75}Se	121 d			0.025–0.402	
^{45}Ca	164 d	0.26			
^{65}Zn	247 d		0.32	1.2	
^{57}Co	270 d			0.123	
^{22}Na	2.6 y	0.54		1.28	
^{60}Co†	5.3 y	0.31		1.17, 1.32	
^{3}H	12.3 y	0.018			
^{226}Ra‡	1622 y			0.19	4.77
^{14}C	5568 y	0.16			

* N.F. XII, † U.S.P. XVII, ‡ Plus radiation from radioactive daughters.

The application of the more important inorganic preparations of radionuclides will be discussed, while organic preparations are described adequately in the relevant pharmaceutical and medical literature. Some preparations have been included in the U.S.P. XVIII and in the N.F. XII, where official specifications and standards of purity are listed.

^{51}Cr.—Diagnostic Injection.[1]—*Sodium Chromate Cr 51 Injection,* U.S.P. XVII, is used for:

1. determining red blood cell volume or mass,
2. studying red blood cell survival time, and
3. evaluating blood loss.

Doses should be kept as small as will be consistent with accurate measurement throughout the time involved. Radioactivity injected in the form of tagged red blood cells is 15 to 20 microcuries for body weights between 100 and 200 lbs., and total dosage in the body at any one time should not exceed 390 microcuries. Because the radioactive tag is stable, repeat doses are seldom indicated, even when measurements are made throughout several weeks. However, repeat doses may be required in conditions in which (1) there is rapid red blood cell destruction and (2) survival studies are indicated before, during, and after treatment.

^{60}Co—Therapeutic Source.—Radioactive cobalt (^{60}Co) for brachytherapy is a cobalt-containing alloy that is highly resistant to chemical corrosion, it is supplied as wire segments. The uses of small ^{60}Co sources are essentially the same as those of similar sources of radium. These ^{60}Co sources are used for gamma-ray therapy at short distances, either by external plaque administration, by placing them into a body cavity (*e.g.,* cervical applicators), or by implanting them in the tissue to be irradiated (as needles). They have been employed mainly in the treatment of carcinoma of the bladder and the uterine cervix, in both early and advanced stages, though they have also been used in the treatment of carcinoma of the uterus, prostate, vagina, urethra, tongue, lip, mouth and the lymph nodes of the neck.

^{57,60}Co—Diagnostic Aids.—*Cyanocobalamin Co 57 Capsules* and *Solution,* U.S.P. XVII, and *Cyanocobalamin Co 60 Capsules* and *Solution,* U.S.P. XVII, are being applied diagnostically by virtue of their radiometallic tracers for the detection of addisonian (pernicious) anemia, in which a lack of intrinsic factor causes malabsorption of vitamin B_{12}. For detailed information about its absorption, metabolism and its principal test procedures by means of fecal and urinary excretion and by liver and serum uptake the specialized literature should be consulted.

[1] The information on this and the following pharmaceutical preparations have been adapted from the commercial literature of the following:
Abbott Laboratories, Radiopharmaceutical Operations, Abbott Park, North Chicago, Illinois 60064.
E. R. Squibb and Sons, Radiopharmaceutical Services, 745 Fifth Ave., New York, N.Y. 10022.

[198]Au—**Diagnostic and Therapeutic Injection.**—As a dilute colloidal solution, this radioactive form of gold is especially useful for these diagnostic purposes:

1. scintiscanning of the liver to determine its size, shape, displacement, and functional integrity,
2. scintiscanning and monitoring of the lymphatics and lymph nodes to evaluate lymph flow and lymph node filtration,
3. scintiscanning of the bones to determine the size and distribution of reticuloendothelial marrow, and
4. monitoring of the blood and liver to measure portal circulation and reticuloendothelial capacity of the liver.

Gold Au 198 Solution, N.F. XII, has found its greatest success and widest application in the symptomatic treatment of peritoneal and pleural effusions associated with malignant neoplasms. The degree of success attained appears to be related directly to the proper selection of the cases. The ideal patient for therapy of malignant effusion with radio-gold ([198]Au) appears to be one whose chief problem is the accumulation of fluid in the abdomen or chest without the presence of large tumor masses or severe constitutional effects from the neoplasm, apart from discomfort by the massive fluid accumulation.

Radio-gold ([198]Au) has been used prophylactically also against dissemination of tumor cells after surgical exposure and/or removal from the serous cavities.

[131]I—**Diagnostic and Therapeutic Injection and Oral.**—1. *Diagnostic.* —*Sodium Iodide I 131 Capsules* and *Solution*, U.S.P. XVII are valuable tools in the appraisal of thyroid function. Radio-iodine tests of thyroid function generally consist of: (1) measurement of isotope excretion in the urine, (2) uptake in the thyroid, (3) level in the blood, or (4) a combination of these measurements. Radio-iodine has also been employed in localizing functional metastases associated with thyroid malignancies.

Radio-iodine tests of thyroid function such as determination of urinary excretion of ^{131}I or uptake of ^{131}I by the thyroid, are based upon the observation that an overactive thyroid gland concentrates radio-iodine faster and in larger quantities than the normal thyroid. Other tracer studies depend upon measurement of inorganic or organically bound radio-iodine levels in the serum, on the rate of appearance of total quantity or organically bound radio-iodine in the blood stream and measurement of clearance rates. Although uptake values depend on the mode of administration and the time of measurement, the following range may be given for 24-hour uptake values, expressed in per cent of administered tracer dose: less than 15 per cent indicates hypothyroid range, more than 50 to 60 per cent indicates hyperthyroid range.

The use of radioactive iodine in connection with diagnosis of thyroid malignancy is based on the fact that malignant thyroid growths sometimes concentrate iodine in similar fashion as the normal thyroid gland. When this occurs, this property can be utilized to localize remote metastases by administration of tracer doses of radioactive iodine.

2. *Therapeutic.*—The official forms of radio-iodine (*q.v.*) are highly useful as therapeutic agents in the treatment of hyperthyroidism, the management of euthyroid heart disease such as angina pectoris and congestive heart failure not responding to other forms of therapy, and the treatment of selected cases of thyroid carcinoma.

The thyroid gland has a high avidity for iodine. The normal thyroid gland concentrates approximately 20 per cent of the total body stores. Ingested iodine is absorbed rapidly and generally can be detected in the thyroid gland and the saliva within minutes after oral administration. Iodine is absorbed from the intestinal tract as iodide and it is removed from the blood stream by the thyroid epithelium. In the thyroid gland, iodide is converted to nascent iodine by an enzymatic process and subsequently it is combined with tyrosine.

The radiation effect of radio-iodine (^{131}I) is primarily due to beta particles which have an effective range of approximately 2 mm. in soft tissue, thereby limiting the radiation to the tissues which concentrate iodine, *i.e.*, the functioning thyroid gland. The first successful remissions of hyperthyroidism utilizing radioactive iodine were reported in 1942 by Hertz and Roberts and Hamilton and Lawrence.

The use of radio-iodine (^{131}I) in the management of severe euthyroid cardiac disease is based on its ability to reduce thyroid activity by radiation thyroidectomy. This lowers the total metabolism of the body and reduces the work load of the heart.

^{192}Ir—**Therapeutic Irradiation Source.**—Radio-iridium (^{192}Ir) seeds in nylon ribbons are prepared for *removable* interstitial implantation therapy. The seeds are stainless-steel ensheathed cylinders of ^{192}Ir, measuring approximately 3 mm. in length and 0.5 mm. in diameter.

The gamma rays emitted by iridium-192 are much softer than those of cobalt-60, with the result that more are absorbed locally by the tumor tissue during interstitial implantation therapy.

Radiation exposure to operating and nursing personnel is also decreased. Protection problems are simplified by the low half-value layer of iridium in lead, compared to the values for cobalt-60 and radium, as shown in the table below. The iridium-192 gamma radiation is still energetic enough, however, to avoid increased absorption in bone.

Isotope	1γ (*Specific Gamma-Radiation Intensity*) (*roentgens/hr/curie at 1 meter*)	*Half-Value Layer* (*mm/Pb*)
Cobalt-60	1.28	12
Iridium-192	0.55	3
Radium	0.84	10

Implantation with nylon ribbons is usually more accurate than with radium needles because, with nylon ribbons, the needles can be positioned unhurriedly, since no radiation exposure occurs during this phase.

The patient is more comfortable than with radium implants, because nylon ribbons are flexible.

^{59}Fe—Diagnostic Injection.—For determining the mechanisms or estimating the status of erythropoiesis and of iron metabolism in normal and diseased persons, radioiron (^{59}Fe) preparations are supplied with which the following parameters of iron metabolism can be measured:

1. Clearance of iron from the plasma,
2. Appearance of iron in the red cells,
3. Appearance of iron in various body sites, and
4. Absorption of iron from the intestine.

Suitable tests for these parameters and the inferences drawn from them are based on the concept of the blood plasma as a medium in which iron is in continuous flux. Although the proportion of the body's iron which is in the plasma is relatively small, the plasma iron can be considered as the focal point of iron metabolism.

Iron enters the plasma from intestinal sites of absorption and from various pools. At the same time, it exits from the plasma to enter erythroid cells of blood-forming organs and to enter the pools. Therefore, following an intravenous tracer dose of radioiron, various counts and calculations can be performed to measure:

1. *Plasma clearance rate*—fraction of plasma iron content leaving the plasma during a unit of time,
2. *Plasma iron transport rate*—total milligrams of iron entering and leaving the plasma per day,
3. *Appearance rate in erythrocytes*—fraction of a tracer dose appearing in the peripheral red cells and the rate of this appearance, and
4. *The metabolic state of various iron pools*—the amount of a tracer dose appearing in various body sites such as the liver and spleen as determined by counting *in vivo*.

^{32}P—Diagnostic and Therapeutic Injection and Oral.—*Sodium Phosphate P 32 Solution*, U.S.P. XVII, is utilized for treatment of *polycythemia vera*. It helps to relieve symptoms of headache, fullness in the head, dizziness, weakness, and dyspnea on exertion. Sodium Phosphate P 32 also reduces the size of the spleen and helps restore to normal or near normal the blood abnormalities of hypervolemia, excessive packed (red) cell volume, and excessive red blood cell count.

Sodium Phosphate P 32 solution is also used for treatment of *chronic leukemia*—myelocytic, lymphocytic, or granulocytic. The objectives of therapy are to (1) maintain the white blood cell count between 10,000 and 20,000, (2) prevent bleeding tendencies, (3) keep the liver and spleen at or above the costal margin, (4) keep lymph nodes not over +1, and (5) keep the patient at his usual work.

Sodium Phosphate P 32 is a valuable diagnostic agent for the *detection of intraocular* tumors, when it is used in conjunction with other tests and clinical evaluation.

Sodium Phosphate P 32 also is being used successfully to localize and demarcate tumors of the brain at surgery. However, gamma emitters are often preferred for this purpose.

[197,203]**Hg—Diagnostic Injection.**—Chlormerodrin Hg-197 and Hg-203 are special radioactive tracers which are used for scintillation (gamma ray) scanning of (1) the brain for suspected tumor and (2) the kidneys for suspected anatomical, pathological, or functional defects. Both procedures are non-traumatic and can be performed on outpatients.

Chlormerodrin Hg-197 and Hg-203 are preferentially concentrated by neoplastic lesions of the brain so that a high tumor-to-background ratio of activity is produced following intravenous administration of the tracer. At the same time, the tracer are rapidly cleared from the blood stream so that little extraneous radioactivity is contributed by the blood and by vascular structures such as the temporal muscles.

Chlormerodrin Hg-197 and Hg-203 are readily concentrated by *functional kidney parenchyma*, especially the cortex. Therefore, scanning with suitable detecting equipment will yield useful functional, pathological, and anatomical information about the kidneys. Such scanning may confirm or amplify that obtained by contrast techniques such as retrograde pyelography, excretory urography and renal angiography. On occasion, it may yield information not revealed by these techniques.

[226]**Ra—Therapeutic Irradiation Source.**—In 1898, M. and Mme. Curie isolated this metallic chemical element from pitchblende, a uranium mineral. It was named *radium*, from the Latin *radius*, a ray, because of its intense radioactivity.

In Nature, this element is found very sparingly associated with uranium. It occurs also in some natural spring waters. The residues remaining after extracting the uranium from Bohemian pitchblende, provide most of the European radium. Most of the world's present supply of radium has its origin either in the uranium deposits in the Belgian Congo in Central Africa, at Great Bear Lake in the Canadian Northwest Territory or in Colorado and Utah.

In general, the properties of radium resemble those of the alkaline earths, especially barium, from which it is separated by the fractional crystallization of its halogen salts, usually the bromide. Its spectrum is characteristic. Its atomic weight, together with its analytical reactions and chemical behavior, place it in Group II. The decay process is described in Table 12.

43

The radiations from radium, like the Roentgen rays, are capable of destroying living cells. This property was unknown until 1901, when Becquerel received a severe burn from a tubed sample which he had carried around for several weeks in his waistcoat pocket. The blood vessels and blood-making organs of the body are especially susceptible to the action of radium rays. Radium, for therapeutic purposes, is applied in the form of one of its salts (usually the bromide, $RaBr_2$) or as the emanation (radon). Radium salts or radium emanation are used to arrest and cure malignant growths. When small gold capsules of radium emanation are buried in cancer tissue, they cause the degeneration of the cancer cells with subsequent reduction in the size of the growth.

^{99m}Tc—Diagnostic Injection.—^{99m}Tc pertechnetate is one of the few radioisotopes used in medicine which is truly carrier-free; therefore, "possible chemical toxicity can be excluded," and the only factors for consideration are "(1) radiation dosage and (2) pyrogen reactions. Sodium Pertechnetate Tc-99m solution is a radioactive tracer for brain scanning, an adjunctive diagnostic aid in detecting and localizing intracranial neoplastic and non-neoplastic lesions. Patients suspected of having a brain lesion can safely receive this tracer. Then, within a relatively short time, appropriate instruments can detect a lesion and indicate its size and position in a visual display. Lesions amenable to detection include primary neoplasms, metastatic neoplasms, and various non-neoplastic lesions.

Use of scintillation scanning does not replace a thorough neurological examination, arteriography, and/or pneumoencephalography. Instead, it confirms and amplifies the results of these techniques. However, arteriography and pneumoencephalography are indirect techniques. In contrast, a positive scan gives direct information about the existence, size, and location of a tumor.

Sodium Pertechnetate Tc-99m, sterile non-pyrogenic solution for oral ingestion or intravenous injection, is offered in two sizes— (1) 10 millicuries in 4 ml. and (2) 15 millicuries in 6 ml. The solution is isotonic, containing 9 mg. of sodium chloride/ml. No bacteriostatic agent is present.

It is eluted from its parent, molybdenum-99 which, itself, is produced by the neutron-gamma reaction on molybdenum-98. Therefore, this product does not contain ruthenium-103, tellurium-132, or iodine-131 which are produced in the fission process.

The Technetium-99m sterile generator is prepared with nonpyrogenic materials and has been sterilized by autoclaving. It consists of a specially designed lead shield containing an alumina-packed glass column which releases ^{99m}Tc upon elution. The lead shield has two access ports so the rubber closures at the top and bottom of the glass column, allowing aseptic elution and storage under conditions of constant shielding. Additional shielding during shipment is provided by a removable lead sleeve which surrounds the entire assembly (Fig. 10).

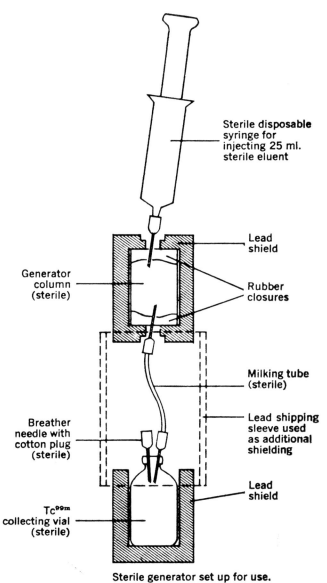

Sterile disposable syringe for injecting 25 ml. sterile eluent

Lead shield

Generator column (sterile)

Rubber closures

Milking tube (sterile)

Breather needle with cotton plug (sterile)

Lead shipping sleeve used as additional shielding

Lead shield

Tc⁹⁹ᵐ collecting vial (sterile)

Sterile generator set up for use.

Fig. 10

APPENDIX

EFFECT OF pH ON INDIVIDUAL DRUGS

I. Drugs which are unfavorably affected by alkali.
   A. Drugs which are precipitated by alkali.
   B. Drugs which are decomposed or inactivated by alkali.

II. Drugs which impart an alkaline reaction to preparations.

III. Drugs which are unfavorably affected by acid.
   A. Drugs which are precipitated by acid.
   B. Drugs which are decomposed or rendered ineffective by acid.

IV. Drugs which impart an acid reaction to preparations.

V. Drugs which undergo color changes with change in pH.

VI. Drugs the activity of which depend upon suitable pH.

VII. Recommended pH for solution of a few drugs.

   I. Drugs which are unfavorably affected by alkali.

      A. Drugs which are precipitated by alkali:

         Alkaloidal salts (*e.g.*, strychnine sulfate, codeine salts).
         Salts of local anesthetics (*e.g.*, procaine salts, "Butyn sulfate").
         Soluble salts of aluminum, calcium, copper, iron, lead, mercury, silver, zinc and certain salts of other metals (*e.g.*, silver nitrate, copper sulfate, mercury bichloride, ferrous sulfate, etc.).

      B. Drugs which are decomposed or inactivated by alkali:

Acetanilid	Hydrogen peroxide
Acetophenetidin	Iodine
Acid Acetylsalicylic	Mild mercurous chloride (Calomel)
Acid Ascorbic (Vitamin C)	Pectin
Acid Tannic	Penicillin
Ammonium salts	Pepsin
Apomorphine HCl	Phenyl salicylate (Salol)
Barbiturates	Pyrogallol
Chloral hydrate	Resorcinol
Chlorobutanol	Resorcinol monoacetate
Cocaine (when sterilized)	Riboflavin
Creosote carbonate	Santonin
Epinephrine ("Adrenalin," "Suprarenin")	Strophanthin
	Thiamine HCl (Vitamin B_1)
Guaiacol carbonate	Vanillin

(665)

II. Drugs which may impart an alkaline reaction to preparations—and which may, therefore, precipitate, decompose or inactivate drugs in Part I:

Aminopyrine
Ammonia water
Ammonium carbonate
Barbital sodium
Bentonite
Calcium hydroxide
Chloramine-T
Dilantin sodium
Ephedrine (base)
Fluorescein sodium
Lead acetate
Milk of Magnesia
Magnesium carbonate
Magnesium oxide
Methenamine
Pentobarbital sodium (Nembutal)
Phenobarbital sodium
Potassium acetate
Potassium bicarbonate
Potassium carbonate
Potassium citrate
Potassium hydroxide

Rose water ointment
Sodium acetate
Sodium benzoate
Sodium bicarbonate
Sodium borate
Sodium carbonate
Sodium citrate
Sodium hydroxide
Sodium perborate
Sodium peroxide
Sodium phosphate
Sodium sulfite
Sulfadiazine sodium
Sulfapyridine sodium
Sulfathiazole sodium
Sulfurated potash
Theobromine and sodium acetate
Theobromine and sodium salicylate
Theophylline ethylenediamine (Aminophylline)
Theophylline and sodium acetate

III. Drugs which may be unfavorably affected by acid:

A. Drugs which may be precipitated by acid:

Barbital sodium
Caffeine and sodium benzoate
Dilantin sodium
Iodophthalein sodium
Mercurochrome
Pentobarbital sodium (Nembutal)
Phenobarbital sodium (and other sodium barbiturates)

Sodium benzoate
Sodium salicylate
Sulfadiazine sodium
Sulfapyridine sodium
Sulfathiazole sodium
Theobromine and sodium acetate
Theobromine and sodium salicylate
Theophylline ethylenediamine
Theophylline and sodium acetate

B. Drugs which may be decomposed or rendered ineffective by acid:

Bicarbonates
Carbonates
Hydroxides
Iodides
Methenamine
Oxides
Paraldehyde
Pancreatin

Penicillin
Sodium nitrite
Sodium sulfite
Sodium thiosulfate
Sulfurated lime solution
Sulfurated potash
Salts of slightly soluble organic acids generally

IV. Drugs which may impart an acid reaction to preparations:

Acacia
Acid Acetylsalicylic
Acid Ascorbic (Vitamin C)
Acid Boric
Acid Tannic (other acids)
Alkaloidal salts
Alum
Aluminum chloride
Aluminum sulfate
Ammonium chloride
Ammonium nitrate
Arsenic tri-iodide
Arsphenamine
Bismuth subnitrate
Calcium chloride
Calcium lactate
Citrated caffeine

Cocaine HCl
Copper sulfate
Ephedrine HCl
Sodium borate (or boric acid) and glycerin
Magnesium salts (soluble)
Mercury bichloride
Pectin pastes
Potassium bitartrate
Silver nitrate
Silver picrate
Sodium biphosphate
Trinitrophenol (Picric acid)
Phenols
Zinc chloride
Zinc iodide
Zinc sulfate

V. Drugs which undergo color changes with change in pH:

Drug	Acid Solution	Alkaline Solution
"Bromsulphalein"	Nearly colorless	Deep bluish-purple
Carmine	Red-orange	Reddish-purple
Cochineal	Orange	Reddish-purple
Cudbear	Light red	Dark red to purplish-red
Fluorescein	Yellowish-orange	Green fluorescence
Gentian violet	Blue	Purple
Methylene blue	Light blue	Blue to slightly violet
Phenolphthalein	Colorless	Red
Phenolsulfonphthalein	Orange or yellow	Red to purplish-red
Syrup cherry	Red	Nearly colorless
Syrup raspberry	Red	Nearly colorless

VI. Drugs the activity of which depend upon suitable pH:

Drug	pH or Reaction Required or Preferable
Acriflavine	Alkaline
Acid Benzoic	Acid
Acid Mandelic	pH 5.5 or less
Acid Salicylic	Acid
Gentian violet	Alkaline
p-Hydroxybenzoic acid esters	Acid
Methenamine	Acid
Pepsin	Acid
Sulfonamides	Alkaline

VII. Recommended pH for solutions of a few drugs. With some drugs it is possible to obtain greater therapeutic efficacy, greater stability or lessened irritation or discomfort to the patient by means of adjustment of the pH of solutions of these drugs to suitable values. The pH values recommended for a few drugs are provided below:

Drugs	*Recommended pH*
Atropine salts	6.8
Alkaloidal salts generally	6.8
Alum	6.0
Butyn sulfate	5.0
Cocaine HCl and Procaine HCl	6.0
Ephedrine and its salts	6.8
Epinephrine ("Adrenalin," "Suprarenin")	6.0
Fluorescein sodium	9.0
Homatropine salts	6.8
Metycaine	5.0
Penicillin	6.3–6.8
Phenacaine HCl (Holocaine)	5.0
Physostigmine salts	7.6 or 6.0
Pilocarpine salts	6.8
Thiamine HCl (Vitamin B_1)	3.5–4.5 (not greater than 5)
Zinc salts	6.0

FREQUENTLY USED PREFIXES, SUFFIXES AND ABBREVIATIONS

a—a prefix denoting without or not.
aa.—an abbreviation meaning "of each."
A.C.S.—American Chemical Society.
A.M.A.—American Medical Association.
A.Ph.A.—American Pharmaceutical Association.
-ate—a suffix indicating a salt of an acid whose name ends in -*ic*, except where the acid begins with *hydro*.
bi—a prefix denoting two or twice.
anhyd.—anhydrous.
B.P.—British Pharmacopoeia.
cryst.—crystals.
d—day.
deca—a prefix meaning ten.
di—a prefix meaning two.
dodeca—a prefix meaning twelve.
EDTA—Ethylene-diaminetetraäcetic Acid.
-emia—a suffix denoting blood.
gal.—gallon.
h—hour.
hepta—a prefix meaning seven.
hexa—a prefix meaning six.
hydro—a prefix meaning presence of hydrogen.
hyper—a prefix signifying abnormal or excessive.
hypo—a prefix denoting deficiency or lack; below or beneath.
-ic—a suffix indicating an element in a compound in a higher valence than in compounds ending in -ous.
-ide—a suffix denoting the negative radical of a binary compound.
-ite—a suffix indicating a salt of an acid whose name ends in -*ous*.
lb.—pound.
liq.—liquid.

m—minute.

meta—an acid derived from the ordinary form of the acid by intra-molecular loss of one molecule of water from one molecule of the acid.

neo—new, *i.e.*, neocalamine, neosilvol.

neut.—neutral.

N.D.—New Drugs.

N.F.—National Formulary.

N.N.D.—New and Nonofficial Drugs (no longer published).

N.N.R.—New and Nonofficial Remedies (no longer published).

nona—a prefix meaning nine.

octa—a prefix meaning eight.

ortho—a prefix denoting an acid in a higher state of hydration than the meta-form.

-ous—a suffix indicating a valence lower than that indicated by *-ic.*

oz.—ounce.

pent—a prefix meaning five.

per—a prefix indicating the presence of an atom having a relatively high valence. (peroxysulfuric acid)

pkg.—package.

po.—powder.

precip.—precipitated.

pyro—an acid derived from the ordinary form of the acid by inter-molecular loss of one molecule of water from two molecules of the acid.

resubl.—resublimed.

R.S.—Reagent Standard.

sec.—secondary.

sesqui—a prefix indicating that three atoms of the specified element are combined with two of another.

sol.—solution.

soln.—solution.

sp. gr.—specific gravity.

sub—a prefix indicating a partially hydrolyzed compound.

sulfo—see thio.

tech.—technical.

tert.—tertiary.

tetra—a prefix meaning four.

thio—a prefix indicating the presence of sulfur in the compound named.

tri—a prefix meaning three.

trideca—a prefix meaning thirteen.

undeca—a prefix meaning eleven.

U.S.P.—United States Pharmacopeia.

y—year.

∞—a symbol meaning equivalent to.

DEFINITIONS

acid—a substance that ionizes in aqueous solution to yield the hydronium (hydrogen) ion as one of the ions formed. See Chap. 10, however.

amphoteric—possessing the ability to react with either acids or bases.

amorphous—a non-crystalline form.

anion—an ion with a negative charge.

atomic number—the number of protons in the nucelus of an atom. This is also the number of electrons which surround the nucleus.

atomic weight—the relative weight of an atom with the oxygen atom as 16.000 as the reference point.

base—a substance that ionizes in aqueous solution to yield the hydroxide ion as one of the ions formed. See Chap. 10, however.

catalytic agent—a substance which alters the rate of a reaction, either increasing or decreasing the rate, and can be recovered unchanged at the end of the reaction.

cation—a positively charged ion.

combining weight—the atomic weight of an element or radical divided by the valence of the element or radical.

complex ion—an ion which contains more than one element, *e.g.*, $Cu(NH_3)_4^{++}$, $[Fe(CN)_6]^{=}$.

compound salt—a salt which does not ionize into the ions that were used originally in its formation., *e.g.*

$$2KI + HgI_2 \rightarrow K_2HgI_4$$
$$\downarrow\uparrow$$
$$2K^+ + HgI_4^{=}$$
$$6KCN + FeCl_2 \rightarrow K_4Fe(CN)_6 + 2KCl$$
$$\downarrow\uparrow$$
$$4K^+ + Fe(CN)_6^{=}$$

decrepitation—crackling or snapping when heated.

double salt—a salt which ionizes into the ions originally used in its formation. *e.g.*

$$KAl(SO_4)_2 \rightarrow K^+ + Al^{+++} + 2SO_4^{=}$$

equilibrium, chemical—the point at which the forward reaction is taking place at the same rate as the reverse reaction.

formula, chemical—the combined symbols with subscripts representing the constituent parts of a compound and their proportions by weight.

gram formula weight—the weight in grams equal to the formula weight.

hydration—the association of one or more molecules of water with an ion or molecule.

hydrolysis—a double decomposition in which water is one of the reactants, with the formation of a weak acid or base.

hypertonic—a relative term in that it has an osmotic pressure *higher* than another solution by which it is compared.

hypotonic—a relative term describing a solution having an osmotic pressure *less* than another solution with which it is compared.

indicator paper—filter paper saturated with a compound which changes from one color to another at a certain hydrogen ion concentration.

ionization constant—$\frac{[M^+] \, [A^-]}{[MA]} = K$, the product of the concentration in moles of the anions and cations of an electrolyte divided by the concentration in moles of the undissociated electrolyte. The constant indicates the degree of ionization.

ionization potential—the energy necessary to remove an electron from a neutral atom in its lowest energy state to form a positive ion. The higher the value, the less will be the tendency of the element to form positive ions.

isohydric—a relative term meaning that a solution has the same pH as another solution with which it is compared.

isotonic—a relative term referring to a solution having the same osmotic pressure as that of body fluids.

K_a—acid ionization constant. (K_b refers to bases.)

molal solution—a solution which contains one mole of solute per 1000 Gm. of solvent.

molar solution—a solution which contains one mole of solute per 1000 ml. solution.

neutralization—a reaction in which an acid and a base react to form water and a salt.

non-polar solvent—a solvent of which the molecules are non-ionic, *i.e.*, the center of negative charge and positive charge coincide (benzine, ether, pet. ether).

normal salt—a salt which contains neither replaceable hydrogen ions nor hydroxide ions.

normal solution—a solution which contains one mole of solute divided by the hydrogen equivalent per 1000 ml. of solution.

osmosis—the diffusion of certain constituents of a solution through a semipermeable membrane.

oxidation—a gain in positive valence by an element or ion by the loss of one or more electrons.

oxidation potential—the energy, expressed in volts, for 1 gram atom of a metal in the solid state to go to a hydrated ion in 1 M. solution. It is a composite determined by the heat of sublimation, ionization potential, hydration energy of the ions, and an entropy effect.

oxidizing agent—an electron acceptor.

periodic law—elements show periodic variations in many of their physical and chemical properties when arranged in the order of their atomic weights or atomic numbers.

pK_a and pK_b— the negative log of K_a or K_b.

polar solvent—a solvent of which the molecules are ionic, *i.e.*, the center of the negative charge and the positive charge do not coincide (water, alcohol, pyridine).

polymorphic—existing in two or more crystalline forms.

reducing agent—an electron donor.

reduction—a loss in positive valence by an element or ion by the gain of electrons.

reversible reaction—a reaction in which the products of the original reaction react with each other to form the original reactants.

salt—a substance that will ionize to form ions other than hydrogen or hydroxide ions.

sequestering agent—a compound which acts by the reduction of the concentration of a multivalent positive ion in solution, by combination with a negative ion to form a complex negative ion, to the extent that the remaining concentration of the multivalent positive ion is insufficient to be precipitated by a given negative ion with which it has a low solubility product constant, (citrates, tartrates, sugars, glycerin, Versene, Calgon, etc.).

solute—the component of a solution which is dissolved in the solvent.

solvent—the component of a solution which dissolves the solute.

valence—the number of atoms of hydrogen (or its equivalent) that an element or ion can hold in combination if negative, or that it can displace if positive.

valence electrons—the electrons of the outer electron shells which are gained, lost, or shared in chemical reactions.

ELECTROMOTIVE SERIES OF THE METALS IN AQUEOUS 1 MOLAR SOLUTIONS OF THEIR IONS AT 25° C.

The chemical reactivity of metals in aqueous solution is conveniently compared by a consideration of their oxidation-reduction half reactions. In the table which follows (Table 15), the metals are arranged in the order of decreasing tendency to proceed in solutions of equal molarity with respect to the metallic cations.

TABLE 15.—ELECTROMOTIVE SERIES OF THE METALS IN
AQUEOUS 1 MOLAR SOLUTIONS OF THEIR IONS, 25°C[1]

Metal	Oxidation-Reduction Half Reaction	Oxidation-Reduction Potential Volts
Potassium	$K = e^- + K^+$	$+2.92$
Barium	$Ba = 2e^- + Ba^{2+}$	$+2.90$
Strontium	$Sr = 2e^- + Sr^{2+}$	$+2.89$
Calcium	$Ca = 2e^- + Ca^{2+}$	$+2.87$
Sodium	$Na = e^- + Na^+$	$+2.71$
Magnesium	$Mg = 2e^- + Mg^{2+}$	$+2.34$
Aluminum	$Al = 3e^- + Al^{3+}$	$+1.67$
Manganese	$Mn = 2e^- + Mn^{2+}$	$+1.05$
Zinc	$Zn = 2e^- + Zn^{2+}$	$+0.762$
Iron	$Fe = 2e^- + Fe^{2+}$	$+0.440$
Cadmium	$Cd = 2e^- + Cd^{2+}$	$+0.402$
Cobalt	$Co = 2e^- + Co^{2+}$	$+0.277$
Nickel	$Ni = 2e^- + Ni^{2+}$	$+0.250$
Tin	$Sn = 2e^- + Sn^{2+}$	$+0.136$
Lead	$Pb = 2e^- + Pb^{2+}$	$+0.126$
Hydrogen	$H_2 = 2e^- + 2H^+$	0.0000
Bismuth	$Bi + H_2O = 3e^- + BiO^+ + 2H^+$	-0.32
Copper	$Cu = 2e^- + Cu^{2+}$	-0.345
Silver	$Ag = e^- + Ag^+$	-0.799
Mercury	$Hg = 2e^- + Hg^{2+}$	-0.854
Platinum	$Pt = 2e^- + Pt^{2+}$	(about) -1.2
Gold	$Au = 3e^- + Au^{3+}$	-1.42

[1] From *General Chemistry* by A. W. Laubengayer, p. 374, courtesy of Rinehart and Co., Inc., New York, N. Y., 1949.

The oxidation-reduction potential is a measure of the tendency (in volts) for a metal to undergo oxidation. American chemists follow Prof. G. N. Lewis in stating that the electrode reaction potential is positive if the reaction at the electrode is one of relatively strong oxidation tendency. In Europe it is opposite. In American practice, a positive sign given to the reaction which occurs at that electrode is one of greater oxidation tendency than the reaction at a standard hydrogen electrode. If oxidation potential is being considered, the electrode reaction is written so that electrons are on the right side. The lower the potential the less tendency the metal has to form a cation in solution, *i.e.* the less active the metal since the driving force in these reactions is the tendency to give up electrons during the reaction. A table such as this is frequently referred to as an *electromotive series* or *electrochemical series* because it compares the possibility of a metal reacting under comparable conditions. Hydrogen is arbitrarily set at zero and provides a convenient reference point in that any metal above it will react with aqueous acids to form cations of the metal and to reduce hydrogen ions to form hydrogen. Metals below hydrogen will not react with acids to produce hydrogen. Although the table does not specifically show it, the tendency to react with oxygen, sulfur and the halogens will also be found to decrease in the same order. In addition, any metal above another metal will reduce it when in contact with it in aqueous solution. For example, a solution of copper sulfate will plate out copper metal onto a brightly polished iron surface with the simultaneous liberation of ferrous ions:

$$Cu^{++} + Fe^{\circ} \rightarrow Cu^{\circ} + Fe^{++}$$

ISOTONIC SOLUTIONS

The demonstration of osmosis requires that two solutions of different osmotic pressures be separated by a semipermeable membrane. In using the term "osmotic pressure" it must be understood that this pressure is dependent on the number of particles (molecules, ions, colloidal particles) in each unit volume in the same manner that the pressure of a gas on its containing vessel is proportional to the number of molecules of the gas per unit volume.

In line with this reasoning, it follows that a gram mole of glucose in a liter of water would exert the same osmotic force as a gram mole of fructose (grape sugar) in a liter of water because each quantity will contribute the same number of particles (molecules) per liter of water. If an attempt is made to extend this by analogy to a glucose solution and sodium chloride solution in equal molar quantities, it will be found that the sodium chloride solution has a much higher osmotic pressure than does the glucose solution. This discrepancy is accounted for by the fact that sodium chloride, being a completely ionic compound, provides two ions in aqueous solution and thereby increases the number of particles per unit volume to double that of glucose. This would imply that the sodium chloride solution would give an osmotic pressure effect double that of the glucose solution. This is not exactly true because of the deviation from an ideal situation as a result of mutual effects that ions have on one another in solution, particularly in concentrated solution.

Preparations intended for parenteral use or collyria present a problem to the pharmacist that should be fully understood. An intravenous injection upon contact with blood cells and tissue cells will exert its osmotic pressure upon these cells. The osmotic pressure of the cellular content along with the cell wall (a semipermeable membrane) then completes the requisites for a demonstration of osmotic pressure. If the osmoti cpressure of the injected solution is higher than that of the cellular contents a withdrawal of water from the cell will result with consequent cell shrinkage, a phenomenon called plasmolysis. In such an instance the injected solution would be referred to as a hypertonic solution. The reverse of this involves a hypotonic solution which is one in which the osmotic pressure of an injected solution is less than that of the cellular contents. Cells that are bathed in hypotonic solution then imbibe more water than is withdrawn and result in swelling, distention, and finally rupture. This course of events is referred to as plasmoptysis.

In addition to hypertonicity and hypotonicity there is a possible third condition that may be attained, and this results from the injection of a solution possessing the same osmotic pressure or tonicity as does the cellular contents, and such a solution is designated as an isotonic solution. Cells bathed in isotonic solutions imbibe the same amount of fluid as is withdrawn, thereby maintaining their shape and function. The blood is, of course, isotonic with cellular contents and any type of injection that will directly or indirectly dilute the blood must also be made isotonic. Intramuscular injections may also be irritant if they are hypotonic or hypertonic.

The adjustment of collyria to isotonicity must be made to prevent the irritation and inflammation that normally occurs with hypotonic or hypertonic preparations. Principles involved in the adjustment are: first, an evaluation of the osmotic pressure of the solution containing only the medicinal agents; and second, subtraction of this evaluation from the osmotic pressure required for isotonicity, the difference obtained being the increase in osmotic pressure required to make the solution isotonic.

Experimental evidence has shown that a 0.9 per cent aqueous solution of sodium chloride is isotonic with all body fluids (including lacrimal fluid). Since sodium chloride is normally found in the extracellular fluids, it follows that this would be the salt of choice for adjustment of tonicity and as a standard by which other compounds can be compared.

Comparisons of the tonicity produced by other compounds with that of sodium chloride can be secured only by experimental evidence. These comparisons are called equivalents, and are listed in the accompanying table. The equivalents or, more appropriately, factors, when multiplied by the weight of the corresponding compound gives a product representing the weight of sodium chloride necessary to produce a solution of the same tonicity, providing the weight of the compound and the derived weight of sodium chloride are both dissolved in equal volumes of water. By this procedure the tonicity of a definite weight of a compound in a known volume of water can be calculated in terms of the amount of sodium chloride necessary to produce the same tonicity in an equal volume.

METHOD OF CALCULATION FOR ISOTONIC SOLUTIONS

To cite an example, consider a 1000 ml. solution containing 0.15 per cent W/V chlorobutanol.

$0.15\% = 0.0015$

$.0015 \times 1000 = 1.5$ Gm. chlorobutanol

By referring to the table it is found that the chlorobutanol factor is 0.18. Therefore $0.18 \times 1.5 = 0.27$ Gm. sodium chloride. This quantity of sodium chloride (0.27 Gm.) when dissolved in sufficient water to produce 1000 ml. will then have a tonicity equal to that of the 0.15 per cent chlorobutanol solution. It is important to note that the quantity of sodium chloride derived in these calculations will produce a solution of equal tonicity only if it is dissolved in sufficient water to produce a volume equal to that in which the medicinal agent is dissolved. Up to this point the calculations have produced the sodium chloride equivalent of the medicinal agent. It must be borne in mind that an isotonic solution of sodium chloride contains 0.9 per cent sodium chloride or 0.9 Gm. per 100 ml. of solution. Medicinal agents present in a solution also contribute toward tonicity and, in finding the weight of sodium chloride that is equivalent to the weight of medicinal agent present, an amount has been determined that must be subtracted from the weight of sodium chloride that would have been used if no medicinal agent were added.

Previously it was found that the sodium chloride equivalent of chlorobutanol (1.5 Gm.) was 0.27 Gm. of sodium chloride. In 1000 cc. of solution the amount of sodium chloride required for an isotonic solution in the absence of chlorobutanol could be determined in the following manner.

$0.9\% = .009$

$.009 \times 1000 = 9$ Gm. sodium chloride

Therefore 9 Gm. of sodium chloride in 1000 ml. of solution would be isotonic, but chlorobutanol (1.5 Gm.) also contributes a tonicity equal to 0.27 Gm. of sodium chloride. Subtracting this quantity from 9 Gm. gives a difference equal to the amount of sodium chloride to be added

9.00
−0.27

8.73 Gm. = amt. of sodium chloride to be added to produce an isotonic solution.

If the same quantity of chlorobutanol were dissolved in a smaller quantity, the preliminary calculations would be the same, but the determination of the amount of sodium chloride necessary to produce isotonicity in the absence of chlorobutanol would give a different result. Thus, if a 90 ml. solution containing 1.5 Gm. of chlorobutanol is to be made isotonic the following calculations would be necessary.

Wt. of chlorobutanol = 1.5 Gm.
Chlorobutanol factor = 0.18
      1.5 × 0.18 = 0.27 Gm. NaCl
Vol. of solution = 90 ml.
% NaCl required = 0.9%
    .009 × 90 = .81 Gm. sodium chloride

Weight of sodium chloride required for
isotonicity in absence of medicinal agents = 0.81 Gm.

Sodium chloride isotonicity weight equivalent
of chlorobutanol (1.5 Gm.)   = 0.27 Gm.

Difference (0.81 −0.27)   = 0.54 Gm.

Weight of sodium chloride to be added to 90 ml. = 0.54 Gm.

Where more than one medicinal agent is present, the procedure is virtually the same. The sodium chloride weight equivalents of all agents are calculated, added together, and subtracted from the weight of sodium chloride required for isotonicity in the absence of medicinal agents.

In those instances where a compound to be included in a preparation is not listed in the accompanying table, an approximation can be relied upon that will, in most instances, suffice. As previously stated, a molar quantity of a relatively nonionized compound such as glucose produces only about half as many particles in solution as does a molar quantity of one that is practically 100% ionized. Therefore 18 Gm. (0.1 molar) of glucose would be tonically equal to 2.9 Gm. (0.05 molar) of sodium chloride.

18 Gm. glucose ≈ 2.9 Gm. sodium chloride

Divide both sides by 18 to get tonicity equivalent of 1 Gm. of glucose.

1 Gm. glucose ≈ 0.16 Gm. sodium chloride

Any quantity of glucose could then be multiplied by this factor (0.16) to obtain the tonicity weight equivalent of sodium chloride.

If the compound is highly ionized, as is sodium chloride, their equal molecular (molar) quantities will produce the same tonicity effect. Using potassium nitrate as an example of a highly ionized substance it can be seen that one gram mole (101 Gm.) should be equivalent tonically to a gram mole of sodium chloride (58.5 Gm.).

101 Gm. potassium nitrate ≈ 58.5 Gm. sodium chloride

Divide both sides by 101 to get sodium chloride tonicity weight equivalent of one gram of potassium nitrate.

1 Gm. potassium nitrate ⬧ .58 Gm. sodium chloride

This approximation is very close to that given in the table (0.60) which is based on experimental results.

Occasionally a prescription may be encountered wherein directions are given to make a solution isotonic with some agent other than sodium chloride. This can readily be accomplished by proceeding in exactly the same manner as before. That is, determine the weight of sodium chloride that would be required to make the solution isotonic, and divide this weight by the factor corresponding to the desired tonicity agent. In the problem previously calculated the amount of sodium chloride required for 90 ml. of solution containing 1.5 Gm. chlorobutanol was 0.54 Gm. If it is desired to make the solution isotonic with boric acid instead of sodium chloride the table should be consulted to find the factor for boric acid.

Weight of sodium chloride required = 0.54

Boric acid weight equivalent = 0.55

0.54 ÷ 0.55 = 0.98 Gm.

Dividing this factor into the weight of sodium chloride gives a quotient of 0.98 Gm. of boric acid that must be added to produce the same tonicity that would result if 0.54 Gm. of sodium chloride had been used.

SODIUM CHLORIDE EQUIVALENTS[1] FOR ISOTONIC COLLYRIA

	NaCl equiv.
Adrenalin (Epinephrine Hydrochloride)*	0.26
Alum (Potassium)	0.19
Alypin hydrochloride (Amydricaine Hydrochloride)*	0.18
Ammonium chloride	1.13
Amydricaine hydrochloride (Alypin Hydrochloride)	0.18
Amylcaine hydrochloride (Stovaine)*	0.20
Antipyrine	0.17
Apothesine hydrochloride*	0.19
Atropine sulfate	0.14
Boric acid	0.55
Butacaine sulfate (Butyn Sulfate)*	0.10
Butamin (Tutocaine Hydrochloride)*	0.20
Butyn sulfate (Butacaine Sulfate)*	0.10
Chlorobutanol	0.18
Cocaine hydrochloride	0.19
Cupric sulfate	0.15
Dextrose	0.16
Dionin (Ethylmorphine Hydrochloride)	0.16

* The above data without the asterisk are calculated from the freezing-point data by Husa and Rossi;[2] those with the asterisk are taken from Wells.[3]

44

	NaCl equiv.
Diothane hydrochloride*	0.13
Ephedrine hydrochloride	0.28
Ephedrine sulfate	0.19
Epinephrine hydrochloride (Adrenalin)*	0.26
Eserine salicylate (Physostigmine Salicylate)	0.19
Eserine sulfate (Physostigmine Sulfate)*	0.12
Ethylhydrocupreine hydrochloride (Optochin HCl)*	0.15
Ethylmorphine hydrochloride (Dionin)	0.16
Eucatropine hydrochloride (Euphthalmine)*	0.18
Euphthalmine (Eucatropine Hydrochloride)*	0.18
Fluorescein sodium*	0.19
Glycerin	0.35
Holocaine hydrochloride (Phenacaine Hydrochloride)*	0.16
Homatropine hydrobromide	0.19
Hyoscine hydrobromide (Scopolamine Hydrobromide)*	0.13
Hyoscine hydrochloride (Scopolamine Hydrochloride)*	0.15
Larocaine hydrochloride*	0.18
Mercuric succinimide	0.14
Metycaine hydrochloride*	0.20
Mild protein silver (Argyrol)	0.19
Morphine hydrochloride*	0.15
Morphine sulfate	0.15
Neosynephrin hydrochloride*	0.22
Nupercaine hydrochloride*	0.18
Optochin hydrochloride (Ethylhydrocupreine Hydrochloride)*	0.15
Pantocaine hydrochloride (Tetracaine Hydrochloride)*	0.19
Phenacaine hydrochloride (Holocaine Hydrochloride)*	0.16
Pilocarpine hydrochloride	0.22
Pilocarpine nitrate*	0.21
Physostigmine salicylate (Eserine Salicylate)	0.19
Physostigmine sulfate (Eserine Sulfate)*	0.12
Potassium chloride	0.84
Potassium nitrate	0.60
Procaine hydrochloride	0.24
Propadrine*	0.31
Scopolamine hydrobromide (Hyoscine Hydrobromide)*	0.13
Scopolamine hydrochloride (Hyoscine Hydrochloride)*	0.15
Silver nitrate	0.39
Silver protein, mild (Argyrol)	0.19
Silver protein, strong (Protargol)	0.04
Sodium bicarbonate	0.69
Sodium biphosphate	0.45
Sodium borate	0.43
Sodium chloride	1.00
Sodium nitrate (no H_2O)	0.62
Stovaine (Amylcaine Hydrochloride)*	0.20
Strong silver protein (Protargol)	0.04
Sucrose	0.10
Syntropan*	0.14
Tannic acid	0.03
Tetracaine hydrochloride (Pantocaine Hydrochloride)*	0.19
Tutocaine hydrochloride (Butamin)*	0.20
Zinc chloride*	0.60
Zinc sulfate	0.15

* The above data without the asterisk are calculated from the freezing-point data by Husa and Rossi;[2] those with the asterisk are taken from Wells.[3]

REFERENCES

1. Brecht, E. A.: Isotonic Collyria, The Merck Report (January, 1945).
2. Husa, W. J., and Rossi, O. A.: A Study of Isotonic Solution, J. Am. Pharm. Assn. Sc. Ed., **31**, 270 (1942).
3. Wells, J. M.: Rapid Method for Calculating Isotonic Solutions, J. Am. Pharm. Assn. Pract. Pharm. Ed., **5**, 103 (1944).

INORGANIC NOMENCLATURE[1]

Compounds composed of only two elements (*e.g.*, NaCl, CaO, K_2S) are termed *binary compounds*. The most electropositive element is named first, followed by the root of the more negative element using the ending *ide*. An exception to this is *cyanide*, the anion of hydrocyanic acid (HCN). Combinations of elements that recur in compounds are termed *radicals* or *groups* (*e.g.*, $SO_4^=$, NO_3^-) and when combined with a metallic cation (*e.g.*, $ZnSO_4$, $CuSO_4$) are spoken of as *ternary compounds*.

Acids containing no oxygen (*e.g.*, HCl, HBr, HCN) are *hydracids* or *hydro acids*. There are no *ous* acids in this class because the more electronegative element exists in only one valence state. Acids containing oxygen (*e.g.*, H_2SO_4, HNO_3) are *oxyacids*. The nomenclature of some of these oxyacids is illustrated in the following table:

Formula	Acid	Salt
HClO	Hypochlorous acid	Hypochlorite
$HClO_2$	Chlorous acid	Chlorite
$HClO_3$	Chloric acid	Chlorate
$HClO_4$	Perchloric acid	Perchlorate
HPH_2O_2	Hypophosphorous acid	Hypophosphite
H_3PO_3	Phosphorous acid	Phosphite
$H_4P_2O_6$	Hypophosphoric acid	Hypophosphate
H_3PO_4	Phosphoric acid	Phosphate
H_3AsO_3	Arsenous acid	Arsenite
H_3AsO_4	Arsenic acid	Arsenate

The terms *hypo—ous*, *ous*, *ic*, and *per—ic* are used when the apparent valence (or oxidation number) varies by 2. An exception is made in the case of hypophosphoric acid because of the two phosphorus atoms in $H_4P_2O_6$. When naming the salts derived from these acids, the ending *ite* is always associated with *ous* acids and *ate* with *ic* acids.

The prefixes *ortho*, *meta* and *pyro* sometimes are used to distinguish between various oxyacids derived from an element in a given oxidation state. *Ortho* is used as a prefix to indicate the most highly "hydroxylated" *known* form of an acid (or its salt or ester). Thus, orthophosphoric acid indicates $(HO)_3P{=}O$ because the hypothetical $(HO)_5P$ ("true ortho acid") is not known. Some examples are:—

[1] For a more extended discussion of nomenclature in this area see "Definitive Rules for Nomenclature of Inorganic Chemistry," (International Union of Pure and Applied Chemistry), J. Am. Chem. Soc., **82**, 5523 (1960).

H_3BO_3 or $(HO)_3B$ Orthoboric acid
H_3AsO_4 or $(HO)_3As{=}O$ Orthoarsenic acid
H_3PO_3 or $(HO)_3P$ Orthophosphorous acid

The *meta* prefix is used to denote that form of the acid remaining after the *intra*molecular removal of a molecule of water from the ortho acid. For example:—

$$H_3BO_3 \longrightarrow HBO_2 + H_2O$$
orthoboric   metaboric
acid   acid

$$H_3PO_4 \longrightarrow HPO_3 + H_2O$$
orthophosphoric   metaphosphoric
acid   acid

Pyro is the prefix used to denote the *inter*molecular removal of one molecule of water between two molecules of the ortho acid. For example:—

$$2H_3PO_4 \longrightarrow H_4P_2O_7 + H_2O$$
orthophosphoric   pyrophosphoric
acid   acid

Thio acids are acids with an atom of sulfur replacing an atom of oxygen in the oxyacid from which the name is derived. Examples of interest to pharmacy students together with their related oxyacids are:

Formula	Acid	Salt
$H_2S_2O_3$	Thiosulfuric acid	Thiosulfate
(H_2SO_4)	(Sulfuric acid)	(Sulfate)
HSCN	Thiocyanic acid	Thiocyanate
(HOCN)	(Cyanic acid)	(Cyanate)

Salts may be of various types. The most important of these are:

(a) *Normal Salts.*—These salts contain only one kind of cation and one kind of anion (*e.g.*, NaCl, KBr). Those in which different valence states of the cation exist use *ic* and *ous* as suffixes to indicate the higher and lower valence states respectively. For example, ferr*ic* chloride = $FeCl_3$ and ferr*ous* chloride = $FeCl_2$.

(b) *Hydrogen Salts.*—These salts contain hydrogen which may be replaced by a metal or which will react with a base. These are often spoken of as *acid salts* and frequently are prefixed with *bi-*. This usage is incorrect to denote an acid salt but common usage, as in the official compendia (*e.g.*, Sodium Bicarbonate, Sodium Bisulfite, Sodium Biphosphate), serves to perpetuate it. The correct terminology is to name the metallic cation first and then name the hydrogen just before the anion. Thus, $NaHCO_3$ is properly described as "sodium hydrogen carbonate" and NaH_2PO_4 is best named as "sodium dihydrogen phosphate." The prefix *bi-* does not even indicate how many hydrogens are present but simply signifies that all of the available hydrogen has not been replaced.

(c) *Mixed Salts.*—These salts may contain two different cations combined with a single anion or they may contain a single cation combined with two or more anions. In naming these the most electropositive element should be named first where there are two cations. Examples are magnesium ammonium phosphate ($MgNH_4PO_4$) and potassium calcium phosphate ($KCaPO_4$).

(d) *Double Salts.*—These salts are obtained when two salts crystallize together to form well-defined crystals containing whole number ratios of each salt. Perhaps the most important of these are the alums. For example, potassium alum has the composition, $K_2SO_4 . Al_2(SO_4)_3 . 24H_2O$. Another example which is not an alum is ferrous ammonium sulfate, $FeSO_4 . (NH_4)_2SO_4 . 6H_2O$.

(e) *Basic, sub and oxy Salts.*—These are known sometimes as *hydroxy salts* also. The nomenclature indicates salts containing a hydroxy (OH^-) or an oxy- ($O^=$) group together with another anion. They are often used to indicate partially hydrolyzed normal salts. These terms are interchangeable and usually refer to the same type of compound. However, *oxy* is customarily reserved to indicate only oxygen in an inorganic compound (*e.g.*, $BiOCl$, bismuth oxychloride). The elements whose salts are prone to partial hydrolysis are Al, Pb, Sb, Bi, Mn and Fe. Magnesium may also be included on the basis of the official magnesium carbonate (*q.v.*).

A basic or sub salt is usually visualized as forming by partial *hydrolysis* of a normal salt, *i.e.*

$$Bi(NO_3)_3 \rightleftarrows Bi^{+++} + 3NO_3^-$$

$$H_2O \quad \rightleftarrows \overset{+}{OH^-} + \overset{+}{H^+}$$
$$\downarrow$$
$$Bi(OH)^{++} + OH^- \rightleftarrows Bi(OH)_2^+$$

The sub salt formed is then a mixture $Bi(OH)(NO_3)_2$ and $Bi(OH)_2NO_3$ and is more soluble than the hydroxide [$Bi(OH)_3$] but less soluble than the normal salt [$Bi(NO_3)_3$]. The above approach is taken in preparing Bismuth Subnitrate N.F. and Lead Subacetate Solution.

A basic or sub salt may also be prepared by partial *neutralization* of a hydroxide; *i.e.*, Aluminum Subacetate Solution U.S.P.

$$\underset{\underset{OH}{\diagdown}}{\overset{\diagup}{Al}}\!\!-\!\!\underline{|OH \quad\quad H|}OOCCH_3 \quad\quad \underline{H|}OOCCH_3 \rightarrow \underset{\underset{OH}{\diagdown}}{\overset{\overset{OOCCH_3}{\diagup}}{Al}}\!\!-\!\!OOCCH_3 + 2H_2O$$

HYDROLYSIS

Hydrolysis is the reaction of a salt with water to reform the base and acid responsible for the original salt (1).

$$(1)\ ZnSO_4 + 2H_2O \rightleftharpoons Zn(OH)_2 + H_2SO_4$$

In a broader sense, hydrolysis may include the decomposition of an ester into an alcohol and acid. Also, compounds of nonmetallic elements, with oxygen or halides, are split by water into two acids (2)

$$(2)\ PCl_3 + 3H_2O \rightarrow H_3PO_3 + 3HCl$$

The hydrolysis of chlorine to HCl and HClO (see chlorine) and the hydrolysis of sulfur and phosphorus are also important.

Hydrolysis is facilitated and increased by a rise in temperature, dilution and by removal of a reaction product through volatilization or precipitation. Of importance also is that, with salts, the weaker[1] the responsible base (or acid) the greater the hydrolysis.

The most important type to pharmacists is the hydrolysis of salts. Salts are electrolytes and, therefore, their hydrolysis must depend upon ionic change wherein the ions react with the ions of water. It amounts to a transfer of a proton from water to an anion, termed protolysis.

Formation of Weak Acid.—A solution of a salt obtained from a weak acid and a strong base will give a basic reaction. Sodium acetate, a strong electrolyte, when dissolved in water dissociates as follows (3).

$$(3)\ CH_3COONa \rightleftharpoons CH_3COO^- + Na^+$$

Each ion now is available to react with the components of water to effect a hydrolysis (4).

$$(4)\ CH_3COOH \rightleftharpoons CH_3COO^- + H^+$$

The significant point is that sodium, as an ion, is strongly electropositive and does not form a molecule with hydroxide ions. This permits an excess of hydroxide ions to build up whereas acetate ion attracts hydrogen ions (protons) to form slightly ionized acetic acid. These reactions remove hydrogen ions and increase hydroxide ions. Therefore, the solution of sodium acetate is basic.

Formation of a Weak Base.—By a similar sequence of reactions ammonium chloride can hydrolyze to give an acid solution (5, 6).

$$(5)\ NH_4Cl \rightleftharpoons NH_4^+ + Cl^-$$
$$(6)\ NH_4^+ + H_2O \rightleftharpoons NH_4OH + H^+$$

---

[1] Meaning a low degree of ionization or that the anion has a high affinity for protons (H^+).

Equation (6) shows the formation of the weak base NH₄OH (slightly ionized) with the liberation of hydrogen ions. There is negligible attraction between hydrogen ions and chloride ions and, therefore, an acid solution results. When the solubility of the formed hydroxide [e.g., Bi(OH)₃ or Al(OH)₃] is low, some will precipitate out as formed and the reaction will proceed to the right until all of the original salt is hydrolyzed and a large amount of precipitate is formed (7).

(7) $(CH_3COO)_3Al + 3H_2O \rightleftarrows Al(OH)_3 + 3CH_3COOH$

It is always confusing to reconcile the hydrolysis of metallic salts that yield acid solutions yet whose hydroxides are always considered insoluble. For example: A solution of aluminum chloride is acid in solution, therefore, how is the removal of hydroxide ions accounted for? Two situations may be considered:

1. A colloidal form exists (8)

(8) $AlCl_3 + 3H_2O \rightleftarrows Al(OH)_3 + 3H^+ + 3Cl^-$
colloidal

or,

2. An incomplete hydroxide or sub form exists (see basic salts) (9, 10). This is the usually accepted explanation.

(9) $Al^{+++} + H_2O \rightleftarrows Al(OH)^{++} + H^+$

or

(10) $Al(H_2O)_6^{+++} + 2H_2O \rightleftarrows Al(H_2O)_5(OH)^{++} + H_3O^+$

Formation of Weak Acid and Weak Base.—In this case both cation and anion of a salt resulting from the reaction of a weak acid and weak base will react with water to form slightly ionized molecules (11).

(11) $CH_3COONH_4 + H_2O \rightleftarrows NH_4OH + CH_3COOH$

In general, salts of this type will exhibit acid or basic solutions depending upon which one is the stronger. However, when the strength is nearly the same a neutral solution will result, although hydrolysis has taken place to a high degree.

Salts of Strong Base and Strong Acid.—Here there is a situation of maximum ionization but negligible hydrolysis which results in a practically neutral solution (12).

(12) $NaCl + H_2O \rightarrow Na^+ + Cl^- + H_2O$

Neither ion shows any affinity for the components of water so the hydrogen ion concentration remains unchanged.

Hydrolysis of salts in solution can be associated with the protonic concept of the Brönsted-Lowry theory for acids and bases. A salt in aqueous solution causes an unbalance in the ratio of hydrogen cations (*i.e.*, hydronium ions, H_3O^+) and hydroxide anions caused by the difference in proton acceptor and donor properties of these ions. For example, ammonium chloride in solution provides ammonium ions (NH_4^+) and chloride ions (Cl^-). An acid solution results because ammonium ions have greater proton donor strength than the chloride ion has proton acceptor strength. Therefore, an excess of hydrogen ions exist and the solution is acid. Other hydrolysis examples such as sodium carbonate, zinc chloride and aluminum chloride can be explained on the same basis.

Hydrolysis may also be thought to depend upon the charge densities of certain cations and anions. The charge, if high enough, will distort the water dipole sufficiently to break it. Those anions (acetate, carbonate, etc.) that become attached to hydrogen of a water molecule release hydroxide ions and provide a basic solution. In a like manner cations (Zn^{++}, Al^{+++}, Hg^{++}, etc.) that break the O–H bond of water become attached to the oxygen of a water hydroxide group thus releasing hydrogen ions that establish an acid solution.

WATER

Water of Hydration, or coordinated water, is that water (as molecules) associated with cations and/or anions of a salt in solution or in crystals. Depending on the coordination number, many cations and anions are often associated with a fixed number of water molecules. Ferric chloride, $FeCl_3 . 6H_2O$, may be visualized as Fe-$(H_2O)_6^{+++} + 3Cl^-$ in solution. There is a strong Fe–O bond formation, so much so that, upon heating the crystalline material, HCl is given off.

In the case of copper sulfate, $CuSO_4 . 5H_2O$, four moles of water are associated with the cupric ion, $Cu(H_2O)_4^{++}$, (cation water) and one with the sulfate $SO_4(H_2O)^=$ (anion water). In a general way the following structure depicts the arrangement.

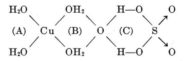

On heating, the two molecules of water attached only to Cu^{++} come off first (A), then the two moles at (B), and finally, at 200° to 300° C., the anion-held mole at (C). Zinc sulfate ($ZnSO_4 . 7H_2O$) also has a mole of anion water.

Anion water is commonly found with salts containing oxyanions such as hypophosphite, thiosulfate and phosphate.

Other less fixed water of crystallization is considered to be held loosely between the cation and anion by mutal attraction to the dipole of water, more or less fitting into the "holes" of the crystalline structure. A physically "held" water or *Zeolytic water* may also be present in a crystal. The loss of this, however, does not alter the crystalline structure.

Lattice water is present in constant amounts because it is held in the definite lattice structure of the crystal but is not attracted by the cations or anions. This is found in compounds containing ions that do not have any attraction for water. Examples are $BaCl_2.-2H_2O$; $KOOCCH_3.4H_2O$; and $SrBr_2.6H_2O$.

EFFLORESCENCE

Efflorescence, the reverse of hydration, is the loss of water molecules (water of crystallization) from a crystalline substance. At any given temperature (*e.g.*, room temperature) a hydrate will establish an equilibrium of vapor pressure around it. Loss of water, or dehydration, is endothermic and therefore increases as temperature rises.

A crystalline hydrate having a vapor pressure greater than the surrounding air will lose water of hydration (*efflorescence*). Crystalline hydrates vary greatly in their ability to effloresce. Magnesium sulfate ($MgSO_4.7H_2O$) and sodium sulfate ($Na_2SO_4.10H_2O$) do so easily in dry air, whereas aluminum sulfate [$Al_2(SO_4)_3.18H_2O$] and dibasic calcium phosphate ($CaHPO_4.2H_2O$) are stable in air.

HYGROSCOPIC PROPERTY

Hygroscopic substances are those that have the ability to remove water from the air. Naturally, this ability varies greatly, and those that take on sufficient water to form a liquid are said to be *deliquescent* (process known as *deliquescence*). When a substance is exposed to air, a film of moisture will condense on its surface (the degree of condensation is controlled by temperature and moisture content of the air). Water attraction is probably influenced by the dipole attraction between water and the ions on the surface of the substance. This will dissolve some of the compound to form a solution. If the solubility is great, such as in calcium chloride, the vapor pressure of this "film" solution will be less than the surrounding vapor pressure. More water, then, is absorbed, which in turn causes more compound to be dissolved. This cycle eventually results in a complete solution.

Substances are known that attract water because of dipole attraction but do not form solutions and may even be insoluble. In this way calcium fluoride has a strong attraction for water. Because of the strong cation charge of silicon, silicon dioxide (SiO_2) "holds" water molecules and is used as a desiccating agent, yet it is insoluble. It can be heated to drive off the water and reused.

Index

A

Index

COMMON LOGARITHMS

N	0	1	2	3	4	5	6	7	8	9
10	0000	0043	0086	0128	0170	0212	0253	0294	0334	0374
11	0414	0453	0492	0531	0569	0607	0645	0682	0719	0755
12	0792	0828	0864	0899	0934	0969	1004	1038	1072	1106
13	1139	1173	1206	1239	1271	1303	1335	1367	1399	1430
14	1461	1492	1523	1553	1584	1614	1644	1673	1703	1732
15	1761	1790	1818	1847	1875	1903	1931	1959	1987	2014
16	2041	2068	2095	2122	2148	2175	2201	2227	2253	2279
17	2304	2330	2355	2380	2405	2430	2455	2480	2504	2529
18	2553	2577	2601	2625	2648	2672	2695	2718	2742	2765
19	2788	2810	2833	2856	2878	2900	2923	2945	2967	2989
20	3010	3032	3054	3075	3096	3118	3139	3160	3181	3201
21	3222	3243	3263	3284	3304	3324	3345	3365	3385	3404
22	3424	3444	3464	3483	3502	3522	3541	3560	3579	3598
23	3617	3636	3655	3674	3692	3711	3729	3747	3766	3784
24	3802	3820	3838	3856	3874	3892	3909	3927	3945	3962
25	3979	3997	4014	4031	4048	4065	4082	4099	4116	4133
26	4150	4166	4183	4200	4216	4232	4249	4265	4281	4298
27	4314	4330	4346	4362	4378	4393	4409	4425	4440	4456
28	4472	4487	4502	4518	4533	4548	4564	4579	4594	4609
29	4624	4639	4654	4669	4683	4698	4713	4728	4742	4757
30	4771	4786	4800	4814	4829	4843	4857	4871	4886	4900
31	4914	4928	4942	4955	4969	4983	4997	5011	5024	5038
32	5051	5065	5079	5092	5105	5119	5132	5145	5159	5172
33	5185	5198	5211	5224	5237	5250	5263	5276	5289	5302
34	5315	5328	5340	5353	5366	5378	5391	5403	5416	5428
35	5441	5453	5465	5478	5490	5502	5514	5527	5539	5551
36	5563	5575	5587	5599	5611	5623	5635	5647	5658	5670
37	5682	5694	5705	5717	5729	5740	5752	5763	5775	5786
38	5798	5809	5821	5832	5843	5855	5866	5877	5888	5899
39	5911	5922	5933	5944	5955	5966	5977	5988	5999	6010
40	6021	6031	6042	6053	6064	6075	6085	6096	6107	6117
41	6128	6138	6149	6160	6170	6180	6191	6201	6212	6222
42	6232	6243	6253	6263	6274	6284	6294	6304	6314	6325
43	6335	6345	6355	6365	6375	6385	6395	6405	6415	6425
44	6435	6444	6454	6464	6474	6484	6493	6503	6513	6522
45	6532	6542	6551	6561	6571	6580	6590	6599	6609	6618
46	6628	6637	6646	6656	6665	6675	6684	6693	6702	6712
47	6721	6730	6739	6749	6758	6767	6776	6785	6794	6803
48	6812	6821	6830	6839	6848	6857	6866	6875	6884	6893
49	6902	6911	6920	6928	6937	6946	6955	6964	6972	6981
50	6990	6998	7007	7016	7024	7033	7042	7050	7059	7067
51	7076	7084	7093	7101	7110	7118	7126	7135	7143	7152
52	7160	7168	7177	7185	7193	7202	7210	7218	7226	7235
53	7243	7251	7259	7267	7275	7284	7292	7300	7308	7316
54	7324	7332	7340	7348	7356	7364	7372	7380	7388	7396
N	0	1	2	3	4	5	6	7	8	9